全国船舶工业职业教育教学指导委员会推荐教材
国家“双高”建设教材

舰船电气设备

主　编　冯　晔
副主编　吴　峰　曹传强
参　编　李武华　陈新梅　罗　彬
　　　　王诲信　王福太
主　审　张选军

哈尔滨工程大学出版社
Harbin Engineering University Press

内容简介

书中介绍了国际航运业采用的最新电气实践内容，旨在帮助轮机员和电气人员了解船舶电气系统、电气设备及其维护。内容安排上从介绍基础知识入手，循序渐进，电气安全和实际工作安全贯穿始终。主要介绍了发电机结构及其控制，发电机的保护和维护；电动机和启动器的结构、操作及保护；船用电动机的调速控制方式；船舶照明、餐饮、制冷、空调、洗衣设备和阴极保护等各种辅助电气设施，以及电池的操作、维护和保养；石油、天然气和化学品船中位于潜在危险区域的电气设备的特殊设计和维护；各种防爆方法以及危险区域的电气设备测试；船舶电力推进系统的应用和操作，以及高压电的操作、安全程序和测试方法。

本书适合轮机工程技术专业、船舶电子电气技术专业全日制士官生、留学生、大专生以及这些专业的社会培训班学员学习使用。

图书在版编目(CIP)数据

舰船电气设备 / 冯晔主编. -- 哈尔滨 : 哈尔滨工程大学出版社, 2025. 1. -- ISBN 978-7-5661-4637-3

Ⅰ. U674.7

中国国家版本馆 CIP 数据核字第 202562YF04 号

舰船电气设备

JIANCHUAN DIANQI SHEBEI

选题策划 张志雯
责任编辑 刘海霞
封面设计 李海波

出版发行 哈尔滨工程大学出版社
社　　址 哈尔滨市南岗区南通大街 145 号
邮政编码 150001
发行电话 0451-82519328
传　　真 0451-82519699
经　　销 新华书店
印　　刷 哈尔滨理想印刷有限公司
开　　本 787 mm×1 092 mm　1/16
印　　张 25.75
字　　数 779 千字
版　　次 2025 年 1 月第 1 版
印　　次 2025 年 1 月第 1 次印刷
书　　号 ISBN 978-7-5661-4637-3
定　　价 85.00 元

http://www.hrbeupress.com
E-mail:heupress@hrbeu.edu.cn

Preface

This book inherits the tradition of marine culture, focuses on the future development of intelligent ships, especially based on the cultivation of innovative personal in ship's electrical management, emphasizes the basic theory, basic knowledge, basic skills content in the compilation, focuses on the "safety, health, environmental protection" navigation culture and cultivate students' practical ability to keep integrity and innovation.

This book is written in line with the training objectives of the China higher vocational marine engineering technology major, and covered some content of the syllabus of the fourth engineer's competency examination of seagoing vessels. In the process of compiling this book, the primary task is to deliver the knowledge of the application of ship electrical equipment, pay attention to the cultivation of electrical equipment management skills, and covered some new technologies, new processes and new equipment so as to provide a certain space for professional thinking and improvement for teaching and learning.

This book consists of nine chapters, which is compiled by ChangJiang MSA Seafarers Examination Center C/E Li Wuhua, a team composed of CMA CGM (Qingdao) yard superintendent Wang Huixin, Wah Kwong Maritime Transport Holding Limited technical superintendent Wang Futai, Wuhan Xinhuihang Seaman Management Co., LTD Cao Chuanqiang, and front-line teachers Feng Ye, Wu Feng, Chen Xinmei, Luo Bin from the Chinese People's Liberation Army Navy Non-commissioned Officer School and Wuhan Institute of Shipbuilding Technology College. Chapter 1 is compiled by Feng Ye and Li Wuhua, chapter 2 is compiled by Li Wuhua, Chen Xinmei amd Wang Huixin, chapter 3 and 4 are compiled by Feng Ye, Cao Chuanqiang and Wang Futai, chapter 5 is compiled by Feng Ye and Wu Feng, chapter 6 is compiled by Feng Ye, Luo Bin and Cao Chuanqiang, chapter 7 is compiled by Feng Ye and Chen Xinmei, chapter 8 is compiled by Feng Ye and Luo Bin, chapter 9 is compiled by Feng Ye and Wu Feng. Feng Ye is responsible for drafting and revising the entire book.

前　言

本书定位于继承海洋文化传统，着眼于智能舰船发展的未来，立足于培养舰船电气管理的创新型人才，在编写中注重“三基”（基本理论、基本知识、基本技能）内容，同时注重向学生传递“安全、健康、环保”的航海文化理念和培养学生守正创新的实践能力。

本书内容符合全国高职轮机工程技术专业的培养目标，并涵盖了部分海船三管轮适任考试大纲的内容。在编写过程中，笔者自始至终以传承舰船电气设备运用知识为首要任务，注重对学生进行电气设备管理技能的培养，并选取了一些舰船新技术、新工艺和新设备等内容，为教与学提供一定的专业发展思考。

全书共9章，由长江海事局船员考试中心李武华轮机长，达飞航运集团（青岛）驻船场机务王诲信，华光船务管理（深圳）有限公司机务王福太，武汉鑫汇航海员管理有限公司专家曹传强以及中国人民解放军海军士官学校、武汉船舶职业技术学院等学校的一线教师冯晔、吴峰、陈新梅、罗彬组成的编写团队编写完成。其中，第1章由冯晔、李武华编写，第2章由李武华、陈新梅、王诲信编写，第3章、第4章由冯晔、曹传强、王福太编写，第5章由冯晔、吴峰编写，第6章由冯晔、罗彬、曹传强编写，第7章由冯晔、陈新梅编写，第8章由冯晔、罗彬编写，第9章由冯晔、吴峰编写。全书由冯晔负责统稿及修改。

目　　录

Chapter 1 Basic Electricity
第1章 电工基础

1.0 Introduction 介绍

The purpose of this course is to give you an insight into the basic electricity. We will learn the difference between AC and DC, how we can read an electric diagram and how to make a diagram, we will also learn the function of the different components in an electric circuit. Finally we will learn how to use the different tools and the safety rules when working on an electric circuit or machinery. In conjunction with this chapter, we will also do some practical exercises that will support the theory in these papers. Hopefully that you will learn, enjoy and gain knowledge from this course, that you can put into practical use in your future activities. In this chapter we are going to address the issues of what electricity is and how it is generated.

本课程的目的是让大家深入了解电学基础。我们将学习交流和直流之间的区别,如何阅读电路图以及如何画电路图,还将学习电路中不同元件的功能,最后学习如何使用不同的工具及其安全守则在电路或机器上工作。结合本章,我们将进行一些实践练习,以对这些内容中的理论提供实践支撑。希望大家能从本课程中学习、享受并获得知识,以便在今后的工作中发挥实际作用。在本章中,我们将讨论什么是电以及如何发电的问题。

1.1 Electricity 电力

Imagine a piece of wire. In the one end of that piece of wire you attach a voltage with a high potential, like the positive end of a battery. Nothing will happen until you connect another potential that is related with the first high potential that you connected, like the negative end of the same battery. Thus you have a CIRCUIT, and when you have a circuit with two different potentials, you will have a CURRENT of electrons flowing. So we have to have a closed circuit to have a current flowing.

想象一下有一根电线。在电线的一端连接一个高电位的电压,就像连接电池的正极。电线的另一端除非连接另一个与已连接的第一个高电位相关的电位,比如同一个电池的负极,否则什么都不会发生。这样你就有了一个电路,当这个电路具有两个不同电势时,便会有一个电子流。所以我们必须有一个闭合的电路,才能有电流流过。

Normally we say that the current flows from the positive (highest) to the negative (lowest) potential, but actually it is the other way round. The current consists of free electrons flowing from the negative (lowest) potential to the positive (highest) potential, as electrons are negatively charged. We could say that the negative end has a surplus of free electrons and that the positive end lacks electrons. So just like a magnet where you have a positive end and a negative end that attracts each other, the positive potential attracts the negative electrons.

通常我们说电流从正(最高)电势流向负(最低)电势,但实际上正相反。当电子带负电时,电流由从负(最低)电势流向正(最高)电势的自由电子组成。可以说负端有多余的自由电子,而正端缺少电子。所以就像磁铁一样,正端和负端相互吸引,正电势吸引负电子。

The difference between the two potentials is called VOLTAGE. On the Fig. 1. 1 the above is shown schematically.

两个电位之间的差值称为电压。图 1. 1 反映了上述内容。

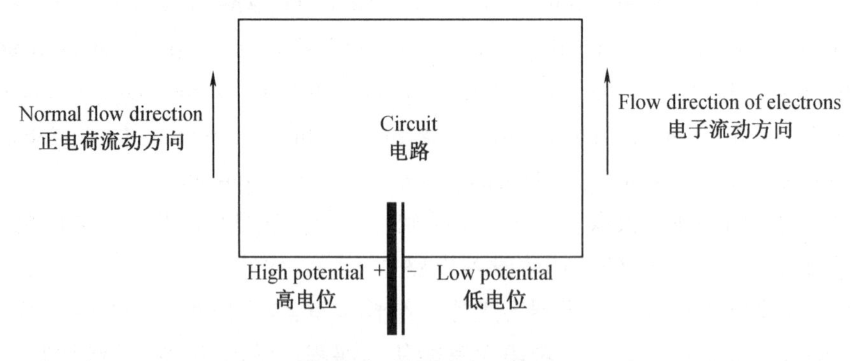

Fig. 1. 1　Short circuit

图 1. 1　短路

The Fig. 1. 1 is showing a state that is normally referred to as a SHORT CURCUIT. The reason being that there is no restriction to the flow of electrons. This restriction is called RESISTANCE. Now we have already introduced some terms that we call units, so let's take a closer look at those units.

图 1. 1 展示了短路状态。短路的原因是对电子的流动没有限制,这种限制称为电阻。现在已经介绍过一些单位的术语,接下来让我们更详细地了解这些单位。

1. 1. 1　Voltage 电压

Voltageis denoted with a U. Voltage is measured in Volts, the abbreviation being V. A normal battery has a voltage of 1. 5 V.

电压用字母 U 表示,以伏特为单位,缩写为 V。普通电池的电压为 1. 5 V。

1. 1. 2　Current 电流

Current is denoted with an I. Current is measured in Amperes, the abbreviation being A. The intensity of current depends of the voltage applied and the resistance present in the circuit, according to Ohm's law.

电流用字母 I 表示,以安培为单位,缩写为 A。根据欧姆定律,电流的强度取决于施加的电压和电路中存在的电阻。

1.1.3 Resistance 电阻

Resistance is denoted with a R. Resistance is measured in Ohms, the abbreviation being the Greek letter omega, Ω. The resistance in an object (circuit) is normally constant, but can alter with the ambient temperature.

电阻用字母 R 表示,以欧姆为单位,缩写为希腊字母 Ω。物体(电路)中的电阻通常是恒定的,但会随环境温度而变化。

The correlation between voltage, current and resistance are best described in Ohm's law:

电压、电流、电阻之间的相关性可用欧姆定律来描述:

$$U=IR$$

1.1.4 Power 功率

Power is denoted with a P. Power is measured in Watts, the abbreviation being W. Power is the given amount of energy per time unit and is a measurement of the size of the device.

功率用字母 P 表示,以瓦特为单位,缩写为 W。功率是单位时间的给定能量,是设备规模的度量。

The correlation between power, voltage, current and resistance can be described as such (the power sentence):

功率、电压、电流和电阻之间的相关性可以这样描述(功率表达式):

$$P=UI$$

And as Ohm's law is like this:

正如欧姆定律是这样的:

$$U=IR$$

You can rewrite the power sentence as follows:

你可以把功率表达式改写如下:

$$P=I^2R$$

Most appliances contain a resistance, like a light bulb. When an appliance is connected in a circuit, it is often referred to as a LOAD. In other words most loads contain a resistance. If we insert a load in the diagram that we have already made, we get the below diagram Fig. 1.2.

大多数电器都有电阻,比如灯泡。当设备连接在电路中时,通常称其为负载。换句话说,大多数负载都有电阻。如果我们在已有电路图中插入一个负载,我们将得到图 1.2。

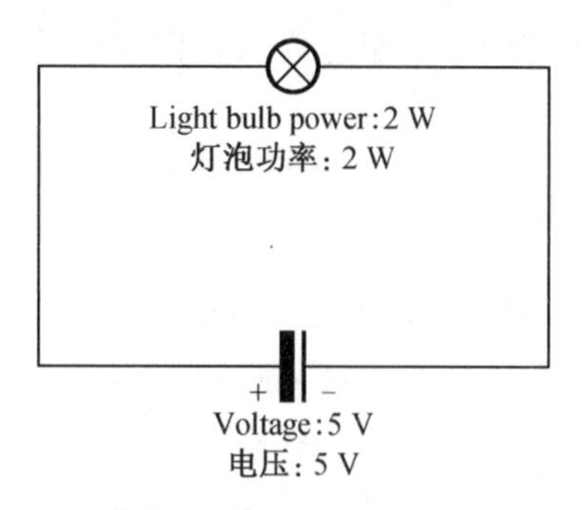

Fig. 1.2 Circuit with load

图 1.2 带负载的电路

We have also got some extra information—The voltage is 5 V and the power consumption is 2 W, this gives us the opportunity to calculate the resistance of the light bulb and the current flowing in the circuit.

我们还得到了一些额外的信息——电压为 5 V,功率为 2 W,这使我们有机会计算灯泡的电阻和电路中流动的电流。

The facts:voltage = 5 V, power = 2 W, according to the power sentence:

已知:$U=5$ V,$P=2$ W,根据功率表达式:

$$P=UI$$

$$2=5I$$

$$I=2/5=0.4\ \text{A}$$

Then according to Ohm's law:

然后根据欧姆定律:

$$U=IR$$

$$5=0.4R$$

$$R=5/0.4=12.5\ \Omega$$

And then we can check it with:

然后我们可以通过下式验算:

$$P=I^2R$$

$$P=0.4\times0.4\times12.5=2\ \text{W}$$

So now we know that the current is 0.4 A and that the resistance is 12.5 Ω.

那么现在我们知道电流是 0.4 A,电阻是 12.5 Ω。

1.2　Generating Electricity 发电

The voltage is being driven by a force. This force is called the electromotive force(e. m. f.). This means that whenever we want to generate a voltage, we have to generate an electromotive force. The most common way to generate an electromotive force, if we disregard batteries, is to move a conductor (wire) in a magnetic field.

电压是由一种力驱动的,这种力叫作电动势。这意味着,每当我们想要产生电压时,我们就必须产生电动势。如果不考虑由电池产生电动势,最常见的产生电动势的方法是在磁场中移动导体(导线)。

A magnet can attract iron objects. We can even magnetize an iron rod,this is caused by the magnetic field lines protruding from a magnet. Below Fig. 1. 3 is shown how this would look if we could see the magnetic field lines.

磁铁能吸引铁质物体。我们甚至可以磁化铁棒,这是由磁铁突出的磁力线引起的。如果我们能看到磁力线,它会是如图 1. 3 所示的样子。

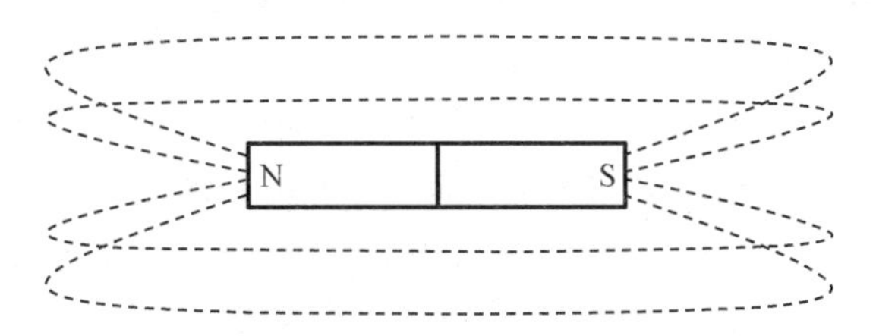

Fig. 1. 3　Magnetic field lines

图 1. 3　磁力线

These field lines can penetrate through other materials, even a vacuum. The direction of the field lines is from the North (positive) pole to the South (negative) pole, outside of the magnet. When a conductor is introduced in a magnetic field, all the atoms in the conductor are affected by the magnetic field. If the conductor is held in a steady position,nothing will happen. But if the conductor is moved through the field(Fig. 1. 4), all of the atoms are subjected to a change in the field and this is what drives the electromotive force.

这些磁力线可以穿透其他材料,甚至是真空。磁力线的方向是从磁铁外部的北极(正极)到南极(负极)。当导体被引入磁场时,导体中的所有原子都受到磁场的影响。如果导体保持在静态位置,则不会发生任何情况。但是如果导体在磁场中移动(图 1. 4),则所有的原子都会在磁场中发生变化,这就是产生电动势的原因。

Another aspect concerning magnetism and electricity is that a magnetic field is surrounding every current carrying conductor. This aspect together with the previously mentioned movement of a conductor in a magnetic field is used in a machine called a GENERATOR, where we of course generate voltage. And when we can generate voltage, we can have a current flowing and when we have that, we say that we generate power.

关于磁和电的另一个知识点是磁场围绕着每个载流导体。这一规律与前面提到的导体在磁场中的运动一起应用于一种叫作发电机的机器中,使其能产生电压。当我们可以产生电压时,便可以使电流流动,当我们有电流时,便产生了功率。

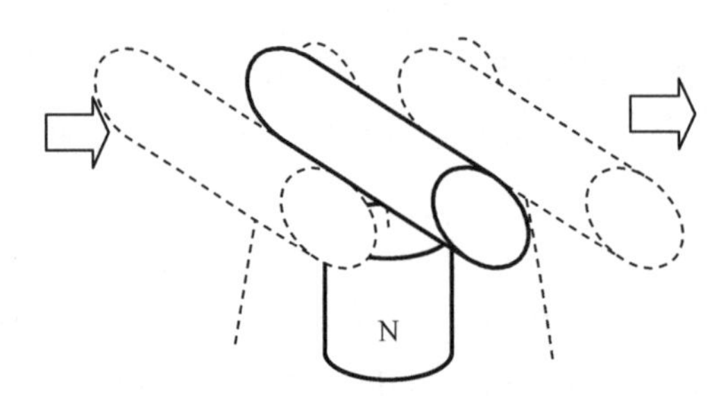

Fig. 1.4 Conductor is moving through the field

图 1.4 导体在磁场中移动

1.3 Generating Magnetism 磁性的产生

The above mentioned aspect of a magnetic field surrounding a conductor can be used to create a relative powerful magnet, an electro-magnet. If we wind up a conductor in a coil, all the small magnetic fields surrounding a conductor will add together to form a single, more powerful field(Fig. 1.5).

上述围绕导体的磁场可用于产生相对较强的磁体,即电磁体。如果我们将导体缠绕成线圈,那么围绕导体的所有小磁场将叠加在一起,形成一个更强大的磁场(图 1.5)。

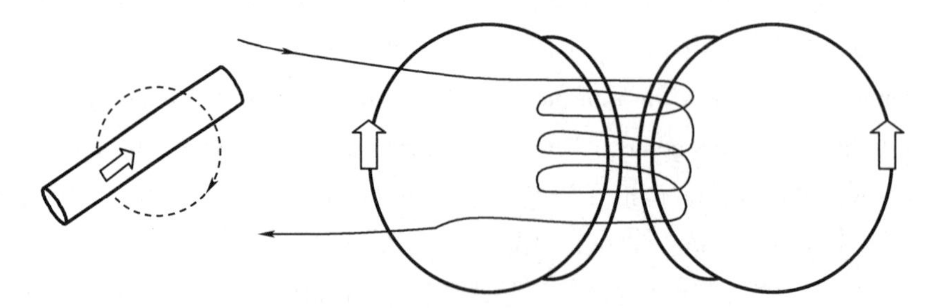

Fig. 1.5 Magnetic fields of a coil

图 1.5 线圈的磁场

This circumstance is used in solenoids and relays, where the forces of the magnetic field are used to move a core and thus close/open a valve or a set of contacts. It is also used in generators to produce a magnetic field powerful enough to generate an electromotive force that can drive a voltage(Fig. 1.6).

这一特性应用于螺线管和继电器,其中磁场的力用于移动铁芯,从而关闭/打开阀或一组触点。它也被应用于发电机,以产生足够强大的磁场,从而产生能够驱动电压的电动势(图 1.6)。

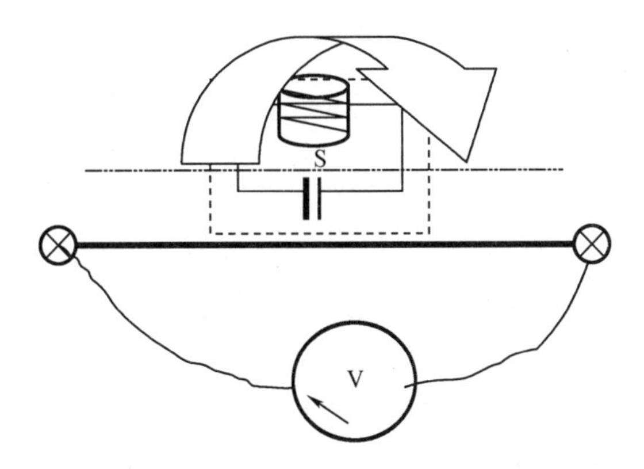

Fig. 1.6 Generate electromotive force

图 1.6 产生电动势

1.4 Batteries 电池

1.4.1 Atoms and Ions 原子和离子

An atom consists of a nucleus and around that nucleus electrons are orbiting. The nucleus consists of neutral neutrons and positive protons. The electrons are negative. Normally there is a balance between the number of positive protons and negative electrons, so if you see the atom as a whole, it is neutral. If, for some reason, the atom loses one or more of the electrons, there is a surplus of positive charges and if you see the atom as a whole, it will be positive. The electrons that the atom has lost will be attached to another atom, which will then have a surplus of negative charges and if you see that atom as a whole, it will be negative. These positive and negative atoms are called ions.

一个原子由一个原子核以及围绕该原子核在轨道上运动的电子组成。原子核由中子和带正电荷的质子组成。电子是带负电荷的。通常,质子和电子的数量是平衡的,所以如果把原子看成一个整体,它是呈中性的。若由于某种原因,原子失去了一个或多个电子,就会有剩余的正电荷,如果将原子看作一个整体,它将呈正电性。原子失去的电子将附着在另一个原子上,该原子就会有多余的负电荷,如果把这个原子看作一个整体,它将呈负电性。这些正负原子都称为离子。

We can chemically create ions. Just take ordinary salt, sodium chloride (NaCl) and dissolve it in water. The Sodium atom will be split from the Chloride atom and then we have a positive Sodium ion and a negative Chloride ion. This goes for all acids, bases and salts.

我们可以用化学方法制造离子。只需将普通的盐,如氯化钠(NaCl)溶解在水中即可。钠原子将与氯原子分裂,然后我们就得到一个带正电荷的钠离子和一个带负电荷的氯离子。这适用于所有酸、碱和盐。

1.4.2 Wet Batteries & Dry Batteries 湿电池和干电池

These circumstances are used in wet batteries to create a high potential and a low potential. The difference between a high and a low potential is what we call the voltage and when we have a voltage and a circuit we can have a current flowing.

这些情况用于湿电池以产生高电位和低电位。高电位和低电位之间的差就是我们所说的电压,当有电压和电路时,就可以产生电流的流动。

Let's take sulphuric acid (H_2SO_4) and dissolve it in water. Then we get hydrogen ions and sulphuric ions in the water. If we then enter a zinc rod and a copper rod into the solution and connect a voltmeter, we will be able to get a reading on the volt meter. That is because zinc and copper have different capabilities to create positive ions. That capability is referred to as electro positivity and metals can be arranged according to their electro positivity into the electromotive series.

将硫酸(H_2SO_4)溶解在水中,可得到氢离子和硫离子。如果在溶液中加入一根锌棒和一根铜棒,并连接一个电压表,则电压表就会有读数。这是因为锌和铜产生正离子的能力不同。这种产生正离子的能力被称为电正性,金属可以根据自身的电正性排列成电动势系列。

As zinc is more electropositive than copper, electrons will flow from the zinc to the copper through the volt meter, as the sulphuric ions, which are negative, are attracted to the positive zinc. When these two components interact, they release electrons. It is these electrons that flow through the volt meter. At the copper rod, the hydrogen ions receive electrons and create free hydrogen(Fig. 1.7).

由于锌比铜更具正电性,电子将通过电压表从锌流向铜,因为带负电荷的硫酸离子被吸引到带正电荷的锌上。当这两种离子相互作用时,它们会释放电子,正是这些电子流过了电压表。在铜棒处,氢离子接收电子并产生自由氢(图 1.7)。

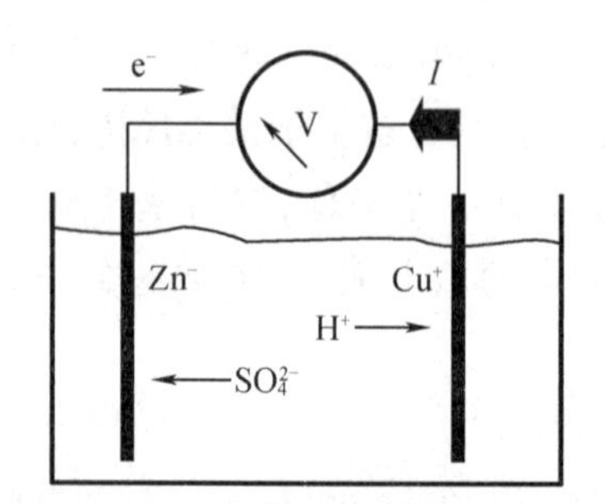

Fig. 1.7 Copper-Zinc primary battery

图 1.7 铜锌原电池

The dry batteries work out of the same principles, but the solution of acid and water is absorbed in a porous material. If you leave dry batteries in an appliance for a long period of time, you will experience that the solution will leak out. Alkaline batteries are also dry batteries, only instead of an acid.

干电池的工作原理与湿电池相同,但是酸和水的溶液是被多孔材料吸收的。如果把干电池放在电器里很长一段时间,你会发现溶液会漏出来。碱性电池也是干电池,只是使用碱代替酸。

Lead accumulators are of the wet type only here, two types of lead is used instead of copper and zinc. Further more, the process can be reversed so you can charge the battery again.

铅蓄电池为湿电池,它使用两种铅代替铜和锌,且反应过程可逆,所以可以再次为电池充电。

1.5 Capacitance & Capacitors 电容和电容器

The operation of charging and discharging a capacitor may be more easily understood if we consider the hydraulic analogy given in Fig. 1.8, where P represents a piston operated by a rod R and D is a rubber diaphragm stretched across a cylindrical chamber C. The cylinders are connected by pipes E and are filled with water.

如果我们考虑图 1.8 中给出的液压模拟,电容器的充电和放电操作可能更容易理解。其中,P 表示由杆 R 驱动的活塞,D 表示延伸穿过圆柱形腔室 C 的橡胶隔膜。气缸通过管道 E 连接,并充满水。

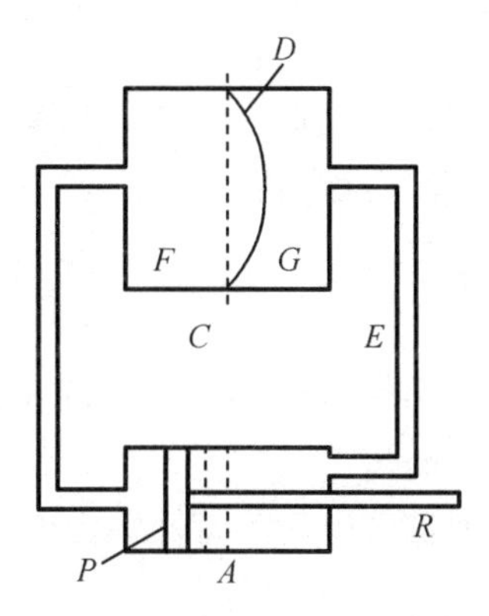

Fig. 1.8 Hydraulic analogy

图 1.8 液压模拟

When no force is being exerted on P, the diaphragm is flat, as shown dotted, and the piston is in position A. If P is pushed towards the left, water is withdrawn from G and forced into F and the diaphragm is in consequence distended, as shown full line. The greater the force applied to P, the greater is the amount of water displaced. But the rate at which this displacement takes place depends upon the resistance offered by pipes E, thus the smaller the cross-sectional area of the pipes, the longer is the time required for the steady state to be reached. The force applied to P is analogous to the e. m. f. of the battery, the quantity of water displaced corresponds to the charge, the rate at which the water passes any point in the pipes corresponds to the current and the cylinder C with its elastic diaphragm is the analogue of the capacitor.

当没有力施加在 P 上时,隔膜是平的,如图中虚线所示,活塞处于适当位置 A。如果 P 被向左推,水从 G 中排出并进入 F,隔膜因此膨胀,如图中实线所示。施加在 P 上的力越大,排出的水量就越多。但这种位移发生的速率取决于管道 E 提供的阻力,因此管道的横截面积越小,达到稳定状态所需的时间就越长。施加在 P 上的力类似于电池的电动势,排出的水量对应于电荷,水通过管道中任何一点的速度对应于电流,具有弹性隔膜的圆柱体 C 类似于电容器。

When the force exerted on P is removed, the distended diaphragm forces water out of F back into G; and if the frictional resistance of the water in the pipes exceeds a certain value, it is found that the piston is merely pushed back to its original position A. The strain energy stored in the diaphragm due to its distension is converted into heat by the frictional resistance. The effect is similar to the discharge of the capacitor through a resistor.

当施加在 P 上的力被移除时,膨胀的隔膜迫使水从 F 返回 G;如果管道中的水的摩擦阻力超过一定值,则发现活塞只是被推回到原来的位置 A。由于隔膜膨胀而储存在隔膜中的应变能通过摩擦阻力转换成热。其效果类似于电容器通过电阻器放电。

No water can pass from F to G through the diaphragm so long as it remains intact; but if it is strained excessively, it bursts, just as the insulation in a capacitor is punctured when the potential difference (p. d.) across it becomes excessive.

只要隔膜完好无损,水就不能从 F 流到 G;但是如果隔膜过度紧张,就会爆裂,就像电容器的绝缘层在其两端的电势差过大时会被击穿一样。

1.5.1 Capacitance 电容

The property of a capacitor to store an electric charge when its plates are at different potentials is referred to as its capacitance.

电容器在极板处于不同电位时储存电荷的特性称为电容。

1.5.2 Capacitors 电容器

Paper-insulated capacitor is shown in Fig. 1.9.

纸绝缘电容器如图 1.9 所示。

The unit of capacitance is termed the Farad (abbreviation F), which may be defined, as the capacitance of a capacitor between the plates of which there appears a potential difference of 1 V when it is charged by 1 C of electricity. It follows from the definition of the Farad that:

电容的单位为法拉,缩写为 F,可以定义为电容器极板之间充入 1 C(库仑)电荷出现 1 V 电势差的电容量。根据法拉的定义有

$$\frac{Q}{U}=C$$

$$Q=CU$$

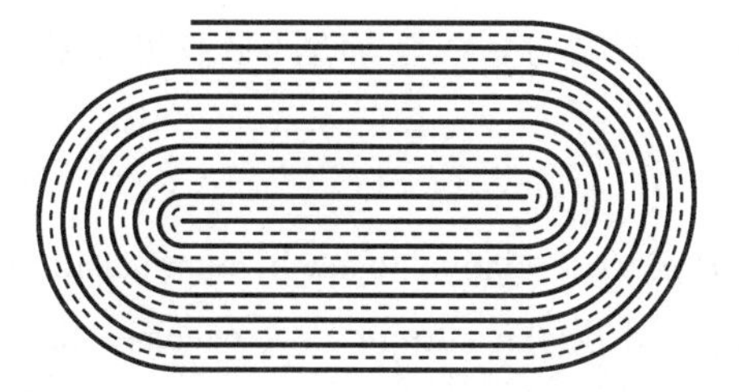

Fig. 1.9 Paper-insulated capacitor

图 1.9 纸绝缘电容器

In practice, if measured in Farad, the value of the capacitor will be very small and the capacitance is usually expressed in microfarads (μF) or in picofarads (pF), where 1 μF = 10^{-6} F and 1 pF = 10^{-12} F.

在实践中,若以法拉为单位,那么电容的数值会非常小,所以电容通常以微法(μF)或皮法(pF)表示,1 μF = 10^{-6} F,1 pF = 10^{-12} F。

1.6 Inductance 电感

The unit of inductance is termed the Henry(abbreviation H), in commemoration of a famous American physicist, Joseph Henry (1797—1878), who, quite independently, discovered electromagnetic induction in 1831.

电感的单位为亨利(缩写为 H),以纪念美国著名物理学家约瑟夫 · 亨利(1797—1878),他在 1831 年发现了电磁感应现象。

A circuit has an inductance of 1 H an e. m. f. of 1 V is induced in the circuit when the current varies uniformly at the rate of 1 A per second. If either the inductance or the rate of change of current is doubled the induced e. m. f. is doubled. Hence if a circuit has an inductance of L and if the current increases from I_1 to I_2 in t the average rate of change of current is $(I_2-I_1)/t$. And average induced e. m. f. is L×rate of change of current = $L \cdot (I_2-I_1)/t$ or $e=L \cdot \mathrm{d}i/\mathrm{d}t$.

一个具有 1 H 电感的电路,当电流以每秒 1 A 的速率均匀变化时,电路中会感应出 1 V 的电动势。如果电感或电流变化率增加 1 倍,则感应电动势增加 1 倍。因此,如果电路的电感为 L,并且电流在时间 t 内从 I_1 增加到 I_2,则电流的平均变化率为 $(I_2-I_1)/t$。平均感应电动势为电感×电流变化率 = $L \cdot (I_2-I_1)/t$ 或电动势 $e=L \cdot \mathrm{d}i/\mathrm{d}t$。

While this term gives the magnitude of the e. m. f. , there remains the problem of polarity. When a force is applied to a mechanical system, the system reacts by deforming, or accelerating or dissipating or absorbing energy. A comparable state exists when a force (voltage) is applied to an electric system, which accelerates (accepts magnetic energy in an inductor) or dissipates energy in heat (in a resistor).

虽然上面给出了感应电动势的大小,但仍然存在极性问题。当力施加到机械系统上时,该系统通过变形、加速、耗散或吸收能量来做出反应。当一个力(电压)被施加到一个电力系统上时,存在类似的状态,该电力系统会加速(吸收电感器中的磁能)或散热(在电阻器中)。

If two coils *A* and *C* are placed relative to each other as in Fig. 1. 10, then, when S is closed, some of the flux produced by the current in *A* becomes linked with *C*, and the e. m. f. induced in *C* circulates a momentary current through galvanometer G. Similarly when S is opened the collapse of the flux inducts an e. m. f. in the reverse direction in *C*. Since a change of current in one coil is accompanied by a change of flux linked with the other coil and therefore by an e. m. f. induced in the latter, the two coils are said to have mutual inductance.

如果两个线圈 *A* 和 *C* 彼此相对放置,如图 1. 10 所示,那么当 S 闭合时,*A* 中的电流产生的磁通量中的一部分与 *C* 相连接,*C* 中感应的电动势通过电流计 G 循环瞬时电流。类似地,当 S 打开时,磁通量的消失会在 *C* 中以相反的方向感应出电动势。由于一个线圈中电流的变化伴随着与另一个线圈相连的磁通量的变化,因此也伴随着在另一线圈中感应的电动势的变化,所以这两个线圈中的现象被称为互感。

If two circuits possess a mutual inductance of M and if the current in one circuit — termed the primary circuit — increases by $\mathrm{d}i$ in $\mathrm{d}t$, e. m. f. induced in secondary circuit is $M \cdot \mathrm{d}i/\mathrm{d}t$.

如果两个电路的互感为 M,并且如果一个电路(称为初级电路)中的电流在时间 $\mathrm{d}t$ 内增加了 $\mathrm{d}i$,则次级电路中的感应电动势为 $M \cdot \mathrm{d}i/\mathrm{d}t$。

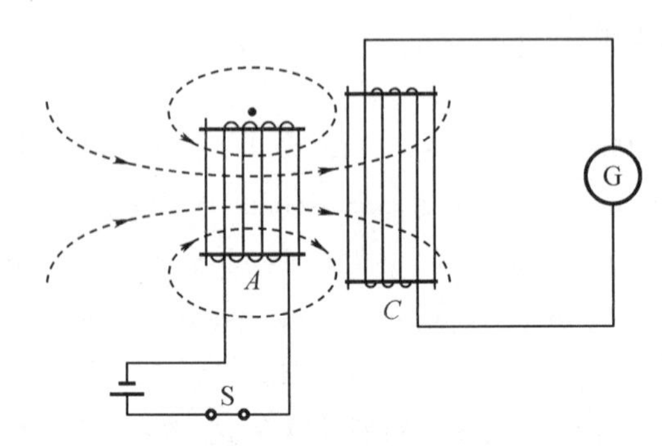

Fig. 1. 10 Mutual inductance

图 1. 10 互感

1.7 Electro Magnetism 电磁学

When a conductor carries an electric current, a magnetic field is produced around that conductor—a phenomenon discovered by Oersted at Copenhagen in 1820. He found that when a wire carrying an electric current was placed above a magnetic needle (Fig. 1. 11), the needle was deflected clockwise or anticlockwise, depending upon the direction of the current. Thus it is found that if we look along the conductor and if the current is flowing away from us, as shown by the cross inside the conductor in Fig. 1. 12, the magnetic field has a clockwise direction and the lines of magnetic flux can be represented by concentric circles around the wire.

当导体携带电流时,该导体周围会产生磁场——1820年奥斯特在哥本哈根发现了这一现象。他发现,当一根带电流的电线放在磁针上方时(图1.11),磁针的法线方向是顺时针还是逆时针取决于电流的方向。因此,如果我们沿着导体看,若电流从我们身边流出,如图1.12中导体内部的十字所示,则磁场是顺时针方向的,磁通线可以用导线周围的同心圆表示。

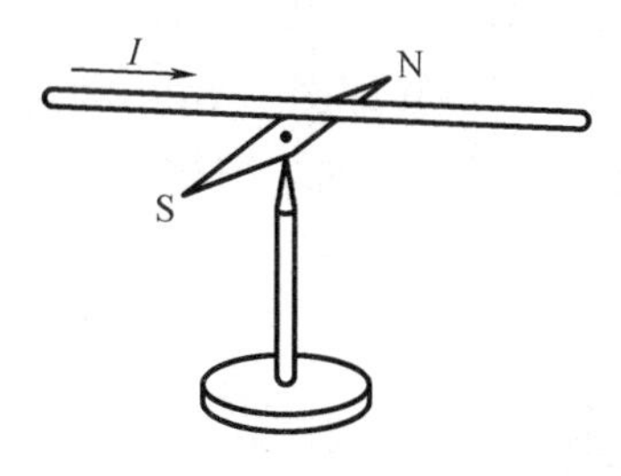

Fig. 1. 11 Oersted experiment
图1.11 奥斯特实验

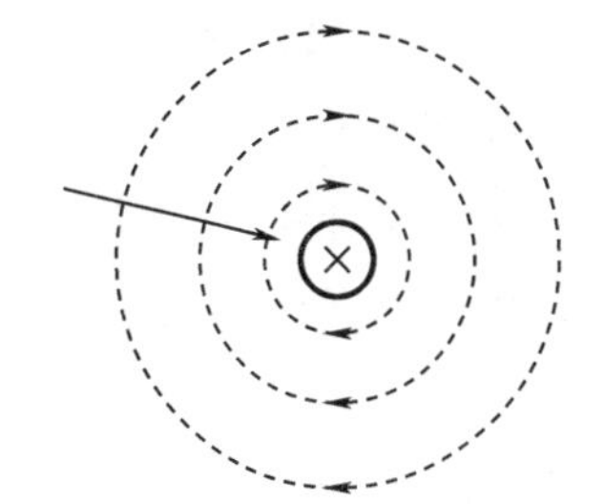

Fig. 1. 12 Magnetic flux due to current in straight conductor
图1.12 直导体通电时的磁场

We should note the interesting convention for showing the direction of current flow in a conductor. In Fig. 1. 13, we have a conductor in which we have drawn an arrow indicating the direction of conventional current flow. However, if we observe the conductor end on, the current would either be flowing towards us or away from us. If the current is flowing towards us, we indicate this by a dot equivalent to the approaching point of the arrow, and if the current is flowing away then it is represented by a cross equivalent to the departing tail feathers of the arrow.

我们应该注意指示导体中电流方向的有趣规律。在图1.13中有一个导体,我们在其中画了一个箭头,指示电流方向。然而,如果我们看向导体末端,电流要么流向我们,要么远离我们。如果电流流向我们,则用一个相当于箭头入射点的点来表示;如果电流正在流出,则用一个等同于箭尾羽离开的十字来表示。

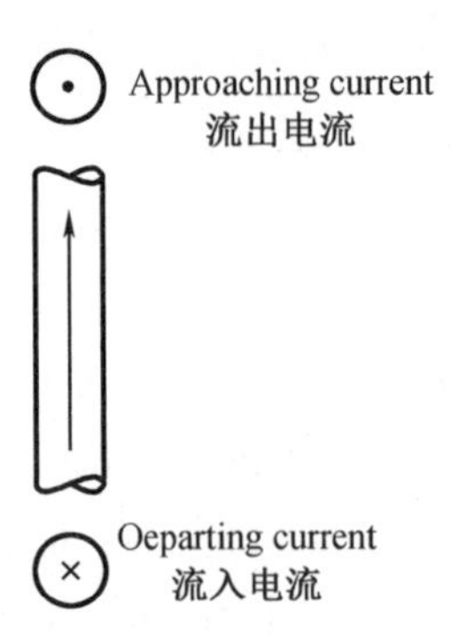

Fig. 1.13 Representation of current

图 1.13 电流的表示

A convenient method of representing the relationship between the direction of a current and that of its magnetic field is to place a woodscrew (Fig. 1.14) alongside the conductor carrying the current. In order that the screw may travel in the same direction as the current, namely towards the right in Fig. 1.14, it has to be turned clockwise when viewed from the left-hand side. Similarly, the direction of the magnetic field, viewed from the same side, is clockwise around the conductor, as indicated by the curved arrow *F*.

表示电流方向与其磁场方向之间关系的一种便捷的方法是在承载电流的导体旁边放置一个木螺钉(图 1.14)。为了使螺钉沿与电流相同的方向移动(即图 1.14 中的右侧),从左侧观察时,必须顺时针转动螺钉。类似地,从同一侧看,磁场的方向是围绕导体沿顺时针方向的,如曲线箭头 *F* 所示。

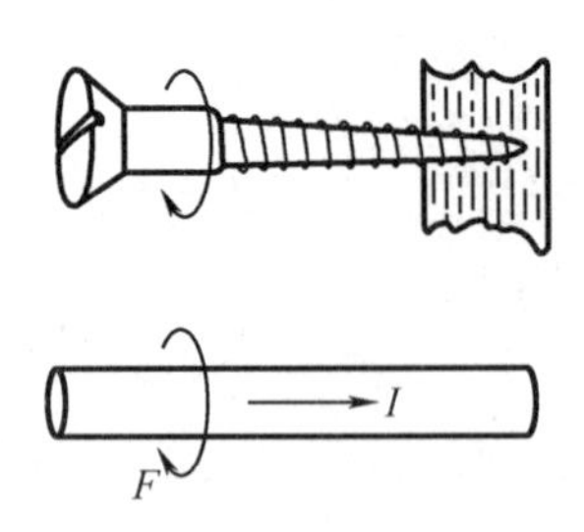

Fig. 1.14 Right hand screw rule

图 1.14 右旋螺丝规则

An alternative method of deriving this relationship is to grip the conductor with the right hand, with the thumb outstretched parallel to the conductor and pointing in the direction of the current, the fingers then point in the direction of the magnetic flux around the conductor.

推导这种关系的另一种方法是用右手握住导体,拇指平行于导体并指向电流方向,则手指指向导体周围的磁通量方向。

1.8 Magnetic Field of a Solenoid 线圈的磁场

If a coil is wound on a steel rod, as in Fig. 1. 15, and connected to a battery, the steel becomes magnetized and behaves like a permanent magnet. The magnetic field of the electromagnet is represented by the dotted lines and its direction by the arrowheads.

如果线圈缠绕在钢棒上,如图 1. 15 所示,并与电池连接,则钢棒会被磁化,就像永久磁铁一样。电磁铁的磁场用虚线表示,其方向用箭头表示。

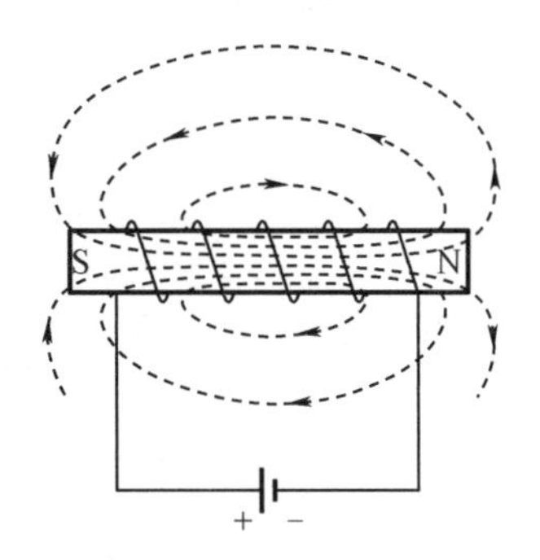

Fig. 1. 15 Solenoid with steel core

图 1. 15 带钢芯的线圈

The grip rule can be expressed thus: if the solenoid is gripped with the right hand, with the four fingers pointing in the direction of the current, i. e. conventional current, then the thumb outstretched parallel to the axis of the solenoid points in the direction of the magnetic field inside the solenoid.

抓握规则可以这样表达:如果用右手抓握螺线管,四手指指向电流方向,那么平行于螺线管轴线的拇指指向螺线管内部的磁场方向。

In 1831, Michael Faraday made the great discovery of electromagnetic induction, namely a method of obtaining an electric current with the aid of magnetic flux. He wound two coils, *A* and *C*, around a steel ring *R*, as in Fig. 1. 16 and found that, when switch S was closed, a deflection was obtained on galvanometer G, and that when S was opened, G was deflected in the reverse direction. A few weeks later, he found that when a permanent magnet N, S was moved relative to a coil *C* (Fig. 1. 17), galvanometer G was deflected in one direction when the magnet was moved towards the coil and in the reverse direction when the magnet was withdrawn; and it was this experiment that finally convinced Faraday that an electric current could be produced by the movement of magnetic flux relative to a coil. Faraday also showed that the magnitude of the induced e. m. f. is proportional to the rate at which the magnetic flux passed through the coil is varied. Alternatively, we can say that when a conductor cuts or is cut by magnetic flux, an e. m. f. is generated in the conductor and the magnitude of the generated e. m. f. is proportional to the rate at which the conductor cuts or is cut by the magnetic flux.

1831 年,迈克尔 · 法拉第发现了电磁感应现象,即借助磁通量获得电流的方法。他将两个线圈 *A* 和 *C* 缠绕在钢环 *R* 上,如图 1.16 所示,他发现当开关 S 闭合时,电流计 G 指针发生偏转,而当 S 断开时,G 指针发生反向偏转。几周后,他发现当永磁体 N、S 极相对于线圈 *C* 移动(图 1.17),磁体朝向线圈移动时,电流计 G 指针向一个方向偏转;当磁体收回时,指针则向相反方向偏转。正是这个实验最终说服了法拉第,使他相信磁通量相对于线圈的运动可以产生电流。法拉第还表明,感应电动势的大小与通过线圈的磁通量变化的速率成正比。或者我们可以说,当导体切割或被磁通量切割时,导体中会产生电磁波,产生的电磁波的大小与导体切割或磁通量切割的速度成正比。

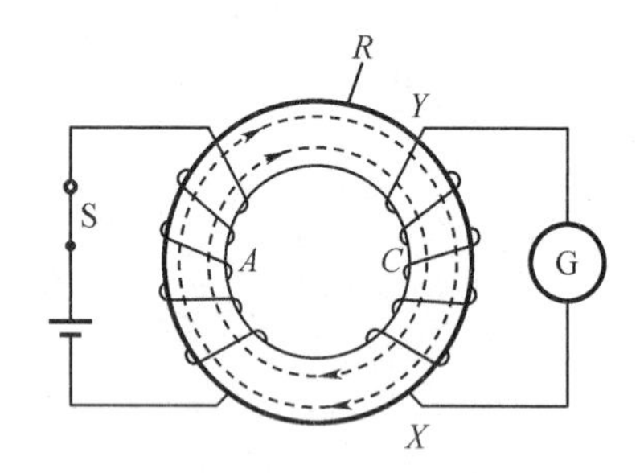

Fig. 1. 16 Electromagnetic induction between coils

图 1.16 线圈间的电磁感应

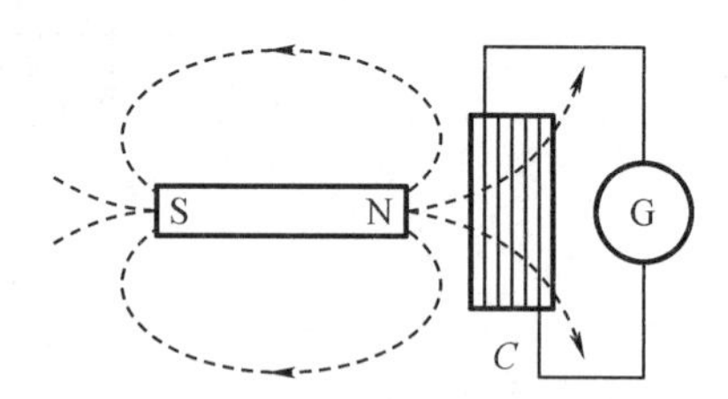

Fig. 1. 17 Electromagnetic induction between coil and permanent magnet

图 1.17 线圈和永磁体间的电磁感应

In 1834, Heinrich Lenz, a German physicist, enunciated a simple rule, now known as Lenz's law, which can be expressed thus: The direction or a induced e. m. f. is always such that it tends to set up a current opposing the motion or the change of flux responsible for inducing that e. m. f.

1834 年,德国物理学家海因里希 · 楞次阐述了一个简单的规则,该规则被称为楞次定律。楞次定律可以这样表述:感应电动势的方向总是这样的,即它倾向于建立一个与导致电动势的运动方向或磁通量变化方向相反的电流。

Let us consider the application of Lenz's law to the ring shown in Fig. 1. 16. By applying either the screw or the grip rule given as above, we find that when S is closed and the battery has the polarity shown, the direction of the magnetic flux in the ring is clockwise. Consequently, the current in *C* must be such as to try to produce a flux in an anticlockwise direction, tending to oppose the growth of the flux due to *A*, namely the flux that is responsible for the e. m. f. induced in *C*. But an anti-clockwise flux in the ring would require the current in *C* to be passing through the coil from *X* to *Y* (Fig 1. 16). Hence, this must also be the direction of the e. m. f. induced in *C*.

让我们考虑一下楞次定律在图 1.16 所示环上的应用。通过应用上面给出的螺钉或抓握规则,我们发现当 S 闭合且电池具有如图所示极性时,环中的磁通量方向为顺时针。因此,环 *C* 中的电流必须试图产生一个逆时针方向的磁通量,倾向于反对环 *A* 引起的磁通量的增长,即导致产生电动势的磁通量。但是环中的逆时针磁通量将要求环 C 中的电流从 X 到 Y 通过线圈(图 1.16),因此这也必须是环 C 中感应电动势的方向。

Two methods are available for deducing the direction of the induced or generated e. m. f. namely (a) Fleming's right-hand rule(Fig. 1. 18) and (b) Lenz's law. The former is empirical, but the latter is fundamental in that it is based upon electrical principles.

有两种方法可用于推导感应或产生的感应电动势的方向,即弗莱明右手定则(图 1. 18)和楞次定律。前者是经验的,但后者是基础的,因为它基于电学原理。

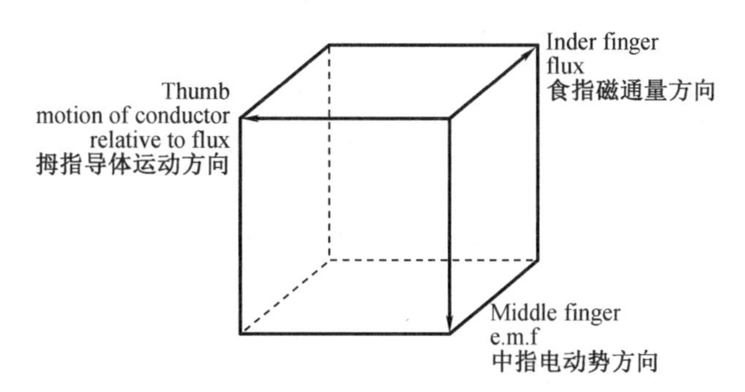

Fig. 1. 18　Fleming's right-hand rule

图 1. 18　弗莱明右手定则

If the right index finger is pointed in the direction of the magnetic flux as in Fig. 1. 18, and the thumb is pointed in the direction of motion of the conductor relative to the magnetic field, then the middle finger, held at right angles to both the thumb and the inder finger, represents the direction of the e. m. f. The fingers and their association with the correct quantity present some difficulty to many students. Easy manipulation can be acquired only by experience: It may be helpful to associate field or flux with inder finger, motion of the conductor relative to the field with thumb and e. m. f. with middle finger. If any two of these are correctly applied, the third is correct automatically.

如果右手食指指向磁通量方向,如图 1. 18 所示,拇指指向导体相对于磁场的运动方向,则中指(与拇指和食指都成直角)表示感应电动势的方向。手指的操作及其与物理量的正确关联给许多学生带来了困难,只有通过实践才能获得熟练操作:将场或磁通量与食指相关联,将导体相对于场的运动与拇指相关联,将电动势与中指相关联。如果其中任意两指应用正确,则第三指自然正确。

Left-hand rule can be summarized as follows:

(1) Hold the thumb, index finger and middle finger of the left hand in the manner indicated (Fig. 1. 19) whereby they are mutually at right angles.

(2) Point the index finger in the field direction.

(3) Point the middle finger in the current direction.

(4) The thumb then indicates the direction of the mechanical force exerted by the conductor.

左手定则可概括如下:

(1)按图 1.19 指示的方式伸出左手的拇指、食指和中指,使它们相互成直角。

(2)将食指指向磁通量的方向。

(3)将中指指向电流的方向。

(4)然后拇指指向导体受力的方向。

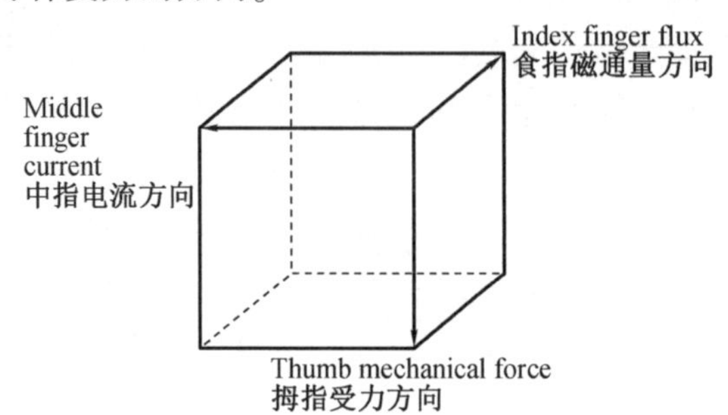

Fig. 1.19 Left-hand rule

图 1.19 左手定则

By trying this with your left hand, we can readily demonstrate that if either the current or the direction of the field is reversed then the direction of the force is also reversed. Also we can demonstrate that, if both current and field are reversed, the direction of the force remains unchanged.

通过用左手如此尝试,我们可以很容易地验证,如果电流或磁场方向反转,那么力的方向也会反转。我们还可以验证,如果电流和磁场都反向,力的方向保持不变。

1.9 Alternating Versus Dirrect 交流电与直流电

Here we are going to look at how the electricity that is provided in the outlets on the walls is generated.

下面我们将研究墙壁上插座中的电力是如何产生的。

We learned how electricity could be generated using magnetism that again was generated from electricity. Now we are going to take a look as to how this looks if we put it into graphics.

我们学过如何利用电产生磁场,又如何利用磁场来发电。现在我们来看看,如果将电压用图形来表示会是什么样子。

The voltage that is produced in a battery is constant, if it is over a shorter period of time. In a diagram where we have the voltage and the time as the two axis's it looks like Fig. 1.20.

如果在较短的时间内观察,电池中产生的电压是恒定的。在一个以电压和时间为两轴的坐标图中,它看起来如图 1.20 所示。

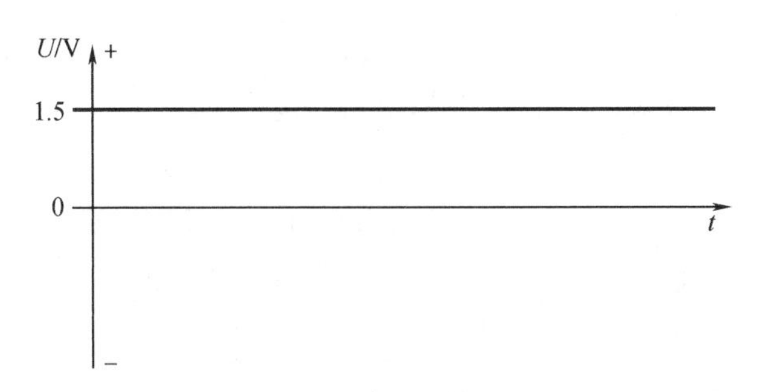

Fig. 1.20 DC voltage

图 1.20 直流电压

As the magnetic field is rotating, the electromotive force that is generated in the conductor will alter simultaneously. When the North Pole is passing the conductor, an electromotive force will be generated in one direction. When the South Pole is passing the conductor an electromotive force will be generated in the opposite direction. This produces the voltage that drives the current (again assuming that we have a closed circuit). The AC voltage looks like Fig. 1. 21.

当磁场旋转时,导体中产生的感应电动势将同时改变。当 N 极经过导体时,将在一个方向上产生感应电动势。当 S 极通过导体时,将产生相反方向的感应电动势。这会产生驱动电流的电压(再次假设我们有一个闭合电路)。交流电压如图 1.21 所示。

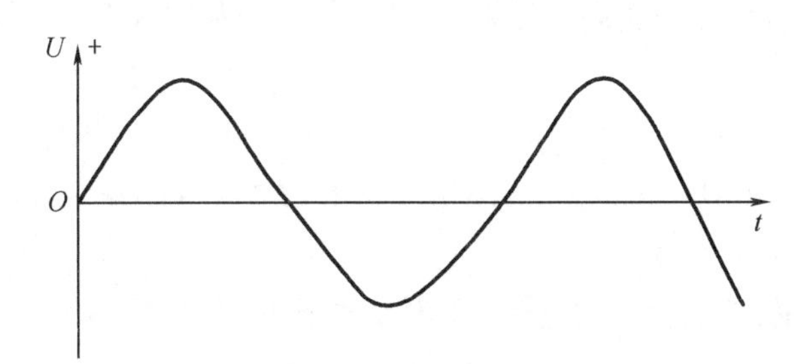

Fig. 1.21 AC voltage

图 1.21 交流电压

The time that has passed for one cycle, that is the time it takes for the North Pole to complete one full revolution, the number of cycles that completedby the north pole for 1 s is referred to as the frequency. The frequency is measured in Hz and is denoted with an f.

一个周期所经过的时间即 N 极旋转完整一圈所需的时间。N 极 1 s 内旋转的周期数称为频率,以赫兹(Hz)为单位测量,用 f 表示。

In Europe and China, the frequency at the outlets is 50 Hz. This means that in 1 s, 50 cycles are completed. On vessels 60 cycles are completed every second.

在欧洲国家和中国,供电频率为 50 Hz。这意味着在 1 s 内完成 50 个周期。在船舶上,每秒完成 60 个周期。

The above curve(Fig. 1. 21) is called a sinus curve, that is because it relates to trigonometry. The full rotation can be seen as a circle and as the curve above. This aspect can be seen in Fig. 1. 22.

图 1. 21 所示曲线称为正弦曲线,这是因为它与三角函数有关。整个旋转可以看作是一个圆及其对应的曲线。这一点可以在图 1. 22 中体现。

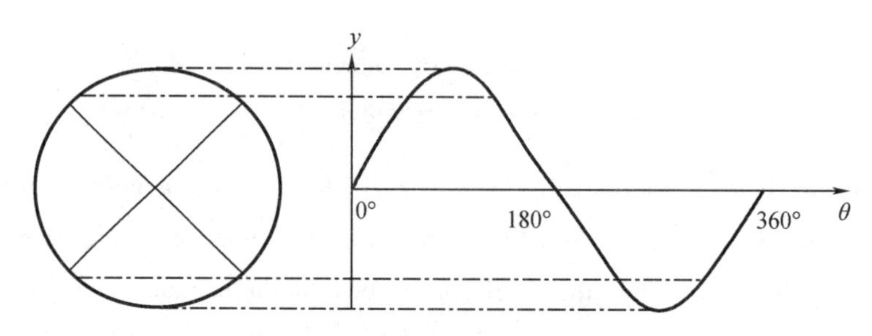

Fig. 1. 22 Circle and sinus curve

图 1. 22 圆与正弦波

As it can be seen, the higher the revolutions, the higher the frequency. You can also calculate the time it takes for one revolution or cycle if you know the frequency, with the following formula:

可以看出,转速越高,频率越高。如果知道频率,可以利用以下公式计算出周期:

$$T=1/f$$

If the frequency is 50 Hz, then we know that in 1 s 50 cycles are completed. So the time for one cycle must be 1/50=0. 02 s.

如果频率是 50 Hz,那么我们知道在 1 s 内完成了 50 个周期。因此,一个周期为 1/50=0. 02 s。

You can also calculate how many revolutions the generator is running at if it has one pair of poles (north and south). If again the frequency is 50 Hz, the generator is revolving 50 times per second. In order to get that in revolutions per minutes you multiply with 60, which gives 3,000 r/min.

如果发电机有一对磁极(N 极和 S 极),还可以计算发电机的转速。再次设频率为 50 Hz,即发电机每秒旋转 50 次。为了得到每分钟的转数就需要乘以 60,于是得到 3 000 r/min。

On vessels, the frequency is 60 Hz, but here the generators normally run at 720 r/min. How can that be?

在船舶上,供电频率为 60 Hz,船上的发电机通常以 720 r/min 的速度运行。这怎么可能呢?

That is because the generator has more than one pair of poles and we can calculate how many pairs it has. If it had one pair of poles, the generator would have to run with 60×60 = 3,600 r/min and if we divide that with 720, we get 5 pair of poles (for a single phase).

这是因为发电机有不止 1 对磁极,我们可以计算一下它有多少对磁极。假设发电机只有 1 对磁极,那么它必须以 60×60 = 3 600 r/min 的速度运行,我们将其除以 720,则得到 5 对磁极(单相)。

Now we are going to take a look at how the current curve looks in a direct and alternating system(Fig. 1.23).

现在我们来看看直流和交流系统中电流的波形(图 1.23)。

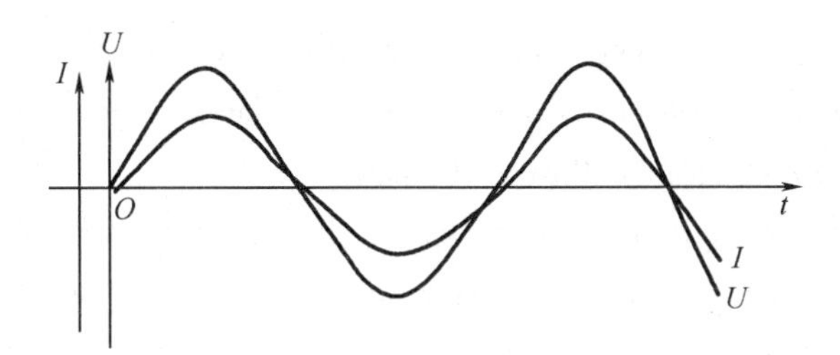

Fig. 1.23 AC voltage and current

图 1.23 交流电压和电流

But there is something called phase shift. Phase shift means that the current is displaced in relation to the voltage (Fig. 1.24). It can be either forward or backward. The reason for the displacement is that not all resistance is "pure" resistance.

但是有一个叫作相移的概念——相移指电流相对于电压发生的位移(图 1.24)。这个位移可以向前或向后。发生位移的原因是并非所有阻力都是"纯"电阻。

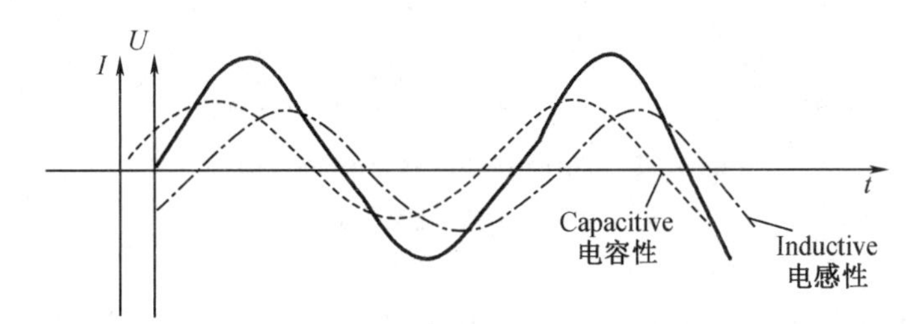

Fig. 1.24 Phase shift

图 1.24 相移

Let us take a coil as an example. Then there is a resistance in the wire in the coil, but because it is a coil and it creates a magnetic field, there is also another component called inductance. This inductance "delays" the current in relation to the voltage. If you take a capacitor, the reverse will happen, then the current will be advanced in relation to the voltage. This is called capacitance.

我们以线圈为例。线圈中的导线存在电阻,但是因为它是线圈,便会产生磁场,还会产生另一个分量,叫作电感。电感能使电流相对于电压滞后。如果在电路中使用电容器,则会发生相反的情况,电流将相对于电压超前,这种特性叫作电容性。

1.10 Three-phase Voltage 三相电压

In the example given in chapter one of how to generate alternating voltage in a generator, we had one conductor exposed to the magnetic field. If we insert two more conductors that is physically placed in a circle with 120° in between (a full circle has 360°) we get a voltage that looks like it is shown as Fig. 1.25 for the three conductors. Also now we don't call it conductors but phases. We name the phases as phase 1, 2 and 3. In the old days, they were called phase R, S and T. Phases 1 is always succeeded by phase 2 and then phase 3 in a normal network. That is of course because it is rotating as it is illustrated below.

在前文中给出的如何在发电机中产生交流电压这一示例中,我们将一个导体暴露在磁场中。如果再插入两个导体,且将这两个导体放置在一个圆圈中,使三个导体彼此之间成120°夹角(一个完整的圆为360°),则得到的电压如图1.25所示。现在我们不再称为导体,而是称为相位。我们将相位命名为相1、相2和相3。在过去,它们被称为R、S和T相。在正常网络中,相1总是由相2和相3接替,因为它们在不停地旋转。

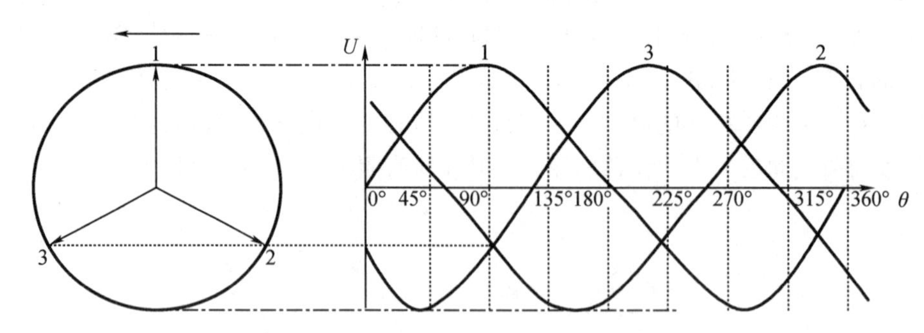

Fig. 1.25 Three-phase AC voltage curve

图1.25 三相交流电压波形

1.10.1 Star and Triangle Connection 星形连接和三角形连接

The 6 ends of the 3 conductors (windings) are taken out to the terminal board of the generator and when you have the 6 ends, you have the choice of connecting the conductors in either star or triangle connection (Fig. 1.26).

3根导线(绕组)的6个端部被引出到发电机的接线板上,当有6个端点时,可以选择以星形或三角形方式连接导线(图1.26)。

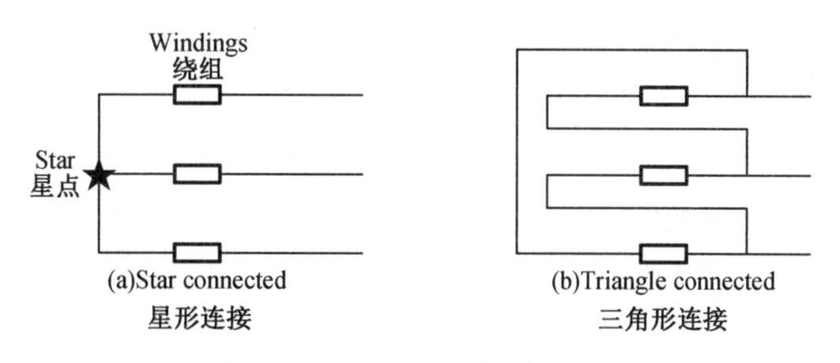

Fig. 1.26 Star and triangle connection

图 1.26 星形连接和三角形连接

Previously, we have learned that it is a single conductor that is moved in a magnetic field, but actually, in a generator of any kind, it is several conductors. This is because a single conductor has a limited capability to generate the kind of voltage that we usually require. So instead of a single conductor, we have a winding for each phase.

之前我们学习过在磁场中移动的单个导体,但实际上在任何类型的发电机中,都有多个导体。这是因为单个导体产生电压的能力有限。因此,发电机中每相都设置了一个绕组,而非单个导体。

The voltage that is generated in the windings can be shown with vectors as well. The voltages are displaced with 120° in between as a result of the physical design of the generator. But then the voltage generated depends on how the windings are connected, whether they are connected in a star or triangle. If the generator is connected in a star connection, the voltages produced will look like Fig. 1.27.

绕组中产生的电压也可以用矢量来表示。由于发电机的物理设计特性,两相电压在120°之间变化。但是,产生的电压与绕组的连接方式(即星形连接或三角形连接)有关。如果发电机以星形方式连接,则产生的电压如图 1.27 所示。

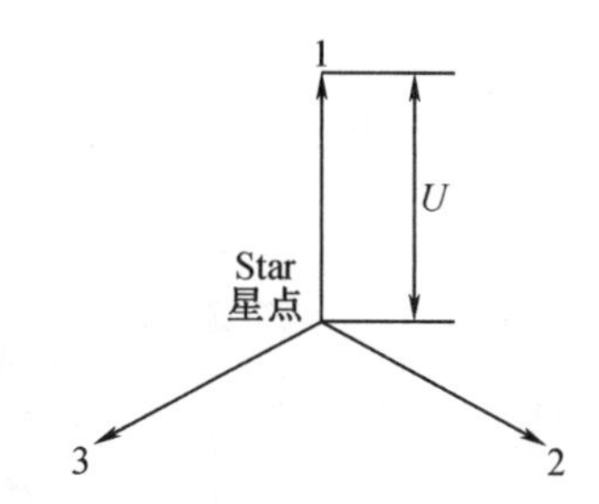

Fig. 1.27 Star connection voltage

图 1.27 星形连接时的电压

The point where the three windings meet is called the star point. The potential at this point is 0 V, under normal load condition (equal phase load). The voltage generated over one winding is then U.

三相绕组的交点称为中性点。在正常负载(平衡负载)条件下,该点的电位为 0 V。在一个绕组上产生的电压为 U。

If we then take a look at the voltages, then we can access the phase voltage U. But we can also get a voltage from each of the "points", this voltage we call line voltage U_{1-2} or U_{1-3} or U_{2-3}, the size is the same as in Fig. 1. 28. That is because when you add the two vectors of the two windings in the star connection you get the final voltage.

如果我们看一下电压向量,就可以得到相电压 U。但是也可以从每个"点"间得到电压,这个电压被称为线电压 U_{1-2} 或 U_{1-3} 或 U_{2-3},它们的大小相同(图 1. 28)。这是因为当把星形连接中两个绕组的两个矢量相加时,就得到了最终的电压。

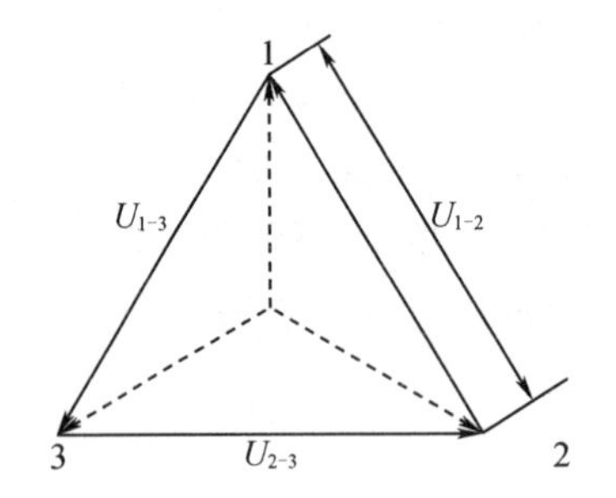

Fig. 1. 28　Voltage between points

图 1. 28　端点间的电压

The fact is that the difference between the voltages in phase and line is $\sqrt{3}$. So the difference between U_1 and U_{1-2} is:

事实上,相电压和线电压相差$\sqrt{3}$倍。所以 U_1 和 U_{1-2} 的关系是:

$$U_{1-2}=\sqrt{3}U_1$$

Below Fig. 1. 29 we can see how a generator is working in principle. In the real world it looks like Fig. 1. 30.

发电机的工作原理如图 1. 29 所示。在现实世界中,它看起来如图 1. 30 所示。

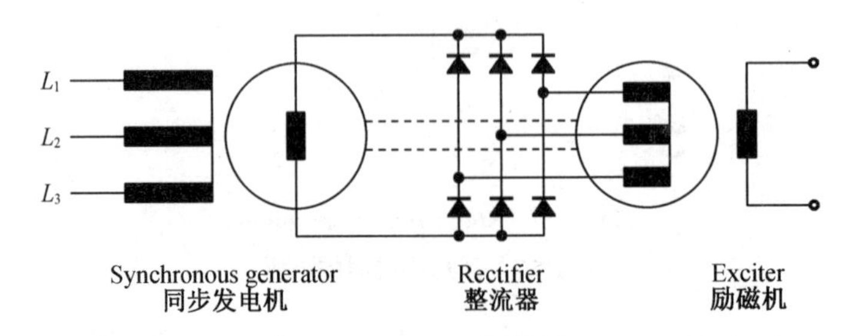

Fig. 1. 29　Synchronous generator principle simple drawing

图 1. 29　同步发电机原理简图

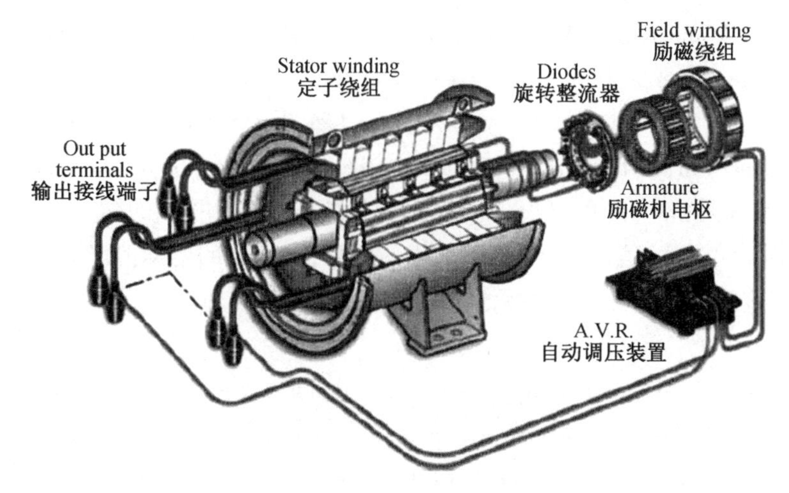

Fig. 1.30 Synchronous generator construction

图 1.30 同步发电机结构

1.10.2 Three-phase System 三相系统

The system utilizing two windings is referred to as a two-phase system and that utilizing three windings is referred to as a three-phase system. Let us consider the three-phase system in detail.

利用两个绕组的系统被称为两相系统,利用三个绕组的系统被称为三相系统。下面我们详细讲解三相系统。

In Fig. 1.31, RR_1, YY_1 and BB_1 represent three similar loops fixed to one another at angles of 120°, each loop terminating in a pair of slip-rings carried on the shaft as indicated in Fig. 1.32. We shall refer to the slip-rings connected to sides R, Y and B as the "finishes" of the respective phases and those connected to R_1, Y_1 and B_1 as the "starts".

在图 1.31 中,RR_1、YY_1 和 BB_1 表示三个类似回路,它们彼此保持 120°的固定角度,每个回路终止于一对滑环,如图 1.32 所示,滑环安装在轴上。将连接到 R、Y 和 B 侧的滑环称为各相的"尾端",将连接到 R_1、Y_1 和 B_1 侧的滑环则称为各相的"首端"。

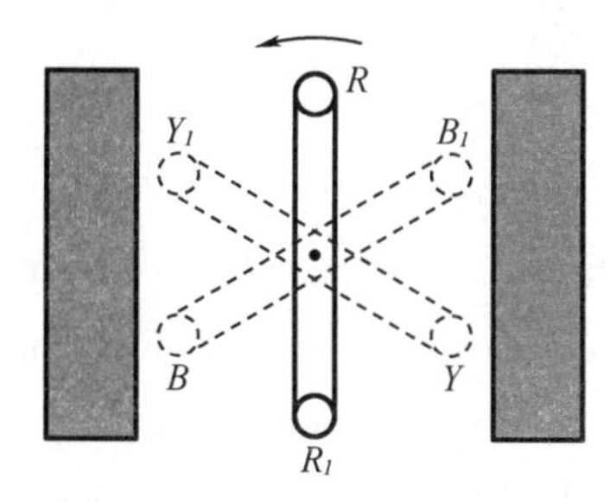

Fig. 1.31 Generation of three phase e. m. f

图 1.31 产生三相电动势

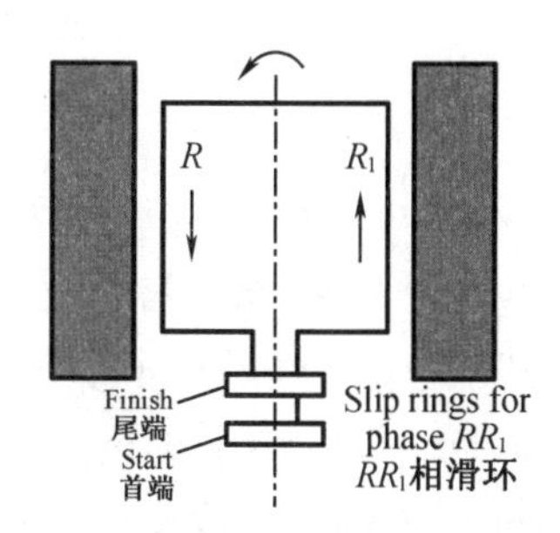

Fig. 1.32 Loop RR_1 at instant max. e. m. f.

图 1.32 回路 RR_1 在瞬时感应电动势最大位置

The letters R, Y and B are abbreviations of "red" "yellow" and "blue", namely the colors used to identify the three phases. Also, "red-yellow-blue" is the sequence that is universally adopted to denote that the e. m. f. in the yellow phase lags that in the red phase by a third of a cycle, and the e. m. f. in the blue phase lags that in the yellow phase by another third of a cycle.

字母 R、Y 和 B 是"red(红色)""yellow(黄色)"和"blue(蓝色)"的缩写,即用于标识三相的颜色。此外,"红-黄-蓝"是一个普遍采用的序列,黄色相的电动势滞后于红色相三分之一个周期,而蓝色相的电动势又滞后于黄色相三分之一个周期。

Suppose three coils are rotated anticlockwise at a uniform speed in the magnetic field due to poles N,S. The e. m. f. generated in loop RR_1 is zero for the position shown in Fig. 1. 31. When the loop has moved through 90° to the position shown in Fig. 1. 32, the generated e. m. f is at its maximum value, its direction round the loop being from the start slip-ring towards the finish slip-ring. Let us regard this direction as positive, consequently the e. m. f. induced in loop RR_1 can he represented by the full-line curve of Fig. 1. 33.

假设由于磁极 N、S 的作用,三个线圈在磁场中以均匀的速度逆时针旋转。回路 RR_1 中产生的电动势在图 1. 31 所示位置为零。当回路 RR_1 移动 90°至图 1. 32 所示位置时,产生的电动势处于最大值,其绕回路的方向是从起点滑环到终点滑环。我们把这个方向视为正方向,则回路 RR_1 中感应的电动势可以用图 1. 33 所示的实线曲线表示。

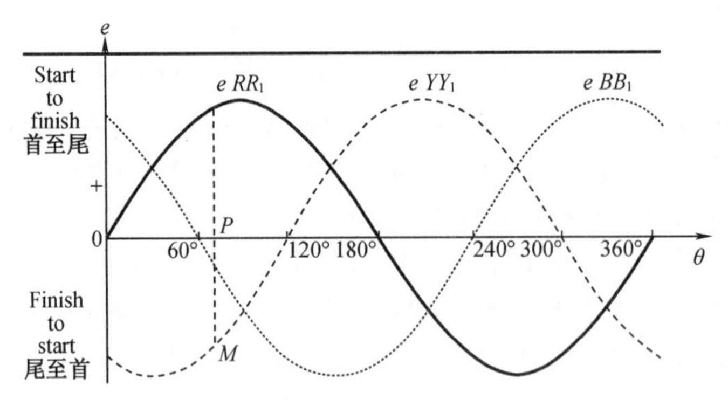

Fig. 1. 33　Wave form of three-phase e. m. f.

图 1. 33　三相感应电动势波形

Since the loops are being rotated anticlockwise, it is evident from Fig. 1. 31 that the e. m. f. generated in side Y of loop YY_1 has exactly the same amplitude as that generated in side R, but lags by 120° (or one-third of a cycle). Similarly, the e. m. f. generated in side B of loop BB_1 is equal to but lags that in side Y by 120°. Hence the e. m. f. s generated in loops RR_1, YY_1 and BB_1 are represented by the three equally spaced curves of Fig. 1. 33, the e. m. f. s being assumed positive when their directions round the loops are from "start" to "finish" of their respective loops.

由于回路是逆时针旋转的,从图 1. 31 中可以明显看出,在回路 YY_1 的 Y 侧产生的电动势与 R 侧的幅值相同,但滞后 120°(或一个周期的三分之一)。类似地,在回路 BB_1 的 B 侧产生的电动势等于但滞后于 Y 侧电动势 120°。因此,回路 RR_1、YY_1 和 BB_1 中产生的电动势由图 1.33 中三条等距曲线表示,当它们围绕回路的方向从各自回路的"首端"到"尾端"时,认为电动势方向为正。

If the instantaneous value of the e. m. f. generated in phase RR_1 is represented by $e_R = e_m \sin I$, then instantaneous e. m. f. in YY_1 is $e_Y = e_m \sin(I-120°)$ and instantaneous e. m. f. in BB_1 is $e_B = e_m \sin(I-240°)$.

如果相 RR_1 中产生的电动势的瞬时值由 $e_R = e_m \sin I$ 表示,则 YY_1 中的瞬时电动势为 $e_Y = e_m \sin(I-120°)$,BB_1 中的瞬时电动势为 $e_B = e_m \sin(I-240°)$。

1.10.3 Delta Connection of Three-phase Windings 三相绕组的三角形连接

The three-phases of Fig. 1.31 can for convenience be represented as in Fig. 1.34 where the phases are shown isolated from one another; L_1, L_2 and L_3 represent loads connected across the respective phases. Since we have assumed the e. m. f. s to be positive when acting from "start" to "finish", they can be represented by the arrows e_R, e_Y and e_B in Fig. 1.34. This arrangement necessitates six line conductors and is therefore cumbersome and expensive so let us consider how it may be simplified. For instance, let us join R_1 and Y together as in Fig. 1.35, thereby enabling conductors 2 and 3 of Fig. 1.34 to be replaced by a single conductor.

方便起见,图 1.31 中的三相可以如图 1.34 中所示,其中各相彼此隔离;L_1、L_2 和 L_3 表示连接在各相上的负载。由于假设当从首端到尾端时,电动势为正值,因此可以用图 1.34 中的箭头 e_R、e_Y 和 e_B 表示各相的电动势。这种布置需要 6 条导电线路,笨重且昂贵,我们来考虑如何简化它。例如,如图 1.35 所示将 R_1 和 Y 连接在一起,从而使图 1.34 中的导体 2 和导体 3 能够被单个导体代替。

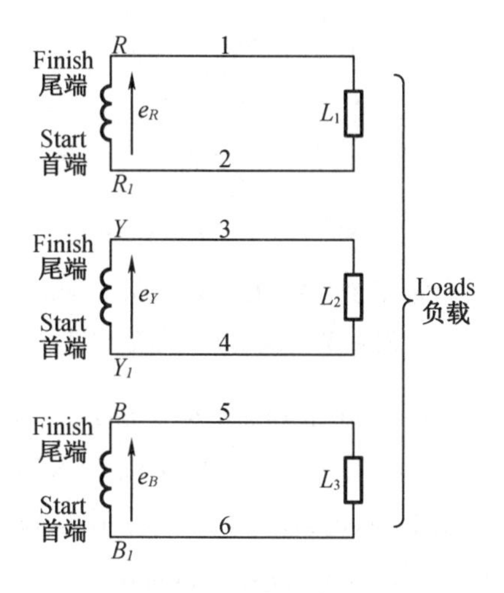

Fig. 1.34 Three-phase winding with 6 conductors

图 1.34 6 导线三相绕组

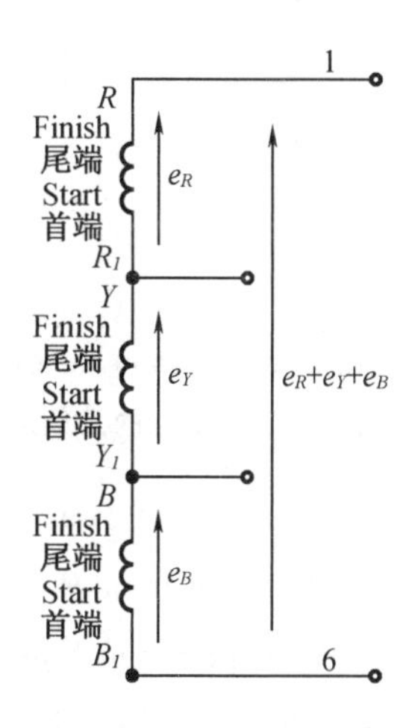

Fig. 1.35 e. m. f. in delta connected winding

图 1.35 三角形连接的感应电动势

Instantaneous value of total e. m. f. acting from B_1 to R is

从 B_1 到 R 产生的总电动势的瞬时值为

$$\begin{aligned} e_R+e_Y+e_B &= e_m[\sin I+\sin(I-120°)+\sin(I-240°)] \\ &= e_m(\sin I+\sin I\cdot\cos 120°-\cos I\cdot\sin 120°+\sin I\cdot\cos 240°-\cos I\cdot\sin 240°) \\ &= e_m(\sin I-0.5\sin I-0.866\cos I-0.5\sin I+0.866\cos I) \\ &= 0 \end{aligned}$$

Since this condition holds for every instant, it follows that R and B_1, can be joined together, as in Fig. 1. 36, without any circulating current being set up around the circuit. The three line conductors are joined to the junctions.

由于此条件在每一瞬间都成立,因此 R 和 B_1 可以连接在一起,如图 1. 36 所示,电路的回路中没有任何循环电流。三线导体与此节点连接。

The circuit derived in Fig. 1. 36 is usually drawn as in Fig. 1. 37 and the arrangement is referred to as delta (from the Greek capital letter Δ) connection also known as a mesh connection.

图 1. 36 中导出的电路通常如图 1. 37 所示,其布局称为三角形(源自大写希腊字母 Δ)连接,也称为网状连接。

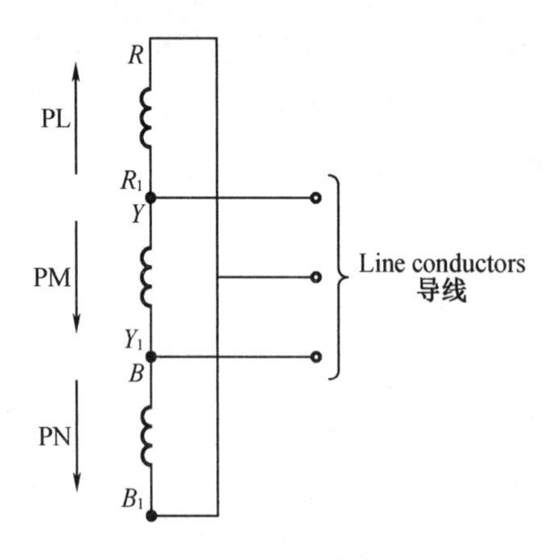

Fig. 1. 36 Delta connection of three-phase winding

图 1. 36 三相绕组的三角形连接

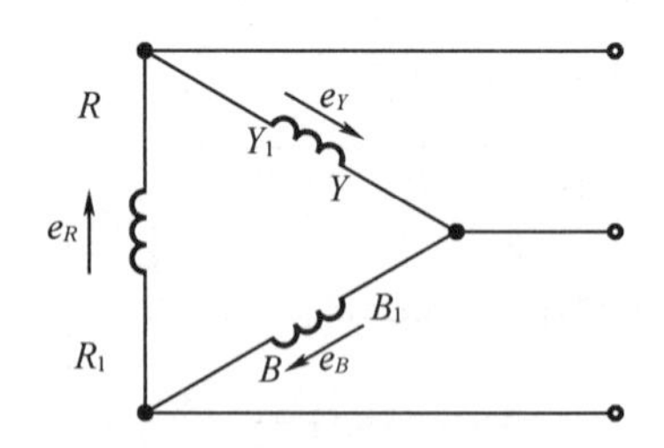

Fig. 1. 37 Mesh connected winding

图 1. 37 绕组的三角形连接

For instance, at instant P in Fig. 1. 33, the e. m. f. generated in phase R is positive and is represented by PL acting from R_1 to R in Fig. 1. 36. The e. m. f. in phase Y is negative and is represented by PM acting from Y to Y_1, and that in phase B is also negative and is represented by PN acting from B to B_1. But the sum of PM and PN is exactly equal numerically to PL, consequently the algebraic sum of the e. m. f. s round the closed circuit formed by the three windings is zero.

例如,在图 1.33 中的瞬间 P,在 R 相中产生的感应电动势为正,并用图 1.36 中从 R_1 到 R 的 PL 表示。Y 相中的电动势为负,用从 Y 到 Y_1 的 PM 表示,B 相中的电动势也是负的,用从 B 到 B_1 的 PN 表示。但 PM 和 PN 之和在数值上与 PL 完全相等。因此由三个绕组形成的闭合电路的电动势的代数和为零。

It should be noted that the directions of the arrows in Fig. 1.36 represent the directions of the e.m.f. at a particular instant, whereas arrows placed alongside symbol e, as in Fig. 1.37, represent the positive directions of the e.m.f.'s.

需要注意的是,图 1.36 中箭头的方向表示特定时刻的感应电动势的方向,图 1.37 中符号 e 旁边的箭头表示感应电动势的正方向。

It would be noticed that in Fig. 1.37, R is connected to Y_1 instead of B_1 as in Fig. 1.36. Actually it is immaterial which method is used. What is of importance is that the start of one phase should be connected to the finish of another phase, so that the arrows representing positive directions of the e.m.f.'s point in the same direction round the mesh formed by the three windings.

应该注意到,在图 1.37 中,R 与 Y_1 连接,而不是与图 1.36 中的 B_1 连接。实际上使用哪种连接方法并不重要,重要的是某相的起点应连接到另一相的终点,以便使表示感应电动势正方向的箭头在三个绕组形成的网格中指向相同的方向。

The voltage given for a three-phase system is always the line voltage unless it is stated otherwise.

除非另有说明,否则三相系统的电压总是线电压。

From Fig. 1.38, it will be seen that I_1 when positive, flows away from line conductor R, whereas I_3, when positive, flows towards it. Consequently, I_R is obtained by subtracting I_3 and I_1. Similarly, I_Y is the phasor difference of I_3 and I_2. From Fig. 1.39, it is evident that the line currents are equal in magnitude and differ in phase by 120°.

从图 1.38 中可以看出,当 I_1 为正时,它从 R 相线流出;当 I_3 为正时,它流向 R 相线。因此,可通过将 I_3 和 I_1 相减获得 I_R。类似地,I_Y 是 I_3 和 I_2 的差。从图 1.39 可以明显看出,线电流大小相等,相位相差 120°。

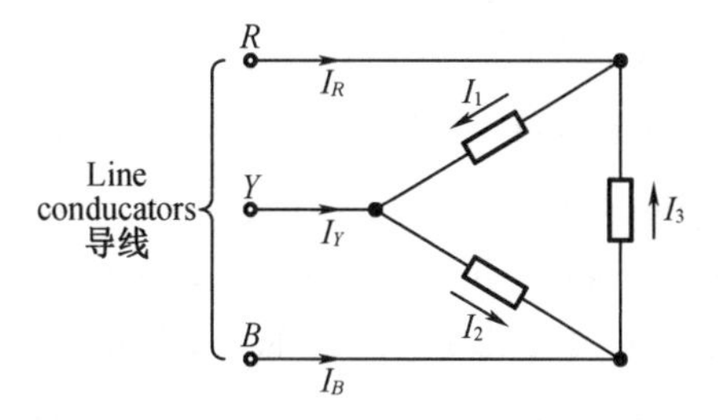

Fig. 1.38　Delta connection system with balanced load

图 1.38　带平衡负载的三角形连接系统

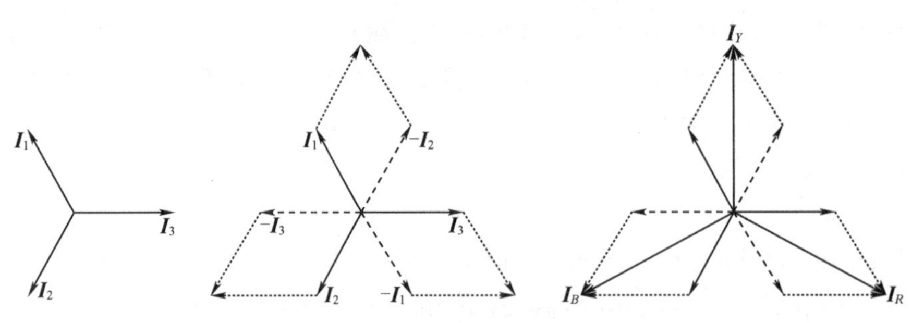

Fig. 1.39 Phasor diagram for Fig. 1.38

图 1.39 图 1.38 的向量图

Also $I_R = 2I_1 \cos 30° = \sqrt{3}I_1$. Hence for a delta connected system with a balanced load, line current = 1.73×phase current ie $I_L = 1.73I_P$. From Fig 1.38, it is obvious that in a delta-connected system the line and the phase voltages are the same, $U_L = U_P$.

而且 $I_R = 2I_1 \cos 30° = \sqrt{3}I_1$,因此对于具有平衡负载的三角形连接系统,线电流 = 1.73×相电流,即 $I_L = 1.73I_P$。由图 1.38 可以看出,在三角形连接系统中,线电压和相电压是相同的,$U_L = U_P$。

1.10.4 Star Connection with Three-phase Windings 三相绕组的星形连接

Let us go back to Fig. 1.34 and join together the three "starts", R_1, Y_1 and B_1 at N, as in Fig. 1.40, so that the three conductors 2, 4 and 6 of Fig. 1.34 can be replaced by the single conductor NM of Fig. 1.40. Since the generated e. m. f. has being assumed positive when acting from "start" to "finish", the current in each phase must also be regarded as positive when flowing in that direction, as represented by the arrows in Fig. 1.40. If I_R, I_Y and I_B are the instantaneous values of the currents in the three phases, the instantaneous value of the current in the common wire MN is $I_R+I_Y+I_B$, having its positive direction from M to N.

让我们回到图 1.34,将三个首端 R_1、Y_1 和 B_1 连接在一起,如图 1.40 所示,这样图 1.34 中的导体 2、导体 4 和导体 6 就可以用图 1.40 中的单个导体 NM 代替。假设从首端到尾端的过程中,产生的感应电动势为正,则如图 1.40 中的箭头所示,各相电流按该方向流动时的方向也必须视为正。如果 I_R、I_Y和 I_B 是三相电流的瞬时值,公共导线 MN 中的电流瞬时值为 $I_R+I_Y+I_B$,正方向从 M 到 N。

As in Fig. 1.41, this arrangement is referred to as a four-wire star-connected system and junction N is referred to as the neutral point. Three-phase motors are connected to the line conductors R, Y and B, whereas lamps, heaters, etc. are usually connected between the line and neutral conductors, as indicated by L_1, L_2 and L_3, the total load being distributed as equally as possible between the three lines. If these three loads are exactly alike, the phase currents have the same peak value, I_m, and differ in phase by 120°. Hence if the instantaneous value of the current in load L_1 is represented by $I_1 = I_m \cdot \sin T$, instantaneous current in L_2 is $I_2 = I_m \cdot \sin(T-120°)$, instantaneous current in L_3 is $I_3=I_m \sin(T-240°)$. Hence instantaneous value of the resultant current in neutral conductor MN (Fig. 1.41) is $I_1+I_2+I_3=I_m[\sin T+\sin(T-120°)+\sin(T-240°)]=I_m \cdot 0=0$.

如图 1.41 所示,这种布置被称为四线星形连接系统,结点 N 被称为中性点。三相电动机连接相线 R、Y 和 B,而灯、加热器等负载通常连接在相线和中性线之间,用 L_1、L_2 和 L_3 表示,总负载尽可能均匀地分布在三条线路之间。如果这三个负载完全相同,各相电流具有相同的峰值 I_m,相位相差 120°。因此,负载 L_1 中的电流的瞬时值为 $I_1=I_m \cdot \sin T$,L_2 中的电流的瞬时值为 $I_2=I_m \cdot \sin(T-120°)$,$L_3$ 中的电流的瞬时值为 $I_3=I_m \sin(T-240°)$。因此,中性线 MN(图 1.41)中合成电流的瞬时值为 $I_1+I_2+I_3=I_m[\sin T+\sin(T-120°)+\sin(T-240°)]=I_m \cdot 0=0$。

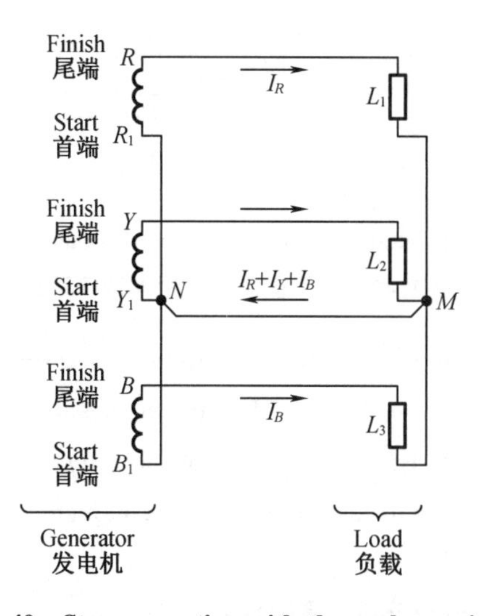

Fig. 1.40 Star connection with three-phase winding

图 1.40 三相绕组的星形连接

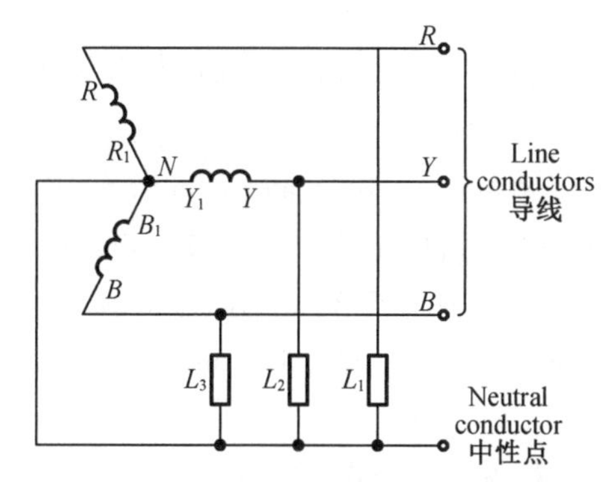

Fig. 1.41 Four wire star connected system

图 1.41 星形连接的四线制系统

i. e. with a balanced load, the resultant current in the neutral conductor is zero at every instant. Hence this conductor can be dispensed with, thereby giving us the three-wire star-connected system shown in Fig. 1. 42.

即在平衡负载下,中性导体中的合成电流在每一瞬间都为零。因此,可以省去这种导体,从而得到图 1. 42 所示的三线星形连接系统。

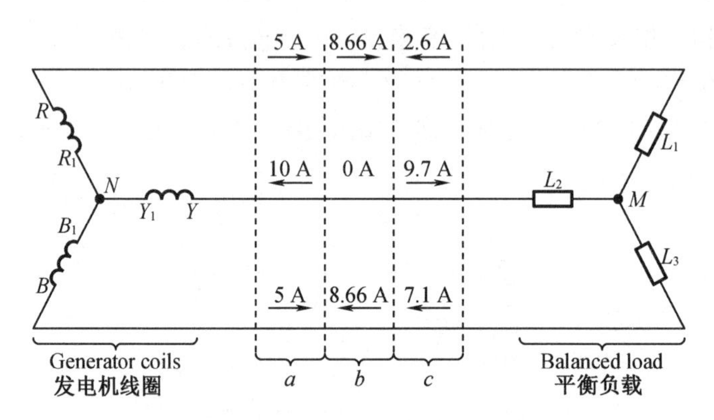

Fig. 1. 42 Star connected system with balanced load

图 1. 42 带平衡负载的星形连接系统

When we are considered the distribution of current in a system, it is helpful to bear mind:

(1) That arrows such as those of Fig. 1. 40 placed alongside symbols indicate the direction of the current when it is assumed to be positive and not the direction at a particular instant.

(2) That the current flowing outward in one or two conductors is equal to that flowing back in the remaining conductor or conductors.

当我们考虑系统中的电流分布时,请记住:

(1)图 1. 40 中符号旁边的箭头表示假设电流为正时的电流方向,而不是特定时刻的电流方向。

(2)在一个或两个导体中向外流动的电流等于流回其余导体中的电流。

Let us consider the second statement in greater details. Suppose the curves in Fig. 1. 43 represent the three currents differing in phase by 120° and having a peak value of 10 A. At instant *a*, the currents in phases *R* and *B* are each 5 A, whereas the current in phase *Y* is −10 A. These values are indicated above an in Fig. 1. 42, i. e. 5 A are flowing outwards in phases *R*, *B* and 10 A are returning in phase *Y*.

让我们更详细地考虑第二种说法。假设图 1. 43 中的曲线表示相位相差 120°且峰值为 10 A 的三个电流。在瞬间时刻 *a*,*R* 相和 *B* 相的电流各为 5 A,而 *Y* 相的电流为−10 A。这些值如图 1. 42 所示,即 5 A 在 *R* 相、*B* 相中向外流动,10 A 流回 *Y* 相。

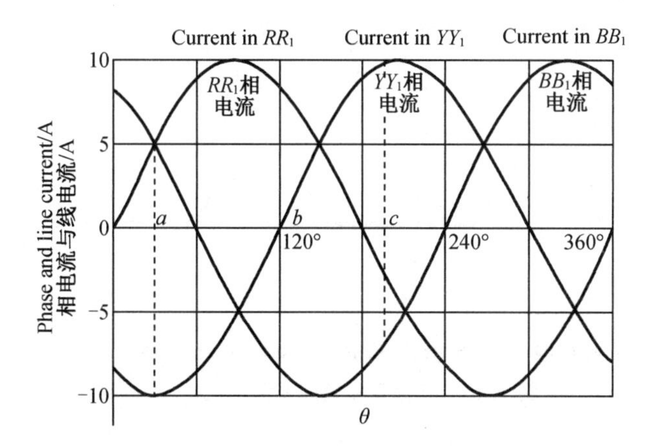

Fig. 1. 43 Waveforms of current in a balanced three-phase system

图 1. 43 三相平衡系统的电流波形

At instant *b*, the current in *Y* is 0 A, that in *R* is 8. 66 A and that in *B* is −8. 66 A, i. e. 8. 66 A are flowing outwards in phase *R* and returning in phase *B*. At instant *c*, the currents in *R*, *Y* and *B* are −2. 6 A, 9. 7 A and −7. 1 A respectively, i. e. 9. 7 A flow outwards in *Y* and return via phases *R* (2. 6 A) and *B* (7. 1 A). It will be seen that the distribution of currents between the three lines is continually changing, but at every instant the algebraic sum of the currents is zero.

在时刻 *b*,*Y* 相的电流为 0 A,*R* 相的电流为 8. 66 A,*B* 相的电流为−8. 66 A,即 8. 66 A 在 *R* 相中向外流动,在 *B* 相中返回。在时刻 *c*,*R*、*Y* 和 *B* 相中的电流分别为−2. 6 A、9. 7 A 和−7. 1 A。即 9. 7 A 在 *Y* 相向外流动,并通过 *R* 相(2. 6 A)和 *B* 相(7. 1 A)返回。可以看出,三条相线之间的电流分布在不断变化,但在每一时刻,电流的代数和都是零。

1. 11 Rectified Voltage 整流电压

It is possible to rectify an alternating voltage so we end up having what appears to be a direct voltage. It is done by means of connecting diodes in a certain way. A diode is a component that allows a current or voltage to have one direction only. We could say it works like a check valve, a one way valve.

对交流电压进行整流,这样就可以得到直流电压。这是通过以某种方式连接二极管来实现的。二极管是允许电流或电压仅具有一个方向的部件,可以说它就像一个单向阀。

If we put a diode in a circuit with alternating voltage, you will only get either the positive or negative part of the sinus curve through the diode. This of course depends on how we turn the diode in the circuit(Fig. 1. 44).

如果把一个二极管接入交流电压的电路中,只能通过二极管得到正弦曲线的正或负半周部分。这取决于如何将二极管接入电路中(图 1. 44)。

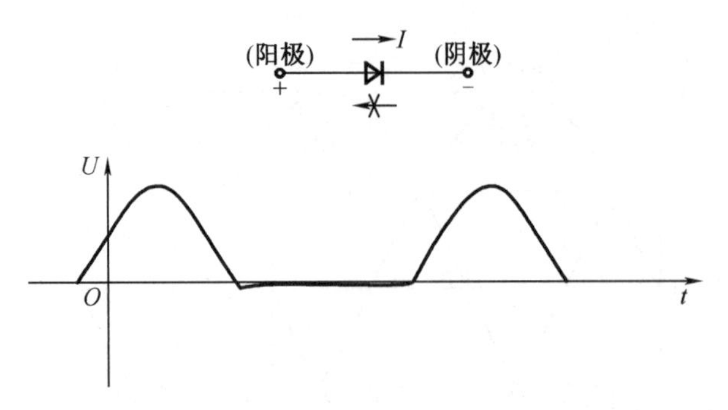

Fig. 1.44 Diode and rectified alternating voltage

图 1.44 二极管和整流交流电压

If we connect 4 diodes in a certain way, you will then get a voltage that is more consistent and more like real direct voltage (Fig. 1.45).

如果我们以某种方式连接 4 个二极管,会得到一个更稳定的电压,也是更接近真实值的直流电压(图 1.45)。

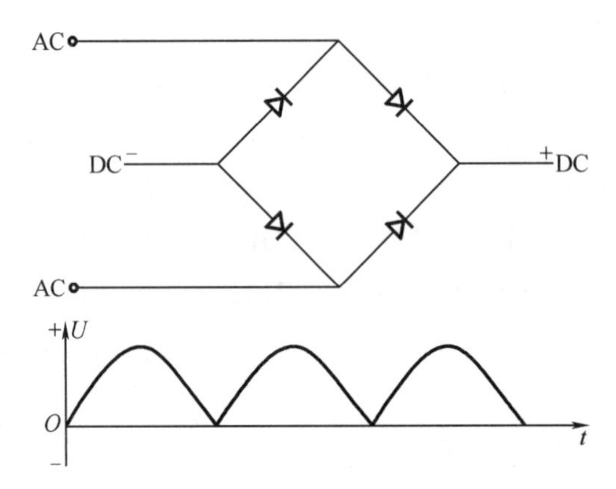

Fig. 1.45 Four diodes rectifier

图 1.45 四二极管整流器

The waveform of the e. m. f. generated in an AC generator undergoes one complete cycle of variation when the conductors move past a N and a S pole, and the shape of the wave over the negative half is exactly the same as that over the positive half.

交流发电机产生的感应电动势波形反映的是导体运动切割 N 极和 S 极产生的感应电动势经历一个周期的变化,并且波形的负半周部分和正半周部分完全相同。

Relationship between frequency, speed and number of pole pairs: If an AC generator has p pairs of poles and if its speed is N revolutions per second, then f= no. of cycles per second = no. of cycles per revolution×no. of revolutions per second.

频率、转速和极对数之间的相互关系:如果交流发电机有 p 对磁极,且其转速为 N(r/s),则频率 f= 每秒的周期数 = 每转的周期数×每秒的转数,即

$$f=pN\ (\text{Hz})$$

1.12 Supply Network 供电网络

We have now learned how electricity is generated, what the difference between AC and DC is, what inductance and capacitance is and how three-phase voltage is generated. Now we are going to look at how the network that supplies the appliances and machines onshore and offshore looks like.

至此我们已经了解了电是如何产生的,交流和直流之间的区别,电感和电容是什么,以及三相电压是如何产生的。现在我们来看看陆上和海上的设备和设施的供电网络(电网)是什么样子的。

1.12.1 Onshore Network 陆上电网

The onshore network basically starts at the power plant and ends in the outlets at the consumer. There is a difference though, the voltage. The voltage at the outlets is 400/230 V, the voltage at the power plant is 400,000 V. So the voltage is transformed under way to the consumer. The reason for the transformation is that there is a resistance in the cables and thus a power loss. If you remember the power sentence it said $P=U \cdot I$ which could be rewritten to $P=I^2 \cdot R$.

陆上电网基本上从发电厂开始,输出到用户端结束。不过两端的电压是有区别的。输出端电压为400/230 V,发电厂电压为400 000 V,即电压被变压至用户端。变压的原因是电缆中存在电阻,从而导致功率损失。公式$P=U \cdot I$可以改写为$P=I^2 \cdot R$。

At the power plant, there is a lot of power produced (peak value for Denmark, consumption of 5,750,000,000 W) and if it was produced at 400 V then the current would have to be very large ($P=U \cdot I \Rightarrow I=14,375,000$ A). And when the current is very large, a lot of power would be lost in the cables as heat is produced ($P=I^2 \cdot R$). Furthermore, because of the high current and the resistance, there would also be a drop in the voltage that would be unacceptable.

发电厂的发电量很大(如丹麦电厂的峰值耗电量为5 750 000 000 W),如果发电电压为400 V,则电流必须非常大($P=U \cdot I \Rightarrow I=14\ 375\ 000$ A)。当电流非常大时,会产生热量,电缆中会损失大量功率($P=I^2 \cdot R$)。此外,由于存在高电流和电阻,也会导致不允许的电压降。

If we have a high voltage and a low current, thus a small power loss and a small drop in the voltage. And then we have to transform the voltages in the network as it can be seen as Fig. 1.46. A transformer works like a generator, only it is not rotating.

如果高电压低电流输电,则功率损耗会很小,电压降也很小。因此,我们必须在网络中变换电压,如图1.46所示。变压器的工作方式与发电机相似,只是它不旋转。

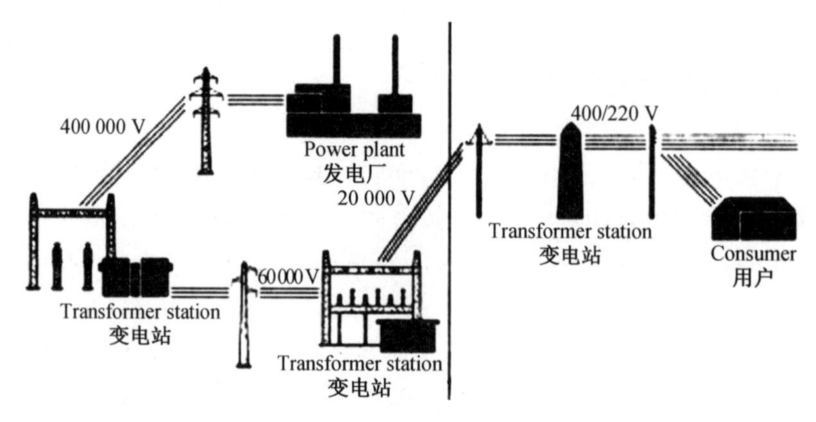

Fig. 1.46 Onshore network

图 1.46 陆上电网

The network that we are going to concentrate on is the 400 V network. The final transformation is done from 20,000 V to 400 V. The voltages that we here speak of is what we call the NET VOLTAGE. So the net voltage which is the voltage between two phases is 400 V. The 20,000/400 V transformer is star connected on the secondary (400 V) side, as Fig. 1.47.

我们将重点关注的网络是 400 V 电网。最终的电压变换是从 20 000 V 到 400 V。这里我们所说的电压就是电网电压。因此，电网电压即两个相之间的电压为 400 V。20 000/400 V 变压器在次级(400 V)侧为星形连接，如图 1.47 所示。

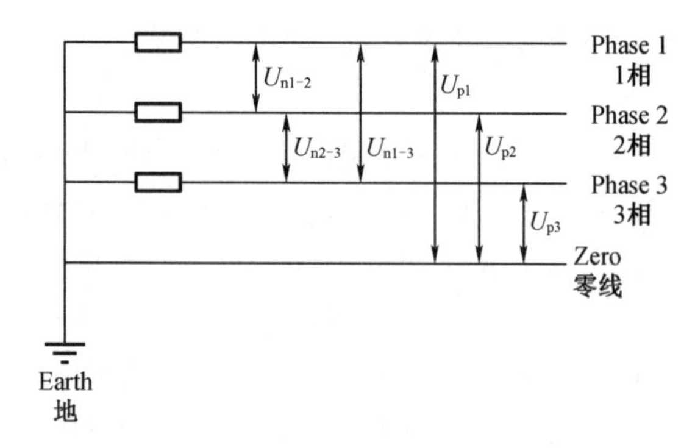

Fig. 1.47 Transformer secondary side connection

图 1.47 变压器二次侧连接

We have also introduced another wire, the Zero wire. It is connected to the star point of the transformer. And under normal conditions, the potential of the star point is 0 V, which is why we call the Zero wire zero. Furthermore, the zero wire is grounded (connected to earth), so we are sure that we have 0 V on the Zero wire.

我们还引入了另一种导线——零线。它连接到变压器的星形结点。在正常情况下，星形结点的电势是 0 V，这就是为什么我们称之为零线。此外，由于零线接地，因此我们确定零线上的电压为 0 V。

The voltage that we can measure between zero and a phase is called the PHASE VOLTAGE. The difference between the two voltages is $\sqrt{3}$. So if the net voltage is 400 V, then the phase voltage is:

我们可以将零线和某相之间测量的电压称为相电压,两种电压之间相差$\sqrt{3}$倍。所以如果电网电压是 400 V,则相电压是:

$$400/\sqrt{3}=231\ \text{V}$$

Then consumer got a slight drop in the voltage, depending on how far from the transformer it is (the length of cable). This type of net is called an earthed net.

之后用户侧的电压会略有下降,大小取决于它与变压器的距离(电缆的长度)。这种类型的电网称为接地电网。

1.12.2　Off Shore Network 海上电网

Off shore, it looks a little different. First of all, we don't have earth, we only have the vessels hull. The hull is made of steel which is an excellent conductor. This means that we cannot take the star point to earth and thus we cannot have a Zero wire. This also means that we only have the net voltage available. This type of net is called isolated net (three-phase three wire system), as Fig. 1.48.

在海上,情况与陆地有所不同。首先,海上没有地面,只有船体。船体是由钢铁制成的,它是一种优良的导体。这意味着我们不能将星形结点接到大地上,因此我们不能获得零线。这也意味着我们只有电网电压可用。这种类型的网络称为中性点不接地网络(三相三线制),如图 1.48 所示。

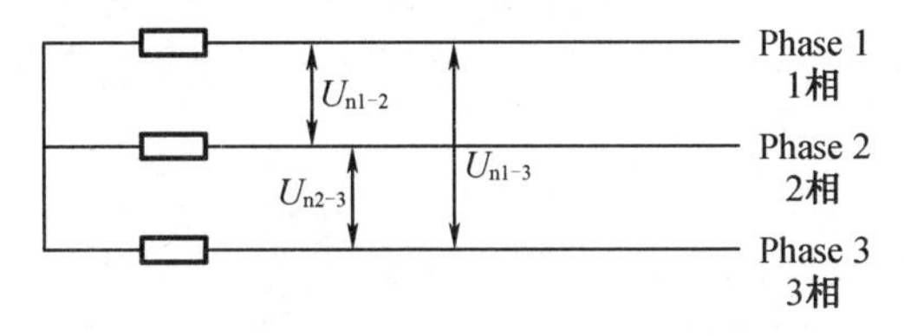

Fig. 1.48　Isolated net connection

图 1.48　中性点不接地网络连接

The off shore network is a three-phased system as the on shore network, but the voltage and frequency are higher. On most ships, the system voltage is 440 V and the frequency is 60 Hz. Another difference is that most off shore networks are isolated networks. This means that the star point in the generator is not used and we don't have a Zero wire. The net voltage (440 V) is the only voltage we can obtain directly. To get the supply voltage for light installations (230 V) a transformer is used, as Fig. 1.49.

海上电网与陆上电网一样是三相系统,但电压和频率更高。在大多数船舶上,系统电压为 440 V,频率为 60 Hz。另一个区别是,大多数海上电网都是孤立的网络。这意味着没有使用发电机中的星形结点,并且没有零线。电网电压(440 V)是我们唯一可以直接获得的电压。为了获得照明设备的电源电压(230 V),采用了变压器,如图 1.49 所示。

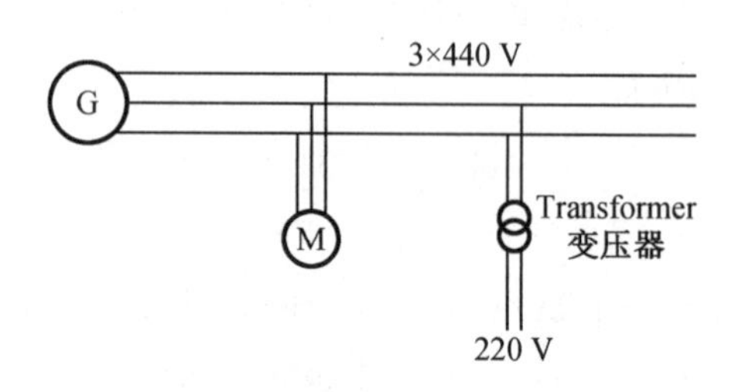

Fig. 1.49 Off shore network

图 1.49 海上电网

By having an isolated system, we gain some advantages. If we have an electrical fault on the system, we can proceed with the current operation and make a repair at first possible opportunity. The electrical fault could be a wire touching the hull of the ship or an internal failure in some electrical equipment (a motor, a faulty lamp etc.).

通过使用中性点不接地系统,我们可以获得一些优势。如果系统出现电气故障,我们可以继续当前的运转,并在第一时间进行维修。电气故障可能是电线接触船体或某些电气设备(电动机、故障灯等)的内部故障引起的。

As described earlier, we must have a closed circuit in order to have a current flowing. Below Fig. 1.50 shows that if we have a fault in an earthed system, we will have a short circuit and we will have to correct the fault before we can operate the system again.

如前所述,必须有一个闭合电路才能有电流流过。图 1.50 显示,如果中性点接地系统出现故障,则会出现短路,我们必须先排除故障,然后才能再次运行系统。

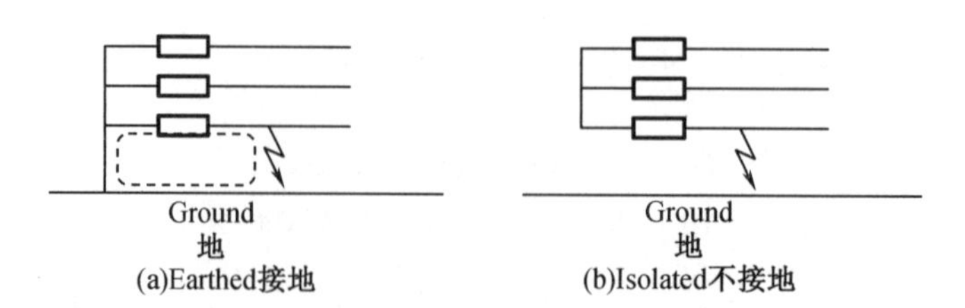

Fig. 1.50 Earthed system and Isolated system

图 1.50 中性点接地系统和中性点不接地系统

In an isolated system, the first earth fault will not result in a short circuit and the operation can proceed.

在中性点不接地系统中,第一个接地故障不会导致短路,运转可以继续。

In isolated networks, it is necessary to monitor if a earth fault has occurred, because if another earth fault occurs you will have a short circuit. On ships, this is done by having a system detect the condition of the isolation to earth and if a fault occurs an alarm is sounded.

在中性点不接地网络中,有必要监测是否发生了接地故障,因为如果发生第二个接地故障,则会引起短路。在船舶上,故障监测是由系统检测对地隔离状态来实现的,如果发生接地故障则会发出警报。

It is very common on vessels to have earth faults on the system. It should be corrected as soon as possible as there is danger in connection with an earth fault.

在船舶上,系统接地故障非常常见。由于存在与接地故障相关的危险,应尽快消除接地故障。

Let's take a look at what happens if we accidentally get in contact with live wires. On shore, it looks like Fig. 1. 51. So in this case you could get $440/\sqrt{3}=254$ V over yourself.

让我们来看看如果不小心触碰到带电的导线会发生什么。在陆地上的情况如图 1. 51 所示。所以这种情况下人体会承受 $440/\sqrt{3}=254$ V 的电压。

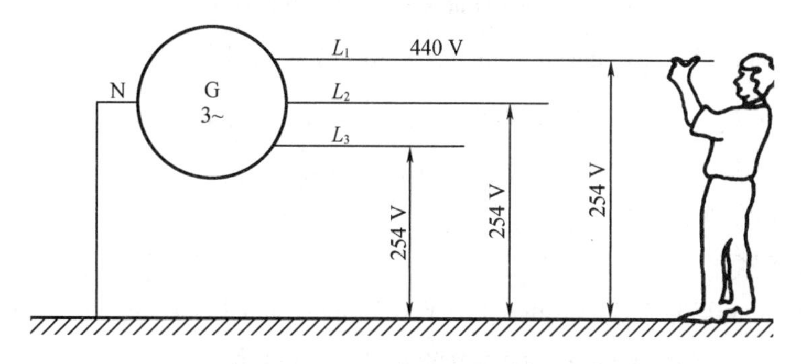

Fig. 1. 51 In contact with live wire on shore

图 1. 51 接触陆地带电导线

Off shore, it looks like Fig. 1. 52. In this case, you have the full net voltage over yourself if there is a earth fault in another phase. If there are no faults then there is no circuit and there will be no current flowing. For your own safety, remove the cause for earth faults.

海上的情况如图 1. 52 所示。在这种情况下,如果另一相出现接地故障,则触电人体会承受全部电网电压。如果没有接地故障,那么就没有回路,就不会有电流流过。因此,为了自身安全,要排除接地故障。

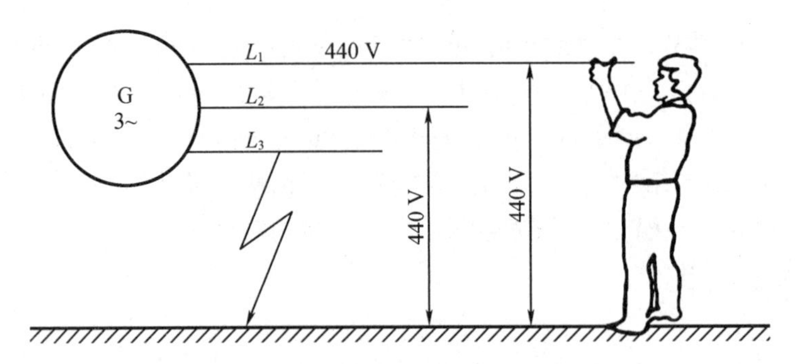

Fig. 1.52 In contact with live wire off shore

图 1.52 接触海上带电导线

1.13 Circuit Calculations 电路计算

The following gives briefs revision of DC and AC circuits and calculations.

下面给出简短的复习直流和交流电路的示例。

$$R_n = R_1 + R_2 + R_3 + \cdots \text{(in series 串联)}$$

$$1/R_n = 1/R_1 + 1/R_2 + 1/R_3 + \cdots \text{(in parallel 并联)}$$

$$U = I \cdot R \text{(Ohm's Law 欧姆定律)}$$

$$\sum \text{emf's} = \sum \text{p. d's (Kirchhoff's Voltage Law 基尔霍夫电压定律)}$$

$$\sum I_{IN} = \sum I_{OUT} \text{(Kirchhoff's Current Law 基尔霍夫电流定律)}$$

$$P = U \cdot I = I \cdot I \cdot R$$

Example 示例:

Using the circuit(Fig 1.53) with a 110 V DC supply and $R_1 = 6\ \Omega$, $R_2 = 5\ \Omega$, $R_3 = 5.5\ \Omega$, calculate all currents, supply power and potential drop across R_1.

在图 1.53 中,直流电源电压为 110 V,$R_1 = 6\ \Omega$,$R_2 = 5\ \Omega$,$R_3 = 5.5\ \Omega$,计算所有电流、功率和穿过 R_1 的电势差。

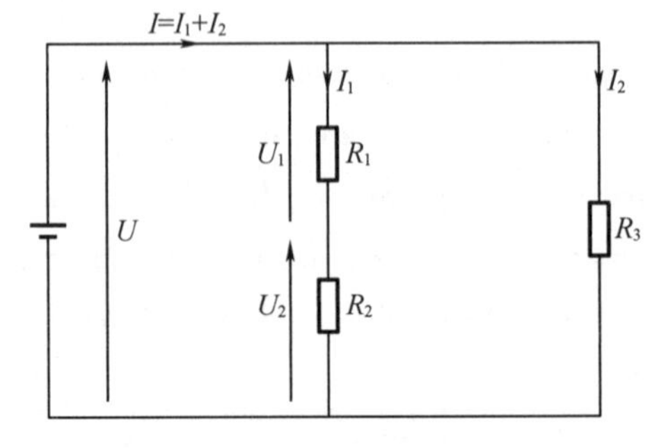

Fig. 1.53 DC circuit

图 1.53 直流电路

Answer 解:

$I_1=110/(6+5)=10$ A,$I_2=110/5.5=20$ A,所以电源电流 $I=I_1+I_2=30$ A

$$P=U\cdot I=110\times30=3.3\ \text{kW}$$

用 $P=\sum I\cdot I\cdot R$ 验算:

经过 R_1 的电势差$=6I_1=60$ V。

$X_L=2\pi fL(\Omega)$, $X_C=1/2\pi fC(\Omega)$,$Z=\sqrt{R^2+X_L^2}$ 或 $Z=\sqrt{R^2+X_C^2}$, $I=U/Z$

Power factor(功率因数)= $\cos\varphi=R/Z=P/S$ (lag or lead 滞后或超前)

$$P=U\cdot I\cdot\cos\varphi \text{ 或 } P=I^2R\ (\text{W})$$

$$Q=U\cdot I\cdot\sin\varphi \text{ 或 } P=I^2X\ (\text{Var})$$

$$S=U\cdot I \text{ 或 } S=I^2Z(\text{kV}\cdot\text{A})$$

Example 示例:

In the circuit shown in Fig. 1.54 with a 220 V, 60 Hz, supply and $R_1=6\ \Omega$, $R_2=5\ \Omega$, $L=0.1$ H, $C=100\ \mu$F. Calculate all currents, supply power, overall power factor and potential drop across the 6 Ω resistor.

在图 1.54 所示的电路中,交流电压 $U=220$ V,$f=60$ Hz,$R_1=6\ \Omega$,$R_2=5\ \Omega$,$L=0.1$ H,$C=100\ \mu$F。计算所有的电流、功率、功率因数和通过 6 Ω 电阻的电势差。

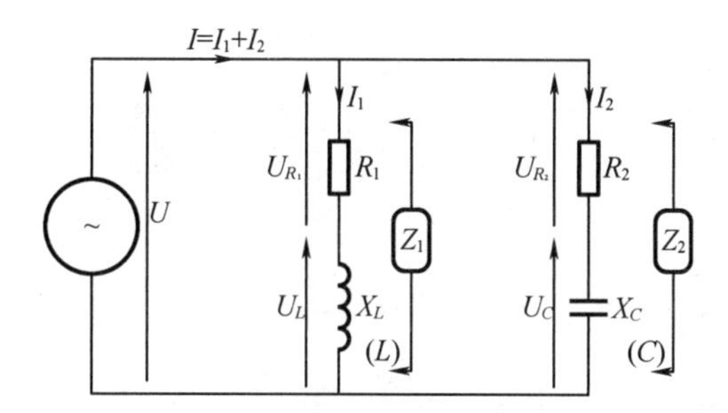

Fig. 1.54 Single phase AC circuit

图 1.54 单相交流电路

Answer 解:

$$X_L=2\pi fL=37.7\ \Omega, X_C=\frac{1}{2}\pi fC=26.5\ \Omega$$

$$Z_1=38.2\ \Omega(81^\circ \text{ lagging 滞后 } 81^\circ)$$

$$Z_2=27\ \Omega\ (79.3^\circ \text{ leading 超前 } 79.3^\circ)$$

So $I_1=220/38.2=5.76$ A lagging U by 81°and $I_2=220/27=8.15$ A leading U by 79.3°. The total supply current is the phasor sum of I_1 and I_2 which must be resolved into "in-phase" (horizontal) and "quadrature" (vertical) components before adding, the result (for you to check) is $I=3.34$ A at 43.8° leading.

所以,电流 $I_1=220/38.2=5.76$ A,滞后于电压 81°,$I_2=220/27=8.15$ A,超前于电压 79.3°。所以矢量电流和就等于 I_1 和 I_2 的和,在相加之前必须分解为同相的水平和垂直分量。得到的结果是 $I=3.34$ A,超前于电压 43.8°。

$$P=220\times3.34\cdot\cos 43.8°=531\text{ W}$$

$$\text{总功率因数}=\cos 43.8°=0.72\text{,超前}$$

$$\text{通过 }6\ \Omega\text{ 电阻的电势差}=6I_1=5.76\times6=34.56\text{ V}$$

$$U_L=\sqrt{3}U_{PH},\ I_L=I_{PH}(\text{in star 星形连接})$$

$$U_L=U_{PH},I_L=\sqrt{3}I_{PH}(\text{in delta 三角形连接})$$

$$P_{PH}=U_{PH}\cdot I_{PH}\cdot\cos\varphi=I_{PH}^2R(\text{W})$$

Balanced three-phases(三相对称时):

$$P=\sqrt{3}U_L\cdot I_L\cdot\cos\varphi$$

Example 示例:

Using the circuit(Fig. 1.55) with a 440 V, three-phase, 60 Hz AC supply and $Z_{PH}=10\ \Omega$ at power factor is 0.8 lagging (balanced load). Calculate phase and line currents and supply power when connected as star and delta.

图 1.55 所示电路为 440 V,60 Hz 的三相交流电路,$Z_{PH}=10\ \Omega$,功率因数为 0.8,滞后(平衡负载)。计算在星形连接和三角形连接中的相电流、线电流、功率。

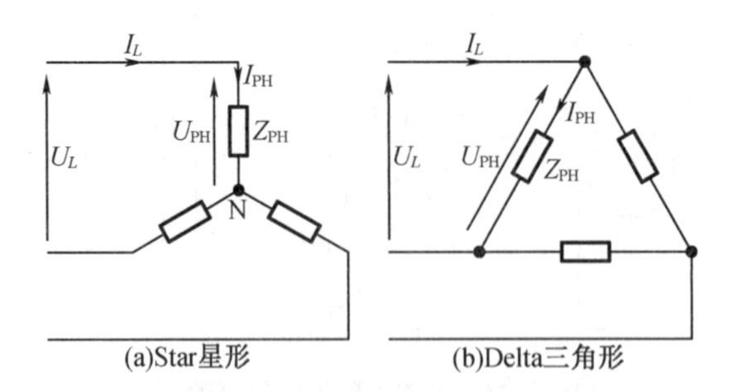

Fig. 1.55 Three-phase AC circuit

图 1.55 三相交流电路

Answer 解:

(1) in star(星形连接)

$$U_{PH}=440/\sqrt{3}=254\text{ V}$$

$$I_{PH}=254/10=25.4\text{ A},I_L=I_{PH}=25.4\text{ A}$$

$$P=\sqrt{3}\times440\times25.4\times0.8=15.49\text{ kW}$$

(2) in delta(三角形连接)

$$U_{PH}=U_L=440\text{ V}$$

$I_{PH}=440/10=44\ A, I_L=\sqrt{3}\times 44=76.2\ A$

$P=\sqrt{3}\times 440\times 76.2\times 0.8=46.46\ kW$ (notice this pauper is three times the value in star 功率是星形连接的 3 倍)

1.14 Basic Digital Logic Circuits 数值逻辑电路基础

1.14.1 Introduction 引言

Digital logic circuits utilize only two states, high and low. These two states can be represented by voltage levels (e.g. 5 V is a logical high and 0 V is a logical low) or any two distinct states of any signal (e.g. 100 ℃ is a logical high and 80 ℃ is a logical low). Arithmetic using binary numbers was formalized by George Boole in 1847 and is termed Boolean algebra. There are seven basic logic gates: NOT, NAND, NOR, AND, OR, XOR and XNOR. This section focuses on the five fundamental gates: NOT, NAND, NOR, AND and OR. NAND and NOR gates are both universal gates. This means that any logic function can be implemented by either a sequence of only NAND gates or only NOR gates. It is impossible to realize or implement an arbitrary logic function with just AND or OR gates. The set of seven basic gates contains no memory and the function produced by their interconnection is called combinational logic. When the inputs to a combinational logic circuit change state, a chain reaction occurs as the digital logic signal traverses the logic circuit.

数字逻辑电路仅有高电平和低电平两种状态。这两种状态可以用电压电平表示(例如,5 V 为逻辑高电平,0 V 为逻辑低电平),也可以用任何信号的任意两种不同状态表示(例如,100 ℃为逻辑高,80 ℃为逻辑低)。1847 年,乔治·布尔标准化了二进制数算术的使用,称为布尔代数。其中,有七个基本逻辑门:非门、与非门、或非门、与门、或门、异或门和同或门。本节讲解的重点是五个基本逻辑门:非门、与非门、或非门、与门和或门。与非门和或非门都是通用门,这意味着任何逻辑功能都可以仅通过与非门或或非门的序列来实现。仅用与门或或门是不可能实现任意逻辑函数的。七个基本逻辑门的集合不包含存储器,它们互连产生的功能称为组合逻辑。当组合逻辑电路的输入状态改变时,数字逻辑信号通过逻辑电路时会发生连锁反应。

No matter how complicated, all digital integrated circuits are made from simple building blocks called gates. Gates are like electronically controlled switches. They are either on or off how do gates work. Let's start with the basics.

无论有多复杂,所有数字集成电路都是由称为门的简单构件制成的。门就像电子控制的开关。它们要么开着,要么关着,可以想象一下闸门是如何工作的。让我们从基础知识开始学习。

1.14.2 Switch Gates 开关门

The three simplest gates can be demonstrated with some pushbutton switches, a battery and a lamp.

三个最简单的门可以用一些按钮开关、电池和灯来演示。

1. AND 与门

The lamp glows only when switches A and B are closed. The Table 1.1 summarizes the gate's operation is called a truth table.

只有当开关 A 和 B 闭合时，灯才会发光。表 1.1 总结了闸门的操作，称为真值表。

Table 1.1 Truth table 1

表 1.1 真值表 1

A	B	OUT
Off	Off	Off
Off	On	Off
On	Off	Off
On	On	On

A truth table contains a list of all possible combinations of inputs and the value of the output as a function of the inputs. For a gate with n inputs, there will be 2^n rows in the truth table.

真值表包含输入端所有可能的输入组合以及不同输入组合对应的输出值。一个有 n 个输入的门，其真值表就会有 2^n 行。

Open switch = off　Closed switch = on

打开开关 = 关　闭合开关 = 开

Demonstrated circuit of AND gate as shown in Fig. 1.56.

与门演示电路如图 1.56 所示。

2. OR 或门

The lamp glows only when switch A or B or both switches A and B are closed. Here's the truth table as shown in Table 1.2.

只有当开关 A 或 B 闭合或开关 A 和 B 都闭合时，灯才会发光。其真值表如表 1.2 所示。

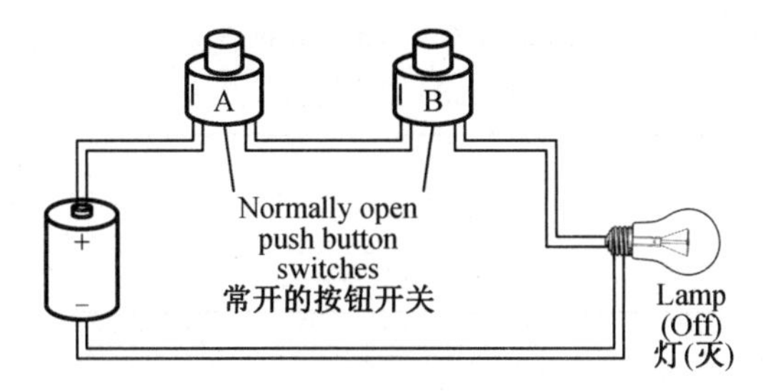

Fig. 1.56 Demonstrated circuit of AND gate

图 1.56 与门演示电路

Table 1.2 Truth table 2

表 1.2 真值表 2

A	B	OUT
Off	Off	Off
Off	On	On
On	Off	On
On	On	On

Demonstrated circuit of OR gate as shown in Fig. 1. 57. The switches are the gate's inputs. The lead without switches is the Common or Ground lead.

或门演示电路如图 1.57 所示。开关是门的输入。不带开关的导线是公共导线或接地导线。

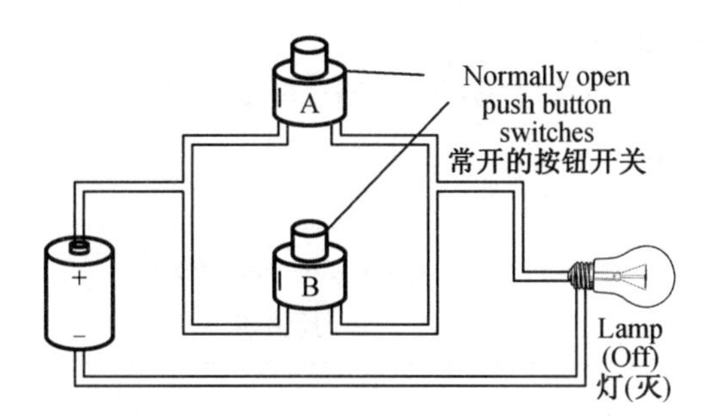

Fig. 1.57 Demonstrated circuit of OR gate

图 1.57 或门演示电路

3. NOT 非门

The lamp normally glows, only when the switch is opened is the lamp off, in other words, the NOT gate reverse the usual action of a switch. Here's the truth table as shown in Table 1. 3.

灯通常会发光,只有当开关打开时灯才熄灭,即非门反转开关的正常动作。其真值表如表 1.3 所示。

Table 1.3 Truth table 3

表 1.3 真值表 3

IN	OUT
Off	On
On	Off

The NOT gate is usually called the inverter. Demonstrated circuit of NOT gate as shown in Fig. 1.58.

非门通常称为反相器。非门演示电路如图 1.58 所示。

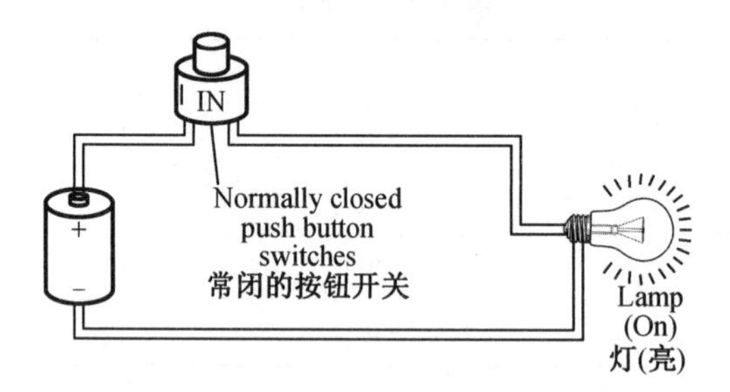

Fig. 1.58 Demonstrated circuit of NOT gate

图 1.58 非门演示电路

4. The Binary Connection 二进制连接

It's possible to substitute the digits 0 and 1 for the off and on state of a switch the truth tables for the gates. The binary representation corresponding to the truth tables of the above gates are shown in Table 1.4 to Table 1.6.

可以用数字 0 和 1 代替开关的关闭和打开状态,以上各门的真值表对应的二进制表示方式如表 1.4 至表 1.6 所示。

Table 1.4 AND gate truth table

表 1.4 与门真值表

A	B	F
0	0	0
0	1	0
1	0	0
1	1	1

The 0 and 1 input (A & B) combinations from number in the two digit (or bit) binary number system in digital electronics, binary numbers serve as codes that represent decimal numbers, letters of the alphabet, voltages and many other kinds of information.

在以两个数码(或二位)0 和 1 作为输入(A & B)组合的二进制数字系统数字电路中，用二进制数表示十进制数字、字母表字母、电压和许多其他类型信息的代码。

Table 1.5　OR gate truth table

表 1.5　或门真值表

A	B	F
0	0	0
0	1	1
1	0	1
1	1	1

Table 1.6　NOT gate truth table

表 1.6　非门真值表

A	F
0	1
1	0

Decimal 十进制	Binary 二进制	Binary-Coded Decimal (BCD) 二进码十进数
0	0	0000 0000
1	1	0000 0001
2	10	0000 0010
3	11	0000 0011
4	100	0000 0100
5	101	0000 0101
6	110	0000 0110
7	111	0000 0111
8	1000	0000 1000
9	1001	0000 1001
10	1010	0001 0000
11	1011	0001 0001
12	1100	0001 0010
13	1101	0001 0011
14	1110	0001 0100
15	1111	0001 0101

1.14.3 Gate Symbols 逻辑门符号

1. NOT 非门

The output F of a NOT gate (or inverter) is the complement (inverse) of the input. The truth table is shown in the Table 1.6.

非门的输出 F 是其输入 A 的反码 $\overline{A}$。其真值表如表 1.6 所示。

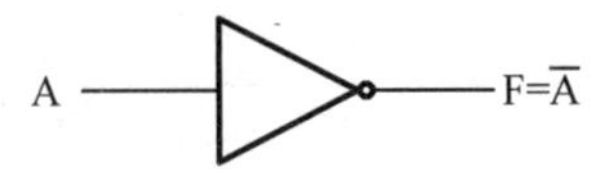

2. AND 与门

The output F of a AND gate is high if and only if both inputs are high. That is, F is 1 if and only if both A and B are 1. The truth table is shown in the Table 1.4.

当且仅当两个输入都为高电平时,与门的输出 F 才为高电平。换句话说,全 1 出 1。其真值表如表 1.4 所示。

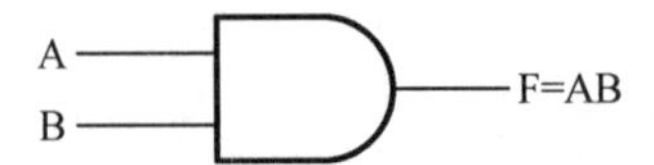

3. NAND 与非门

The output F is low of a NAND gate if and only if both inputs are high. The NAND function is the complement of the AND function. The truth table is shown in the Table 1.7.

当且仅当两个输入都为低电平时,与非门的输出 F 才为高电平。与非门就是与门的反码。其真值表如表 1.7 所示。

Table 1.7 NAND gate truth table

表 1.7 与非门真值表

A	B	F
0	0	1
0	1	1
1	0	1
1	1	0

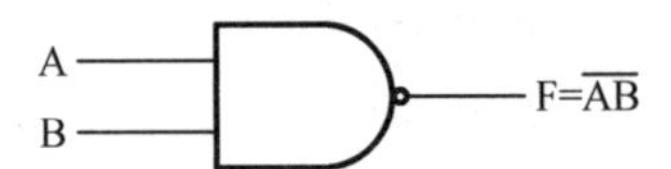

4. OR 或门

The output F of OR gate is high if and only if either of the inputs is high including the case when both inputs are high. The output is high if A or B is high. The truth table is shown in the Table 1.5.

当且仅当任意输入为高电平时(包括两个输入都为高电平的情况)或门的输出 F 才为

高电平。A 或 B 有高电平输出就为高电平。其真值表如表 1.5 所示。

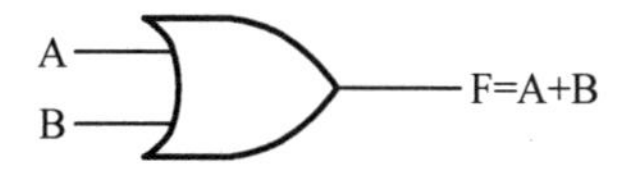

5. NOR 或非门

The NOR gate produces a high output if and only if both inputs are low. It produces the complement of the OR gate function. The truth table is shown in the Table 1.8.

当且仅当任意输入为低电平时,或非门才产生高电平输出,其产生的输出是或门的反码。其真值表如表 1.8 所示。

Table 1.8　NOR gate truth table

表 1.8　或非门真值表

A	B	F
0	0	1
0	1	0
1	0	0
1	1	0

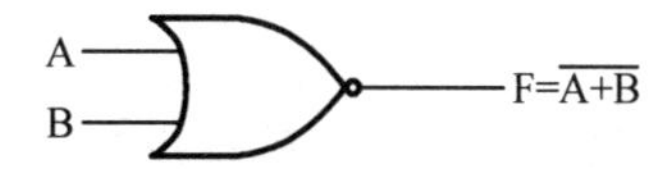

6. XOR 异或门

The output of an XOR gate is high if and only if a single input is high. The truth table is shown in the Table 1.9.

当且仅当只有一个输入为高电平时,异或门的输出才为高电平。其真值表如表 1.9 所示。

Table 1.9　XOR gate truth table

表 1.9　异或门真值表

A	B	F
0	0	0
0	1	1
1	0	1
1	1	0

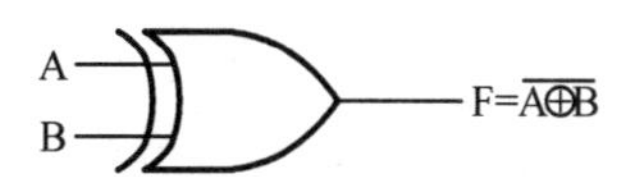

7. XNOR 同或门

The output of an XNOR gate is the complement of the XOR function. The truth table is shown in the Table 1. 10.

同或门的输出是异或门的反码。其真值表如表 1. 10 所示。

Table 1. 10　XNOR gate truth table

表 1. 10　同或门真值表

A	B	F
0	0	1
0	1	0
1	0	0
1	1	1

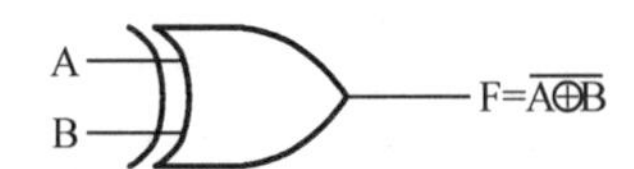

All of the above gates, except the NOR gate, have two inputs. Gates exist with several inputs, but the chips are more costly to fabricate. It is useful to consider the case when a logic function must be implemented using gates with only two inputs. The NOT gate never has more than one input.

以上这些逻辑门,除非门之外,都有两个输入端。也存在更多输入端的逻辑门,但是其制作成本较高。将一个逻辑功能视为必须采用两个输入端的逻辑门是很有帮助的。非门只有一个输入端。

1. 14. 4　Digital IC 数字集成电路

Each IC (or chip) contains a specific logic network or assortment of various logic functions.

每个集成电路(IC)(或芯片)包含由多种逻辑功能组成的特定逻辑网络或搭配。

The DIP is fabricated with an IC in a plastic enclosure with metal pins extending from the sides of the package that connect the integrated circuit inside the package with external circuitry. The metal pins extending from the sides of the DIP are bent downward so that the DIP can fit into a breadboard for rapid prototyping of a circuit, as Fig. 1. 59.

双列直插式封装(DIP)是指由集成电路、塑胶外壳和伸出两侧并与其内部集成电路连接的金属引脚组成的封装形式。DIP 两侧伸出的金属引脚向下弯曲以便插入插接板,迅速形成电路,如图 1. 59 所示。

All digital logic gates get their power from an external DC power supply, which can be a battery or a bench top DC power supply.

所有的数字逻辑门都由外部直流电源供电,可以采用电池或板式直流电源。

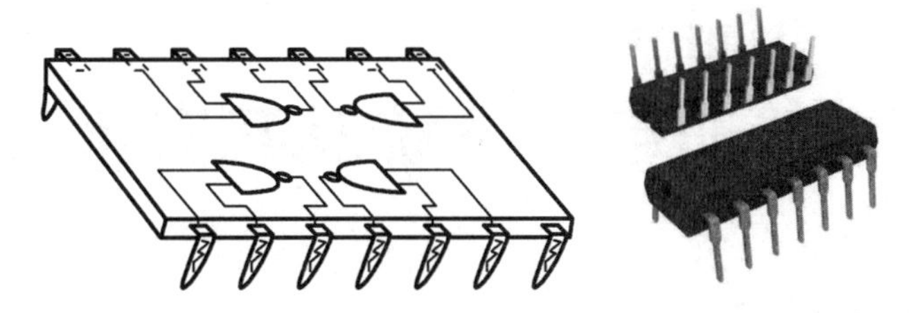

Fig. 1.59 Generic dual in line package (DIP) often referred to as a "chip"

图 1.59 双列直插式封装(DIP)通常指芯片

Question 思考题

Given the logic circuit in Fig. 1.60, determine its output F.

逻辑电路如图 1.60 所示,计算输出 F 的表达式。

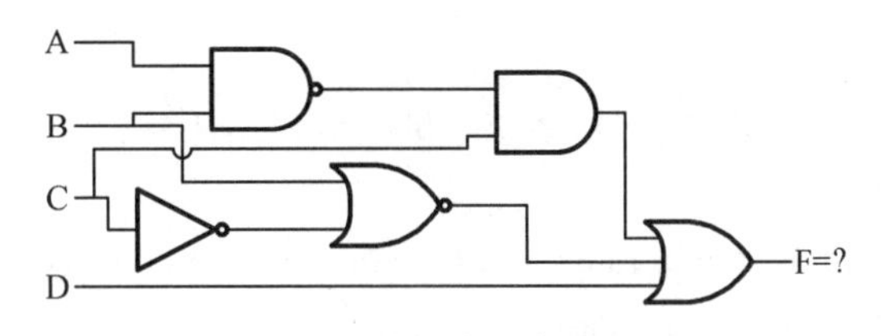

Fig. 1.60 Logic circuit

图 1.60 逻辑电路示例

Answer 答案

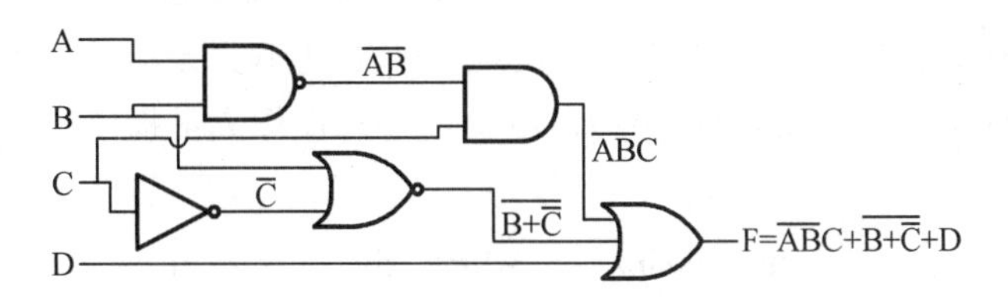

Chapter 2 Ships' Electrical Systems, Safety and Maintenance

第2章 船舶电气系统及其安全与维护

2.0 Introduction 介绍

This chapter provides an overview of a ship's electrical system is presented and describes various types of circuit diagrams used in electrical work. Electrical calculations, safety precautions, circuit diagrams and testing methods are outlined together with a description of general electrical maintenance and fault finding techniques.

本章概述了船舶的电气系统,并描述了在电气工作中使用的各种类型的电路图,介绍了电气计算、安全注意措施、电路图和测试方法,以及一般的电气维护和故障查找技术。

2.1 Ships' Electrical System 船舶电气系统

Auxiliary services on board ship range from engine room pumps, compressors and fans, deck winches and windlasses, to general lighting, catering and air conditioning. Electrical power is used to drive these auxiliary services. The electrical power system on board ship is designed to provide a secure supply to all loads with adequate built-in protection for the equipment and operating personal.

船上的辅助设施涵盖机舱泵、压缩机和风扇、甲板绞缆机和锚机,以及一般照明、餐饮和空调等设备。电力用于驱动这些辅助服务设施。船上的电力系统用于给所有负载提供一个安全稳定的电源,电源自带的内置保护可以给设备和操作人员提供足够的安全防护。

The distribution system is the means by which the electrical power produced by the generators is delivered to the various motors, lighting, galley services, and navigation aids, etc. which comprise the ship's electrical load.

配电系统是将发电机产生的电力输送至构成船舶电力负载的各种电动机、照明设备、厨房设施和导航设备等的装置。

The general scheme of a ship's electrical power system is common to nearly all ships.

一个船舶电力系统的保护方案几乎是所有船都通用的。

The electrical energy is routed through the main switchboard, and then distributed via cables to section and distribution boards then, ultimately to the final load consumers.

电能通过主配电板布线,然后通过电缆分配到各分区和分配电板,最终分配到负载用户。

The main AC generators (sometimes called alternators) produce the electrical power. It is supplied to the main switchboard and then distributed via cables to section and distribution boards, ultimately to the various auxiliary services comprising the electrical load. An emergency generator and emergency switchboard maintain supplies in the event of a main power failure.

主交流发电机(有时也称为交流发电机)产生电力。电力通过电缆供应到主配电板,然后分配到各分区和分配电板,最终分配到各种用途的电气负载。应急发电机和应急配电板在主电源故障时使用。

Compare this general layout in Fig. 2. 1 with the system on your ship. Note the great similarities and also note the differences—all ships' systems differ in some respect.

比较一下图 2. 1 中船舶电力系统的总体布局。注意一下它们的差异,所有船舶的电力系统在某些方面都有所不同。

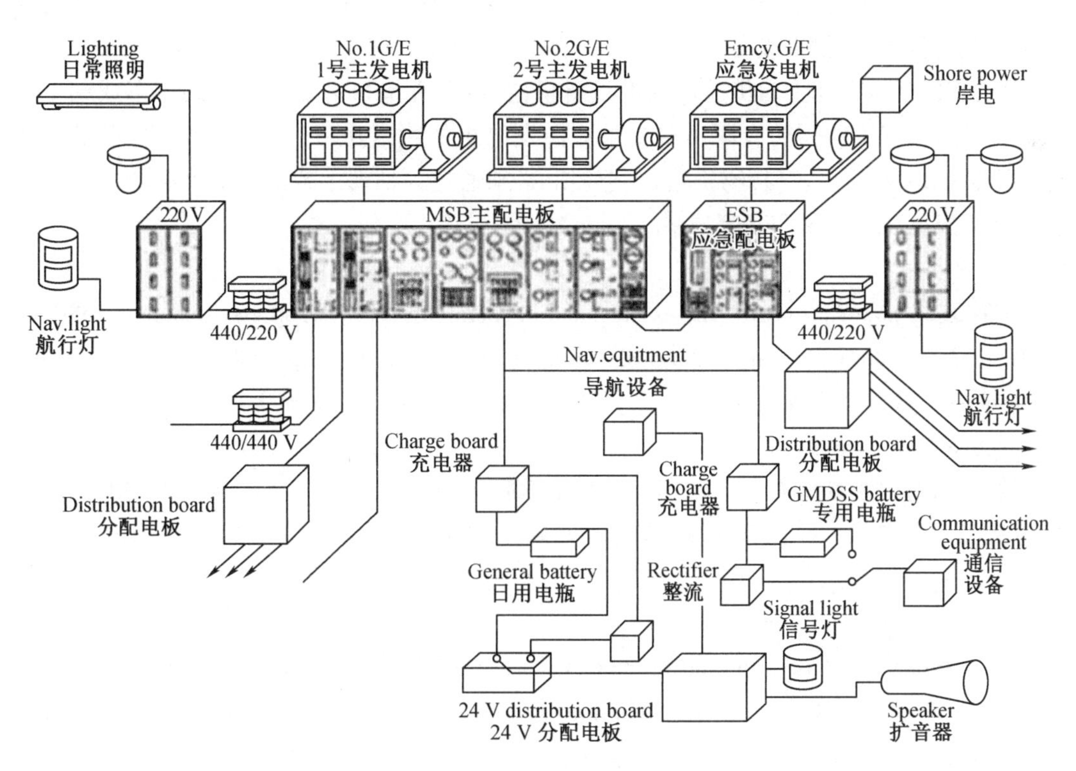

Fig. 2. 1 Electric power system

图 2. 1 船舶电力系统

The generators may be driven by a diesel engine, by a steam or gas turbine, or by the main propulsion engine as a shaft generator. The type of prime mover is determined by the design of the ship and by economic factors.

发电机可以由柴油机、蒸汽或燃气涡轮机驱动,或由作为轴带发电机的主推进装置驱动。原动机的类型取决于船舶的设计和经济因素。

The combined power rating of the generators is determined by the overall demand of the ship's electrical load.

发电机的组合额定功率是由船舶电力负载的总体需求决定的。

Large passenger ships usually have four large generators rated at 10 MW or more to supply the electric propulsion motors and the extensive hotel services on board. A cargo ship may have two main generators typically rated from 350 to 1,000 kW which are sufficient to supply the engine room auxiliaries while at sea and the winches or cranes for handling cargo while in port. The limited load required during an emergency requires that an emergency generator may be rated from about 10 kW for a small coaster to about 300 kW or more for a cargo liner. The shipbuilder must estimate the number and power rating of the required generators by assessing the power demand of the load for all situations whether at sea or in port.

大型客船通常有四台额定功率为 10 MW 或超过 10 MW 的大型发电机,以为电动机和船上的其他设备(如酒店设备)提供电力。货船可以有两个额定功率为 350~1 000 kW 的主发电机,它们足以在海上为机舱的辅助设备供电,以及在港口为处理货物的绞车或起重机供电。紧急情况下所需的有限负载要求应急发电机的额定功率约为 10 kW(小型沿海货轮)到约 300 kW 或更多(货物班轮)。造船厂必须通过评估海上或港口的负载功率需求来估计所需发电机的数量和额定功率。

Electrical power on board ship is commonly generated at 440 V,60 Hz(sometimes 380 V, 50 Hz). Ships with a very large electrical power demand will require generators that operate at a high voltage (3.3 kV, 6.6 kV or 11 kV) to limit the size of normal load current and the prospective fault current.

船上的电力通常为 440 V,60 Hz(有时是 380 V,50 Hz)。电力需求非常大的船舶需要发电机产生高电压(3.3 kV、6.6 kV 或 11 kV),以限制正常负载电流和预期故障电流的大小。

The British Standard (BS) and International Electrotechnical Commission (IEC) definition of low voltage is 50 V AC to 1,000 V AC (the IEC give this definition to harmonise British and European standards).

英国标准(BS)和国际电工委员会(IEC)对低压的定义为 50~1 000 V 交流电(IEC 给出这一定义的目的是协调英国和欧洲的标准)。

Lighting and other low power ancillary services usually operate at 110 V or 220 V, single-phase AC. Transformers are used to reduce the 440 V system voltage to these lower voltage levels.

照明和其他低功率辅助设施通常使用 110 V 或 220 V 单相交流电。变压器用于将 440 V 系统电压降低到较低的电压水平。

Where portable equipment is to be used in dangerous, hot and damp locations, it is advisable to operate at 55 V or even 24 V supplied again by a step-down transformer. Occasionally, transformers are also used to step-up voltages, e. g. supplying a large 3. 3 kV bow thruster motor from a 440 V switchboard supply.

如果便携式设备用于危险、炎热、潮湿的地方,建议由降压变压器以 55 V 甚至 24 V 的电压运行。偶尔变压器也用于提高电压,例如从 440 V 开关板电源提供一个 3. 3 kV 电压给船首侧推器电动机。

Batteries for various essential services operate at 12 V or 24 V DC but sometimes higher voltages are used if such loads require a large power supply.

各种必要设施的电池在 12 V 或 24 V 直流下运行,但如果这些负载需要较大的电源时会使用更高的电压。

2. 2 Electrical Diagrams 电气图

There are various types of diagram which attempt to show how an electrical circuit operates. Symbols are used to represent the various items of equipment. The ship builder provides a complete set of ship's electrical diagrams. It is important that you study these diagrams to be able to read and understand them competently, and to use them as an aid in locating electrical faults.

电气图有各种各样的类型,用以展示一个电路如何运行。在电气图中用符号来表示各种设备元件。造船厂会提供一套完整的船舶电气图。研究这些图是很有必要的,以便我们能够熟练地阅读和理解它们,并使用它们帮助找出电气故障。

2. 2. 1 Block Diagrams 框图

Block diagrams describes the way a process works and which way signals run. It is a simple way to get a general overview of how a system works without going into detail. Block diagram consists of blocks. These blocks symbolize a source or a receiver (or both) of signals, they are connected with process lines showing which way the signals run.

框图描述了流程的工作方式以及信号的运行方式。这是一种简便方法,可以在不用详细说明的情况下获得系统工作原理的一般概述。框图由模块组成,这些模块表示信号的发出或接收(或两者),以显示信号运行方式的流程顺序相连。

A block diagram shows in simplified form the main inter-relationships of the elements in a system, and how the system works or may be operated. Such diagrams are often used to depict control systems and other complex relationships. The block diagram in Fig. 2. 2(a) describes the main functions of an overcurrent relay (OCR) used for protection. Fig. 2.2(b) shows one way of realizing the overall OCR function.

方框图以简化的形式显示系统中元素的主要相互关系,以及系统是如何工作或如何操作的。这样的图通常被用来描述控制系统和其他复杂的关系。图 2.2(a)描述了用于保护的过流继电器(OCR)的主要功能。图 2.2(b)显示了实现整体 OCR 功能的一种方法。

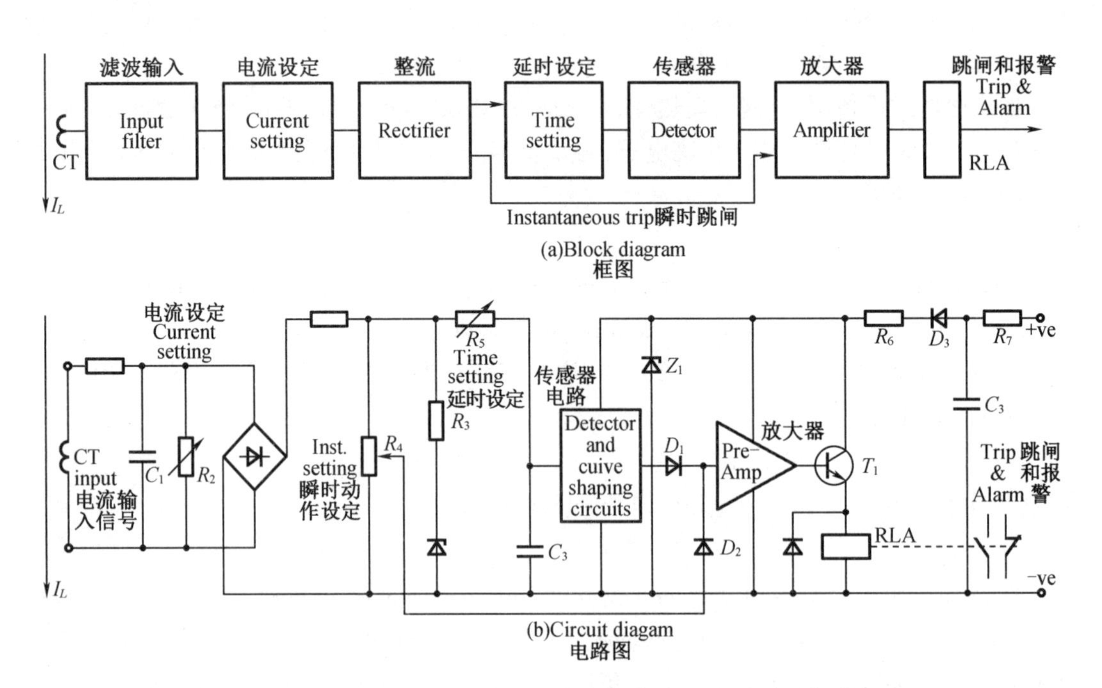

Fig. 2.2 Electronic overcurrent relay block diagram and circuit diagram

图 2.2 过流继电器框图和电路图

Diagrams like this state the function of each block but usually do not give any information about the components in each block or how the blocks are actually interconnected.

用这样的图说明每个方框的功能,但通常不提供任何关于每个方框中的组件的信息或这些方框实际上是如何相互连接的。

2.2.2 A System Diagram 系统图

A system diagram, as in Fig. 2.3, shows the main features of a system and its bounds, without necessarily showing cause-to-effect. Its main use is to illustrate the ways of operating the system. Detail is omitted in order to make the diagram as clear as possible, and so, easily understood.

系统图 2.3 展示了一个系统的主要特征及其界限,而不必展示因果关系。它的主要用途是说明系统的工作方式。为了使图尽可能一目了然,我们省略了一些细节。

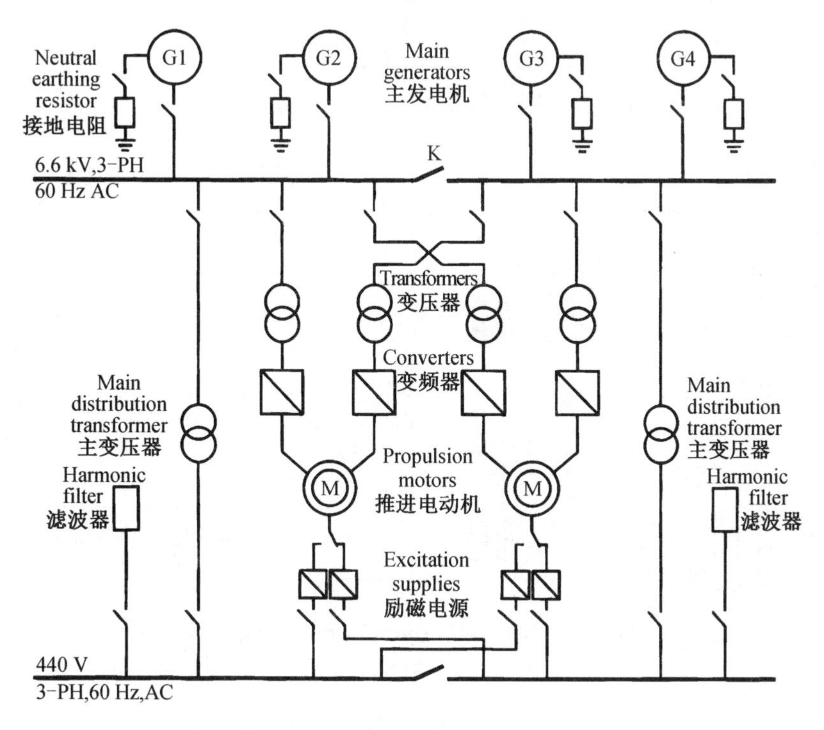

Fig. 2.3　Power system diagram

图 2.3　电力系统图

2.2.3　A Circuit Diagram 电路图

A circuit diagram shows the functioning of a circuit fully. All essential parts and connections are depicted by means of graphical symbols arranged to show the operation as clearly as possible but without regard to the physical layout of the various items, their parts or connections.

电路图完整地展示了电路的功能。所有的基本部件和连接都用图形符号表示,以尽可能清楚地说明其运行过程,但不考虑各种部件的物理布局或连接。

The electrical connections in Fig. 2.4 for a motor starter are clearly shown in the simplest way. A most important point is that no attempt is made to show the moving contacts of a relay or contactor alongside the coil that operates them (where they are actually physically located). Instead, the coil and its related contacts are identified by a common number or letter. Although there are international agreements as to the symbol to be used to represent electrical components, you must be prepared to meet various different symbols representing the same component.

图 2.4 以最简单的方式清晰地展示了一个电动机启动器的电气连接。最重要的是,不必将继电器或接触器的动触点展示在操作它们的线圈旁边(它们的实际位置)。相反,线圈及其相关触点由一个共同的数字或字母来识别。关于用来表示电气组件的符号有不同的国际标准,因此我们必须为遇到用各种不同符号代表相同组件这一情况做好准备。

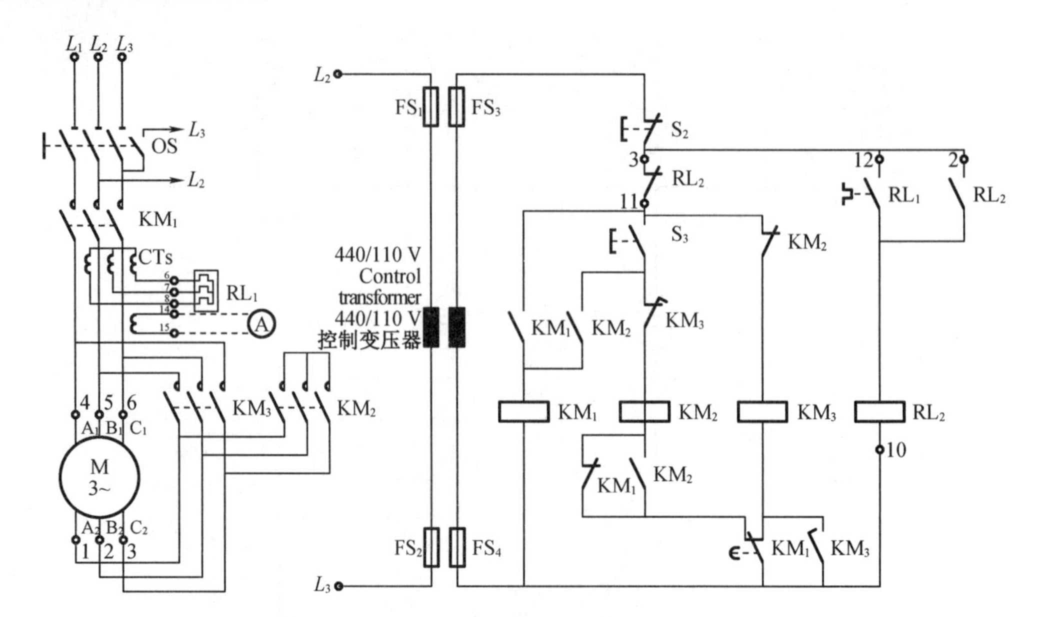

Fig. 2.4 Star-delta control circuit diagram

图 2.4 星-三角控制电路

The use of a circuit diagram is to enable the reader to understand the operation of the circuit, to follow each sequence in the operation from the moment of initiating the operation (e. g. by pressing a start button) to the final act (e. g. starting of the motor). If the equipment fails to operate correctly, the reader can follow the sequence of operations until he comes to the operation that has failed. The components involved in that faulty operation can then be examined to locate the suspect item. There is no need to examine other components that are known to function correctly and have no influence on the fault, so the work is simplified. A circuit diagram is an essential tool for fault finding.

电路图的使用是为了使读者能够理解电路的运行情况,并了解从运行启动的时刻(例如通过按下启动按钮)到最终动作(例如启动电动机)的每个动作顺序。如果设备不能正常运行,读图者可以根据动作顺序找到失败的动作点,然后检查该动作故障所涉及的部件,以确定可疑部件,而不需要检查那些已知的能正常工作且对故障没有影响的其他零部件,从而简化工作。电路图是查找故障的必备工具。

2.2.4 Wiring Diagram 接线图

A wiring diagram shows the detailed connections between components or items of equipment, and in some cases the routing of these connections. An equipment wiring diagram shows the components in their approximate positions occupied within the actual enclosure. The component may be shown complete (e. g. a contactor coil together with all the contacts it drives) or may be simply represented by a block with the necessary terminals clearly marked. A different thickness of line can be used to differentiate between power and control circuit connections. The wiring diagram in Fig. 2. 5 is of the same starter shown for the circuit diagram of Fig. 2. 4.

接线图展示了设备组成部分或组件之间的连接细节，在某些情况下包含这些连接的路径。设备接线图展示了组件在实际设备中所处的大致位置。图中可以完整展示组件（例如接触器线圈及其驱动的所有触点），也可以用框图简洁清晰地标记必要的端子排。不同宽度的线条可用于区分电源电路和控制电路。图 2.5 中的接线图与图 2.4 中的电路图所示的启动器相同。

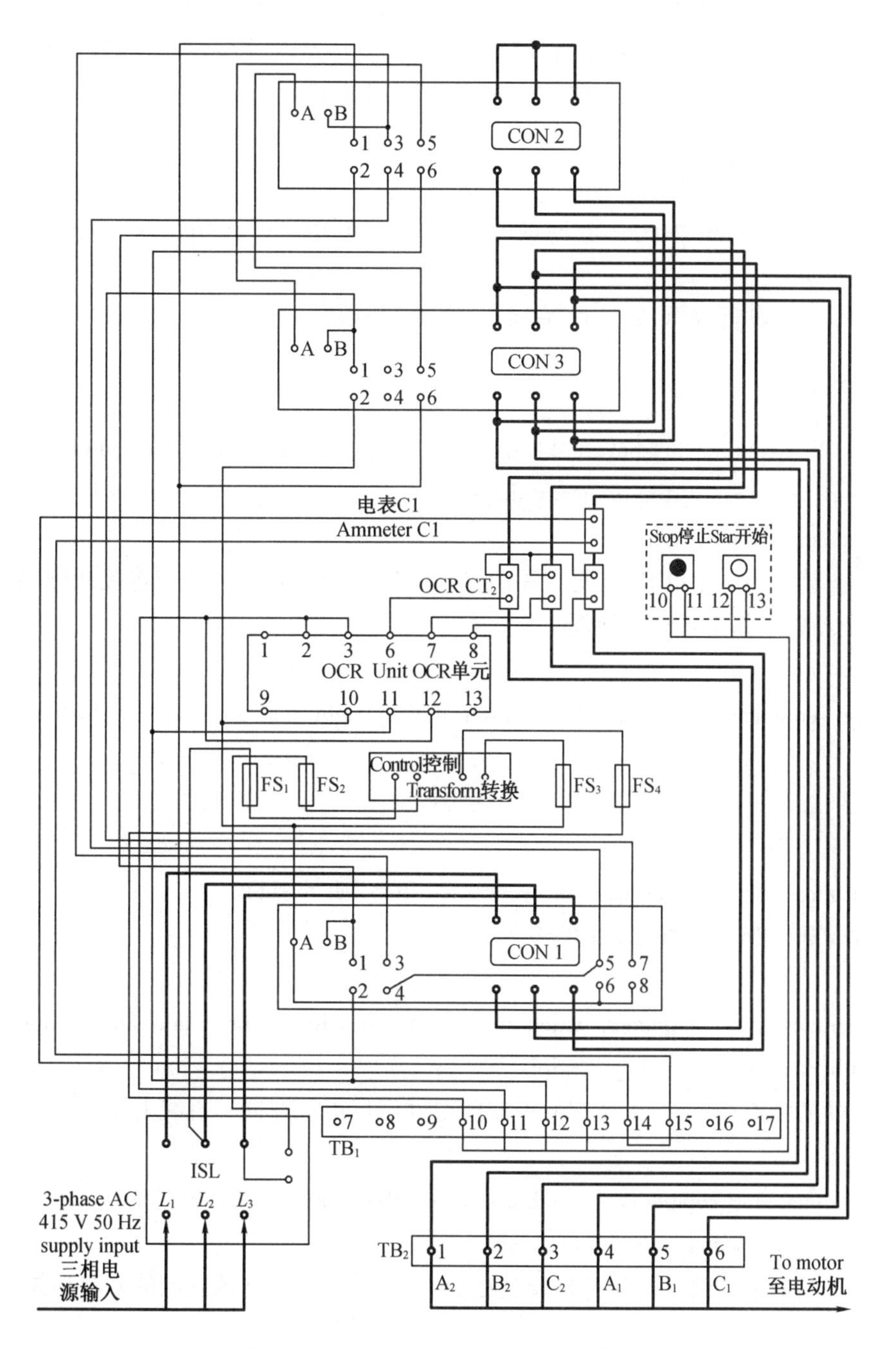

Fig. 2.5　Star-delta starter wiring diagram

图 2.5　星–三角启动器接线图

A wiring diagram may be of a fairly simple circuit, but its layout makes it quite difficult to use and to understand the sequential operation of the circuit. The purpose of a wiring diagram is mainly to instruct the wiring installer how to construct and connect the equipment. It is of little use in trouble shooting apart from identifying the exact position of suspect components, terminals and wires.

接线图可能是一个相当简单的电路,但它的布局使得其不便使用且难以用于了解电路的动作顺序。接线图的作用主要是指导布线安装人员构造和连接设备。它可用于识别可疑部件、端子和电线的确切位置,而在故障排除方面用处很小。

Question 思考题

What to do if difficulties arise in locating a fault on an item of equipment and only a wiring diagram is available?

如果难以定位设备故障,且只有接线图,该如何处理?

Answer 答案

It may well save time to convert the wiring diagram into a much simpler and more useful circuit diagram. When converting a wiring diagram into a circuit diagram certain basic rules and conventions should be followed.

将接线图转换为一个更简单、更有用的电路图可能会节省时间。当将接线图转换为电路图时,应遵循以下基本规则和惯例。

- Every sequence should be drawn from left to right and from top to bottom (where possible).

  每个序列应尽可能从左到右,从上到下绘制。

- Each stage should be in order of occurrence from left to right.

  每个阶段都应按从左到右发生的顺序进行。

- All contacts and components which are in series should be drawn in a straight line (where possible) with the component they control.

  所有串联的触点和组件,以及它们控制的组件应尽可能在同一直线上绘制。

- All contacts and components which are in parallel should be drawn side by side and at the same level to emphasis their parallel function.

  所有并联的触点和组件都应并排绘制在同一水平线上,以强调它们的并联功能。

- All major components operating at bus-bar voltage should be drawn at the same level (or aligned horizontally) to help identify the required components quickly.

所有在母线电压下工作的主要组件应在相同水平线上(或水平对齐),以帮助快速识别所需的部件。

• All contacts should be shown open or closed as in their normal or de-energised condition.
所有触点应在非动作状态或断电状态下断开或闭合。

There are other conventions but these cover the main points of good systematic diagrams. Block, system, circuit and wiring diagrams are the main types in general use for electrical work. Other types of diagram are sometimes used to give information for which the basic types are unsuitable (e. g. a pictorial view of a component).

还有其他的规则,但这些规则都包含良好系统图的要点。框图、系统图、电路图和接线图是电气作业的主要图表类型。有时使用其他类型的图表来提供以上类型图表无法表达的信息(例如,部件的图形视图)。

We should study the ship's electrical diagrams to gain an understanding of equipment operation prior to carrying out maintenance or fault finding. Diagrams should be regarded as an essential tool when carrying out work on electrical equipment.

在进行维护或故障查找之前,我们应该研究船舶的电气图纸,以了解设备的运行情况。图纸是进行电气设备作业的必要工具。

2.3　Electrical Safety 电气安全

Large power equipments utilize high forces. Electrical, mechanical, thermal and chemical changes produce the desired operation. Very high values of voltage, current, power, temperature, force, pressure etc., create the possibility of danger in an engineering system.

大型电力设备的力矩大,它们通过电气、机械、热和化学方面的变化实现所需的操作。工程系统中的电压、电流、功率、温度、力、压力等的高数值,可能带来危险。

To minimize the safety risk to personnel and equipment, a system must be designed and manufactured to the latest high standards and be correctly installed. During its working life, the equipment must be continuously monitored and correctly maintained by professionally qualified personnel who understand its operation and safety requirements.

为了将对人员和设备的安全风险降到最低,系统的设计和制造必须达到最新的高标准,并正确安装。在其工作寿命内,必须由了解其操作和安全要求的合格专业人员对设备进行持续的监控和正确的维护。

Before attempting any electrical work, there are some basic safety precautions we must bear in mind. The possible dangers arising from the misuse of electrical equipment are well known.

Electric shock and fire can cause loss of life and damage to equipment.

在尝试任何电气作业之前,我们必须牢记一些基本的安全注意事项。滥用电气设备可能产生的危险是众所周知的。触电和火灾会造成生命损失和设备损坏。

Regulations exist to control the construction, installation, operation and maintenance of electrical equipment so that danger is eliminated as far as possible. Minimum acceptable standards of safety are issued by various bodies including national governments, international governmental, national and international standards associations, learned societies, classification societies, etc. Where danger arises it is usually due to accident, neglect or some other contravention of the regulations.

对于电气设备的施工、安装、运行、维护有相应的规范,以尽可能消除危险。最低可接受的安全标准由各机构发布,包括国家政府、国际政府、国家和国际标准协会、学会、船级社等。当出现危险时,通常是由事故、疏忽或其他违反规定的行为造成的。

Ships' staff must operate equipment in a safe manner and maintain it in a safe condition at all times. Failure to do so will cause danger with serious consequences arising. Keep in mind an essential list of DO's and DO NOT's when working with electrical equipment.

船员必须以安全的方式操作设备,并始终使其保持安全状态。如果不这样做,将造成危险,并产生严重后果。在使用电气设备时,请注意"一定要"(DO)和"不要"(DO NOT)的基本清单。

DO get to know the ship's electrical system and equipment. Study the ship's diagrams to pinpoint the location of switches and protection devices supplying distribution boards and essential items of equipment. Write down this information in a note book. Become familiar with the normal indications on switchboard instruments so that abnormal operation can be quickly detected.

一定要了解船上的电气系统和设备。研究船舶图纸,以确定提供配电板和设备基本部件的开关及保护设备的位置。把这些信息写在一个笔记簿中。熟悉配电板仪表上的正常指示符,以便快速检测到异常操作。

DO operate equipment according to the manufacturer's recommendations.

一定要根据制造商的建议操作设备。

DO maintain equipment according to the manufacturer's recommendations or the shipowner's maintenance procedures.

一定要根据制造商的建议或船东的维护程序来维护设备。

DO ensure that all guards, covers and doors are securely fitted and that all bolts and fixings are in place and tight.

一定要确保所有防护罩、盖和门安装牢固,所有螺栓和固定件都安装到位且牢固。

DO inform the officer of the watch before shutting down equipment for maintenance.

一定要在关闭设备进行维修之前通知值班人员。

DO switch off and lock-off supplies, remove fuses, and display warning notices before removing covers of equipment for maintenance.

一定要在打开设备盖子前关闭电源,拆卸熔断器,并显示警告通知。

DO confirm that circuits are DEAD (by using an approved voltage tester) before touching conductors and terminals.

一定要在接触导线和端子之前确认电路已断电(通过使用经批准的电压测试器)。

DO NOT touch live conductors under any pretext.

不得以任何理由接触带电导体。

DO NOT touch rotating parts.

不要接触旋转部件。

DO NOT leave live conductors or rotating parts exposed.

不要暴露带电导体或旋转部件。

DO NOT overload equipment.

不要使设备过载。

DO NOT neglect or abuse equipment.

不要忽视或滥用设备。

You should think SAFETY at all times and so develop a safety conscious attitude. This may well save your life and the lives of others. Most accidents occur due to a momentary loss of concentration or attempts to short-circuit standard safety procedures.

应该一直考虑安全,所以要加强安全意识。这很可能会挽救你和他人的生命。大多数事故的发生是由暂时不专心或试图在标准安全程序中走捷径造成的。

2.4 Electric Shock 触电

Many people have experienced an electric shock at some time. At best it is an unpleasant experience, at worst it is fatal. Electrical safety warning sign as shown Fig. 2. 6.

很多人都有过触电的经历。最好的情况下这只是一种不愉快的经历,而最坏的情况下这是致命的。电气安全警示标志如图 2.6 所示。

Fig. 2.6 Electrical safety warning sign

图 2.6 电气安全警示标志

Anyone who has access to live electrical equipment must be fully aware of first-aid and safety procedures related to electric shock as described in relevant safety acts. Copies of these safety procedures should be displayed on board ship. Electric shock is due to the flow of current through your body. This is often from hand to hand or from hand to foot. A shock current as low as 15 mA AC or DC may be fatal. Obviously the size of shock current is related to the applied voltage and body resistance. Unfortunately, body resistance goes down as the applied voltage goes up. This means that the shock current is further increased at high voltages. The size of body resistance also depends on other factors such as the state of health, the degree of contact with live wires and the perspiration or dampness on skin.

任何使用带电电气设备的人都必须充分了解相关安全规范中所述的与触电有关的急救和安全程序。这些安全程序的副本应张贴在船上。触电是由电流通过人体引起的,通常是从手到手或从手到脚。低至 15 mA 的交流电或直流电可能会造成致命后果。显然,触电电流的大小与所施加的电压和人体电阻有关。不幸的是,人体电阻会随着施加电压的升高而下降。这意味着在高压下,触电电流会进一步增大。人体电阻的大小还取决于其他因素,比如健康状况、与带电电缆的接触程度以及皮肤上的潮湿程度。

Typical dry full-contact body resistance is about 5,000 Ω at 25 V falling to about 2,000 Ω at 250 V.

典型的完全接触时的干燥人体电阻为:25 V 时约 5 000 Ω,250 V 时约 2 000 Ω。

Question 思考题

What would the equivalent shock current levels be at 25 V and 250 V?

25 V 和 250 V 时的触电电流分别是多少?

Answer 答案

5 mA, 125 mA.

Voltages of about 60 V and below are regarded as reasonably safe for portable hand tools. This is why special stepdown isolating transformers are used with portable tools and handlamps. These transformers supply the tool or lamp at 110 V AC but because the secondary winding is centre-tapped to earth, the maximum shock voltage to earth is 55 V AC.

大约 60 V 及以下的电压被认为是便携式手持工具的合理安全电压。这就是为什么特殊的降压隔离变压器被用于便携式工具和手提灯。这些变压器为工具或灯提供 110 V 的交流电压,但由于二次绕组的中性点是接地的,因此接地的最大触电电压为 55 V(交流).

Electric shock is often accompanied by falling, which may cause additional physical injury and require first-aid action. If the shock victim is unconscious, resuscitation must take priority over first aid methods.

触电常伴有跌倒,这可能会造成额外的身体伤害,需要急救。如果触电者失去意识,必须优先采用心肺复苏的急救方法。

2.5 Insulation Resistance 绝缘电阻

All electrical equipment has insulation. The purpose of the insulation is to keep electric currents in the conductors and to prevent contact with live wires. The electrical resistance of insulation must be very high (MΩ) to prevent current leaking away from conductors. Insulation resistance is measured between: conductors and earth, conductors.

所有电气设备均配有绝缘材料。绝缘的目的是保持电流在导体中,并防止人员接触带电的电线。绝缘电阻必须非常高(MΩ),以防止电流从导体上泄漏。测量以下绝缘电阻:导体对地的电阻、导体之间的电阻。

The insulation resistance includes the resistance of the insulation material and also the resistance of any surface deposits of dirt, oil, moisture, etc. Surface deposits can reduce the insulation resistance.

绝缘电阻包括绝缘材料的电阻以及污垢、油、水分等表面沉积的电阻。表面沉积物可降低绝缘电阻的性能。

The flow of leakage currents through such surface deposits is called tracking which is also affected by the creepage and clearance distances between terminals as shown in Fig. 2. 7. Equipment must be maintained in a clean condition to prevent tracking and to maintain a high value of insulation resistance (usually at least 1 MΩ).

通过表面沉积物而使电流泄漏的现象被称为爬电，而绝缘电阻也受到端子之间的爬电距离和间隙的影响(图 2.7)。设备必须保持在清洁的状态下，以防止爬电和保持较高的绝缘电阻值(通常至少为 1 MΩ)。

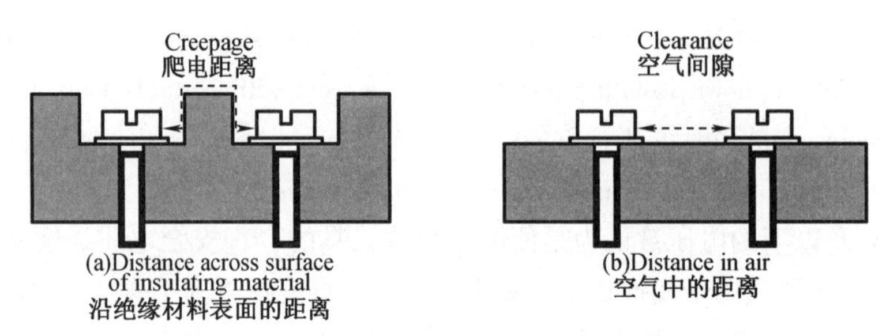

Fig. 2.7 Creepage and clearance distance

图 2.7 爬电距离和空气间隙

Insulation materials are non-metallic and have very few of the generally good physical properties associated with metals. Insulation is adversely affected by many factors such as humidity, temperature, electrical and mechanical stress, vibration, chemicals, oil, dirt and, of course, old age.

绝缘材料是非金属的，一般不具有像金属那样良好的物理性能。绝缘性能受到许多不利因素的影响，如湿度、温度、电气和机械应力、振动、化学品、油、污垢，当然还有老化。

Traditional insulation materials include cotton, silk, paper, etc. They may be either dry or treated with suitable varnishes or resins to exclude moisture and other harmful substances. Other materials include mica, fibre glass, etc., and more modern materials such as PVC and other plastics and compounds. An extensively used medium not normally considered as an insulation material is the air surrounding the electrical components.

传统的绝缘材料包括棉、丝绸、纸张等。它们可以是干燥的，或用适当的清漆或树脂处理，以排除水分和其他有害物质的影响。其他材料包括云母、玻璃纤维等，以及更现代的材料，如聚氯乙烯、其他塑料和化合物。一种被广泛使用，却通常不被认为是绝缘材料的介质，就是电气元件周围的空气。

The majority of insulation materials in common use cannot withstand temperatures much in excess of 100 ℃. All electrical equipment heats up when carrying load current with the consequent rise in temperature. This temperature rise is above that of the ambient cooling air temperature.

大多数常用的绝缘材料不能承受远超 100 ℃的温度。所有的电气设备在承载负载电流时都会升温。此温升高于环境冷却空气的温度。

All marine electrical equipment is constructed and rated to work satisfactorily in a maximum ambient air temperature of 45 ℃ (Lloyd's Register of Shipping). Under this condition, the expected temperature rise will not exceed the permitted temperature limit set for the insulation material. It is therefore the insulation material that dictates the maximum permitted operating temperature of the electrical equipment.

所有船用电气设备应能在 45 ℃(英国劳氏船级社)的最高环境温度下正常工作。在这一条件下,预期的工作温升将不会超过为绝缘材料设定的允许温度限值。因此,绝缘材料决定了电气设备的最高允许运行温度。

For this purpose, insulation is classified according to the maximum temperature at which it is safe to operate. Various classes of insulation are listed in British Standards (BS) and classes A, E, B and F are used for marine electrical equipment. The maximum temperature allowed for each of these classes as shown in the Table 2.1.

为此,绝缘是根据其安全运行的最高温度进行分类的。英国标准(BS)中列出了各种类型的绝缘材料,船舶电气设备采用 A、E、B 和 F 类。每种类别所允许的最高温度如表 2.1 所示。

Table 2.1 Insulation class

表 2.1 绝缘等级

绝缘等级	A	E	B	F	H	C
最高温度/℃	105	120	130	155	180	>180

These are steady surface temperatures measured with equipment stopped and no flow of cooling air. Hot-spot temperatures of 105 ℃ (Class A) and 130 ℃ (Class B) are generally accepted as normal at the centre of coils and windings of machines with these surface temperatures. A machine operating continuously with these hot-spot temperatures would have an expected life of 15 to 20 years before the insulation failed completely. However, the life expectancy would be halved for every 10 ℃ above these allowed hot-spot temperatures.

这些稳定的表面温度要在设备停止,并且没有冷却空气流动的情况下测量。在具有这些表面温度的机器线圈和绕组中心,105 ℃(A 级)和 130 ℃(B 级)的热点温度被公认为正常温度。在这些热点温度下连续运行的机器在绝缘完全失效之前的预期寿命为 15~20 年。然而,每超过这些允许的热点温度 10 ℃,预期寿命将减半。

2.6 Insulation Testing 绝缘测试

A measurement of the insulation resistance (IR) gives one of the best guides to the state of health of electrical equipment. The resistance should be measured between insulated conductors and earth, and between conductors.

对绝缘电阻(IR)的测量是了解电气设备健康状况的最佳方式之一。应测量绝缘导体与接地之间以及导体之间的电阻。

An insulation tester is a high reading resistance meter using a high test voltage — usually 500 V DC(Fig. 2. 8). The test voltage is produced either by an internal hand-driven generator or by a battery and electronic voltage charger. A test voltage of 500 V DC is suitable for testing ships' equipment rated at 440 V AC. Test voltages of 1,000 V and 5,000 V are used for high voltage (HV) systems on board ship.

绝缘测试仪是一种使用高测试电压的高读数电阻计,通常使用 500 V 直流电(图 2. 8)。测试电压是由内部手动驱动的发电机或电池和电子电压充电器产生的。测试电压为 500 V 的直流电适用于测试额定电压为 440 V 的船舶交流设备。船上的高压(HV)系统采用 1 000 V 和 5 000 V 的测试电压。

1—Earth(接地端);2—G(电压测量输入负极);3—V(电压测量输入正极);4—Line(绝缘测试电压输出孔);
5—Display(显示屏);6—Backlight(背光按钮);7—PI/DAR(吸收比和极化指数测量转换按钮);
8—Test(绝缘电阻测量按钮);9—Function switch(功能旋钮)。

Fig. 2. 8 Insulation resistance tester

图 2. 8 绝缘测试仪

To prove the basic operation of the tester, short the two probes together, switch to "MΩ" and press the test button or rocker switch. The pointer should indicate approximately "0 Ω". Before applying the test, the equipment to be tested must be disconnected from the live power supply and locked-off according to standard safety procedures.

为了验证绝缘测试仪的基本功能,将两个探头短接,切换至"MΩ"挡并按下测试按钮或摇杆开关。此时指针应该大约指示"0 Ω"。在进行测试前,必须将被测试的设备按照标准的安全程序切断带电电源并锁定。

A Megger type IR tester can be used to check whether the circuit to be tested is live. Switch the instrument to "MΩ" and connect the probes to pairs of equipment terminals. DO NOT press the button. The meter will now indicate that the circuit is live or not. If the circuit is dead, it is then safe to press the test button. Confirm that a reliable earth connection is obtained by connecting the probes to two separate earth points on the equipment frame while testing for low resistance continuity.

梅凯绝缘测试仪可以用来检查待测试的电路是否带电。将仪器切换到"MΩ"挡,将探头连接到设备端子,不要按下这个按钮。仪表此时会指示电路是否带电。如果电路不带电,则按下测试按钮是安全的。在测试低电阻连续性时,将探头连接到设备框架上的两个独立接地点,以获得可靠的接地连接。

For an IR test on a three-phase machine, measure and log the phase-to-phase insulation resistance values. Three readings should be measured as U-V, V-W, W-U as shown in Fig. 2. 9.

在三相机器上进行绝缘测试,测量并记录各相之间的绝缘电阻值。三个读数应以 U-V、V-W、W-U 的形式进行测量,如图 2. 9 所示。

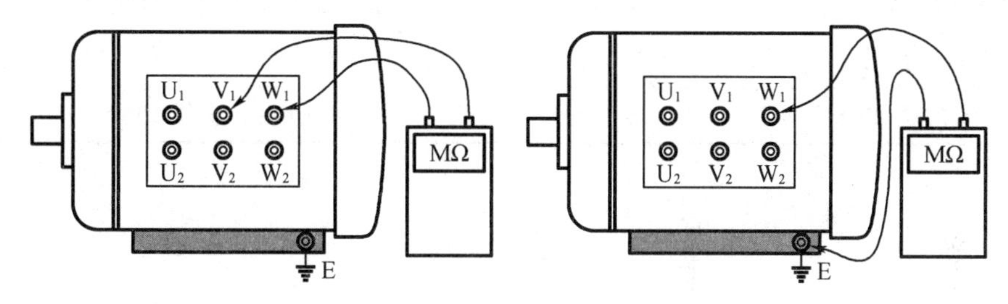

Fig. 2. 9 IR test connections

图 2. 9 绝缘测试接线

Measure and log the phase-to-earth insulation resistance values. Three readings should be measured as U-E, V-E, W-E.

测量并记录相对地绝缘电阻值。三个读数应按 U-E、V-E、W-E 进行测量。

Note: Insulation resistance decreases with increase of temperature.

注:绝缘电阻随温度的升高而降低。

Question 思考题

Why should the measurement of the insulation resistance of a machine ideally be made while machine is hot?

为什么最好在机器变热时测量机器的绝缘电阻?

Answer 答案

Insulation becomes more leaky (its IR value falls) at high temperatures. So testing while hot shows the realistic IR value at, or near, its working temperature. Insulation resistance can vary considerably with changing atmospheric conditions. A single reading gives little information. However, the regular recording of test results may show a downward trend which indicates impending trouble which can be remedied by preventive maintenance(Table 2.2,Fig. 2.10).

在高温下会发生绝缘泄漏(绝缘电阻值下降)。因此,热测试显示了其工作温度下或附近的真实绝缘电阻值。绝缘电阻会随着大气条件的变化而发生很大变化。一次测量所能提供的信息很少,而定期记录测试结果可显示下降趋势,显示即将出现的问题,从而通过预防性维修来补救(表2.2、图2.10)。

Table 2.2 AC compressor motor no. 1 IR LOG

表2.2 1号空压机绝缘记录

Date(日期)	IR/MΩ	Comments(备注)
5 Jan(1月5日)	17	ER cold (dry-dock)(机舱冷态(干坞中))
8 May(5月8日)	12	warm(暖态)
16 Oct(10月16日)	5	hot and humid(热态且潮湿)
12 Mar(3月12日)	2	warm, cleaned & dried(暖态、洁净且干燥)
13 Mar(3月13日)	25	repeat test(重复测量)

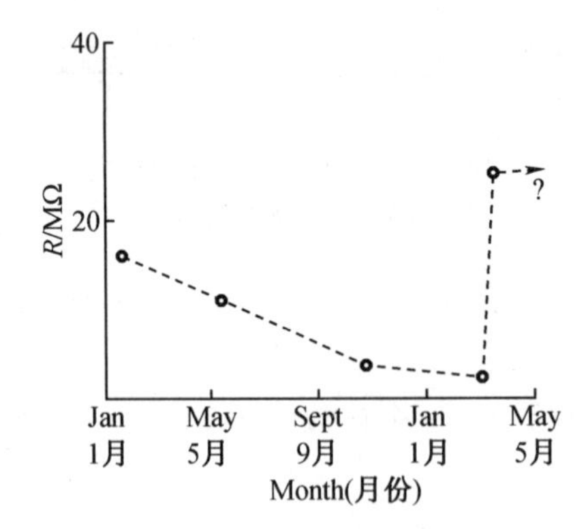

Fig. 2.10 IR trend

图2.10 绝缘曲线

2.7 Circuit Testing 电路测试

This section looks at the various electrical circuit testing operations you may need to carry out, and at the instruments you will need. The main tests as shown in the Table 2.3.

本节将介绍工作中需进行的各种电路测试操作,还有需要用到的仪器。主要的测试内容如表2.3所示。

Table 2. 3 Electrical circuit testing

表 2. 3 电路测试

Insulation Resistance (IR) 绝缘电阻(IR)	Using a (megger) tester (at 500 V DC for a 440 V circuit) Do not use a multimeter for this task 绝缘测试仪(500 V 直流用于 440 V 电路)不要使用万用表
Continuity Resistance(Low Ω) 持续电阻(低阻值)	Typically using a multimeter 一般使用万用表
Component Resistance(Ω or kΩ) 部件电阻(Ω 或者 kΩ)	
Voltage (AC or DC) 电压(交流或者直流)	
Current 电流	Using a clampmeter (or multimeter for small currents) 钳形电流表(或者万用表测量小电流)

2. 8 Continuity Testing 连续性测试

An insulation tester normally also incorporates a low voltage continuity test facility (Fig. 2. 11). This is a low resistance instrument for measuring the continuity (or otherwise) of conductors. It can be used to measure the low resistance of cables, motor windings, transformer windings, earthing straps, etc. The procedure for use is similar to that for the insulation tester:

(1) Prove the correct operation of the instrument;

(2) Isolate and lock off the equipment to be tested;

(3) Prove the equipment to be dead;

(4) Switch the instrument to "Ω" or "continuity";

(5) Connect the probes to the circuit;

(6) Operate the test switch and check the indication on the scale, log all readings.

绝缘测试仪通常还包含一个低压连续性测试装置(图 2. 11)。这是一种用于测量导线(或其他)连续性的低电阻的仪器。其可用于测量电缆、电动机绕组、变压器绕组、接地带等,使用方法与绝缘测试仪相似:

(1)证明仪表能正常工作;

(2)隔离和锁定待测试的设备;

(3)证明设备已断电;

(4)将仪器切换到"Ω"或"连续性";

(5)将探头连接到电路上;

(6)操作测试开关,查看"Ω"的读数,记录所有读数。

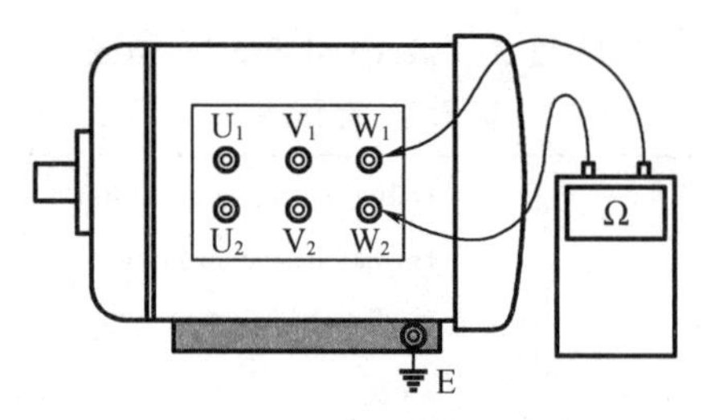

Fig. 2. 11 Continuity test connections

图 2. 11 连续性测试接线

In the case of three-phase motors and transformers, etc. the comparison between readings is usually more important than the absolute value of the readings. All readings should be identical. If one reading is significantly smaller than the others, this could indicate the possibility of short-circuited turns in that winding. Conversely, a high continuity resistance value indicates a high resistance fault or an open-circuit (e. g. a loose connection).

对于三相电动机、变压器等,读数之间的比较通常比读数的绝对值更重要。所有读数均应相同。如果一个读数明显小于其他读数,则可能表明该绕组中有短路的可能性。相反,高连续性电阻值表示高电阻故障或断路(例如,连接松动)。

Some models of insulation/continuity testers also provide facilities to measure resistance in the "kΩ" range and "AC" voltage.

一些型号的绝缘/连续性测试仪还可测量千欧(kΩ)范围内的电阻和交流电压。

To measure very low continuity resistance values such as those between bus-bar joints and circuit breaker contacts, it is necessary to use a micro-ohmmeter. This type of tester drives a set DC current(e. g. 10 A) through the circuit while measuring the resulting volt-drop across it.

为了测量极低的连续性电阻值,如母线接头和断路器触点之间的电阻值,需要使用微欧姆计。这种类型的测试仪驱动着一组直流电流(比如 10 A)通过电路,同时测量由此产生的电压降。

A set of four test leads are used — two to apply the current and two to measure the volt-drop directly at the current injection points.

由四个测试引线组成的一组测试表,使用两根引线来提供电流,两根引线来直接测量电流注入点的电压降。

The meter then calculates $R=U/I$ (Ohm's Law), and displays the result as a digital readout in milli-ohms (mΩ) or micro-ohms (μΩ).

然后仪表通过公式 $R=U/I$ (欧姆定律)计算数值,并以毫欧(mΩ)或微欧(μΩ)为单位显示结果。

2.9 Multimeters 万用表

Routine electrical test work involves measuring current(A), voltage(V) and resistance (Ω). This is most conveniently done by using a multimeter with all the necessary functions and ranges. The instrument may be the traditional switched-range analogue type (pointer and scale) or the more common digital type with auto-ranging and numerical display(Fig. 2.12).

常规的电气测试工作包括测量电流(A)、电压(V)和电阻(Ω)。使用具备全部必要功能和量程的万用表来测量是最方便的。该仪表可以是传统的手动选择量程的模拟型(指针和刻度),或更常见的具有自动选择量程和数字显示的数字型(图2.12)。

Fig. 2.12　Digital multimeter

图2.12　数字型万用表

Digital multi meter have a clear numeric readout which may be supported by a bar-graph display. Where distorted voltage waveforms are likely (e.g. with variable frequency motor drives), it is necessary to use a "true-rms" meter for accuracy. Digital meters are also available which display the test voltage waveform shape with a storage oscilloscope facility on the LCD screen.

数字型万用表有一个清晰的数字读数区,可以用柱形图显示读数,如果可能存在失真的电压波形(例如,变频电动机驱动器),需要使用"真有效值"仪表来提高精度。数字型万用表也可通过存储示波器设备在液晶屏幕上显示测试电压的波形形状。

In all instrument models, an internal battery is fitted for use when measuring resistance.

在所有型号的仪表中,内部都安装有电池,用于测量电阻。

Before measuring the resistance of a component, it is essential that the circuit is switched off, locked off, and any capacitors discharged. The instrument is likely to be damaged otherwise.

在测量一个组件的电阻之前,必须关闭、隔离电路,将电容放电。否则仪器可能会损坏。

The multimeter should be proved for correct operation before use. The manufacturer's instructions should be carefully followed for this but a general procedure is as follows.

使用前应通电确认万用表是否能正常工作。应仔细阅读制造商的说明书，但一般程序如下。

Use the correct probe leads and insert into the correct sockets on the meter.

使用正确的探头导线，并插入仪表上的对应插座。

(1) If the multimeter is an analogue type: Ensure the pointer indicates zero-adjust if necessary. Set selector switches to "Ω" and connect probe tips together. Pointer should deflect to indicate 0 Ω. If not at the zero point adjust trimming controls. Check each resistance range in this way.

(1)如果万用表是模拟类型：确保指针指示为零，必要时应进行调整。设置选择器开关到"Ω"挡，并将探头尖端连接在一起。指针应偏转以表示 0 Ω。如果不在零点，则应调整调节旋钮。用此方式检查各电阻量程范围。

Set selector switch to "acV" (highest range). Connect probes to a suitable known live supply (with CARE) such as the electrical workshop test panel. Pointer should indicate correct voltage.

将选择器开关设置为 acV(最高量程)。将探头连接到合适的已知带电电源(小心)，如电气车间测试面板。指针应指示正确的电压。

Very special care is necessary when using a multimeter to check for a live voltage. If the multimeter has been accidentally set to the current or resistance range, the instrument acts as a low resistance across the live supply. The resulting short-circuit current may easily cause the meter to explode with local fire damage and very serious consequences for the operator. Fused probe leads are therefore highly recommended for use with a multimeter.

当使用万用表检查带电电压时，需要非常小心，如果万用表意外设置为电流或电阻范围，则此时仪表充当带电电源的低电阻。由此产生的短路电流很容易导致仪表爆炸，造成局部火灾，对操作人员造成非常严重的伤害。因此，强烈推荐使用表笔带熔断器的万用表。

Instrument battery failure is checked when the instrument is set to read "Ω" with the probe tips connected together. If the pointer fails to reach "0 Ω" after adjustment of the resistance range trimmer, the battery must be replaced. The instrument should be switched-off when not in use to preserve battery life.

当万用表的挡位设置为"Ω"挡时，将探头尖端连接在一起，可检查仪表电池故障。如果在调整了电阻量程调节器后，指针不能达到 0 Ω，则必须更换电池。仪表在不使用时应关闭，以延长电池寿命。

(2) If the multimeter is a digital type: Switch on and connect the two probe tips together. Set selector switches to "dcV" (highest range). Display should indicate zero(000).

(2)如果万用表是数字类型:打开并将两个表笔尖端连接在一起。将选择开关设置为dcV(最高量程)。显示器应显示零(000)。

Repeat for all "dcV" selector switch positions and note the shift of the decimal point. Separate the probe tips. Set selector switches to "Ω" (highest range). Display should indicate "OL" (over-range) or "100" (depends upon model). Connect probe tips together-display should indicate zero (000).

对所有"dcV"选择开关位置重复进行同样的操作,并注意小数点的位移。分离表笔。选择开关设置为"Ω"挡(最高量程),显示器应指示"OL"(超出量程)或"100"(取决于型号)。将表笔连接在一起,显示器应显示零(000)。

Repeat for all "Ω" selector switch positions and note movement of the decimal point. Set selector switches to "acV" (highest range). Connect probes to a suitable known live supply. Display should indicate correct voltage.

重复执行所有"Ω"挡选择器的开关位置,并注意小数点的移动。将选择开关设置为"acV"(最高量程)。将表笔连接到合适的已知带电电源。显示器应显示正确的电压。

Test the DC voltage range also and note the polarity indication on the meter.

检测直流电压量程,同时注意仪表上的极性指示。

Instrument battery failure is usually indicated by the numeric display. The display may include "BT" or the decimal point may blink, or some other display effect may be used.

仪表电池故障通常由数字显示器表示,显示可能包括"BT"或小数点闪烁,或者使用其他显示方式。

These simple proving tests should be performed every time before using the instrument for real. It is obviously very dangerous to touch conductors believing them to be dead having checked them with a faulty instrument.

在实际使用该万用表之前,每次都应该进行这些简单的验证。如果用有故障的仪器来进行检测,误认为导体已经不带电了,然后去接触导体,显然这是非常危险的。

2.9.1 To measure resistance 电阻的测量

(1) Prove the correct operation of the instrument.

(2) Isolate and lock off the equipment to be tested.

(3) Prove the equipment to be dead.

(4) Switch the instrument to the appropriate resistance range, connect the probes to the

equipment and note the resistance value.

(5) Disconnect the probes and switch off the instrument.

(1)验证仪表能正常工作。

(2)隔离和锁闭待测试的设备。

(3)验证设备不带电。

(4)将仪表切换到适当的电阻挡,将表笔连接到设备上,并记录电阻值。

(5)断开表笔,并将仪表关闭。

2.9.2 To measure voltage 电压的测量

(1) Prove the correct operation of the instrument.

(2) Switch the instrument to the highest voltage range (either AC V or DC V as appropriate).

(3) Connect the probes to the terminals being tested. Take great care not to touch the probe tips and remember that the equipment being tested is LIVE.

(4) Note the voltage reading.

(1)验证仪表能正常工作。

(2)将仪表切换到最高电压挡(视情况选择交流电压挡或直流电压挡)。

(3)将表笔连接到被测试的终端上。触摸表笔时要特别小心,牢记被测试的设备是带电的。

(4)记录电压的读数。

If a lower voltage range would give a more accurate reading, adjust the selector switches accordingly to shift the decimal point. However, most digital meters have an auto-ranging facility.

较低的电压量程可提供更准确的读数,相应地需要调整选择开关以移动小数点。大多数数字仪表都有一个自动调节量程的装置。

No harm will be caused to the instrument by operating, the voltage selector range switches while still connected to a live supply. But GREAT CARE must be taken not to switch into either the current or resistance mode. This would almost certainly operate the instrument overload device and may cause severe damage to the instrument and danger to yourself. Take your time to operate the selector switches during the operation and THINK about what you are doing. Fused probe leads are highly recommended. Disconnect the probes and switch off the instrument.

在已连接带电电源时,操作电压量程选择开关不会对仪表造成伤害。但是必须非常小心,因为它不能切换到电流挡或电阻挡。否则肯定会触发仪表的过载装置,并可能对仪表造成严重损坏并给操作者带来危险。在操作过程中,思考自己在做什么,慢慢操作选择开关。强烈推荐使用带熔断器的表笔。测量完毕后断开探头,然后关闭仪表。

2.9.3 To measure current 电流的测量

Most test instruments can only measure up to a few amps (usually 10 A maximum). The current measuring facility is intended only for small-current components, and in particular, for electronic circuits. The instrument will almost certainly be damaged if it is used to measure the current to motors and other power circuits.

大多数测试仪器只能测量几安培(通常最大为 10 A)的电流。电流测量设备仅适用于小电流元件,特别是电子电路。如果该仪器被用来测量电动机和其他电源电路的电流,那么肯定会被损坏。

The basic current range can be extended by using external shunts (DC) and current transformers (AC). These accessories are generally purchased separately from the instrument manufacturers.

通过使用外部分流器(直流)和电流互感器(交流)可以扩大仪表的基础电流量程。这些配件通常从仪表制造商处单独购买。

The procedure to be used to measure current in a small current circuit:

(1) Prove the correct instrument operation.

(2) Switch the instrument to the highest current range (either AC A or DC A as appropriate).

(3) Turn off the power to the circuit to be tested and discharge all capacitors.

(4) Open the circuit in which current is to be measured—removing a fuse-link often gives a convenient point for current measurement.

(5) Securely connect the probes in series with the load in which current is to be measured.

(6) Turn on the power to the circuit being tested. Note the current size on the meter display.

(7) Turn off the power to the circuit being tested and discharge all capacitors.

(8) Disconnect the test probes and switch the instrument to off. Reconnect the circuit that was being tested.

用于测量小电流电路中的电流的操作步骤:

(1)验证仪表能正常工作。

(2)将仪表切换到最大电流量程(适当的交流挡或直流挡)。

(3)关闭待测试电路的电源,并对所有电容器放电。

(4)接通要测量的电路,拆除熔断器,这通常会为进行电流测量提供一个方便的连接点。

(5)将表笔与要测量电流的负载串联,牢固地连接在一起。

(6)打开被测试电路的电源。注意仪表显示屏上的电流大小。

(7)关闭被测试电路的电源,并对所有电容器放电。

(8)断开测试探头,并将仪表关闭。重新还原被测试的电路。

Often, the most convenient way to measure current is to use a clampmeter which is simply clamped around an insulated conductor.

通常,最方便的测量电流的方法是使用一个钳形电流表,简单地夹在一根绝缘的导线上。

2.10 Diode Tests 二极管测试

Electronic diodes, and other semiconductor devices with PN junctions (e. g. the base-emitter of a transistor) can be tested using a digital type instrument using the following procedure:

(1) Prove the correct instrument operation.

(2) Switch the instrument to diode test. If the diode is still in circuit, turn off the power to the circuit, discharge all capacitors and remove fuses. In this test the instrument drives a small DC current (a few mA) through the diode PN junction while it also acts as a voltmeter to measure the volt-drop across it.

(3) Connect the two probes across the diode.

(4) Read the forward volt-drop across the diode. This should be between 500 mV and 900 mV (0.5-0.8 V) for a healthy silicon diode or PN junction.

(5) Reverse the probe connections and the display should indicate over-range.

电子二极管和其他具有 PN 结的半导体器件(例如,晶体管的基极-发射级)可以使用数字型仪器按以下程序进行测试:

(1)验证仪表能正常工作。

(2)将仪表切换到二极管测试挡。如果二极管仍接在电路中,请关闭电路电源,将所有电容器放电并拆下熔断器。在此测试中,仪表驱动一个小的直流电流(几毫安)通过二极管的 PN 结,同时它也作为一个电压表来测量其电压降。

(3)两个探头连接二极管。

(4)读取穿过二极管的正向电压降。对于一个正常的硅二极管或 PN 结,电压降应为 500~900 mV(0.5~0.9 V)。

(5)对调表笔连接,显示器应该指示超出量程。

If the display indicates over-range in bath directions, the diode is open circuit faulted. If the display indicates less than 1 V in both directions, the diode may be short circuit faulted.

如果两种接法都显示超过量程,则二极管存在开路故障。如果两种接法都显示小于 1 V,则二极管可能存在短路故障。

The associated diode circuitry may be giving false readings, so the diode must be disconnected from the circuit then re-tested.

相关的二极管电路可能会给出错误的读数,因此二极管必须与电路断开,然后重新测试。

2.11　Current Clampmeters 钳形电流表

Power currents (AC) can be measured simply by means of a clampmeter which acts as a current transformer. The instrument tongs are clipped round a single insulated conductor — the circuit is not interrupted.

功率电流(交流)可以通过作为电流互感器的钳形电流表来测量。仪器钳夹在一个不间断的绝缘导线上。

The value of current is obtained from the magnetic flux around the conductor and is usually displayed on a digital display.

导体周围的磁通量会产生电流,其数值通常显示在仪表的数字显示器上。

Many modern clampmeters are virtually multimeters with the addition of facilities to measure voltage and resistance as well as measuring currents up to 1,000 A(Fig. 2. 13).

许多现代的钳形电流表实际上也是万用表,只是增加了测量电压和电阻以及测量高达 1 000 A 的电流的设备(图 2. 13)。

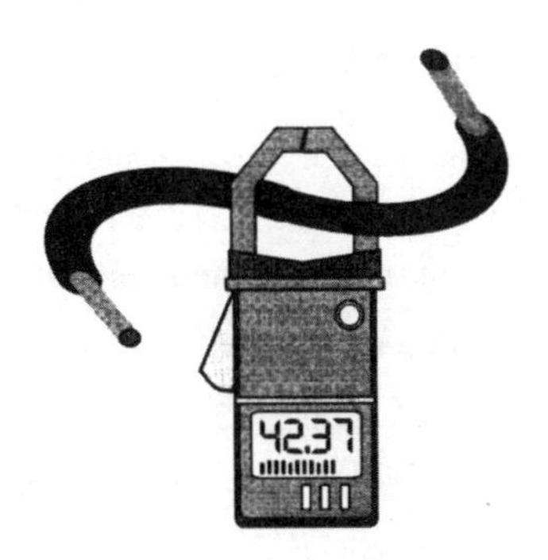

Fig. 2. 13　Current clampmeter

图 2. 13　钳形电流表

CARE must be taken when measuring the current in uninsulated conductors.

在测量非绝缘导体中的电流时,必须格外小心。

More advanced clampmeters can indicate power and power factor in single and three-phase AC circuits by using additional connections to measure voltage.

更先进的钳形电流表可以通过使用额外的连接来测量电压,从而指示单相和三相交流电路中的功率和功率因数。

Question 思考题

What would a clampmeter indicate if clipped around a 3-core cable which is known to be carrying 100 A AC to motor?

已知电动机电缆通过 100 A 的交流电,如果夹在这根 3 芯电缆周围,钳形电流表会怎样显示?

Answer 答案

Zero. This is because the clampmeter monitors the magnetic flux around the cable which is produced by the current in a balanced 3-core(or 2-core for that matter) cable, the net flux is zero. This is why the clampmeter is only connected around a single conductor.

显示零。这是因为钳形电流表检测的是电流产生在电缆周围的磁通量。在平衡的 3 芯(或 2 芯)电缆中,净磁通量为零。这就是钳形电流表只测一根导线的原因。

2.12 Live Line Testers 带电线路测试

When equipment is to be inspected for maintenance, it is important that supplies be switched OFF and locked OFF. The equipment must then be PROVED to be dead to eliminate the danger of electric shock. A live line tester is a simple device to check only whether or not a voltage exists at terninals.

当对设备进行维护检查时,必须关闭电源并锁闭。然后,必须验证该设备已断电,以消除触电的风险。验电器是一种简单的设备,仅用于检查端子是否存在电压。

Live-line testers, up to 500 V, are of various types—some light up (e. g. screwdriver type with a neon indicator), some make a noise, others operate LED's or mechanical indicators (flags) to indicate the approximate value of voltage.

验电器的检测范围高达 500 V,其有各种类型——有的是亮灯型(带氖灯指示灯的螺丝刀类型),有的可发出报警音,还有的可通过发光二极管(LED)或机械指示灯(标志)来指示电压的近似值。

It is important that voltage testers themselves be PROVED to operate correctly before use. This can be conveniently carried out at the electrical workshop test panel.

重要的是,验电器在使用之前要确保其能正常工作。这可以方便地在电工间测试屏上进行测试。

Home-made test lamps should not be used as they can be dangerous because protective equipment, e. g. fuses and finger guards, are not fitted. Great care is required with high voltage circuits where a special HV tester must be used(Fig. 2. 14).

不应使用自制的测试灯,由于没有安装如熔断器和手指保护装置等保护设备,它们可能存在危险。测试高压电路时需要特别注意,应使用特殊的高压验电器(图 2. 14)。

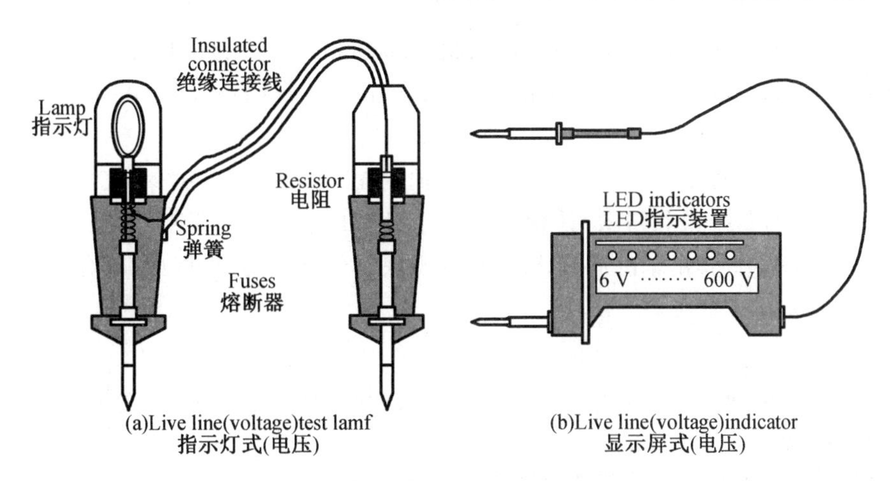

Fig. 2. 14　Live line tester

图 2. 14　验电器

2. 13　General Electrical Maintenance 日常电气维护

All equipment is subject to wear and tear, eventually reaching the end of its useful life when it must be replaced. As equipment nears the end of its safe working life its condition can deteriorate to such an extent as to be a danger to personnel and other plant. The purpose of maintenance, therefore, is to extend the useful life by repair and/or replacement of defective parts and to maintain it in a safe and serviceable condition.

所有设备都会发生磨损,最终在达到其使用寿命时必须更换。当设备接近安全工作寿命时,其状况可能恶化,以致对人员和其他设备带来危险。因此,维护的目的是通过维修和/或更换有缺陷的部件来延长设备的使用寿命,并使其保持在安全和可使用的状态。

The marine environment is particularly arduous for electrical equipment due to the damp, salt-laden atmosphere, extremes of temperature and constant vibration. Shipboard equipment is in particular need of correct maintenance.

由于海洋环境中的电气设备受潮湿、含盐的大气、极端温度和持续振动的影响,因此更需要正确的维护。

The continuous operation of equipment on board ship demands high efficiency keep operational costs to a minimum to maintain financial competitiveness.

船上设备的持续运行需要高效率和获得最佳的经济效益,以帮助船舶将运营成本保持在最低水平,从而具有市场竞争力。

Nearly all equipment needs maintenance. An efficient maintenance engineer must get to know the power system and its equipment; the ship's drawings and circuit diagrams must be checked and updated to relate them to the actual equipment; electrical services and equipment must be kept under continuous observation so that normal healthy operating conditions become known, and abnormal operation becomes quickly apparent, faults can then be pin-pointed and corrected before a breakdown occurs.

几乎所有的设备都需要维护。一个高效的维护工程师必须了解电力系统及其设备;必须检查和更新船舶的图纸和电路图,并将其与实际相关的设备联系起来;对电气服务和设备必须持续观察,以了解其正常的运行状况,从而很快发现异常运行,保证在故障发生前精确定位并纠正故障。

Maintenance can be classified as: breakdown maintenance, planned maintenance, and condition monitoring.

维护工作可分为故障维护、计划维护和状态监测。

Breakdown maintenance (corrective maintenance) is when equipment is left untouched until a breakdown occurs. At this time, the equipment is repaired or replaced and any other specified maintenance procedure carried out.

故障维护(纠正性维护)是指直至发生故障再维护。此时,设备将被维修或更换,并执行任何其他规定的维护程序。

Planned maintenance (preventive maintenance) is when equipment is regularly inspected and maintained according to a fixed timetable and set of procedures specifying the actual work to be done to prevent equipment failure.

计划维护(预防性维护)是指按照固定的时间表和程序对设备进行定期检查和维护,并规定要做的实际工作,以防止设备故障。

Condition monitoring (another form of preventive maintenance) is when equipment is regularly monitored and tested. When monitoring indicates that a breakdown is imminent, the equipment is repaired or replaced and any other specified maintenance procedures are carried out. Regular insulation testing and vibration testing are two forms of condition monitoring.

状态监测(另一种形式的预防性维护)是指对设备进行定期监测和测试。当监测到设备故障时,对其进行维修或更换,并执行其他规定的维护程序。定期的绝缘试验和振动试验是状态监测的两种形式。

There are several disadvantages in breakdown maintenance:

(1) A serious breakdown of equipment may cause sufficient down-time to put the ship out of commission until it is repaired.

(2) If several breakdowns occur simultaneously the available manpower on board ship may not be able to cope adequately, resulting in delays.

(3) Some items of equipment may need the specialist services of the manufacturer to carry out repairs which may cause further delays.

故障维护存在以下缺点：

(1)设备的严重故障可能会导致很长的停机时间，使船舶无法使用，直到修理完毕。

(2)如果同时发生几处故障，船上的可用人力可能无法充分应对，导致维修延误。

(3)某些设备可能需要制造商指派专业人员来进行维修，这可能会导致进一步的维修延误。

Planned maintenance is carried out at fixed regular intervals whether the equipment needs it or not and the aim is to prevent breakdown.

无论是否需要，都应对设备进行定期计划维护，以防止设备故障导致的停机。

Planned maintenance has the following advantages:

(1) Fewer breakdowns and reduced down time produces higher levels of operating efficiency.

(2) Maintenance is carried out at times favourable to the operation of the plant.

(3) More effective labour utilisation because maintenance is carried out at times favourable to the ship's staff.

(4) Replacement equipment can be ordered in advance.

(5) Equipment is maintained in a safe condition with reduced possible dangers.

(6) Where a specialist manufacturer's services are required these can be obtained at convenient times to suit the ship operation.

(7) Replacement of short-life components at scheduled intervals.

计划维护具有以下优点：

(1)减少故障和缩短停机时间，提高操作效率。

(2)有利于设备在运行时进行维护。

(3)更有效的劳动力利用，因为有利于船上的工作人员进行维护。

(4)可提前订购需更换的设备。

(5)设备保持在安全状态，减少可能的危险。

(6)如果需要专业制造商的服务，这些服务可以在方便的时间获得，以适合船舶操作。

(7)按计划的时间间隔更换短寿命的零部件。

Condition monitoring is also carried out at fixed regular intervals. The aim is to forestall breakdown by predicting probable failure from the TREND shown by the monitoring results.

状态监测也应定期进行，目的是通过监测结果显示的趋势预测可能的故障来防止故障发生。

The advantage of this type of maintenance is that equipment is not subjected to unnecessary maintenance. Equipment is regularly condition monitored according to a monitoring schedule. Measurements are taken of insulation resistance, temperature and vibration (of motors), contacts and other parts subject to deterioration are inspected. All findings are recorded in an historical record file. No maintenance is carried out until the trend of test results indicate that it has become necessary. The equipment is then either replaced, repaired or subjected to a major overhaul as specified on a job card.

这种维护的优点是减少不必要的设备维护。监测设备会根据时间表定期进行设备状态监控,测量绝缘电阻、温度和振动(电动机),检查触点和其他可能损坏的部件。所有的监测结果都被记录在一个历史记录文件中。在测试结果表明有必要进行维护之前不维护。然后,根据工作卡上的规定对设备进行更换、修理或大修。

A maintenance records system is required. The recorded measurements of insulation resistance may show a falling trend indicating a progressive degradation of insulation. The equipment should be inspected and repaired before the insulation resistance falls to a dangerously low value.

建立一个维护记录系统是很有必要的,例如记录的绝缘电阻显示出下降趋势,表明绝缘正逐渐退化,在绝缘电阻降至危险的低值之前,应对设备进行检查和修复。

Hot-spot temperatures emitted from live electrical equipment can be monitored from a safe distance using an infra-red detector or camera.

带电电气设备散发的温度可以通过红外线探测器或照相机在安全距离进行监测。

The recorded measurements of the vibration of a motor may follow a rising trend indicating progressive bearing deterioration. Bearings should be replaced before failure occurs. Immediate repair or maintenance is probably not necessary but should be put in hand at the earliest convenient moment.

电动机振动的测量结果可能呈上升趋势,这表明轴承逐渐磨损,应在发生故障前更换轴承。然而立即进行维修或维护可能是不必要的,但应该在方便的时刻尽早进行。

2.14 Fault Finding 故障查找

Generally, fault finding is not an easy task. It is essential to have a good understanding of the operation of the particular equipment and general insight into some of the diagnostic skills used to solve the problem.

一般来说,查找故障并不是一件容易的事。它要求技术人员对特定设备的操作有很好的了解,并对用于解决问题的一些诊断技能有全面的掌握。

Below is a list of the general techniques used.

以下是常用的查找技术列表。

1. Planning 计划

A good fault-finder has a mentally planned strategy. The evidence is carefully considered before deciding what action to take. In contrast, the "muddler" acts on impulse. A good diagnostician will use most of the following mental abilities:

(1) Memory;

(2) Logical thinking;

(3) Perception;

(4) Special technical ability;

(5) Social skills;

(6) Persistence;

(7) Background (underpinning) knowledge.

一个好的故障查找人员会在心里计划好策略。在决定采取任何行动之前,要仔细考虑依据。相比之下,“糊涂者”凭冲动行事。一个好的诊断专家将运用以下大部分的能力:

(1)回忆;

(2)逻辑思维;

(3)感知;

(4)专业技术能力;

(5)社交能力;

(6)坚持不懈;

(7)知识背景(基础)。

Together with the mental abilities above, knowledge and experience are essential. This is wide ranging and includes knowledge of components, methods and systems together with their operational characteristics. The combination of knowledge and direct practical experience with the equipment is a powerful aid to fault finding.

除了上述智力能力外,知识和经验也是必不可少的。这一范围广泛,包括对组件、方法、系统及其操作特性的了解。知识和设备实践经验的直接结合对发现故障有很大帮助。

2. Diagnostic performance 性能诊断

In addition to the necessary skills of the diagnostician, systematic use of “job aids” will improve fault finding method. Examples are: Fault charts; A list of typical symptoms and faults for a particular equipment plus suggested remedies. These lists should be updated according to experience to show the most probable faults.

除了必要技能外,系统地使用“工作辅助工具”将改进故障查找方法。例如,故障图,一个特定设备的典型症状和故障清单,以及建议的补救措施。这些列表应根据经验进行更新,以显示最可能出现的故障。

The seven letters of the mnemonic “FACERAP” are the key steps to logical fault finding:

F—fault: the name and classification of a fault.

A—appearance: the description of the fault or its related symptom.

C—cause: the operational reason for the fault.

E—effect: the consequential effect of the fault.

R—responsibility: the correct person to take remedial action.

A—action: the standard procedure adopted to rectify the fault.

P—prevention: the procedure to avoid repetition of the fault.

有助于记忆的七个字母“FACERAP”是故障查找逻辑的关键步骤:

F——故障:故障的名称和分类。

A——现象:对故障及相关特征的描述。

C——原因:造成故障的原因。

E——影响:故障造成的相应影响。

R——责任:采取补救措施的正确人员。

A——行动:为进行故障纠正所采用的标准程序。

P——预防:避免重复故障的程序。

3. Search strategy 查找策略

Once the diagnostician can visualise the circuit or machine as a series of functions and/or use a job aidz a search strategy can be applied to locate the fault in the minimum time.

一旦诊断人员能够将电路或机器可视化为一系列功能和/或使用工作辅助工具,就可以应用查找策略在最短的时间内定位故障。

A “six step approach” is summarised as:

(1) Collect evidence (stop and think);

(2) Analyse evidence (check assumptions);

(3) Locate fault (inspect and test);

(4) Determine and remove cause;

(5) Rectify fault;

(6) Check system.

“六步方法”总结为:

(1)收集依据(停止并思考);

(2)分析依据(检查假设);

(3)查找故障(检查和测试);

(4)确定和消除故障原因;

(5)纠正故障;

(6)检查系统。

4. Conclusion 总结

Fault finding is not easy. However, a logical approach supported by knowledge and experience will certainly help.

查找故障并不容易。然而,一种由知识和经验支持的逻辑方法肯定会有所帮助。

Chapter 3 Electrical Distribution
第 3 章 电力分配

3.0 Introduction 介绍

This chapter examines a ship's electrical distribution network in detail. Particular attention is paid to earth faults and their detection together with a survey of the range and purpose of the various types of electrical switchgear and protection equipment. Ship's electric cables with their glanding, terminations and testing are reviewed.

本章详细描述了船舶的配电网。尤其是接地故障及其检测,围绕着各种类型的电气开关设备和保护设备的范围和用途展开。最后回顾了船舶的电缆及其接地、接线和测试。

3.1 Power Distribution System 配电系统

The function of a ship's electrical distribution system is to safely convey the generated electrical power to every item of consumer equipment connected to it. Probably the most obvious part in the system is the main distribution centre, i. e. the ship's main switchboard. The main board supplies bulk power to motor group starter boards (often part of the main board), section boards and distribution boards. Protection, e. g. circuit-breakers and fuses, strategically placed throughout the system automatically disconnects a faulty circuit within the network. Transformers interconnect the high voltage and low voltage distribution sections of the system.

船舶配电系统的功能是安全地将产生的电力输送到连接它的每一个用电设备。该系统中最明显的部分是主配电中心,即船舶的主配电板。主配电板向电动机启动屏(通常是主配电板的一部分)、区域配电屏和分配电屏提供电源。保护措施,即断路器和熔断器,策略性安装在整个系统中,会自动断开网络内的故障电路。采用变压器把系统的高、低压配电部分互连起来。

The operational state of a distribution system is indicated by the monitors for power, voltage, current and by protection relays for overcurrent and earth-fault at each main control centre.

配电系统的运行状态由电源、电压、电流监控,并由每个主控制中心的过流和接地故障的保护继电器监测保护。

The vast majority of ships have an alternating current (AC) distribution system in preference to a direct current (DC) system. The required electrical services are broadly considered as main and emergency supplies.

绝大多数船舶的交流电配电系统都优先于直流电配电系统。所需的电力服务大体上分为主电源和应急电源供电。

3.1.1 Main Supply 主电源

An AC network is cheaper to install and operate than a DC system. In particular, AC offers a higher power/weight ratio for the generation, distribution and utilisation of electricity. Transformers efficiently step-up or step-down AC voltages where required. Three-phase AC is effectively converted into rotary mechanical power in simple and efficient induction motors.

交流电网的安装和运行成本比直流电网便宜。特别是,交流电为电力的发电、配电和利用提供了更高的功率转化比。变压器在需要交流电压时有效地升压或降压。三相交流电可通过简单高效的感应电动机有效地转化为旋转机械功率。

A ship's electrical distribution scheme generally follows shore practice. This allows normal industrial equipment to be used on board ship after being marinized where necessary, towithstand the rigours of a sea-life (e. g. it must withstand the vibration, humidity, high temperature, ozone, sea-water, etc. encountered in various parts of the ship).

船舶的配电方案一般遵循岸上的惯例。这使得正常的工业设备可以在"航海化"后在船上使用,以承受海洋环境的考验(例如,它必须承受在船的各个位置遇到的振动、湿度、高温、臭氧、海水腐蚀等)。

The majority of ships have a three-phase AC, 440 V insulated-neutral system. This means that the neutral point of star-connected generators is not earthed to the ship's hull. For continental European vessels, a 380 V, three-phase system is common.

大多数船舶采用三相交流、440 V 中性点绝缘系统。这意味着星形连接的发电机的中性点没有接地到船体上。对于欧洲的船只,比较常见的是 380 V,三相系统。

Ships with very large electrical loads have generators operating at high voltages (HV) of 3.3 kV, 6.6 kV and even 11 kV. Such high voltages are economically necessary in high power systems to reduce the size of current, and hence reduce the size of conductors and equipment required. Operating at such high voltages is becoming more common as ship size and complexity increase, e. g. for large container ship. Offshore oil and gas production platforms operate at up to 13.8 kV, where equipment weight saving is important. Distribution systems at these high voltages usually have their neutral points earthed through a resistor or earthing transformer to the ship's hull.

电力负载非常大的船舶会装有 3.3 kV、6.6 kV 甚至 11 kV 的高压发电机。在高功率系统中,这种高压电在经济性上是必要的,以减小电流,从而减小所需的导体和设备的规格。随着船舶尺寸和复杂性的增加,在如此高的电压下运行变得越来越普遍,如大型集装箱船。对于海上油气生产平台来说,减小设备质量非常重要,因此采用了最高达 13.8 kV 的配电系统。这些高压配电系统通常有中性点通过电阻器或接地变压器接地到船体。

The frequency of an AC power system can be 50 Hz or 60 Hz. In most of the world, the national frequency is 50 Hz but is 60 Hz in North America and in a few other countries. The most common power frequency adopted for use on board ships and offshore platforms is 60 Hz. This higher frequency means that motors and generators run at higher speeds with a consequent reduction in size for a given power rating.

交流电源系统的频率可以为 50 Hz 或 60 Hz。世界上大部分国家的供电频率是 50 Hz，北美地区和某些国家是 60 Hz。在船上和海上平台上最常用的供电频率为 60 Hz。这种较高的频率意味着电动机和发电机以更高的速度运行，从而在给定的额定功率下减小设备的尺寸。

Lighting and low power single-phase supplies usually operate at the lower voltage of 220 V AC although 110 V AC is also used. These voltages are derived from step-down transformers connected to the 440 V system.

照明设备和低功率单相电源通常在 220 V 的低电压交流电下工作，但有时也使用 110 V 交流电。这些电压均来自连接于 440 V 系统的降压变压器。

The distribution system is the means by which the electrical power produced by the generators is delivered to the various motors, lighting, galley services, navigation aids, etc. which comprise the ship's electrical load.

配电系统将发电机产生的电力输送到各电动机、照明设备、厨房服务设备、导航辅助设备等，这些设备构成了船舶的电气负载。

The electrical energy is routed through the main switchboard, then distributed via cables to section and distribution boards then ultimately to the final load consumers.

电能通过主配电板、电缆分配到组合启动屏和分配电板，最终到达用电负载。

The circuit-breakers and switches are the means of interrupting the flow of electric current, and the fuses and relays protect the distribution system from the damaging effects of large fault currents.

断路器和开关是中断电流流动的设备，熔断器和继电器保护配电系统免受大故障电流的破坏性影响。

Fig. 3. 1 shows an HV/LV layout of a ship's distribution system. The system is called a radial or branching system. This distribution system has a simple and logical structure. Each item of load is supplied at its rated voltage via the correct size of cable and is protected by the correctly rated protection device.

图 3.1 展示了船舶高压/低压配电系统的布局。该配电系统被称为放射式系统或多分支系统,具有简单、逻辑化的结构。每一项负载通过正确尺寸的电缆获得额定电压,并由正确的额定保护装置保护。

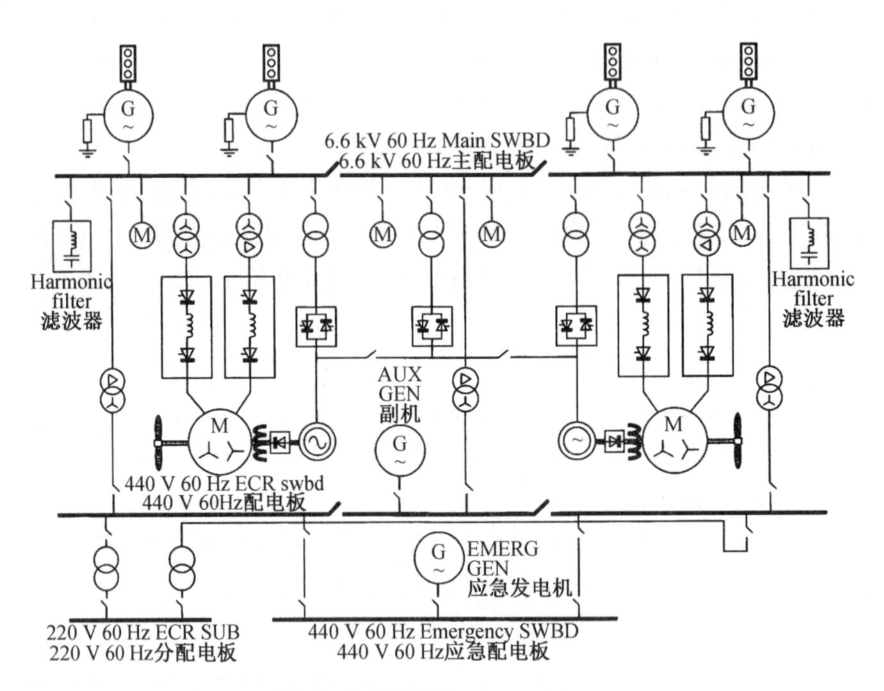

Fig. 3.1 HV/LV power system

图 3.1 高压/低压电力系统

The main electrical load is divided into essential and non-essential services. Essential services are those required for the safety of personnel and for the safe navigation and propulsion of the ship. They include certain supplies to navigational aids, communications, machinery spaces, control stations and steering gear. The essential services may be supplied directly from the main switchboard or via section boards or distribution boards.

主要的电气负载分为必要负载和非必要负载。必要负载是指为保障人员安全和船舶安全航行所需的设施,包括导航辅助设备、通信、机舱、控制站和舵机。必要负载的电源可直接从主配电板获得,或者由组合启动屏或者分配电屏提供。

Emergency supplies are necessary for loads which are required to handle a potentially dangerous situation.

应对潜在危机状况所需的负载,需要具备应急电源。

To maintain generator operation during an overload, a preferential load shedding arrangement is employed. This is achieved by a special overload relay, called a preferential trip relay.

过载时为了维持发电机的持续运行,采用了分级卸载处理。这是通过一个特殊的过载继电器来实现的,该继电器称为分级卸载继电器。

If a generator overload develops, the preferential trip relay raises an alarm and acts to trip selected non-essential loads. This reduces the generator load so that it may continue to supply essential circuits.

如果发电机过载,分级卸载继电器触发报警并使选定的次要负载脱扣。这样就降低了发电机的负载,从而使其可以继续给必要负载电路供电。

Each generator has its own overcurrent relay to trip its own circuitbreaker which is typically high set at 150%, instantaneous operation. In addition, each generator has its own preference overload trip, this being low set generally at 110% current with a 20 s delay.

每个发电机都有过载继电器,用来使其断路器瞬时脱扣,通常设置为额定电流的 150%(高)。此外,每个发电机都有分级卸载脱扣设备,一般设置为额定电流的 110%(低),延迟 20 s。

If a generator overload condition develops, its preference trip will operate to energize the timing relay. The timing relay then operates to disconnect non-essential services in a definite order at set time intervals, e. g.

- 1st trip:air conditioning and ventilation−5 s.
- 2nd trip:refrigerated cargo plant−10 s.
- 3rd trip:deck equipment−15 s.

如果出现发电机过载的情况,其优先脱扣将动作,给时间继电器通电。然后,时间继电器在设定的时间间隔内以设定的顺序断开非必要的负载,例如:

- 一级脱扣:空调和通风,时间 5 s。
- 二级脱扣:冷藏货物,时间 10 s。
- 三级脱扣:甲板设备,时间 15 s。

This order of tripping obviously varies with the ship type. When sufficient non-essential load has been disconnected, the preference overload trip resets and no further load is disconnected. The generator preference trip system can also be initiated by low generator frequency or by low speed at the generator prime-mover.

这种脱扣的顺序随船舶类型的不同而不同。当断开足够的非必要负载时,首选优先脱扣重置,不再断开负载。发电机优先脱扣系统也可以由发电机频率低或发电机原动机转速低触发。

In many cases, the preference trip protection is incorporated in a combined electronic relay which also monitors generator overcurrent and reverse power.

在许多情况下,优先脱扣保护被纳入组合电子继电器中,同时监测发电机过流和逆功率情况。

To maintain the preference relay trip settings as originally specified, they must be periodically tested by calibrated current injection. Preferential load shedding, generator scheduling and load sharing is usually part of an overall power management system (PMS) under computer control.

为了保持优先脱扣继电器初始设置,它们必须通过定期注入电流进行校准测试。优先减载、发电机调度和负荷分配通常是计算机控制下的整体电站管理系统(PMS)的一部分。

3.1.2 Emergency Supply 应急电源

An emergency electrical power supply must be provided on board in the event of a main power failure. Such a supply is required for emergency lighting, alarms, communications, watertight doors and other services necessary to maintain safety and to permit safe evacuation of the ship.

当发生主电网失电时,船上必须提供紧急电力供应,为应急照明、警报、通信、水密门和其他必要的设施供电,以保障安全并且使船舶安全疏散。

Regulations require that the emergency power source be a generator, or batteries, or both. The emergency power source must be self-contained and not dependent upon any other engine room power supply. A battery when fully charged is obviously self-contained. An emergency generator must have an internal combustion engine as prime mover and have its own fuel supply tank, starting equipment and switchboard in the near vicinity.

法规要求应急电源应是发电机或电池,或两者兼有。应急电源必须是独立的,而不依赖于任何其他机房电源。当电池充满电时,电池显然是独立的电源。应急发电机必须有一个内燃机作为原动机,并且在附近必须有自己的燃料供应柜、启动设备和配电板。

The emergency power source must come into action following a total mains failure. Emergency batteries can be arranged to be switched into service immediately following a main power failure. Emergency generators can be hand cranked, but are usually automatically started by compressed air or a battery to ensure immediate run-up following a main power failure.

应急电源必须可在总电源故障后投入使用。应急电池可以设置成在主电源故障后立即投入使用。应急发电机可以手动启动,但通常由压缩空气或电池自动启动,以确保其在主电源故障后可立即启动。

Although regulations may permit a battery to be the sole source of emergency power, in practice a suitable battery may be physically very large and hence a diesel driven generator is usually installed with its own small starting battery or air-start supply. Other small batteries may also be installed to locally supply control and communication equipment.

虽然法规允许电池作为应急电源,但在实际中,合适的电池体积可能非常大,因此柴油机驱动的发电机通常安装有自己的小型启动电池或空气启动气源。其他小型电池也可以安装在本地供电控制和通信设备中。

On passenger ships, regulations require that the primary emergency power supply be provided by a diesel driven generator for up to 36 h(18 h for non-passenger vessels). In addition, an emergency transitional battery must also be installed to maintain vital services (mainly lighting) for a short period — typically a minimum of 3 h. This emergency battery is to ensure that a total blackout cannot occur in the transitional period between loss of main power and the connection of the emergency generator.

在客船上,法规要求主应急电源由柴油发电机提供,供电长达 36 h(非客船为 18 h)。此外,还必须安装应急过渡电池,以在短期内维持非常重要的负载供电(主要是照明),通常至少为 3 h。安装应急电池是为了确保船舶在主电网失电之后,应急发电机未连接上的过渡期间不会发生完全停电。

A typical ship's distribution system is shown in Fig. 3. 2. The system incorporates emergency power supplies.

一个典型的配电分布系统如图 3. 2 所示。该系统包括应急电源。

There is no standard electrical supply arrangement, all ships differing in some respect. It will be seen that both the main and the emergency consumers are supplied by the main service generators during normal operating conditions. In the event of an emergency, only the emergency services are supplied by the emergency generator.

供电布局没有统一的标准,各船舶在某些方面都有所不同。可以看出,在正常运行条件下,主用电负载和应急用电负载都由主发电机供电。在紧急情况下,应急发电机才提供应急供电服务。

The emergency power system must be ready and available at all times. Such reliability requires special care and maintenance. At regular intervals, it must be tested to confirm that it does operate correctly. The testing is normally carried out during the weekly emergency fire and boat drill practice sessions. The main generators are not shut down but the emergency power sources are energized and connected to supply the emergency services for the period of the practice session.

应急电力系统必须随时准备就绪并可用。这种可靠性需要特殊的注意和维护。必须定期进行测试,以确认它是否能正常工作。测试通常在每周的紧急消防和弃船演习期间进行。此时主发电机不停机,但应急电源通电并连接应急配电屏,以在演习期间给应急负载供电。

The regulations governing the emergency source of power are detailed in International Conventions(e. g. SOLAS), National regulations[e. g. IEEE Regulations for the Electrical and Electronic Equipment of Ships (UK)] and in the regulations of the Classification Societies(e. g. Lloyds, Det Norske Veritas) etc.

管理应急电源的规定详见国际公约(如 SOLAS)、国家规定[如 IEEE 关于船舶电气和电气设备的规定(英国)]和船级社规定(如劳氏船级社、挪威船级社的规定)等。

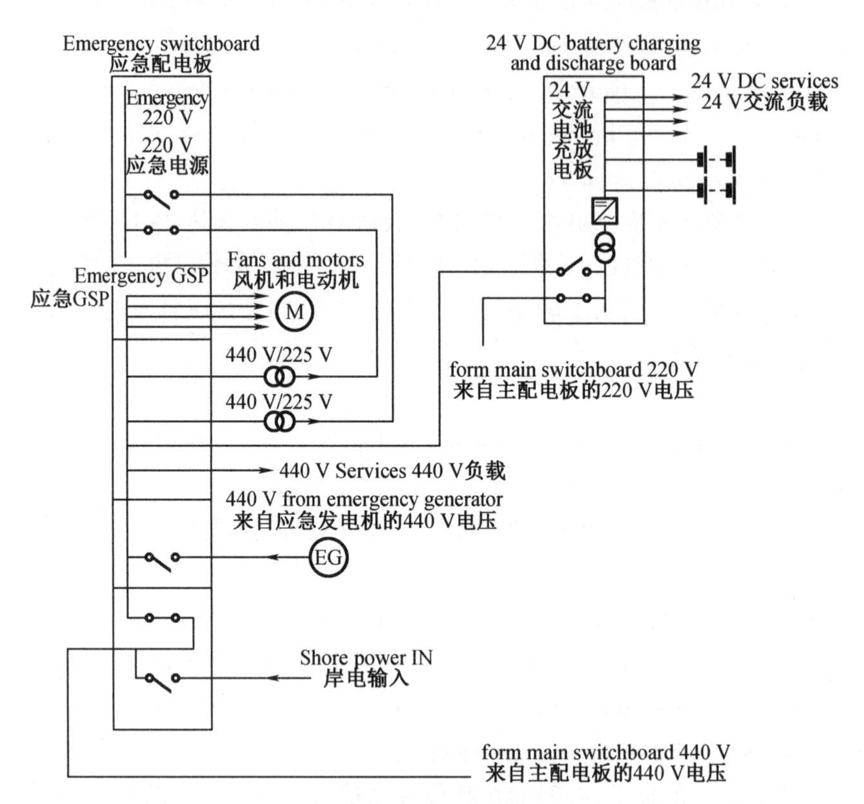

Fig. 3.2　Emergency power supply

图 3.2　应急电源

3.2　Insulated and Earthed Neutral System 绝缘和中性点接地系统

An insulated system is one that is totally electrically insulated from earth (ship's hull). An earthed system has the supply neutral point connected to earth, as Fig. 3.3.

绝缘系统是指完全对地(船体)绝缘的系统。接地系统的电源中性点已连接到地上,如图 3.3 所示。

Shipboard main LV systems at 440 V AC are normally insulated from earth (ship's hull). Similar systems ashore are normally earthed to the ground. HV systems (>1,000 V AC) are usually earthed to the ship's hull via a neutral earthing resistor (NER) or through a high impedance transformer to limit earth fault current.

船舶的主低压电系统 440 V 交流电通常与地(船体)绝缘。岸上的类似系统通常接地。高压电系统(>1 000 V 交流)通常通过中性点接地电阻(NER)或通过高阻抗变压器接地到船体,以限制接地故障电流。

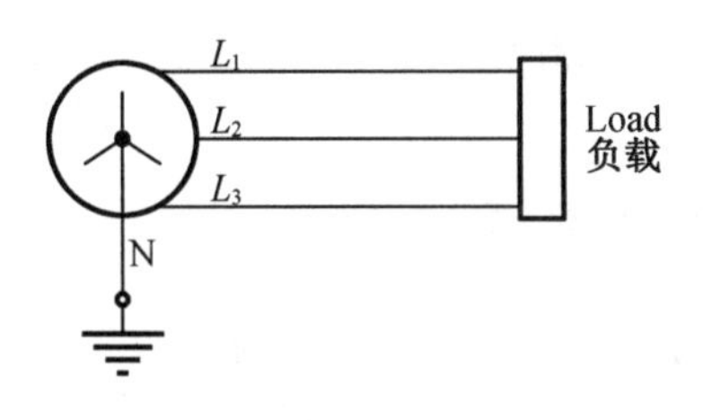

(a) Earthed neutral system 中性点接地系统

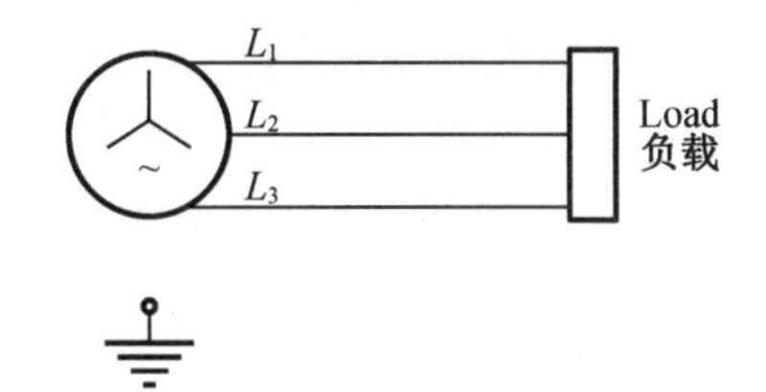

(b) Insulated neutral system 中性点不接地系统

Fig. 3. 3　Insulated and earthed neutral system

图 3. 3　中性点不接地和接地系统

The priority requirement on board ship is to maintain continuity of the electrical supply to essential equipment in the event of a single earth-fault occurring. The priority requirement ashore is the immediate isolation of earth-faulted equipment which is automatically achieved by an earthed system.

船上的优先要求是,在发生单相接地故障时,保持对必要设备电力供应的连续性。岸上的优先要求是,通过接地系统自动实现接地故障设备的立即隔离。

A circuit consists essentially of two parts:

(1) Conductor, the part which carries current through the circuit.

(2) Insulation, the part which keeps the current inside the conductor.

一个电路主要由以下两部分组成:

(1)导体,电路中电流通过的部件。

(2)绝缘体,将电流保持在导体内的部分。

Three basic circuit faults can occur (Fig. 3. 4):

(1) An open circuit fault: is due to a break in the conductor, as at A, so that current cannot flow.

(2) An earth fault: is due to a break in the insulation, as at B, allowing the conductor to touch the hull or an earthed metal enclosure.

(3) A short circuit fault: is due to a double break in the insulation, as at C, allowing both conductors to be connected so that a very large current by-passes or short-circuits the load.

可能会发生三种基本的电路故障(图 3. 4):

(1)开路故障:由导体断裂引起,如 A 点,因此电流不能流动。

(2)接地故障:由绝缘断裂引起,如 B 点,允许导线接触船体或接地的金属外壳。

(3)短路故障:由绝缘的双重断裂引起,如 C 点,允许两个导体连接,形成一个非常大的旁路电流或使负载短路。

The size of fault current that will occur depends on the overall impedance left in the circuit under fault conditions.

故障电流的大小取决于故障条件下电路中存在的整体阻抗。

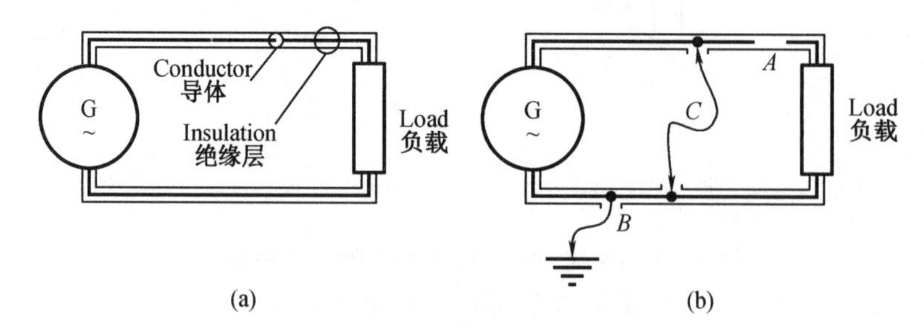

Fig. 3. 4 Circuit fault

图 3. 4 电路故障

Question 思考题

A 15 A motor operates from a 220 V insulated system. The supply cables have a total impedance of 0. 02 Ω. If:

(a) An open circuit fault;

(b) An earth fault;

(c) A short circuit fault;

What circuit current would flow in each case?

15 A 电动机在一个 220 V 的绝缘系统中运行,电源电缆的总阻抗为 0. 02 Ω。如果:

(a)开路故障;

(b)接地故障;

(c)短路故障;

每种情况下会产生什么样的电路电流?

Answer 答案

(a) The open-circuit fault has infinite impedance, so:

开路故障的阻抗为无穷大,因此:

$$I = U/Z = 220\ \text{V}/\infty\ \Omega = 0\ \text{A}$$

(b) The earth fault has NO effect on the circuit current, so I remains at 15 A. (Because this is an INSULATED system)

接地故障对电路电流没有影响,所以 I 还保持在 15 A。(因为这是一个绝缘系统)

(c) The short-circuit fault impedance is limited only by the 0. 02 Ω of the cables, so:

短路故障阻抗仅受电缆 0. 02 Ω 的限制,因此:

$$I = U/Z = 220\ \text{V}/0.02\ \Omega = 11\ 000\ \text{A}\ (11\ \text{kA})$$

The majority of earth faults occur within electrical equipment due to an insulation failure or a loose wire, which allows a live conductor to come into contact with its earthed metal enclosure.

大多数接地故障发生在电气设备内部,由于绝缘故障或导线松动,使带电导线接触到接地金属外壳。

To protect against the dangers of electric shock and fire that may result from earth faults, the metal enclosures and other non-current carrying metal parts of electrical equipment must be earthed. The earthing conductor connects the metal enclosure to earth (the ship's hull) to prevent it from attaining a dangerous voltage with respect to earth. Such earth bonding of equipment ensures that it always remains at zero volts.

为防止接地故障可能造成的触电和火灾危险,电气设备的金属外壳和其他非载流金属部件必须接地。接地导线连接金属外壳和地(船体),以防止其达到危险的对地电压。这种设备的接地连接确保了它始终保持在零电位。

3.3 Significance of Earth Faults 接地故障的重要性

If a single earth fault occurs on the live line of an earthed distribution system, it would be equivalent to a short-circuit fault across the generator through the ship's hull. The resulting large earth fault current would immediately cause the line protective device (fuse or circuit breaker) to trip out the faulty circuit. The faulted electrical equipment would be immediately isolated from the supply and so rendered safe. However, the loss of power supply could create a hazardous situation, especially if the equipment was classed essential, e. g. steering gear. The large fault current could also cause arcing damage at the fault location.

如果接地配电系统的带电线路上发生单相接地故障,则相当于通过船体使发电机短路。由此产生的大电流将立即导致线路保护装置(熔断器或断路器)断开故障电路。故障电气设备将立即与电网隔离,从而确保电网安全。无论如何,断电可能会造成危险的情况,特别是在该设备被列为必要设备的情况下,例如舵机。较大的故障电流可能会导致故障部位被电弧损坏。

In contrast, a single earth fault "*A*" (图 3. 5) occurring on one line of an insulated distribution system will not cause any protective trip to operate and the system would continue to function normally. This is the important point: equipment continues to operate with a single earth fault as it does not provide a complete circuit so no earth fault current will flow.

相比之下,绝缘配电系统中一条线路上的单相接地故障(图 3.5 中 *A* 点)不会导致任何保护跳闸动作,系统将继续正常工作。这点很重要:即使有一个单相接地故障,设备也能继续正常运行,因为它不能形成一个完整的回路,因此没有接地故障电流流动。

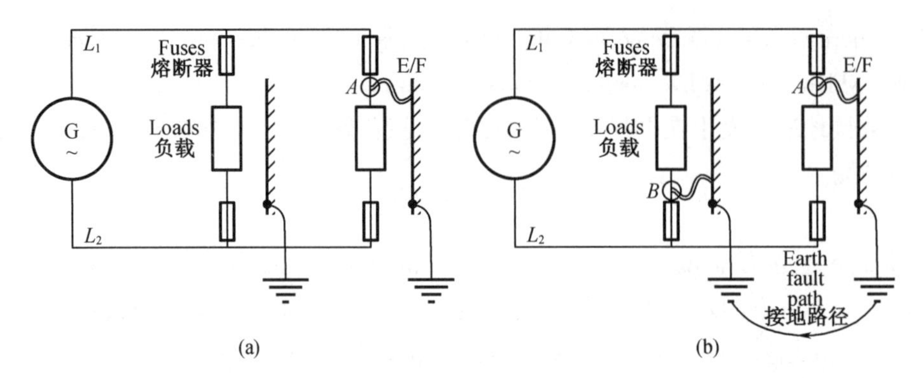

Fig. 3.5 Earth faults in an insulated system

图 3.5 绝缘系统中的接地故障

If a second earth fault on another line in the insulated system, the two earth faults together would be equivalent to a short-circuit fault (via the ship's hull) and the resulting large current would operate protection devices and cause disconnection of perhaps essential services creating a risk to the safety of the ship.

如果绝缘系统的另一条线路发生第二个接地故障,则两个接地故障一起相当于短路故障(通过船体),由此产生的大电流将激活保护装置,可能导致必要负载断电,给船舶带来安全风险。

An insulated distribution system therefore requires two earth faults on two different lines to cause an earth fault current to flow. In contrast, an earthed distribution system requires only one earth fault on the line conductor to create an earth fault current which will trip out the faulty circuit. An insulated system is, therefore, more effective than an earthed system in maintaining continuity of supply to essential services. Hence its adoption for most marine electrical systems.

因此,绝缘配电系统需要两条不同线路上的两个接地故障才能导致接地故障时的电流流动。相比之下,接地配电系统只需要线路导线上的一个接地故障即可产生接地故障电流,从而切断故障电路。由此可见,绝缘系统比接地系统能更有效地维持必要负载的持续供电,故它被应用于大多数船舶电气系统中。

Note: Double-pole switches with fuses in both lines are necessary in an insulated single-phase circuit.

注:在绝缘的单相电路中,两条线路上都需要带有熔断器的双极开关。

High voltage systems (3.3 kV and above) on board ship are normally neutral earthed. Such systems are usually earthed via a resistor connecting the generator neutrals to earth as shown in Fig. 3.6.

船上的高压电系统(3.3 kV 及以上)的中性点一般接地。这种系统通常通过中性接地电阻连接发电机中性点来实现接地,如图 3.6 所示。

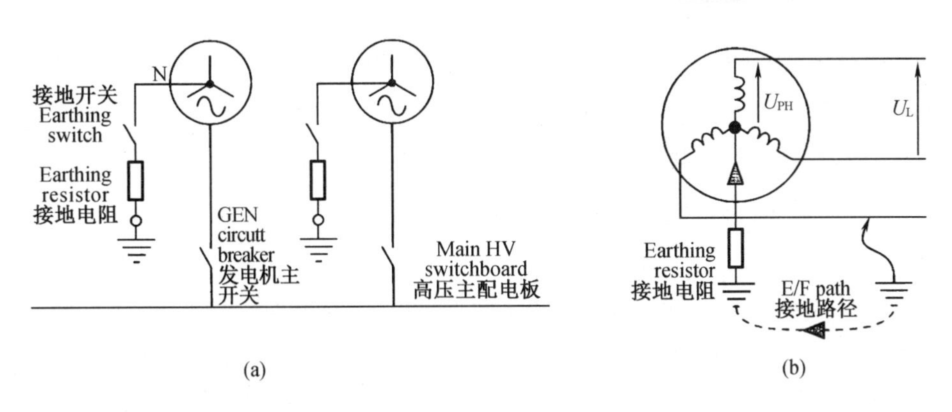

Fig. 3. 6　Neutral earthed in HV system

图 3. 6　高压电系统中的中性点接地

The ohmic value of each earthing resistor is usually chosen so as to limit the maximum earth fault current to not more than the generator full load current. Such a Neutral Earthing Resistor (NER) is usually assembled from metallic plates. The use of such an earthed HV system means that a single earth fault will cause current to flow in the neutral connection wire. This is monitored by an earth fault (E/F) relay to create alarm and trip functions.

通常每个接地电阻阻值的选择以限制最大接地故障电流不超过发电机满载电流为依据。这种中性接地电阻器(NER)通常由金属板组装而成。使用这种中性点接地的高压电系统意味着单个接地故障将导致电流在中性连接线中流动。这将由接地故障(E/F)继电器进行监控,以激活报警和跳闸功能。

Question 思考题

What would be the ohmic value of an NER to limit the earth fault current to the full load rating of a 2 MW, power factor is 0. 8, 6. 6 kV, three-phase AC generator?

在一个满负荷为 2 MW,功率因数为 0. 8,6. 6 kV 的三相交流发电机中,中性接地电阻的阻值应为多少才能限制接地故障电流?

Answer 答案

In a three-phase system, $P=\sqrt{3}U_L \cdot I_L \cdot \cos\varphi$, where U_L is line voltage (3. 3 kV), I_L is the line current and $\cos\varphi$ is the power factor.

在一个三相系统中, $P=\sqrt{3}U_L \cdot I_L \cdot \cos\varphi$,其中, U_L 是线电压(3. 3 kV), I_L 是线电流, $\cos\varphi$ 是功率因数。

The generator full load current is:

发电机满负荷的电流为:

$$I=2\ 000\ 000/(\sqrt{3}\times 6\ 600\times 0.8)=218\ \text{A}$$

Under E/F conditions, a phase voltage of $U_{PH}=6,600/\sqrt{3}=3,810$ V drives the fault current through the NER. So its ohmic value has to be 3,810/218 = 17.5 Ω.

在接地故障条件下，相电压为 $U_{PH}=6\ 600/\sqrt{3}=3\ 810$ V，驱动故障电流通过中性接地电阻。所以中性点接地电阻的阻值应该为 3 810/218 = 17.5 Ω。

Certain essential loads (e. g. steering gear) can be supplied via a transformer with its secondary unearthed to maintain security of supply in the event of a single-earth fault.

某些必要负载(例如舵机)可通过不接地的次级变压器提供电源，以保持单接地故障时的供电安全。

Regulations insist that tankers have only insulated distribution systems. This is intended to reduce danger from earth fault currents circulating in the hull within hazardous zones which may cause an explosion of the flammable cargo.

法规要求，油轮只能使用带绝缘的配电系统。这是为了减少在船体危险区域内循环的接地故障电流的危险，因为可能会引起易燃货物爆炸。

An exception allowed by regulating bodies occurs where a tanker has a 3.3 kV earthed system. Such a system is permitted providing that the earthed system does not extend forward of the engine room bulkhead and into the hazardous area.

法规允许有个特例，如果油轮有一个 3.3 kV 的接地系统，且这个接地系统不从机舱舱壁向前延伸并到达危险区域，则允许该系统存在。

Electrical supplies forward of the engine room bulkhead are usually three-phase 440 V insulated and obtained from a three-phase 3.3 kV or 6.6 kV/440 V transformer.

机舱舱壁朝前铺设的电源通常为三相 440 V 绝缘电源，从三相 3.3 kV 或 6.6 kV/440 V 变压器获得。

Regulations require that an earth fault monitor is fitted to the main switchboard to indicate the presence of an earth fault on each isolated section of a distribution system, e. g. on the 440 V and 220 V sections. An earth fault monitor can be either a set of indicator lamps or an instrument (calibrated in kΩ or MΩ) to show the system IR value to earth.

法规要求在主配电板上安装接地故障监测器，以指示配电系统的每个隔离部分上的接地故障，例如 440 V 和 220 V 部分上的接地故障。接地故障监测器可以是一组指示灯或仪器(以 kΩ 或 MΩ 校准)，以显示系统对地的绝缘电阻值。

Earth indication lamps in a three-phase AC system are arranged as shown in Fig. 3. 7. When the system is healthy (no earth faults) then the lamps glow with equal half brilliance. If an earth fault occurs on one line, the lamp connected to that line goes dim or extinguished. The other lamps experience an increased voltage so will glow brighter than before. Earth indication lamps have been the most common method used for many years, being an inexpensive installation, which is easy to understand. Their major disadvantage is that they are not very sensitive and will fail to indicate the presence of a high impedance earth fault. This has led to the development of instrument type earth fault indicators which are being increasingly used.

三相交流系统中的接地指示灯布置如图 3. 7 所示。当系统正常(无接地故障)时,所有灯发出同等亮度。如果一条线路发生接地故障,则连接到该线路的灯会变暗或熄灭;其他灯的电压会增加,所以会比以前更亮。接地指示灯多年来一直是最常用的方法,是一种易于理解并且廉价的方式。主要缺点是它们不是非常敏感,并且会错误显示存在高阻抗的接地故障。这推动了仪表型接地故障指示器的发展。

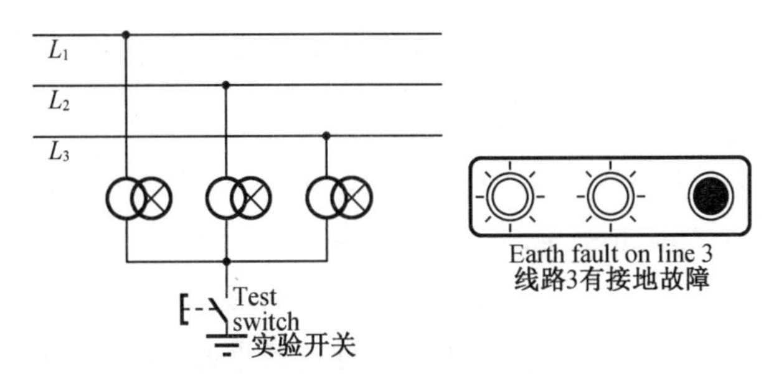

Fig. 3. 7 Earth fault monitoring with lamps

图 3. 7 接地灯监测

One common type of earth fault instrument—monitor connects a small DC voltage to the distribution system. Any resulting DC current is a measure of the insulation resistance of the system(Fig. 3. 8).

一种常见的接地故障仪表——接地故障监测器将一个小的直流电压连接到配电系统中。任何直流电流的产生都能反映系统的绝缘电阻(图 3. 8)。

The injection-type instrument limits the maximum earth fault monitoring current to only 1 mA (compared with about 60 mA for earth lamps), and the meter indicates insulation resistance directly in kΩ or MΩ. The monitor triggers an alarm when its set value is reached.

注入式仪表将最大接地故障监测电流限制在 1 mA(接地灯约为 60 mA),仪表直接以 kΩ 或 MΩ 表示绝缘电阻值。当监视器达到其设定值时,会触发警报。

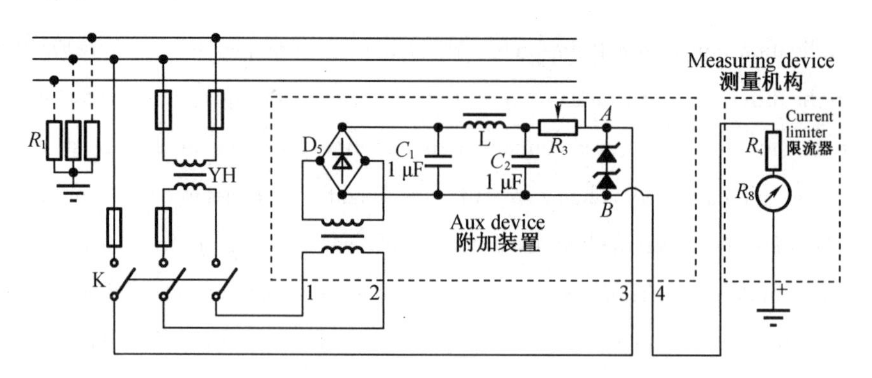

Fig. 3.8　Earth fault monitoring by DC injection

图 3.8　直流注入式接地故障监测

This type of arrangement has been developed to meet regulations which demand that on tankers, for circuits in or passing through hazardous zones, there must be continuous monitoring of the system insulation resistance. Visual and audible alarms are given if the insulation resistance falls below a pre-set value.

这种布置是为了满足油轮对进入或通过危险区域的电路必须连续监测系统绝缘电阻的要求而设计的。当绝缘电阻低于设定值时,会发出声光警报。

An HV system (1 ~ 11 kV) is usually earthed at the generator neutral point via a neutral earthing resistor (NER). This arrangement allows the neutral (and hence earth fault) current to be monitored for alarm/trip by a current transformer (CT) and E/F relay(Fig. 3.9).

一个高压电系统(1 ~11 kV)中发电机的中性点通常通过接地电阻(NER)来接地。这种布局允许通过电流互感器(CT)和接地故障继电器来监控中性点(以及接地故障)电流以进行报警/跳闸(图 3.9)。

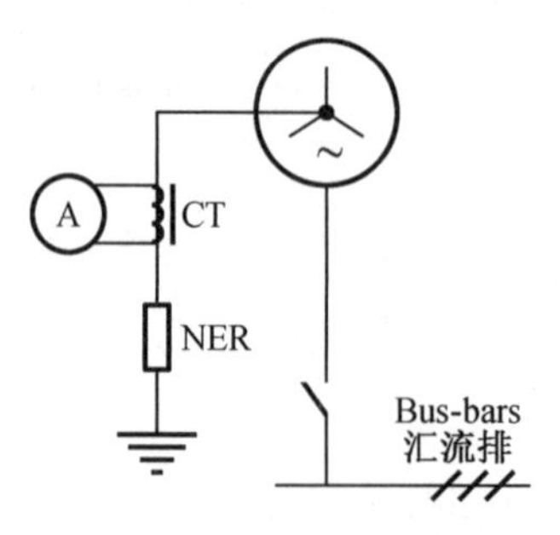

Fig. 3.9　NER circuit

图 3.9　中性点接地电阻电路

Alternatively, a special three-phase earthing transformer is connected to the HV system bus-bars. This high impedance earthing transformer is arranged to limit the maximum permitted E/F current and initiate an alarm/trip voltage signal to a connected protection relay.

或者,将特殊的三相接地变压器连接到高压系统母线。该高阻抗接地变压器用于限制最大允许的接地故障电流,并向连接的保护继电器发出报警/跳闸电压信号。

Measurement of the earth fault current in an earthed system can be provided by various means, one method is shown in Fig. 3. 10.

接地系统中接地故障电流的测量方法有很多种,一种方法如图 3. 10 所示。

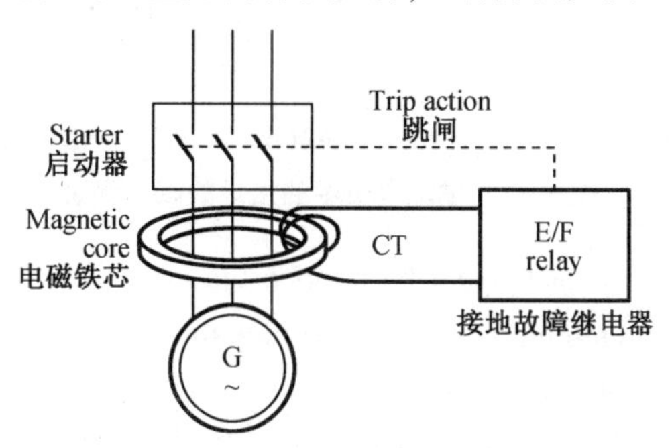

Fig. 3. 10　Core-balance CT

图 3. 10　三芯平衡互感器

Here the current transformer (CT) measures the phasor sum of the 3 line currents supplied to the motor. If the motor is healthy (no earth faults), the phasor sum of the currents measured by the CT is zero.

这里,电流互感器(CT)测量提供给电动机的 3 个线电流的相量和。如果电动机正常(无接地故障),则 CT 测量的电流的相量和为零。

If an E/F occurs in the motor, an earth fault current flows and the phasor sum of the currents is now not zero. The current monitored by the E/F relay is used to trip the contactor in the starter to isolate the faulty motor circuit. Earth fault monitors in main switch board as shown in the Fig. 3. 11.

如果电动机发生接地故障,则接地故障电流流动,且电流的相量和不为零。由接地故障继电器监测的电流,用于跳闸启动器中的接触器,以隔离有故障的电动机电路。主配电板中的接地故障监测装置如图 3. 11 所示。

The earth fault monitor on the switchboard shows the presence of an earth fault on the distribution system. It is up to the maintenance staff to trace (search for) the exact location of the fault and then to clear it as quickly as possible.

配电板上的接地故障监测器显示在配电系统上存在接地故障。由维护人员负责跟踪(搜索)故障的确切位置,然后尽快清除故障。

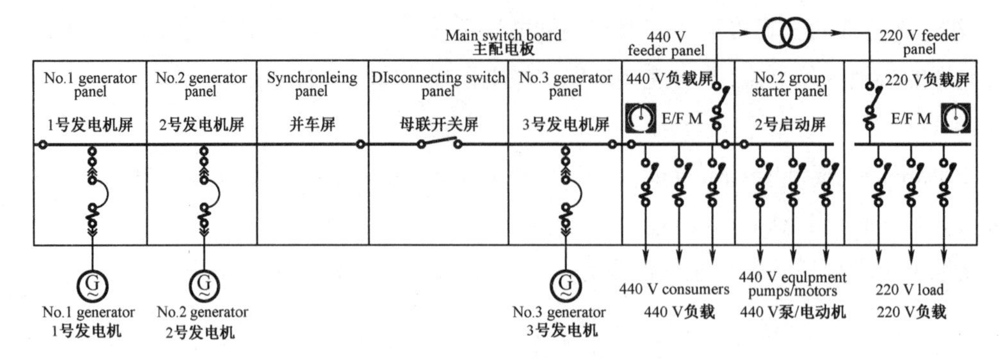

Fig. 3. 11　Earth fault monitors in main switch board

图 3. 11　主配电板中的接地故障监测装置

An apparently simple method would be to open the circuit-breakers feeding loads A, B, C, etc. one at a time and by watching the earth fault monitor while observing which circuit-breaker, when tripped, clears the earth fault, the earth fault must then be on that particular circuit.

一种明显简单的方法是依次打开断路器供电负载 A、B、C 等,一次一个,观察接地故障监测器,同时观察哪个断路器断开时接地故障清除,那么接地故障必是在那个特定的电路上。

In practice, circuits cannot be disconnected at random in this way, some vital service may be interrupted causing the main engines to stop, perhaps in dangerous narrow waters.

在实践中,电路不能以这种方式偶然断开,否则可能会导致一些重要的设施断电,从而导致主机停止,若此时航行在狭窄水域则会更加危险。

Tracing the earth fault must be coordinated with the operational requirements of the ship's electrical services. The method of earth fault clearance will be described fully for a lighting distribution circuit shown in Fig. 3. 12.

追踪接地故障必须与船舶电气设施的运行要求相协调。图 3. 12 所示为照明配电电路接地故障清除的方法。

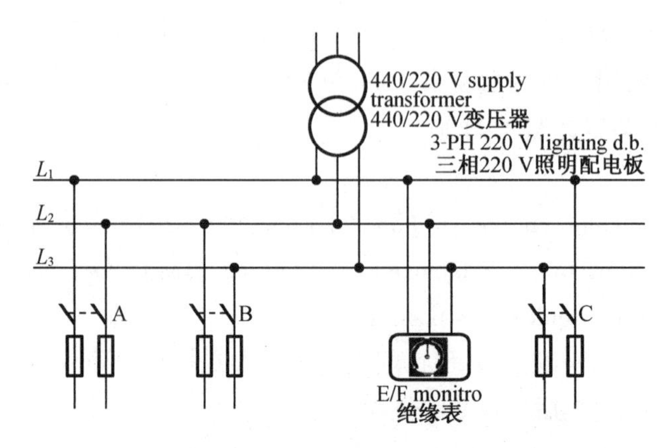

Fig. 3. 12　Three-phase to single-phase distribution

图 3. 12　三相变单相配电

Suppose the earth fault monitor on the 220 V lighting distribution board (d. b.) indicates the presence of an earth fault. Switches A,B,C are sequentially opened and closed in turn until the earth fault monitor indicates the earth faulted circuit. Suppose this is switch B. Circuit B supplies a distribution fuse board (d. f. b.) located near its lighting circuits. Here there is no earth fault monitor so an IR (megger) tester must be used.

假设 220 V 照明配电板(d. b.)上的接地故障监视器显示存在接地故障。开关 A、B、C 依次打开和关闭,直到接地故障监测器指示接地故障电路。假设开关 B 有接地故障。电路 B 提供配电熔断板(d. f. b.)位于其照明电路附近。这里没有接地故障监测器,因此必须使用绝缘测试仪。

At this d. f. b. fuse-pair breaker B is opened to isolate the supply to the load(Fig. 3. 13). The IR tester (megger) is now connected with one lead to earth (hull) and the other lead to "*b*" (the outgoing terminal as shown), and a test applied. If healthy (IR > 1 MΩ), connect the test lead to "*a*" and repeat the test. If both "*a*" and "*b*" are healthy, circuit B is healthy and breaker B can be closed.

配电熔断板断开断路器开关 B,以隔离对负载的电源(图 3. 13),此刻绝缘测试仪一条导线接地(船体),另一条导线连接"*b*"(输出端),进行测试。如果正常 (IR>1 MΩ),则将测试导线连接到"*a*"并重复测试。如果"*a*"和"*b*"都正常,电路 B 正常,可以闭合断路器开关 B。

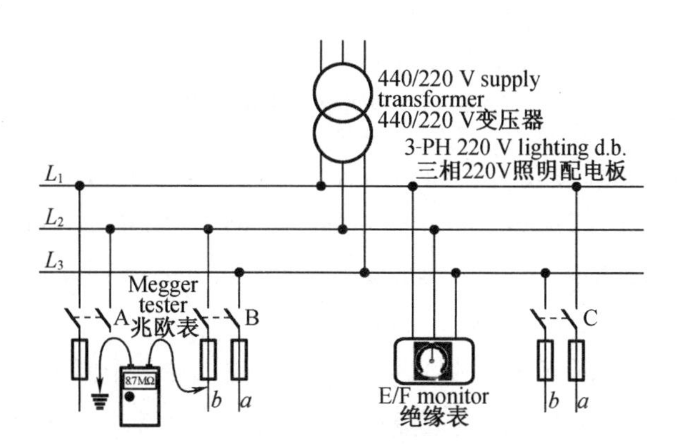

Fig. 3. 13 IR testing at distribution fuse board

图 3. 13 配电容短板绝缘测试

Breaker C is now opened and tested at "*a*" and "*b*". If an earth fault is indicated (IR = low) then the faulted circuit has been located. All breakers are checked in turn to confirm whether healthy or faulted.

现在断开断路器开关 C,并在"*a*"和"*b*"上进行测试。如果显示存在接地故障(IR 值较低),则已找到故障电路。依次检查所有断路器,以确认回路是正常还是有故障。

This breaks the circuit into several isolated conductor sections. At the supply distribution board, test at "*a*" and then at "*b*". If both have an IR>1 MΩ then the conductors connected to "*a*" and "*b*" are clear and healthy.

这样做是将电路分解成几个孤立的导体部分。在电源配电板的"*a*"和"*b*"测试,如果两者都有 IR>1 MΩ,那么导线连接正常。

Close the switch and re-test at "*a*". If the IR is low then the earth fault lies on the conductors beyond the switch.

闭合开关,然后重新在"*a*"处测试,如果绝缘值较低,则接地故障位于此开关的导体上。

At the faulted circuit, the fuses should be removed, all switches should be opened, and all lamps taken out as shown in Fig. 3. 14.

在故障电路处,应拆除熔断器,断开所有开关,并拆除所有灯,如图 3. 14 所示。

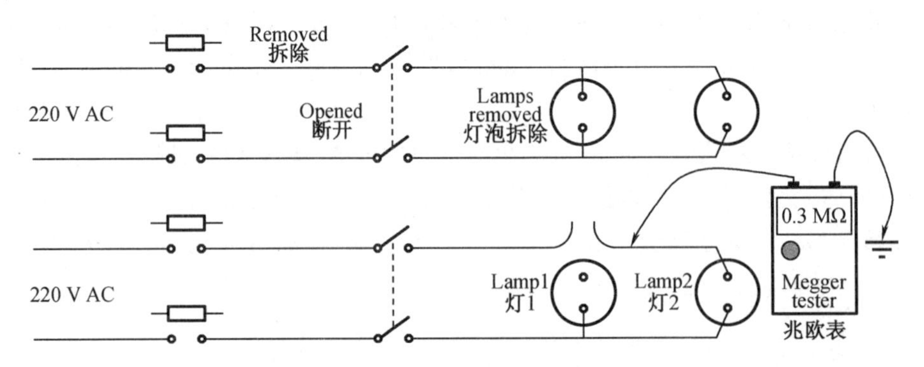

Fig. 3. 14　IR testing on lighting circuit

图 3. 14　照明电路绝缘检测

At lamp 1, remove the fitting and disconnect the conductors as shown to further break down the circuit. Use the IR tester on each of these disconnected leads. If one conductor is indicated as having an earth fault (suppose it is the conductor between lamp 1 and lamp 2) then the earth fault lies at lamp 1 or lamp 2 or on the conductor.

在灯 1 处,拆卸接头,断开导线,以进一步断开电路。在每个断开的导线上使用绝缘测试仪。如果一个导线被指示为有接地故障(假设是灯 1 和灯 2 之间的导体),则接地故障位于灯 1 或灯 2 或导体上。

Both lamp fittings must now be opened and visually inspected to trace the exact location of earth fault.

现在必须将两个灯打开并目视检查,以追踪接地故障的确切位置。

The method of tracing the earth fault is essentially that of continually breaking down the circuit into smaller and smaller sections until it is finally located.

追踪接地故障的方法基本上是通过不断地将电路分解成越来越小的部分,直到故障最终被定位。

When located, the damaged insulation must be repaired. The method of repairing the earth fault depends upon the cause of the earth fault and this is determined by visual examination.

在找到故障后,必须修复损坏的绝缘材料。修复接地故障的方法取决于产生接地故障的原因,这是通过目视检查来确定的。

A lamp fitting that is damaged must be replaced. Dampness in insulation must be dried out by gentle heat and then some precaution must be taken to prevent the future ingress of moisture. Insulation that has been mechanically damaged or weakened by overheating must be made good again. If surface dirt is the cause, a thorough cleaning will probably cure the fault.

更换损坏的灯具配件;若潮湿则通过温和的加热进行干燥,然后采取措施以防止水分进入;修复因过热而机械损坏或减弱的绝缘;如果故障是由表面污垢引起的,则需彻底清洁。

3.4 Distribution Circuit-breakers 配电断路器

Details of main circuit-breakers for main generators and main feeder circuits are included in Chapter 5.

主发电机和主馈线电路的主断路器的详细信息见第 5 章。

The function of any circuit-breaker is to safely make onto and break open the prospective short-circuit fault current expected at that point in the circuit. The main contacts must open rapidly while the resulting arc is transferred to special arcing contacts above the main contacts. Arc chutes with arc-splitters quickly stretch and cool the arc until it snaps. The circuit-breakers is open when the arc is quenched.

任何断路器的功能都是安全地接通和当电流达到预设的短路电流故障时断开电路。主触点必须迅速打开,而产生的电弧被转移到主触点上方的特殊电弧触点上。带电弧分离器的灭弧室可以快速延伸和冷却电弧,直到电弧结束。当电弧被淬灭时,电路断路器就会打开。

Feeder and distribution circuits are usually protected by the molded-case (MCCB) type or the miniature (MCB) type of circuit-breakers.

馈线和配电电路通常由塑壳断路器(MCCB)或微型断路器(MCB)进行保护。

3.4.1 MCCB 塑壳断路器

These small, compact air circuit breakers fitted in a molded plastic case. They have a lower normal current rating (50-1,500 A) than main breakers and a lower breaking capacity. See Fig.

3.15.

这些小型、紧凑的空气断路器安装在一个成型的塑料外壳内。它们比主断路器具有较低的额定电流(50~1 500 A),断路容量更低。如图 3.15 所示。

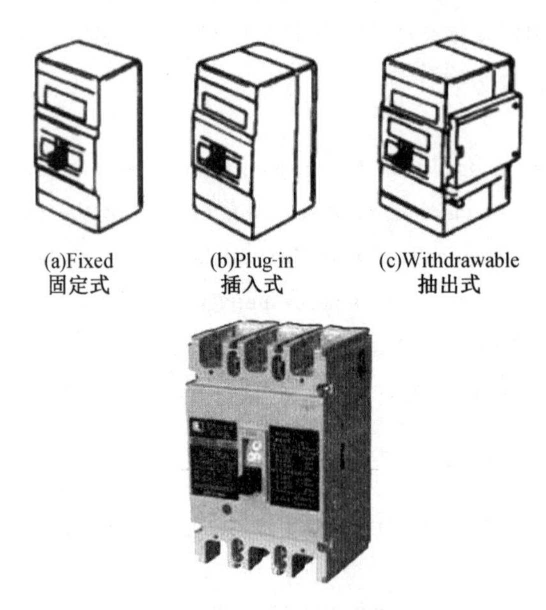

Fig. 3.15　MCCB outline

图 3.15　塑壳断路器外形

They usually have an adjustable thermal overcurrent setting and an adjustable or fixed magnetic overcurrent trip for short-circuit protection built into the case. An undervoltage trip coil may also be included within the case.

它们通常有内置的一个可调的热过流设备和一个可调或固定的磁过流跳闸设备作为短路保护。一个低电压跳闸线圈也可以内置在外壳内。

Operation to close is usually by a hand operated lever but motor-charged spring closing can also be fitted. MCCBs are reliable, trouble free and require negligible maintenance. If the breaker operates in the ON position for long periods, it should be tripped and closed a few times to free the mechanism and clean the contacts. Terminals should be checked for tightness otherwise overheating damage will develop.

通常是通过手动操作杆来进行合闸操作的,也可以通过安装电动机充能弹簧来进行合闸操作。塑壳断路器可靠、无故障,需要的维护可以忽略不计。如果断路器长时间处于开位置,则应跳闸并闭合几次,以活络机械装置和清洁触点。还应检查端子是否紧固,若不紧固则会出现过热损坏。

The front cover of larger MCCBs (around 1,000 A rating) can usually be removed for visual inspection and cleaning. Following tripping under a short circuit fault, the breaker should be

Inspected for damage, checked for correct operation, and its insulation resistance measured. A test result of at least 5 MΩ is usually required. Any other faulty operation usually requires replacement or overhaul by the manufacturer.

较大的塑壳断路器(约 1 000 A 额定值)的前端盖通常可以被移除,以进行目视检查和清洁。在短路故障下跳闸后应检查断路器是否损坏,检查是否正确操作,并测量其绝缘电阻。通常需要至少 5 MΩ 的测试结果。其他故障操作通常需要由制造商更换或大修。

MCCBs can be used for every application on board ship from generator breakers to small distribution breakers. The limited breaking capacity may demand hat back-up fuses be fitted for very prospective short-circuit fault levels.

塑壳断路器可用于船上从发电机断路器到小型配电断路器的每一种应用。有限的断开容量可能要求安装一个短路故障电流预设值很高的备用熔断器。

3.4.2 MCB 微型断路器

These are very small air circuit-breakers in molded plastic cases, see Fig. 3. 16. They have current ratings of 5 – 100 A and generally thermal over-current and magnetic short-circuit protection. They have a very limited breaking capacity (about 3,000 A) and are commonly used in final distribution boards instead of fuses. The d. b. is supplied via a fuse or MCCB with the required breaking capacity.

微型断路器是非常小的空气断路器,安装在成型的塑料外壳中,如图 3. 16 所示。它们的电流额定值为 5~100 A,一般为热过流保护和磁短路保护。它们有一个非常有限的断开容量(约 3 000 A),通常用于最终端的配电板,而不是熔断器。直流电通过所需的断开容量的熔断器或塑壳断路器提供电源。

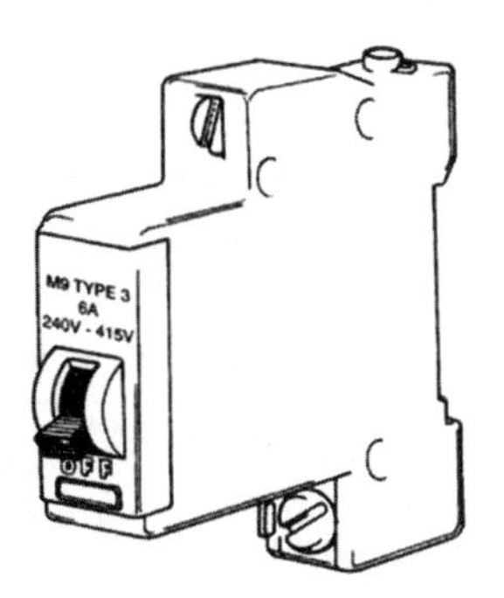

Fig. 3. 16 MCB outline

图 3. 16 微型断路器外观

MCBs must be replaced if faults develop — no maintenance is possible.

如果微型断路器出现故障,则必须更换,不能进行维护。

3.5 Transformers 变压器

Electrical generation on board ship is typically at three-phase AC 440 V 60 Hz, while fixed lighting and other low power loads are supplied with 220 V AC single-phase from very efficient (typically > 90%) static transformer units. Ships with HV generation require three-phase transformers to supply the LV engine-room and accommodation sub-switchboards e. g. using 6,600/440 V units. See Fig. 3. 17.

船舶发电通常为三相、440 V、60 Hz 的交流电,固定照明和其他低功率负载为单相 220 V 交流电,由一个非常高效的(通常>90%)单相静态变压器单元供电。装有高压发电机的船舶需要一个三相变压器降压后给机舱和生活区的分配电板供电,例如使用 6 600/440 V 的降压变压器。如图 3. 17 所示。

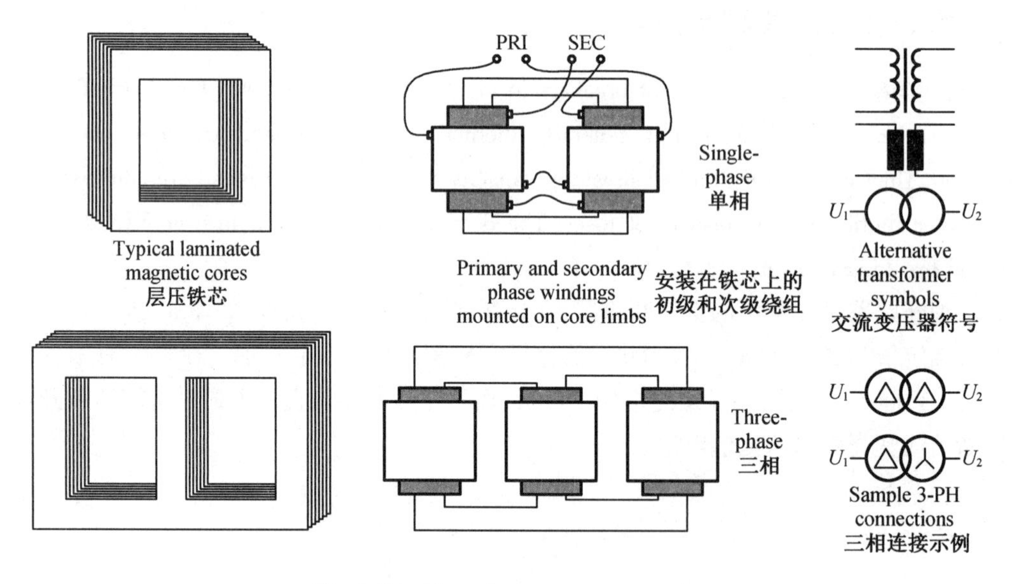

Fig. 3. 17 Transformer arrangements

图 3. 17 变压器布局

In a transformer, we have two windings, a primary winding (N_1) and a secondary winding (N_2) (Fig. 3. 18). Both of them are placed on the same core. This means that the magnetic field induced by the primary winding, will travel in the core and induce a voltage in the secondary winding.

在变压器中有两个绕组,一个初级绕组(N_1)和一个次级绕组(N_2)。它们都放在同一个铁芯上(图 3. 18)。这意味着由初级绕组感应的磁场将在铁芯中传播,并在次级绕组中感应出电压。

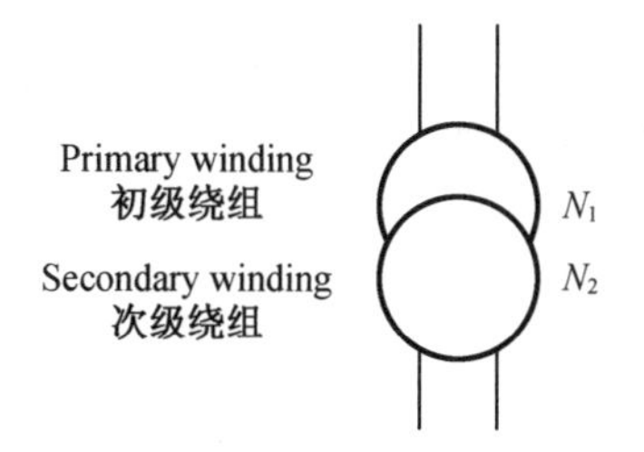

Fig. 3.18 Transformer

图 3.18 变压器

It is then a question of how many turns each winding has that determines the ratio of transformation. The abbreviation for the ratio is n.

因此,决定变比的因素是每个绕组有多少匝。变比的缩写是 n。

$$n = N_1 / N_2$$

If a transformer has 40 turns on the primary winding and 20 turns on the secondary winding, then the ratio will be 40/20 = 2.

如果变压器的初级绕组上有 40 匝,次级绕组上有 20 匝,那么比率将为 40/20 = 2。

The principle of operation of a single phase transformer is simple. An applied AC voltage (U_1) to the primary winding sets up an alternating magnetic flux in the laminated steel core.

单相变压器的工作原理比较简单。对主绕组施加交流电压 U_1,在绝缘铁芯中设置交流磁通量。

The flux induces an e. m. f. in the secondary whose size is fixed by the ratio of primary and secondary turns in the pair of phase windings (N_1 and N_2) to give: $U_1/U_2 = N_1/N_2$. The secondary voltage U_2 is available to drive current through a load.

这个磁通量在次级绕组里面产生一个电磁场,次级绕组的大小由相对绕组(N_1 和 N_2)中主绕组和次级绕组的比率决定,给出 $U_1/U_2 = N_1/N_2$。次级绕组电压 U_2 可通过负载驱动电流。

It is the load connected to the secondary that sets the size and power factor angle of the load current I_2. This is matched on the primary side from: $U_1/U_2 = I_2/I_1$, Transformers are rated in apparent power (VA or kVA) units.

连接到次级绕组的负载决定负载电流 I_2 的大小和功率因数。这和主绕组侧匹配: $U_1/U_2 = I_2/I_1$。变压器被认为是视在功率(VA 或 kVA)单元。

Question 思考题

A 440/210 V single phase transformer supplies a load of 10 kW at 0. 85 power factor load. Calculate secondary and primary currents (ignoring the transformer power losses).

给 440/220 V 单相变压器提供一个 10 kW,功率因数为 0.85 的负载,计算主绕组跟次级绕组的电流(忽略变压器的功率损耗)。

Answer 答案

由 $P_2=U_2 \cdot I_2 \cdot \cos\varphi$ 得

$$I_2=P_2/(U_2 \cdot \cos\varphi)=10\,000/(220\times0.85)=53.47\ \text{A}$$

$$I_1=I_2 \cdot U_2/U_1=53.47\times220/440=26.73\ \text{A}$$

或者由 $P_1=U_1 \cdot I_1 \cdot \cos\varphi$ 开始计算。

The transformers are generally air cooled, being mounted in sheet steel enclosures which are often located adjacent to the main switchboard. Alternatively, they may be fitted within the switchboard so transformer enclosures are not required.

变压器通常是风冷的,安装在钢板外壳中,位于主配电板附近。或者,它们可以安装在配电板内,就不需要变压器外壳了。

Three-phase 440/220 V lighting transformers are usually composed of three separate single-phase units interconnected to form a three-phase arrangement. This enables easy replacement of a single-phase unit if it develops a fault. The alternative is to use a single three-phase unit with all windings mounted on a common magnetic core. This type has to be completely isolated in the event of a fault on one phase only.

三相 440/220 V 照明变压器通常由三个独立的单相单元组成,相互连接,形成三相布局。这使得单相单元在发生故障时很容易更换。另一种选择是使用一个单一的三相单元,所有绕组都安装在一个共同的铁芯上。就算只有一个单相单元发生故障,此类型的变压器也必须完全隔离。

Transformers for use on three-phase insulated systems are generally interconnected in a delta-delta circuit configuration using copper links between the phase windings. See Fig. 3. 19.

用于三相绝缘系统的变压器通常在相绕组之间用铜线连接成三角形-三角形电路结构。如图 3. 19 所示。

If a fault develops on one phase of such an arrangement, the faulty unit can be disconnected (via the links) creating an open delta or "V" connection and a three-phase supply will still be available, although at a reduced power capacity. This is obviously a useful safeguard. In some cases, a spare 4th transformer is available to replace the faulty unit.

如果这种布局中的一个单元出现故障,则故障单元可以断开(通过链路),创建一个开路三角形或"V"形连接,三相电源仍然可用,但容量降低。这显然是一个有用的保障措施。在某些情况下,会有一个备用的第四个变压器用来代替故障单元。

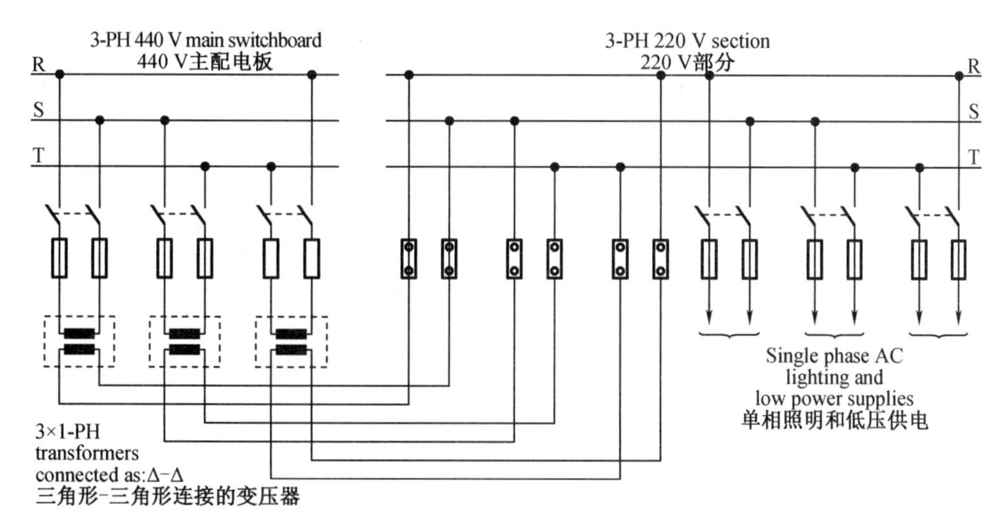

Fig. 3.19　Delta-delta transformer connection

图 3.19　三角形-三角形变压器连接

Transformers for use on three-phase HV/LV earthed systems ashore are generally connected delta-star to provide a three-phase, four-wire LV supply, e. g. a 6,600/400 V ratio gives a secondary line voltage of 400 V plus a line-neutral phase voltage of $400/\sqrt{3}=230$ V. An earth fault occurring on a such neutral-earthed system will immediately operate the protective fuse or circuit-breaker. This interruption of supply leads to rapid identification of the faulty circuit.

在岸上,用于三相高压/低压接地系统的变压器通常是三角-星形连接,以提供三相四线低压电源,例如 6 600/400 V 比值提供次级绕组线路电压 400 V, 加上一个中性相线电压 $400/\sqrt{3}=230$ V。在这种中性接地系统中发生接地故障将立即触发保护熔断器或断路器,电源中断,会快速识别故障电路。

Transformers are static items of equipment which are usually very reliable and trouble-free. However, like all electrical equipment, transformers must be subjected to the usual maintenance checks.

变压器通常是设备中非常可靠、无故障的静态部件。但是,与所有电气设备一样,变压器必须接受常规的维护检查。

At regular specified intervals, transformers must be disconnected, covers removed and all accumulated dust and deposits removed by a vacuum cleaner and suitable brushes. Windings must be inspected for any signs of damage or over-heating. Winding continuity resistance values are measured, recorded and compared with each other for balance. Any differences in continuity readings will indicate winding faults such as short-circuited turns. The insulation resistance of all windings must be measured both with respect to earth and to the other phase windings. The cause of any low insulation resistance reading must be investigated and rectified. Cable connections must be checked for tightness. Covers must be securely replaced and the transformers recommissioned.

按照规定的时间间隔断开变压器,打开盖板,用吸尘器和适当的毛刷清除所有堆积的灰尘。必须检查绕组是否有损坏或过热的迹象。测量绕组连续性阻值,记录并在相间进行比较是否平衡。连续性读数上的任何差异都将表明绕组故障,如出现短路。必须测量所有绕组对地和对其他相绕组间的绝缘电阻。必须检查和纠正造成任何绝缘电阻读数较低的原因。必须检查电缆连接是否紧固。必须安装并固定好变压器盖板,并重新启动变压器。

All test results and observations should then be recorded for future reference.

所有的测试结果和观察结果都应被记录下来,以备将来参考。

3.6 Instrument Transformers 仪表变压器

Transformers are used to supply instruments and protection relays with proportionally small currents and voltages derived from the large currents and voltages in a high power network. See Fig. 3. 20.

在一个大功率电网中,变压器用于给仪器和保护继电器提供由大电流和电压产生的按比例缩小的小电流和电压。如图 3. 20 所示。

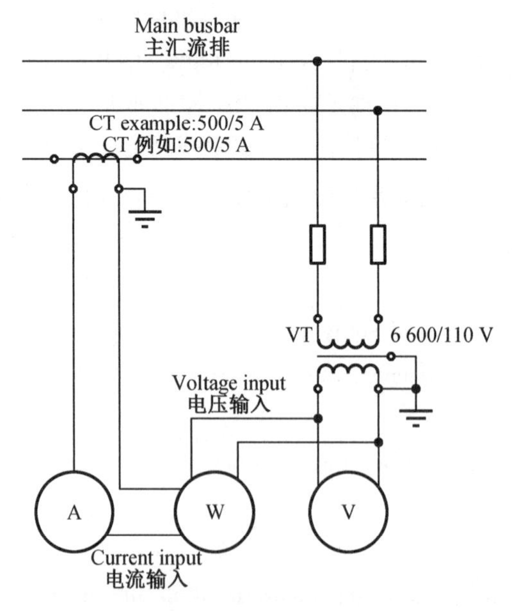

Fig. 3. 20 Instrument connections

图 3. 20 仪表连接

Voltage transformers (VT) supply voltmeters and the voltage operated coils of instruments and relays. A standard secondary voltage of 110 V is used. Current transformers (CT) supply ammeters and the current operated coils of instruments and relays with a standardized 5 A or 1 A. Wattmeter has current and voltage inputs.

电压互感器(VT)向电压表、仪表和继电器的电压线圈供电。采用次级绕组电压为

110 V 的标准变压器。电流互感器(CT)向电流表、仪表和继电器的电流线圈提供标准的 5 A 或 1 A 的电流。功率表有电流和电压输入信号。

The use of VTs and CTs allows standardized instruments and relays to be used. They also improve safety by providing low voltage and low current isolated supplies for monitoring instruments and protection relays.

电压互感器和电流互感器允许使用标准化的仪表和继电器。它们还通过为监测仪器和保护继电器提供低压和低电流隔离电源来提高安全性。

VTs are built like small power transformers. They are not normally used at voltages less than 3 kV. CTs can be of the wound primary or bar primary type.

电压互感器就像小型电力变压器。它们通常不会用于 3 kV 以下的电压。电流互感器可以是绕线式或者条形电流互感器。

The bar primary type CT is used with very high primary current ratings, the wound primary type being used for small step-down ratios, e. g. 1,000/5 A bar primary, 50/5 A wound primary. The ratio specified on a VT details its input and output voltages, e. g. 3. 3 kV/110 V is used on a 3. 3 kV mains circuit and steps,the voltage down to 110 V. The associated instrument will have its scale calibrated 0–6. 6 kV and will be marked "6. 6 kV/110 V VT ratio".

条形电流互感器适用于非常高的一次绕组电流,绕线式电流互感器适用于小的降压比,例如 1 000/5 A 条形电流互感器,50/5 A 绕线式电流互感器。在电压互感器上指定的比率准确表示其输入和输出电压,例如 3. 3 kV/110 V 用于电压为 3. 3 kV 的主电路,并且降压到 110 V。相关仪表的比率将校准在 0~6. 6 kV,并标记为"6. 6 kV/110 V VT 比率"。

The ratio specified on a CT similarly details its input and output currents, e. g. 150/5 A CT is used on a 150 A mains circuit and steps the current down to 5 A. The associated instrument will have its scale calibrated "0–150 A" and will be marked "150/5 A CT ratio".

电流互感器上指定的比率也准确表示了其输入和输出电流,例如 150/5 A 电流互感器用于 150 A 主电路上,并将电流降至 5 A。相关仪表将校准为"0~150 A"并标记为"150/5 A CT 比率"。

The use of instrument transformers does not eliminate danger to operators. The 110 V output from a VT would apply a severe, possibly lethal shock to unsuspecting fingers. The secondary circuit of a CT must never be opened while mains primary load current is flowing. Excessive heating will be developed in an open circuited CT with an extremely high voltage arising at the open secondary terminals. If an ammeter is to be removed from circuit, the CT secondary output terminal must be first short circuited, with the primary circuit switched off. The secondary short circuit will not damage the CT when the primary current is switched on. For further safety, one end of the secondary winding of a CT or VT is connected to earth.

仪表变压器的使用并不能消除其对操作人员的危险。电压互感器的 110 V 输出电压会使接触它的手指受到严重甚至可能致命的电击。在一次侧负载有电流流动时,不得断开电流互感器的次级绕组电路。过热将会导致电流互感器次级开路,开路的次级绕组端子处会产生极高的电压。如果要从电路上取下电流表,必须先关闭一次侧电路,并且短接次级绕组的输出端子。当主回路通电时,次级绕组短路将不会损坏电流互感器。为了确保安全,电流互感器或电压互感器的次级绕组的一端接地。

Status indicator lamps on switchboards are commonly of the transformer type, having a small transformer built into the lamp fitting. The transformer provides a 6 V or 12 V output. The lamp is of low wattage with small bayonet cap fitting. Although not an accurate instrument transformer, the lamp transformer is similar in function to a VT.

配电板上的状态指示灯通常为变压器类型,在灯配件中内置一个小变压器。该变压器提供了一个 6 V 或 12 V 的输出电压。灯是带卡口灯座的低瓦数灯。这虽然不是一个精密的仪表变压器,但指示灯的变压器在功能上与电压互感器类似。

3.7 Shore Power Supply 岸电

A shore-supply is required so that the ship's generators and their prime-movers can be shut down for major overhaul during a dry-docking period.

为了使船舶的发电机和主机能够在坞修期间停机大修,需要配备岸电。

There must be a suitable connection box conveniently located to accept the shore power cable. The connection box is often located at the entrance to the accommodation or in the emergency generator room.

必须有一个合适的接线箱,以方便船舶接受岸电电缆。接线箱通常位于生活区的入口或应急发电机间。

The connection box must have suitable terminals to accept the shore supply cable, including an earthing terminal to earth the ship's hull to the shore earth.

接线箱必须有合适的端子来接受岸电电缆,包括一个接地端子将船体与陆地连接。

The connection box must have a circuit breaker or an isolator switch and fuses to protect the cable linking the connection box to the main switchboard, with a data plate giving details of the ship's electrical system (voltage and frequency) and showing the method for connecting the shore supply cable. A voltmeter is fitted to indicate polarity of a DC shore supply.

接线箱必须有断路器或隔离开关和熔断器,以保护连接接线箱和主配电板的电缆,数据面板显示船舶电气系统的参数(电压和频率),并显示岸电供电电缆的连接方法。且安装了一个电压表来表示直流岸电的极性。

For an AC shore supply, a phase sequence indicator is fitted to indicate correct supply phase sequence. This indicator may be arranged as two lamps connected as an unbalanced load across the three phases via resistors and capacitors. The sequence is "right" when the green lamp is bright and the red one is dark. An alternative P. S. L indicator is a rotary pointer driven by a small three-phase induction motor.

对于交流岸电电源,安装一个相顺序指示器来指示正确的供电相序。该指示器有两个灯,通过电阻和电容器以不平衡负载形式跨接三相。当绿灯亮,红灯暗时,相序“正确”。另一种相序指示器是由一个小型三相感应电动机驱动的旋转指针。

At the main switchboard an indicator is provided, usually a lamp, to indicate that the shore supply is available for connection to the bus-bars via a connecting switch or circuit-breaker. It is not normally possible to parallel the shore supply with the ship's generators. The ship's generators must, therefore, be disconnected before the shore supply can be connected to the main switchboard. Normally, the shore supply switch on the main switchboard is interlocked with the generator circuit breakers so that it cannot be closed if the generators are still connected. But some new ship's main generator can be paralleled with the shore power when only one generator is onload.

在主配电板上提供了一个指示,通常是一盏灯,以指示岸电可通过连接开关或断路器连接到汇流排。通常不能将岸电与船舶的发电机并网。因此,在岸电连接到主配电板之前,必须断开船上的发电机。通常,主配电板上的岸电电源开关与发电机断路器互锁,因此如果发电机仍然连接,则无法闭合岸电开关。但是一些新型船舶的发电机在一台发电机在网的情况下可以与岸电并网。

Question 思考题

Why is it essential to know if the phase sequence of the incoming shore supply is "correct"?
为什么必须知道接入岸电的相序是否“正确”?

Answer 答案

By "correct" we mean that it is the same sequence as the ship's supply (R-S-T), A reversed phase sequence (R-T-S) will produce a reversed shaft rotation in all three-phase motors because the direction of their rotating magnetic fields will be reversed with disastrous results.

我们所说的“正确”的意思是它与船舶的供电相序相同(R-S-T)。反相序列(R-T-S)将使所有三相电动机轴反向旋转,而它们的旋转磁场方向反转将产生灾难性的后果。

This problem is remedied by interchanging any two conductors of the shore supply cable at the connection box.

此问题可以通过在接线箱处交换岸电供电电缆的任意两个电缆线来解决。

Fig. 3. 21 shows a typical shore connection arrangement but some variations occur. For example, the shore supply may be connected directly to the emergency board which then back-feeds to the main switchboard.

图 3.21 所示为典型的岸电连接布局,但有一些变化。例如,岸电供应可以直接连接到应急配电板,然后应急配电板再反馈到主配电板。

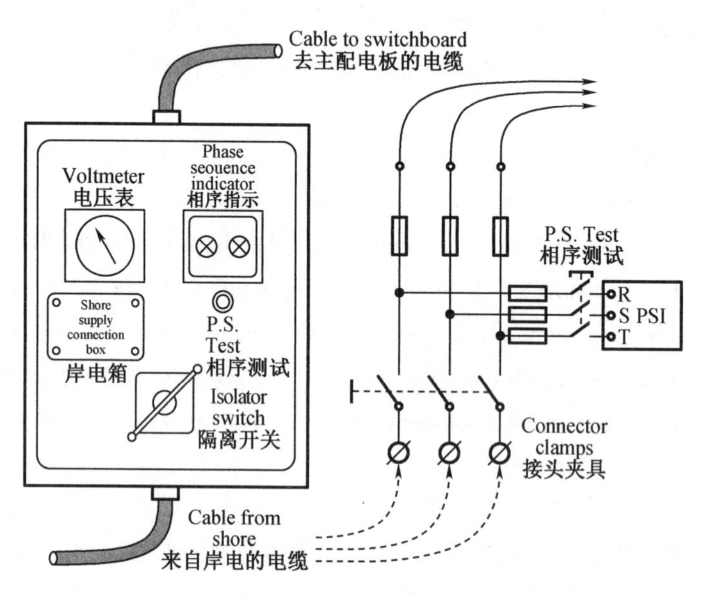

Fig. 3. 21　Shore connection box and indicators

图 3.21　岸电箱及指示

The shore supply may have a different frequency and/or voltage to that of the ship's system. A higher frequency will cause motors to run faster, be overloaded and overheat. A higher voltage will generally cause equipment to take excess current and overheat. It will also cause motors to accelerate more rapidly and this may overstress the driven loads. A lower voltage is generally not so serious but may cause motors to run slower and overheat, and may cause motors to stall.

岸电供应可能具有与船舶供电系统不同的频率和/或电压。更高的频率会导致电动机运行更快,超载和过热。较高的电压通常会导致设备过电流和过热,还会导致电动机加速更快,对驱动的负载造成过大压力。较低的电压带来的后果通常不那么严重,但可能导致电动机运行较慢和过热,并可能引起电动机失速。

If the shore supply frequency differs from the ship's normal frequency then, ideally, the shore supply voltage should differ in the same proportion.

如果岸电供应频率与船舶供电系统的正常频率不同,那么理想情况下,岸电供应电压应相差相同的比例。

Question 思考题

If your ship is designed for 60 Hz at 440 V, what value should the shore supply voltage be, if operating at 50 Hz?

一艘船舶的供电系统被设计为 440 V,60 Hz,如果在 50 Hz 频率下工作,岸电电源电压应该是多少?

Answer 答案

Supply voltage should be reduced to about 380 V.

岸电电源电压应降低到 380 V 左右。

3.8 Circuit Protection 电路保护

Many forms of electrical protection are available which are designed to protect the distribution system when a fault occurs. Protection relays are used to monitor overcurrent, over/under voltage, over/under frequency, earth leakage, unbalanced loading, over-temperature, reverse power (for generators) etc. The HV power system shown in Fig. 3.22 lists typical protective relay functions.

电路保护有许多形式,在发生故障时可保护配电系统。保护继电器用于监测过电流、过/欠电压、过/欠频率、接地、不平衡负载、过热、逆功率(对发电机)等。高压电力系统如图 3.22 所示,图中列出了典型的保护继电器功能。

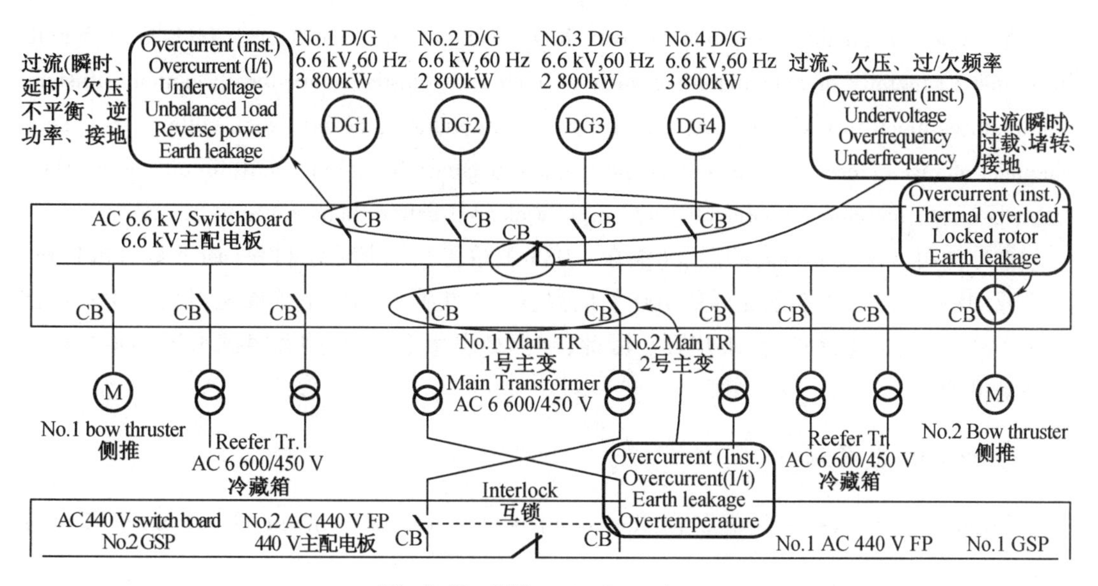

Fig. 3.22 HV protection scheme

图 3.22 高压电保护方案

As most protection relays monitor current and/or voltage, we will limit our examination to overcurrent and undervoltage protection together with an appreciation of protective discrimination.

由于大多数保护继电器监测电流和/或电压,我们将把检查限制在过电流和过电压保护上,并了解保护的区别。

No matter how well designed and operated, there is always the possibility of faults developing on electrical equipment. Faults can develop due to natural wear and tear, incorrect operation, accidental damage and by neglect.

无论设计和操作多么好,电气设备都有可能出现故障。故障可能会由自然磨损、操作不当、意外损坏和疏忽而引发。

The breakdown of essential equipment may endanger the ship, but probably the most serious hazard is FIRE. Overcurrent (I^2R resistive heating effect) in cables and equipment will cause overheating and possibly fire.

必要设备的故障可能会危及船舶,但最严重的危害可能是引起火灾。设备和电缆的过电流(I^2R 电阻发热效应)会导致过热并可能发生火灾。

The size of conductor used in cables and equipment is such that with rated full load current flowing, the heat developed does not raise the temperature beyond about 80 ℃ (i. e. 35 ℃ rise above an ambient of 45 ℃).

电缆和设备中使用的导体尺寸的选择,要使在额定满载电流下,产生的热量不会使温度超过 80 ℃(即环境温度 45 ℃上升超过 35 ℃)。

A copper conductor can withstand very high temperatures (melts at 1,083 ℃), but its insulation (generally organic materials such as cotton or plastic compounds) cannot withstand temperatures much in excess of 100 ℃. At higher temperatures, the insulation suffers irreversible chemical changes, loses its insulation properties and becomes burnt out. Short-circuit and overload currents must, therefore, be detected and rapidly cleared before damage occurs.

铜导体可以承受非常高的温度(铜在 1 083 ℃熔化),但其绝缘材料(通常是有机材料,如棉或塑料化合物)不能承受远超 100 ℃的温度。在更高的温度下绝缘材料会发生不可逆的化学变化,失去绝缘性能,被烧毁。因此,在损坏发生之前,短路和过载电流必须被检测到并被迅速消除。

Question 思考题

Suggest three reasons why protection equipment is essential in an electrical distribution system.

给出保护装置在电气故障诊断系统中至关重要的三个原因。

Answer 答案

(1) To disconnect and isolate faulty equipment in order to maintain the power supply to the

remaining healthy circuits in the system.

(2) To prevent damage to equipment from the thermal and magnetic forces that occur during short circuit and overload faults.

(3) To protect personnel from electric shock.

(1)断开和隔离故障设备,以维护对系统中剩下的健康电路的电源。

(2)防止在短路和过载故障时产生的热量和磁通量损坏设备。

(3)保护工作人员免受触电事故造成的伤害。

The protection scheme consists of circuitbreakers, fuses, contactors, overcurrent and undervoltage relays. A circuit breaker, fuse or contactor interrupts the fault current. An overcurrent relay detects the fault current and initiates the trip action.

该保护方案由断路器、熔断器、接触器、过流和过压继电器组成。断路器、熔断器或接触器会中断故障电流。过流继电器检测到故障电流并启动跳闸动作。

The circuit-breaker or fuse must be capable of safely and rapidly interrupting a short-circuit current. They must be mechanically strong enough to withstand the thermal and magnetic forces produced by the fault current. The size (strength) of the circuit-breaker or fuse is specified by its breaking capacity which is the maximum fault current it can safely interrupt.

断路器或熔断器必须能够安全、快速地分断短路电流。它们的机械强度必须足够高,以承受故障电流产生的热应力和电磁力。断路器或熔断器的大小(强度)由其分断容量决定,该分断容量是它可以安全分断的最大故障电流。

For example, an MCCB may be continuously rated at 440 V with a rated current of 600 A. Its breaking capacity may be 12. 5 MVA which means it can safely interrupt a fault current of 16,400 A ($12.5\times10^6/\sqrt{3}\times440=16,400$ A).

例如,塑壳断路器可以连续工作的额定电压为 440 V,额定电流为 600 A。它的分断容量可能是 12.5 MVA,这意味着它可以安全地分断 16 400 A 的故障电流($12.5\times10^6/\sqrt{3}\times440=16\ 400$ A)。

The prospective fault current level at a point in a circuit is the current that arises due to a short-circuit at that point. See Fig. 3. 23.

电路中某个点的预期故障电流等级是由该故障点短路而产生的电流升。如图 3. 23 所示。

The size of this short-circuit fault current is determined by the total impedance of generators, cables and transformers in the circuit between the generator and the fault, see Fig. 3. 24. This total impedance is generally very small, so the maximum fault current (called the prospective fault current) can be very large.

该短路故障电流的大小由发电机与故障电路之间的发电机、电缆和变压器的总阻抗决定,如图 3.24 所示。此总阻抗通常非常小,因此最大故障电流(称为预期故障电流)可能非常大。

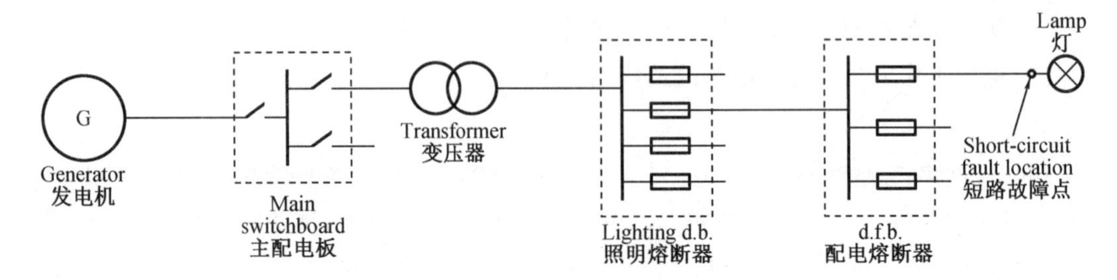

Fig. 3.23 Short-circuit fault location

图 3.23 短路故障点

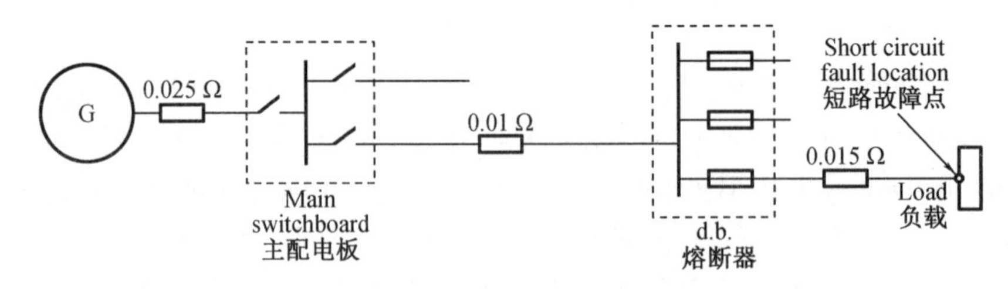

Fig. 3.24 Fault circuit

图 3.24 故障电路

Example 示例:

A 440 V, 10 kW, power factor is 0.85 three-phase load is supplied as shown in Fig. 3.24. The normal full load POWER is $P=\sqrt{3}\,U_L I_L\cos\varphi$. So the load full load current is $I_L=\dfrac{P}{\sqrt{3}\,U_L\cos\varphi}=\dfrac{10.000}{\sqrt{3}\times440\times0.85}=15.44$ A.

Suppose now a short-circuit fault occurs at the load terminals, the total impedance is:

$$Z_F=0.025+0.01+0.015=0.05\ \Omega$$

and the prospective short-circuit faulty 440 V current is:

$$I_F=\frac{U}{Z_F}=\frac{440}{0.05}=8,800\ \text{A}$$

So the prospective fault current level at the load is 8,800 A.

And, for a short-circuit at the d. b the fault level is:

$$\frac{440}{0.025+0.01}=12,571\ \text{A}$$

for a short-circuit at the main switchboard the fault level is:

$$\frac{440}{0.025}=17,600\ \text{A}$$

如图 3.24 所示,这是一个 440 V,10 kW,功率因数为 0.85 的三相负载。通常来说,满载功率是 $P=\sqrt{3}U_{L}I_{L}\cos\varphi$,所以负载的满载电流为 $I_{L}=\frac{P}{\sqrt{3}U_{L}\cos\varphi}=\frac{10\ 000}{\sqrt{3}\times440\times0.85}=15.44\ \text{A}$。

假设现在负载端子出现了短路故障,总阻抗为

$$Z_{F}=0.025+0.01+0.015=0.05\ \Omega$$

440 V 短路故障中的期望电流为

$$I_{F}=\frac{U}{Z_{F}}=\frac{440}{0.05}=8\ 800\ \text{A}$$

所以,负载在短路电路故障中的预期电流为 8 800 A。

在熔断器处的短路故障电流为

$$\frac{440}{0.025+0.01}=12\ 571\ \text{A}$$

主配电板处的短路故障电流为

$$\frac{440}{0.025}=17\ 600\ \text{A}$$

Note that the fault level increases, the nearer the fault occurs to the generator. The circuit-breaker or fuse must have a breaking-current capacity in excess of the prospective fault current level expected at the point at which it is fitted. If less, the circuit breaker (or fuse) is liable to explode and cause fire.

请注意,故障电流的等级越高,故障点就越靠近发电机。断路器或熔断器的电流分断容量必须超过其安装时的预期故障电流等级。否则,断路器(或熔断器)容易爆炸并引起火灾。

The ability of a protection system to disconnect only the faulted circuits and to maintain the electrical supplies to healthy circuits is called protective discrimination. Discrimination is achieved by coordinating the current ratings and time settings of the fuses and overcurrent relays used between the generator and the load as shown in Fig. 3.25. The protective devices nearest the load having the lowest current rating and shortest operating time. Those nearest the generator having the highest current rating and longest operating time.

保护系统只断开故障电路并维持健康电路电源的能力被称为选择性保护。选择性保护是通过协调发电机和负载之间使用的熔断器和过电流继电器的当前额定值及时间设置来实现的,如图 3.25 所示。最接近负载的保护装置具有最低的额定电流和最短的动作时间。离发电机最近的负载具有最高的额定电流和最长的动作时间。

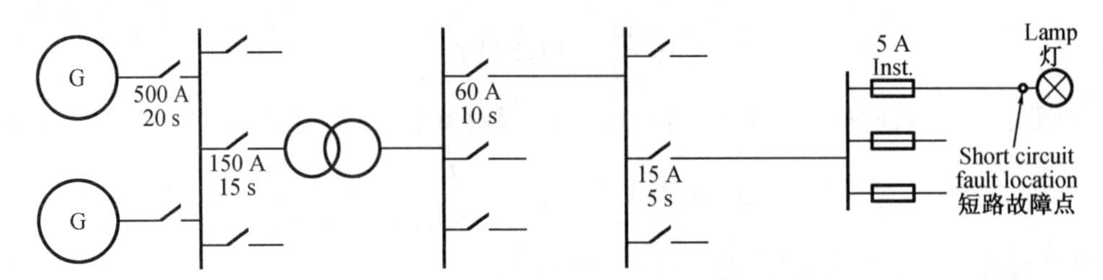

Fig. 3.25 Protective discrimination scheme

图 3.25 选择性保护方案

If a short-circuit fault occurs in the lamp holder in Fig. 3.25, the fault current will be large enough to operate all protection devices from the generators to the fault. However, the 5 A fuse protecting the lamp circuit has the lowest current rating and shortest operating time in the system so will be the quickest to operate. This action will clear the fault and leave all other healthy circuits still connected.

如果图 3.25 中的灯座出现短路故障,故障电流将大到足以使从发电机到故障点的所有保护装置动作。然而,保护灯回路的 5 A 熔断器具有系统中最低的额定电流和最短的工作时间,因此将是最先动作的。此动作将隔离故障,并使所有其他健康电路保持连接。

In the case of fuses, it is generally accepted that discrimination will be achieved if consecutive fuses have a ratio of about 2:1. The shipbuilder specifies the current ratings of fuses, together with the current and time settings of relays, in the protection scheme. It is important that the original settings are maintained to achieve correct discrimination.

在熔断器故障的情况下,一般认为,如果层级间熔断器的比例约为 2:1,则将实现层级保护。船舶制造者会在保护方案中指定熔断器的电流额定值,以及继电器的电流和时间设置。重要的是要保持原厂设置,以实现正确的层级保护。

3.8.1 Overcurrent Protection 过电流保护

The general term "overcurrent" applies to a relatively small increase over the full load current (FLC) rating (e.g. due to mechanical overloading of a motor) rather than the massive current increase caused by a short-circuit fault.

一般术语"过电流"适用于比全负载电流(FLC)额定值相对较小的电流增加(例如由于电动机的机械过载),而不是由于短路故障引起的大规模电流增加。

Generally, an overcurrent, supplied from a CT, is detected by a relay with an appropriate time-delay to match the protected circuit.

一般来说,由电流互感器提供的过电流可以由继电器检测到,这个继电器具有和受保护电路匹配的适当延时设置。

Short-circuit faults in LV distribution circuits are mainly detected and cleared almost instantaneously by fuses, MCCBs or MCBs.

低压配电电路中的短路故障主要是通过熔断器、塑壳断路器或微型断路器即时检测和清除的。

Main supply feeders are usually protected against short-circuits by circuit breakers with instantaneous magnetic trip action.

主电源馈线通常通过具有瞬时磁跳闸动作的断路器保护,以防止短路。

Overcurrent relay types:Magnetic,thermal,electronic.

过流继电器类型有磁过流继电器、热过流继电器、电子过流继电器。

All relay types have an inverse current time characteristic called overcurrent inverse time (OCIT), ie the bigger the current the faster it will operate. See Fig. 3. 26. The basic inverse *I-t* curve would tend towards zero time for the highest currents. To make the relay action more precise at very high fault currents the action is arranged to operate at a definite minimum time which is fixed by the design. This type is called an overcurrent inverse and definite minimum time (OCIDMT) relay action. The OCIDMT can also be combined with an instantaneous (high set) trip to give the fastest action against extremely high currents due to a short circuit fault.

所有的继电器类型都有一个逆电流时间特征,称为过流逆电流时间(OCIT),即电流越大,其动作速度就越快。如图 3.26 所示。对于最高的电流,基本的逆电流时间 *I-t* 曲线将趋于零时间。为了使继电器在极高的故障电流下动作更精确,该动作被安排为在由设计固定的特定的最小时间内操作。这种类型被称为逆过流和最小确定时间(OCIDMT)继电器动作。OCIDMT 还可以与瞬时(高设置)跳闸相结合,以对由短路故障导致的极高电流提供最快的动作。

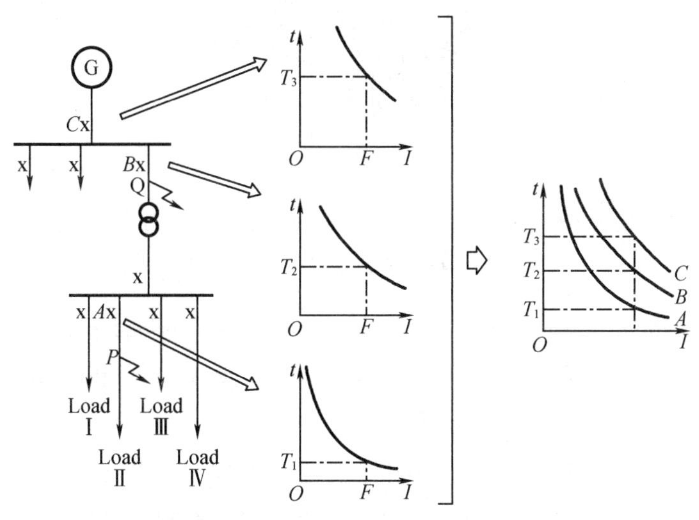

Fig. 3. 26 Inverse current-time(*I-t*) curve

图 3.26 电流-时间反时限曲线

A magnetic relay, as shown in Fig. 3. 27, directly converts the current into an electromagnetic force to operate a trip switch. One type is the attracted armature action similar in construction to a simple signalling relay but with an adjustment for the current setting. The time of operation is fixed at a definite minimum time which is usually less than 0. 2 s. This is regarded as instantaneous i. e. with no deliberate time-delay.

磁过流继电器如图 3.27 所示,它直接将电流转换为电磁力,以操作跳闸开关。一类是吸引衔铁动作,类似于简单的信号继电器,但具有一个电流调节器。操作时间固定在一个确定的最短时间内,通常小于 0. 2 s。这就是瞬时动作,没有特地延时。

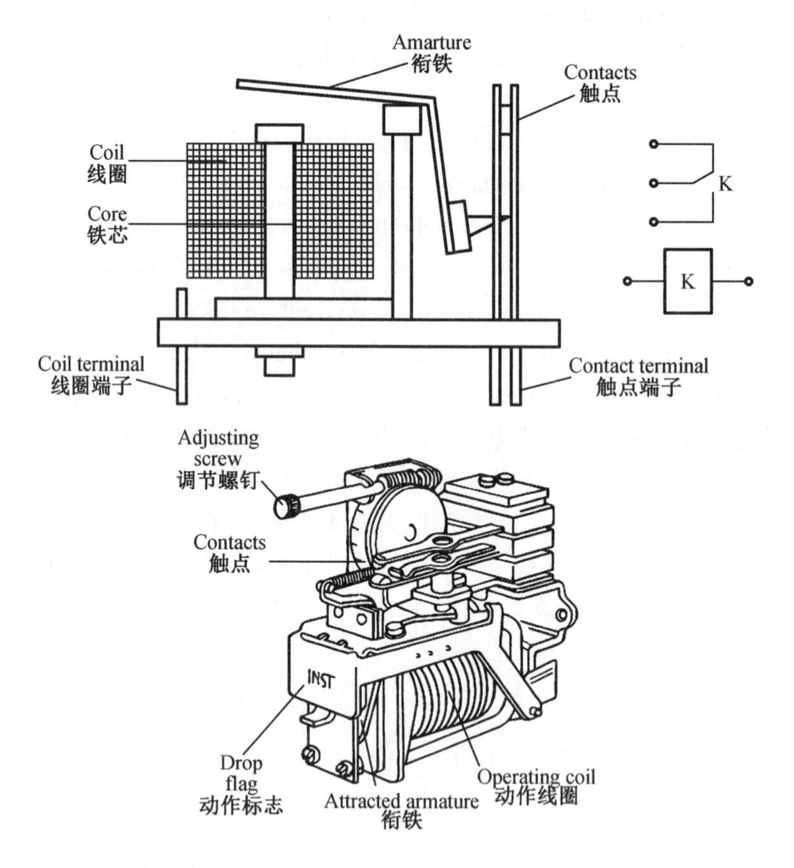

Fig. 3. 27 Magnetic overcurrent relay (instantaneous action)

图 3. 27 磁过流继电器(瞬时动作)

To obtain a magnetic inverse-time action, e. g. for motor overload protection, an induction disc movement is usually employed. This construction is similar to a kWh energy meter used in a house but the disc movement is constrained by a spring so is not allowed to actually rotate. The disc travel is very small but sufficient to operate a set of trip switch contacts. Both current and time settings are adjustable. A combined relay including an attracted armature element and induction disc element will give an instantaneous action (high set current) and an inverse/time characteristic.

为了获得磁逆时间动作,例如用于电动机过载保护,通常使用感应盘。这种结构类似于在房子中使用的电能表,但圆盘的运动受到弹簧的限制,所以不能发生实际旋转。感应盘行程非常小,但足以操作一组跳闸开关触点,电流和时间设置都可以调节,包括吸引电枢元件和感应盘元件的组合继电器将产生一个瞬时动作(高设定电流)和一个逆/时间特性。

Fig. 3. 28 shows a thermal relay which utilizes the bending action of a bimetallic bar (one per phase) to open a normally-closed (NC) contact which then trips a contactor or circuit-breaker. A small circuit current will be allowed to flow directly through the bimetallic strip but larger currents will be directed through a heater coil surrounding the strip. The three bimetal strips in a three-phase relay, all bend in the same direction with balanced overcurrent to cause a trip. A mechanical bell-crank trip arrangement can also operate with unbalanced (differential) currents. This is particularly effective with a single phasing motor fault. In this case, two of the bimetal strips bend further in the normal direction with increased line current, while the other cools down allowing this strip to move relatively backwards (differential action).

图 3.28 所示为一个热过流继电器,它利用双金属条(每相一个)的弯曲作用来打开一个常闭(NC)触点,然后使继电器或者断路器跳闸。小的电路电流将可直接通过双金属条,但更大的电流将通过双金属条周围的加热线圈。三相继电器中的三个双金属条,均匀过流时都向同一方向弯曲,导致跳闸。机械钟形曲柄跳闸装置也可以在过电流不平衡的情况下工作。这对于单相电动机故障尤其有效。在这种情况下,两个双金属条随着线电流的增加沿正常方向进一步弯曲,而另一条则冷却,使该条相对向后移动(不同的作用)。

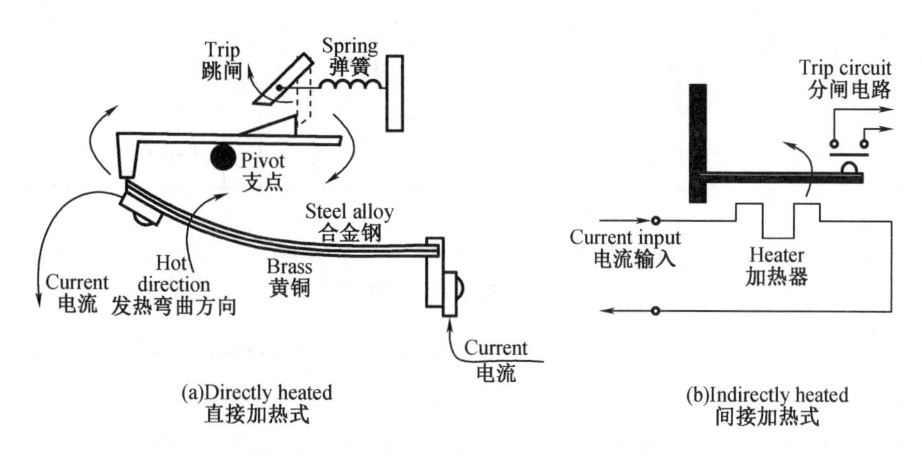

Fig. 3. 28 Bimetallic thermal relay action

图 3. 28 双金属条热过流继电器动作

The time taken to heat the bimetal strip to cause sufficient bending fixes the required time to trip. Resetting the relay can only be achieved after the strip has cooled down back to the ambient temperature. The inverse *I-t* overcurrent characteristic of a thermal relay is very useful for the indirect temperature protection of motors. Its thermal time delay is, however, far too long for a short-circuit fault so back-up instantaneous protection must also be used in the form of fuses or a circuit breaker.

加热双金属条以引起足够的弯曲所需的时间,决定了跳闸所需的时间。只有在金属条冷却至室温后才能重置继电器。热过流继电器的反时限 I–t 的过电流特性对于电动机的间接温度保护非常有用。但是对于短路故障来说,它的热时间延迟太长了,因此熔断器或断路器形式的瞬时保护作为备用也必须使用。

An electronic overcurrent relay usually converts the measured current into a proportional voltage. This is then compared with a set voltage level within the monitoring unit which may be digital or analogue. In an analogue unit (as shown in Fig. 3. 29), the time delay is obtained by the time taken to charge up a capacitor. This type of relay has separate adjustments for overcurrent and time settings together with an instantaneous trip. The electronic amplifiers within the relay require a low voltage de power supply, e. g. 24 V DC derived from a 110 V AC auxiliary supply.

电子过流继电器通常将测量的电流转换成一个比例电压。然后将其与监测单元内的数字或模拟的设定电压电平进行比较。在一个模拟单元中(图 3. 29),时间延迟由给电容器充电所需的时间获得。这种类型的继电器对过流和时间设置以及瞬时跳闸有单独的调整。继电器内的电子放大器需要一个低电压直流电源,例如来自 110 V 的交流电辅助电源的 24 V 直流电。

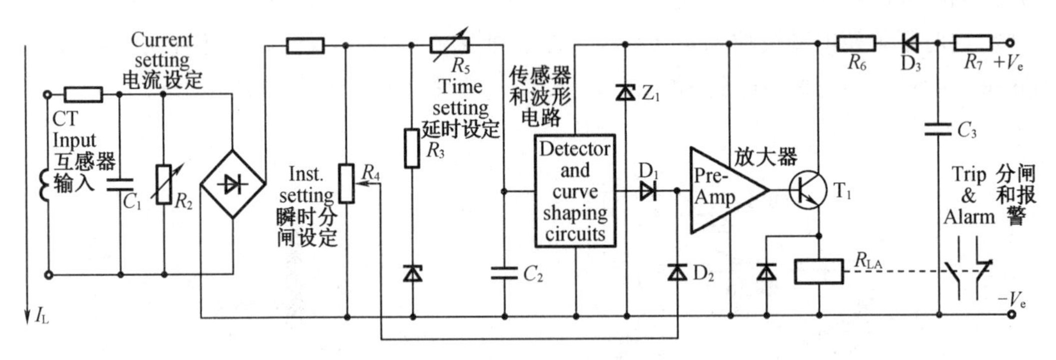

Fig. 3. 29 Electronic overcurrent relay

图 3. 29 电子过流继电器

Here, the input from a line CT is rectified to produce a DC voltage which is proportional to the line current. This voltage charges capacitor C_2 at a rate set in conjunction with potentiometer R_5 which determines the inverse-time characteristic for the relay. When this capacitor voltage exceeds the predetermined level (set by R_2), the detector circuit drives power transistor T_1 to operate the output electromagnetic relay RLA which switches trip and alarm contacts in the external circuits.

在这里,由电流互感器输入的电流被整流以产生与线电流成正比的直流电压。该电压以由电位器 R_5 设置的速率给电容器 C_2 充电,以确定继电器的反时限特性。当该电容器电压超过预设电压(由 R_2 设定)时,检测器电路驱动功率晶体管 T_1 导通以使电磁继电器 RLA 工作,其在外部电路中的跳闸和报警开关触点动作。

An instantaneous trip operation is obtained by applying the output of the bridge rectifier directly to the input of the amplifier with a voltage set by R_4. Hence, for higher values of fault current, the inverse-time delay circuit is by-passed.

通过将桥式整流器的输出直接施加在由 R_4 设置电压的放大器输入端,实现瞬时跳闸。因此,对于较高的故障电流值,将旁通反时限电路。

Both the magnetic and electronic relays can be designed to give an almost instantaneous trip (typically less than 50 ms) to clear a short circuit fault.

磁过流继电器和电子过流继电器都可以做到瞬时(通常小于 50 ms)产生跳闸信号来消除短路故障。

Thermal relays are commonly fitted in MCCBs and in MCBs to give a "long time" thermal overcurrent trip in addition to a magnetic action for an instantaneous trip with a short-circuit fault.

热过流继电器通常安装在塑壳断路器和微型断路器中,它除了可以提供短路故障的电磁作用瞬时跳闸外,还可以提供"长时间"的热过电流跳闸。

Overcurrent protection relays in large power circuits are generally driven by CTs. The CT secondary usually has a 5 A or 1 A rating for full load current in its primary winding.

大型功率电路中的过电流保护继电器通常由电流互感器驱动。电流互感器的次级绕组电流对于其主绕组的满载电流通常为 5 A 或 1 A 额定电流。

All overcurrent relays can be tested by injecting calibrated test currents into them to check their current trip levels and time delay settings.

所有过流继电器都可以通过通入经校准的测试电流来进行测试,以检查其当前的跳闸等级和时间延迟设置。

Primary injection is where a calibrated test current is fed through the normal load circuit. This requires a large current injection test set. The test set is essentially a transformer and controller rather like a welding set, i. e. it gives a low voltage-high current output.

初级输入是指校准后的试验电流向正常负载电路输入的地方。这需要一个较大的电流通入测试设备。测试设备本质上是一个变压器和控制器,就像焊接设备,即它提供了一个低压-高电流输出。

Small secondary injection currents (5-50 A) are fed current directly into the overcurrent relay usually via a special test plug/socket wired into the relay. Secondary injection does not prove the CT performance (as it is disconnected during the test) but is the usual method for testing an overcurrent relay.

小的次级注入电流(5~50 A)通常通过连接到继电器中的专用测试插座直接输入过流

继电器。次级注入不能验证电流互感器性能(因为它在测试中是断开的),但却是用来测试过流继电器的常用方法。

The setting up of an overcurrent relay is obviously critical to its protective duty so is carried out in strict accordance with the manufacturer's instructions. Such setting up is done during new ship trials and at subsequent periodic surveys.

过流继电器的设置显然对其保护作用至关重要,因此要严格按照厂家的说明进行。这种设置是在新船试验和随后的定期调查中进行的。

3.8.2 Fuse Protection 熔断器保护

A fuse is the most common type of protection against a short-circuit fault in LV distribution circuits, motor circuits and for portable appliances. It is relatively simple, inexpensive and reliable. As rewireable fuses tend to be less reliable than the cartridge type and are open to abuse (fitting the wrong size of fuse wire), they are not recommended for marine practice. HRC (high rupturing capacity—e. g. 80 kA) cartridge-type fuse links are normally used. A typical construction is shown in Fig. 3. 30.

在低压配电电路、电动机电路和便携式电器中,熔断器是最常见的短路保护形式。它相对简单、便宜、可靠。由于重新连接的熔断器往往不如管型熔断器可靠,并且容易被滥用(安装规格错误的熔丝),因此不推荐用于海上环境,通常使用高分断容量(HRC,例如80 kA)管型熔断器。其典型的熔断器结构如图 3. 30 所示。

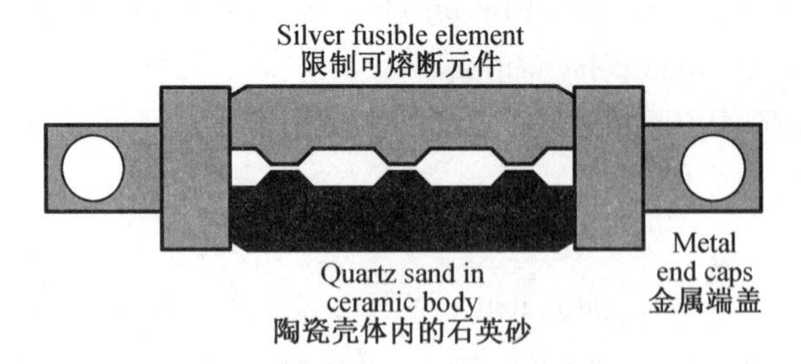

Fig. 3. 30　HRC fuse construction

图 3. 30　HRC 熔断器结构

A disadvantage of a fuse is its insensitivity to small overcurrents. An HRC fuse will blow at currents as low as 25% overload, but only after about 4 h.

熔断器的一个缺点是它对较小的过电流不敏感。HRC 熔断器会在电流低至 25%的过电流时熔断,但在大约 4 h 后才动作。

The advantage of a fuse is its very high speed of operation (a few milliseconds) at high short-circuit fault current — faster than a circuit-breaker.

熔断器的优点是它在高短路故障电流下熔断速度非常快(几毫秒),比断路器动作还要快。

Fuses are fitted in circuits to give protection against short-circuits. Protection against relatively small overcurrents (e. g. due to shaft overloading on a motor) is provided where necessary by an overcurrent relay (OCR).

熔断器安装在电路中，以防短路故障。必要时，通过过流继电器(OCR)来防止相对较小的过流(例如电动机过载引起的过流)。

A starter overcurrent relay protects the motor against relatively small over currents. The fuse links provide back-up protection for the supply cables and generators against a short-circuit fault.

启动器的过流继电器可保护电动机免受相对较小的过流影响。熔断器为电源电缆和发电机提供备用保护，以防止短路故障带来的损害。

Motor fuses are typically rated at 2-3 times, the motor full load current in order to withstand the large starting current surge (up to 6 times full load) of the motor. The motor manufacturer will specify the correct rating of fuse link for a particular motor rating. Hence a typical fuse designation for a motor circuit could be "32M63" which indicates a continuous rating of 32 A, but a rating of 63 A for the brief starting period.

电动机熔断器的额定电流通常为电动机满载电流的2~3倍，以承受电动机的大启动电流激增(高达6倍满载电流)。电动机制造商将给特定电动机指定正确额定参数的熔断器。如给电动机电路指定一个标有"32M63"的典型熔断器，这表示电动机持续工作的额定电流为32 A，额定的短时启动电流为63 A。

Important points to note concerning fuses are:

(1) In the event of a fuse blowing, the cause of the fault must be located and repaired before the fuse link is replaced.

(2) The replacement fuse link must be of the correct current rating, grade and type. Usually this means the replacement fuse link is identical to the blown fuse link.

(3) Replace all three fuses in a three-phase supply even if only one is found blown after a fault. The others may be seriously weakened which makes them unreliable for future use.

关于熔断器，需要注意以下几个要点：

(1) 如果熔断器烧断，必须在更换熔断器连接之前找到并修复故障。

(2) 更换的熔断器必须具有正确的额定电流、等级和类型，即更换的熔断器与熔断的熔断器要相同。

(3) 三相电源中，即使在故障后仅发现一个熔断器熔断，也要同时更换三个熔断器。这是因为其余熔断器性能可能被严重削弱，使得它们在将来的使用中不可靠。

The reference symbols used on an HRC fuse link are devised by the particular manufacturer.

They include the current rating, voltage, application (e. g. motor, transformer, diode, general use), physical size, and type of fixing arrangement.

HRC 熔断器的参考符号是由各制造商设计的。它们包括额定电流、电压、应用对象(例如电动机、变压器、二极管、一般用途)、物理尺寸和固定装置的类型。

3.8.3 Undervoltage Protection 欠压保护

An undervoltage (U/V) release mechanism is fitted to all generator breakers and some main feeder circuit-breakers. Its main function is to trip the breaker when a severe voltage dip (around 50%) occurs. This is achieved by lifting the mechanical latch (which keeps the contacts closed) to allow the trip spring to function which opens the breaker contacts. The U/V release on a generator circuit-breaker also prevents it being closed when the generator voltage is very low or absent.

所有发电机断路器和一些主要馈线断路器都安装有一个欠压(U/V)释放机构。其主要功能是在发生严重电压下降(约 50%)时触发断路。这是通过提升机械锁闩(保持触点闭合)来实现的,以使跳闸弹簧能够打开断路器触点。发电机断路器上的欠压释放也可以防止断路器在发电机电压很低或没有时处于闭合状态。

As shown in Fig. 3. 31, an undervoltage relay, which may be magnetic or electronic, also provides back-up protection to short-circuit protection. As an example, suppose during generator paralleling procedures, an attempt was made to close the wrong circuit-breaker e. g. the breaker of a stopped and dead generator. If this circuit-breaker was closed, the dead generator would be the equivalent of a short-circuit fault on the bus-bars and cause a blackout. The undervoltage relay prevents the closure of the circuit-breaker of the dead generator.

如图 3. 31 所示,欠压继电器可以是电磁或电子继电器,为短路保护提供备用保护。假设在发电机并车过程中,试图闭合错误的断路器,例如停止和失电的发电机断路器。如果此断路器合闸,失电的发电机将相当于将母线短路,并导致全船失电。欠压继电器防止失电发电机的断路器合闸。

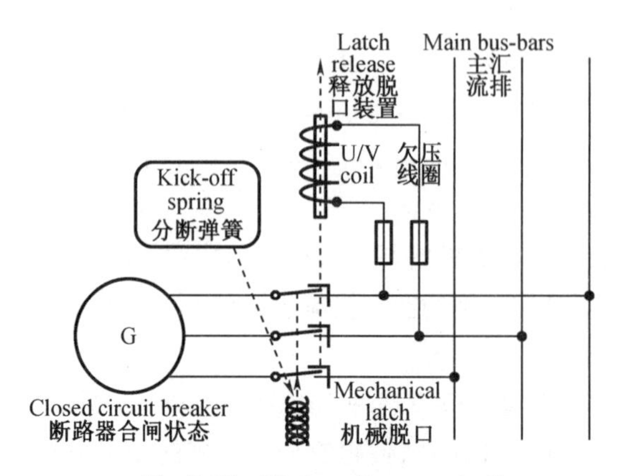

Fig. 3. 31 Undervoltage protection

图 3. 31 欠压保护

Question 思考题

A three-phase short-circuit occurs on the main bus-bars and the short-circuit trip of the running generator breaker fails to operate. Please explain how the undervoltage relay provides a back-uptrip.

主汇流排发生三相短路故障,正在运行的发电机断路器在短路故障中没有跳闸。请解释欠压继电器怎样提供备用跳闸。

Answer 答案

The short-circuit reduces the bus-bar voltage to zero which causes the U/V release to trip the breaker.

短路故障将主汇流排电压降低到0,导致欠压继电器欠压释放跳闸。

Undervoltage protection is also required for motor starters. The starter contactor normally provides this protection as it drops out when the supply voltage is lost or is drastically reduced. The starter circuit will not normally allow the motor to restart when the voltage supply is restored except when special automatic re-starting facilities are provided.

电动机启动器也需要欠压保护。启动触点通常在电源失电或电压大幅降低时断开来提供保护。启动电路通常不允许在恢复电源时重新启动,除非提供特殊的自动重新启动设施。

Undervoltage protection can be electromagnetic or electronic.

欠压继电器可以是电磁的或电子的。

Checking and calibration of generator undervoltage relays can only be done accurately by calibrated voltage injection. A known variable voltage is directly applied to the undervoltage relay to check:

(1)The voltage at which the relay pulls-in;

(2)The voltage at which the relay drops-out.

发电机欠压继电器只能通过校准的电压注入来准确地校准和检查。将已知的可变电压直接施加到欠压继电器上,以检查:

(1)继电器接通时所处的电压;

(2)继电器分闸时的电压。

Generator U/V relays are usually slugged to allow a time-delay which prevents spurious tripping during transient voltage dips (typically 15%) caused by large motor starting currents.

发电机欠压继电器通常运行缓慢,允许延时,以防止由大电动机启动电流引起瞬时电压降(通常为15%)期间发生误跳闸。

3.9 Electric Cables 电力电缆

Ship wiring cables have to withstand a wide variety of environmental conditions, e. g. extremes of ambient temperature, humidity and salinity. Improved materials have led to ship wiring cables of a fairly standard design that are safe, durable and efficient under all conditions.

船舶布线电缆必须承受各种各样的环境条件,例如极端的环境温度、湿度和盐度。改进材料性能后形成了适当的船舶布线电缆设计标准,在所有条件下都是安全、耐用和高效的。

The normal distribution voltage on ships is 440 V and cables for use at this voltage are designated 600/1,000 V, i. e. 600 V to earth or 1,000 V between conductors.

船上常用的配电电压是 440 V,在这个电压下的电缆指定为 600/1 000 V,即对地电压 600 V 或者导体间电压 1 000 V。

Higher voltage systems require cables with appropriate ratings, e. g. for a 3. 3 kV three-phase earthed neutral system the required cable rating is 1,900/3,300 V. For three-phase insulated systems, the cable rating would be 3,300/3,300 V.

更高电压的系统要求电缆具有相适应的额定值,例如对于 3. 3 kV 中性点接地三相系统,要求的电缆额定值为 1 900/3 300 V。对于三相绝缘系统,电缆额定值为 3 300/3 300 V。

Cables are constructed of several basic parts:

(1) Conductors are of annealed stranded copper which may be circular or shaped. Cables with shaped conductors and cores are usually smaller and lighter than cables with circular cores.

(2) Cable insulation has a thickness appropriate to the system voltage rating. Insulation materials are generally organic plastic compounds. Butyl rubber, which is tough and resilient, has good heat, ozone and moisture resistance. These excellent properties enable butyl rubber to replace natural rubber as an insulant. Even so, butyl rubber has now been largely superseded by ethylene propylene rubber (EPR) insulation. EPR has similar electrical and physical properties to butyl rubber but with better resistance to moisture and ozone. It should not, however, be exposed to oils and greases.

电缆由以下几个基本部分组成:

(1)导体是经过退火的绞合铜,可以是圆形的或其他形状的。带形状的导体和线芯的电缆通常比圆芯电缆更小、更轻。

(2)电缆绝缘层的厚度与系统电压额定值相适应。绝缘材料一般是有机塑料化合物。丁基橡胶坚韧,有弹性,具有良好的耐热、抗臭氧和防潮性能。这些优异的性能使丁基橡胶能够取代天然橡胶作为绝缘体。即便如此,丁基橡胶现在已经基本上被乙烯丙烯橡胶(EPR)绝缘所取代。EPR 具有与丁基橡胶相似的电气和物理性能,但具有更好的抗潮湿和臭氧性能。然而,它不能暴露在油和油脂中。

Cross-linked polyethylene (XLPE) as shown in Fig. 3. 32, is also used as an insulant but has inferior mechanical and thermal properties when compared with EPR. Polyvinyl chloride (PVC) is not generally used for ships' cables, even though it is very common ashore. PVC tends to soften and flow at high temperatures (melts at 150 ℃), and hardens and cracks at low temperatures (−8 ℃). Even at normal temperatures, PVC tends to flow and become distorted under mechanical stress for example necking occurs at cable glands causing the gland to lose its watertight properties.

交联聚乙烯(XLPE)如图 3. 32 所示,也被用作绝缘体,但与 EPR 相比,其机械性能和热性能较差。聚氯乙烯(PVC)通常不用作船用电缆,尽管它在岸上很常见。PVC 在高温下趋于软化和流动(在 150 ℃下融化),在低温下(−8 ℃)会硬化和开裂。即使在常温下,PVC 也会在机械应力下流动并变得扭曲,例如,电缆密封套会发生颈缩现象,导致密封套失去水密性能。

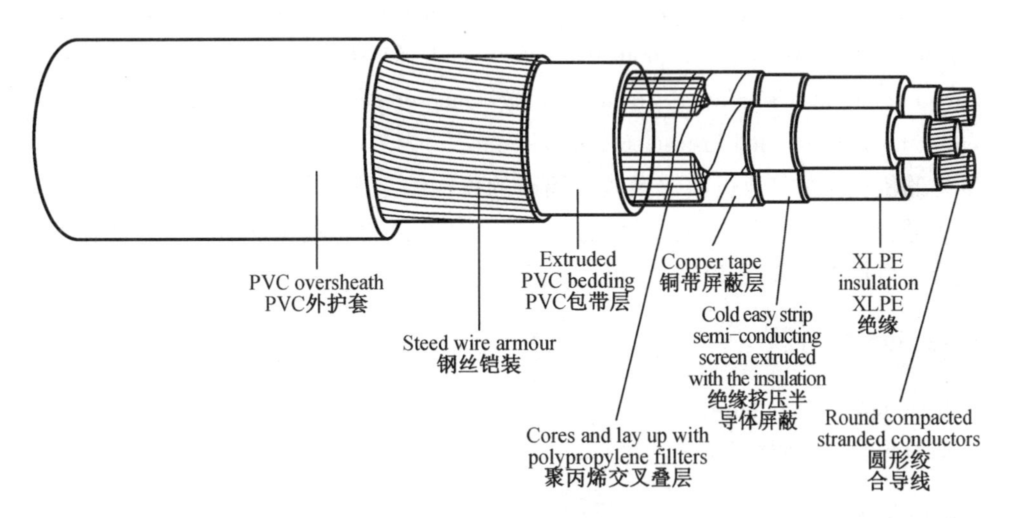

Fig. 3. 32 XLPE cable construction

图 3. 32 XLPE 电缆结构

Multicore ship wiring cables have the cores identified by either color, printed numerals on untaped cores or numbered tapes on taped cores.

多芯船用电缆的线芯用颜色区别,或者是在线芯胶皮上编号。

Question 思考题

What is the purpose of the sheath on a cable?

电缆护套的用途是什么?

Answer 答案

The sheath of a cable protects the insulation from damage and injury — it is not classed as an insulant. Sheath materials are required to be heat, oil and chemical resistant and flame retardant (HOFR). The sheath must also be tough and flexible.

电缆的护套可以保护绝缘体免受损坏,它不被列为绝缘体。护套材料需要耐热、耐油和化学阻燃(HOFR)。护套也必须是坚韧和柔软的。

Polychloroprene (PCP or neoprene) is a common sheath material but has been largely superseded by chlorosulphonated polyethylene (CSP or hypalon). CSP-HOFR sheathing compound is well suited to shipboard conditions. It offers good resistance to cuts and abrasions, resists weather and ozone, acid fumes and alkalis, and is flexible.

聚氯丁烯(PCP 或氯丁烯)是一种常见的护罩材料,但已被氯磺化聚乙烯(CSP 或海普龙)取代。CSP-HOFR 护套复合物非常适合船上的环境。它具有良好的抗切割和磨损性能,能抵抗海上气候和臭氧、酸性烟雾和碱的腐蚀,并且很柔韧。

Extra mechanical protection is provided by armouring with basket-woven wire braid of either galvanised steel or tinned phosphor bronze. The non-magnetic properties of phosphor bronze are preferred for single-core cables. A protective outer sheath of CSP compound covers the wire braid. The wire braiding also acts as a screen to reduce interference (caused by magnetic fields) in adjacent communication and instrumentation circuits.

额外的机械保护是通过镀锌钢或镀锡磷的青铜编织而成的铠装。镀锡磷青铜的非磁性性能更适合于单芯电缆。CSP 化合物组成的保护性外护套覆盖了钢丝编织铠装,钢丝编织的铠装还可作为屏蔽层,以减少相邻通信和仪器电路中的干扰(由磁场引起)。

Question 思考题

Will cable materials burn?

电缆材料会燃烧吗?

Answer 答案

Yes, all organic materials will eventually burn in a severe fire. Cable sheath materials commonly in use are organic plastic compounds that are classed as flame retardant, i. e. will not sustain a fire. Most cable materials now achieve this property by developing chlorine gas and acid fumes to smother the flame. PVC is notorious for its release of deadly acid fumes, but PCP and CSP do the same. EPR and XLPE do not. Some new materials do not produce acid fumes when burning — an important feature for fire-fighting personnel. However, burning cable materials still tend to produce dense black smoke.

是的,所有的有机材料都会在一场大火中燃烧。电缆护套材料通常使用有机塑料化合物,被归类为阻燃物,即不会保持燃烧。现在,大多数电缆材料通过产生氯气和酸雾来覆盖火焰以实现这一特性。PVC 以释放致命的酸烟雾而臭名昭著,但 PCP 和 CSP 也是一样的,而 EPR 和 XLPE 则不会。一些新材料在燃烧时不会产生酸性烟雾——对消防人员来说这是一个很重要的特性。然而,燃烧的电缆材料仍然会产生浓密的黑烟。

3.9.1 MIMS Cables　MIMS 电缆

Mineral insulated, metal sheathed cables are very useful in high temperature, fire-risk areas. These cables have a magnesium oxide powder as insulation with a metal sheath — usually copper (MICC — Mineral insulated, copper covered) which is further covered with PVC for weatherproofing where necessary. A special termination is used with MIMS cables to provide a moisture-proof seal for the hygroscopic insulation powder. For an MICC cable this is achieved by a compound filled brass pot screwed directly on to the copper sheath as shown in Fig. 3. 33.

矿物绝缘、金属护套电缆在高温、有火灾危险的区域非常有用。这些电缆有一种氧化镁粉末作为绝缘,加上铜护套(MICC——矿物绝缘,铜覆盖),再覆盖 PVC,以在必要时防风雨。MIMS 电缆采用一种特殊的端子,为吸湿绝缘粉末提供防潮密封。MICC 电缆通过一个复合填充的黄铜罐直接拧在铜护罩上,如图 3. 33 所示。

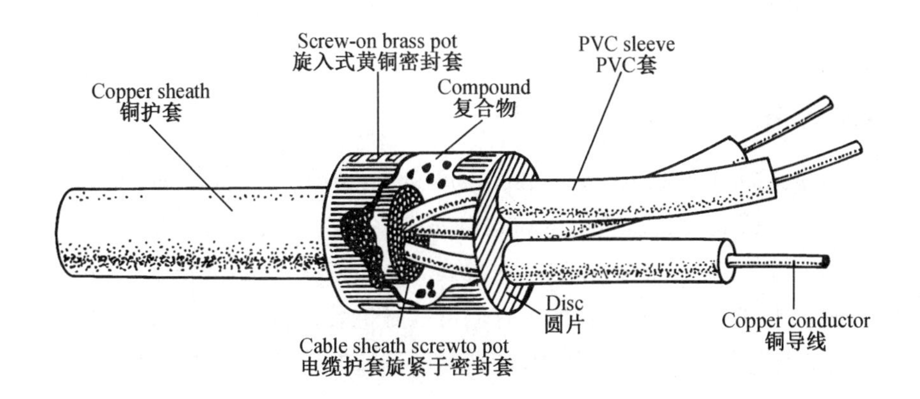

Fig. 3. 33　MICC cable termination

图 3. 33　矿物绝缘电缆

The current rating of a cable is the current the cable can carry continuously without the conductor exceeding 80 ℃ with an ambient air temperature of 45 ℃ (i. e. a 35 ℃ rise). This rating must be reduced (derated) if the ambient exceeds 45 ℃, or when cables are bunched together or enclosed in a pipe or trunking which reduces the effective cooling.

电缆的额定电流是指电缆可以持续携带的电流,当环境温度为 45 ℃时,其导体不超过 80 ℃(即温度上升不超过 35 ℃)。如果环境温度超过 45 ℃,或者当电缆串在一起或封闭在管道或管槽中,有效冷却降低时,该额定值必须降低(降级)。

MICC cable current ratings are based upon a copper sheath temperature of 150 ℃ maximum.
MICC 电缆电流额定值是基于最大 150 ℃的铜护套温度。

For all types of cable the size of conductors required for a particular installation is estimated from current rating tables issued by suppliers. These tables show current ratings for a range of cable types, conductor area and volt-drop/amp/meter.

对于所有类型的电缆,特定安装所需的导线尺寸将根据供应商提供的电流额定值表进行估算。这些额定值表显示了一系列电缆类型、导体面积和电压降/电流/长度对应的电流额定值。

The volt drop in cables from the main switchboard to the appliance must not exceed 6% (in practice it is about 2%). The cables installed must comply with both the current rating and the volt-drop limitation. Cable volt drop only becomes a problem in very long cables.

从主配电板到设备的电缆的电压降不得超过 6%(实际上约为 2%)。所安装的电缆必须同时符合电流额定值和电压降限制。电缆电压降只在非常长的电缆中成为问题。

Question 思考题

What is the purpose of a cable gland?

电缆密封套的作用是什么?

Answer 答案

Cables are insulated, mechanically protected and watertight. They may be armoured and suitable for installation in a hazardous explosive area. A cable gland maintains these properties where the cable is terminated at an appliance, e. g. at a motor terminal box.

电缆是绝缘的、机械保护和水密的。它们可以是铠装的,适合安装在危险的爆炸区域。电缆密封套保持电缆在设备终端连接的水密特性,例如电动机终端接线盒。

The cable gland is screwed into the appliance terminal box. Nuts on the gland compress sealing rings to maintain watertight seals on the inner and outer sheaths and to clamp the armor braiding. The gland must be matched to the size and type of cable. A typical Ex-protected gland construction (which is more complicated than an equivalent industrial type) is shown in Fig. 3. 34.

电缆密封套拧入设备端子盒。密封套上的螺母压紧密封圈,以保持内外护罩上的防水密封,并夹住编织铠装。该密封套必须与电缆的大小和类型相匹配。一种典型的防爆密封套结构(比同等的工业类型更复杂)如图 3. 34 所示。

In most cases earthing of the cable armoring is done by the cable gland. Where cables pass through watertight bulkheads and fire-stop barriers they must be specially glanded to maintain the integrity of such bulkheads.

在大多数情况下,电缆铠装的接地是由电缆密封套实现的。当电缆通过水密舱壁和防火屏障时,必须进行特别加固,以保持这些舱壁的完整性。

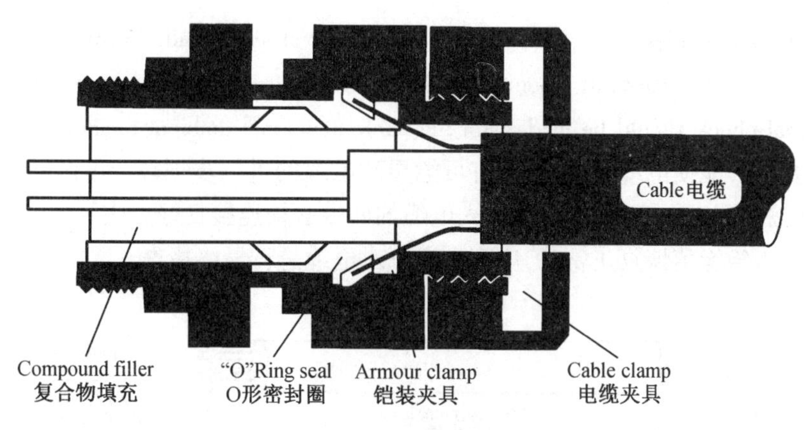

Fig. 3. 34　Exd cable gland

图 3. 34　防爆电缆密封套

Conductor termination sockets can be soldered to the conductors but are more frequently crimped onto each wire by a compression tool.

导体终端插座可以焊接在导体上,但更多的是通过压力工具压在每条导线上。

Cable sockets must be securely attached to the appliance terminal screw by nuts and shakeproof washers. A loose terminal will invariably become a source of localised overheating. Periodic maintenance should always include checking the tightness of terminal connections.

电缆插座必须通过螺母和防震垫片牢固地连接到电器端子螺钉上,松动的端子总会使局部过热。定期维护始终应包含终端连接的紧密性检查。

Small cables are terminated in terminal blocks of various designs.

小电缆通过各种设计连接到接线排上。

Cables should be periodically inspected and tested, ideally when checking their connected appliances. Cable insulation resistance should be measured and the value recorded. Cables in exposed and damp situations, e. g. for deck lighting, may develop a low insulation resistance. Usually this is a result of mechanical damage or a faulty gland permitting the ingress of water. Cables can be dried out by injecting a heating current from a current injection set or a welding transformer as shown in Fig. 3. 35.

电缆应定期检查和测试,最好是在检查其连接的器件时进行。应测量电缆绝缘电阻,并记录其阻值。在暴露和潮湿环境下的电缆,比如用于甲板照明的电缆,可能会产生低绝缘电阻。通常这是由于机械损坏或一个失效的密封套进水引起的。电缆可以通过电流注入装置或变压器的加热电流来干燥,如图 3. 35 所示。

The procedure requires care not to overheat the cables which could cause further damage. The cable should be disconnected at both ends from equipment, and connected as shown in Fig.

3.35. The injection cables must have good connections at each end. Current flow and cable temperature should be carefully monitored. When satisfactory insulation values have been restored, a final check should be made with the cable at normal ambient temperature.

该步骤要求不能使电缆过热,因为有可能导致电缆的进一步损坏。电缆的两端都应与设备断开,并按如图3.35所示连接。输入电缆的两端必须连接良好。应仔细监测电流大小和电缆温度。当绝缘值恢复正常时,应在常温下对电缆进行最终检查。

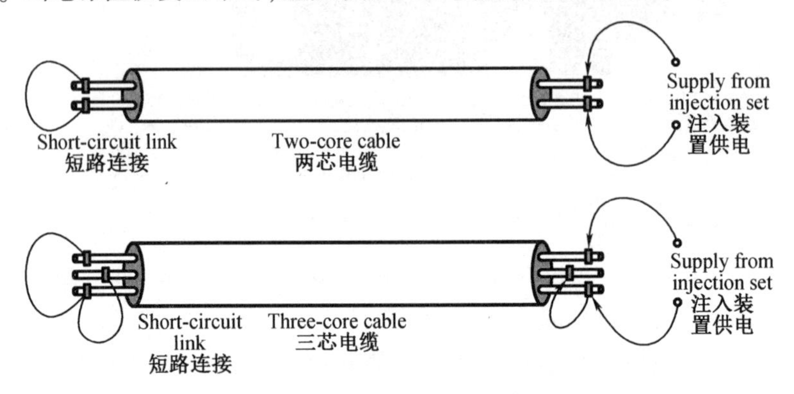

Fig. 3.35 Cable dry out connection

图3.35 电缆干燥法接线

The injected heating current must never exceed the rated current for the cable — it is advisable to use an ammeter and to start at the lowest available setting on the injection set. The voltage should be in the region of 30 to 55 V depending upon the current setting. The cable temperature can be measured with a contact thermometer secured to the cable or with an infrared sensor and should not be allowed to exceed a temperature rise of 30 ℃. Temperature and insulation resistance should be measured and recorded every hour. When the insulation resistance becomes steady the heating should be carried out for a further four hours before switching off. Final readings of at least 20 MΩ to earth and 100 MΩ between cores should be expected.

注入的加热电流不得超过电缆的额定电流,建议使用电流表并从可设置的最低电流开始注入。根据电流设置,电压应为30~55 V。电缆温度可以通过固定在电缆上的接触温度计或红外传感器测量,不允许超过30 ℃。应每小时测量并记录温度和绝缘电阻。当绝缘电阻稳定时,应再加热4 h后再关闭。对地绝缘电阻最终读数不低于20 MΩ,线芯之间的绝缘电阻至少为100 MΩ。

Mechanical damage to cables must be made good either by repairing the damage or replacing that section of cable. Unprotected metal armoring and insulation material are vulnerable to attack by moisture, chemicals and corrosive gases, while exposed live conductors are obviously dangerous. A temporary repair may be effected by preparing and binding the damaged section with a suitable adhesive plastic electrical insulating tape.

电缆的机械损坏必须通过修复或更换损坏部位来解决。未受保护的金属铠装和绝缘材料容易受到水气、化学物质和腐蚀性气体的侵蚀,此时裸露的带电导体显然很危险。可以用适当的塑料电绝缘胶带包裹损坏的部分来进行临时修复。

Such a repair will not be acceptable in a hazardous zone on a tanker. Permanent cable repairs must be made as soon as possible.

这种临时维修在油轮的危险区域不可使用,必须尽快进行永久性的电缆维修。

Chapter 4 Motors and Starters
第4章 电动机及其启动器

4.0 Introduction 介绍

The drive power for compressors, pumps and fans aboard ship comes from electric motors. By far the most common type of motor is the three-phase AC cage-rotor induction motor. It is popular because it is simple, tough and requires very little attention. Another advantage is that starting and stopping these motors can be done with simple and reliable direct-on-line contactor starters. Three-phase induction motors are usually supplied at 440 V, 60 Hz, but 3.3 kV and 6.6 kV, 60 Hz are sometimes used for very large drives such as bow thrusters, cargo pumps, air compressors and gas compressors.

船上的压缩机、泵和风机的驱动力来自电动机。到目前为止,最常见的电动机类型是三相交流笼型转子感应电动机。它很受欢迎,因为它简单、耐用,而且不需要太多关注。另一个原因是,可以使用简单可靠的接触器直接启动和停止这些电动机。三相感应电动机通常以440 V,60 Hz供电,3.3 kV和6.6 kV,60 Hz有时用于非常大的驱动器,如船首推进器、货泵、空气压缩机和气体压缩机。

Special types of motor can also befound on board ships. DC commutator motors are sometimes used for driving deck machinery where speed control is important. Single-phase AC motors are used in low power drives such as galley equipment and power tools.

船上也有特殊类型的电动机。直流换向器电动机有时用于驱动转速控制非常重要的甲板机械。单相交流电动机用于厨房设备和电动工具等低功率驱动器。

High power synchronous AC motors are frequently used for electric propulsion drives, see Chapter 8.

大功率同步交流电动机通常用于电力推进驱动,见第8章。

This chapter will deal principally with the three-phase AC cage rotor induction motor, together with its control and protection. Additionally, the more common types of motor speed control methods are outlined, followed by maintenance procedures for motors and starters.

本章主要讨论三相交流笼型转子感应电动机及其控制和保护。此外,还概述了更常用的电动机转速控制方法,以及电动机和启动器的维护程序。

4.1 Motor Construction 电动机结构

The induction motor has two main components, the stator and the rotor. The stator carries three separate insulated phase windings which are spaced 120°(electrical) apart and lying in slots cut into a laminated steel magnetic core. This type of stator winding is similar to the construction used for an AC generator. The ends of the stator windings are terminated in the stator terminal box where they are connected to the incoming cable from the three-phase AC power supply.

感应电动机有两个主要部件,定子和转子。定子带有三个独立的绝缘相绕组,相差120°(电气)并位于切割成叠层钢片的磁芯槽中。这种类型的定子绕组与交流发电机的结构类似。定子绕组的末端接在定子接线盒中,并与三相交流电源的进线电缆连接。

The rotor consists of copper or aluminium conductor bars which are connected together at their ends by short-circuiting rings to form a cage winding. The conductor bars are set in a laminated steel magnetic core. The essential reliability of the induction motor comes from having this type of simple, robust rotor which usually has no insulation on the conductor bars and does not have any troublesome rotary contacts like brushes, commutator or sliprings. The diagram in Fig. 4. 1 and Fig. 4. 2 identifies the main items used in the construction of a typical totally enclosed, fan ventilated (TEFV) induction motor.

转子由铜或铝导条组成,导条两端通过短路环连接在一起,形成笼型绕组。导条设置在叠层钢片磁芯中。感应电动机的基本可靠性来自这种简单、耐用的转子,该转子的导条通常不设绝缘,并且没有任何麻烦的旋转触点,如电刷、换向器或滑环。图4.1和图4.2标明了典型全封闭风扇冷却型(TEFV)感应电动机结构中使用的主要部件。

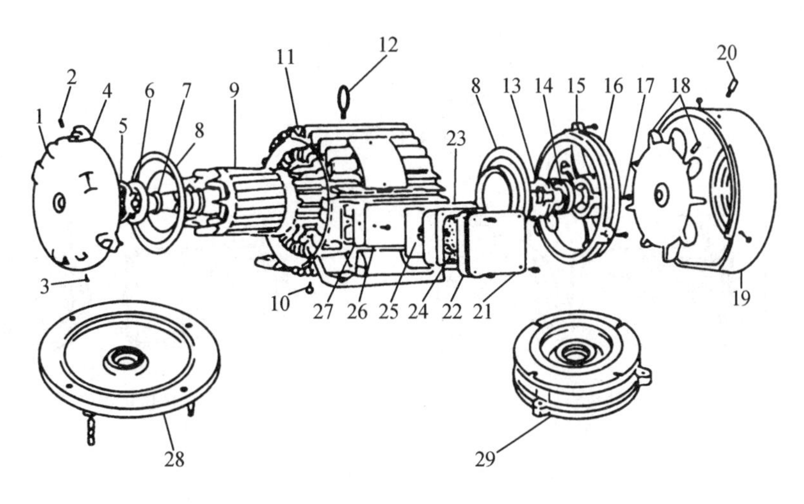

Fig. 4. 1 Induction motor components

图 4. 1 感应电动机元件

No.	Component 部件	No.	Component 部件	No.	Component 部件
1	Endshield, driving end 端盖,传动端	11	Stator frame 机座	21	Terminal box cover 接线盒罩
2	Grease nipple 牛油嘴	12	Eyebolt 吊环	22	Terminal box gasket 接线盒垫片
3	Grease relief screw 卸油螺钉	13	Inside cap 内盖	23	Terminal board 接线端子排
4	End securing bolt 端部固定螺栓	14	Ball bearing 滚珠轴承	24	Terminal box 接线盒
5	Anti-bump nuts 防撞弹片	15	Circlip 卡簧	25	Terminal box gasket 接线盒垫片
6	Ball bearing, driving end 滚珠轴承,传动端	16	Endshield 端盖	26	Raceway plate 槽板
7	False bearing shoulder 间接轴承肩	17	Inside cap screws 内盖螺丝	27	Raceway gasket 槽板垫片
8	Flume 水密环	18	Fan 风扇	28	D flange D 型法兰
9	Cage rotor 笼型转子	19	Fan cover 风罩	29	C face flange C 面法兰
10	Drain plug 排污旋塞	20	Lubricatior extension pipe 润滑延长管		

Fig. 4. 1(Continued)

图 4. 1(续)

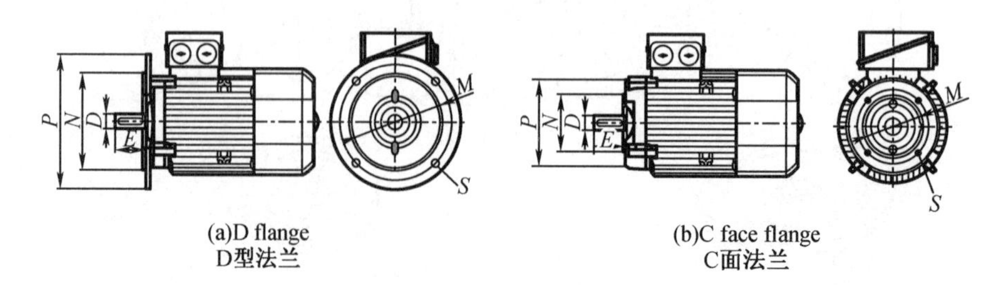

Fig. 4. 2　Flange measurement

图 4. 2　法兰尺寸测量

4.2 Enclosures and Ratings 外壳及其额定参数

4.2.1 Motor Enclosures 电动机壳

The main purpose of motor enclosure is to provides protection from environment impacts such as rain, corrosive, rusty and many more in which motor installed.

电动机外壳的主要用途是保护电动机免受安装环境的影响,如雨水、腐蚀、生锈等。

This protection can make motor more life span and can running in suitable condition. It also provide a types of cooling system for a motor depend on their types of enclosure.

这种保护可延长电动机寿命,并使其能在适当的条件下运行。根据电动机外壳的特点可将电动机冷却系统分为不同的类型。

1. Open Drip Proof (ODP)开式防滴型

This type have a design with vent opening to prevent solids and liquids foreign material entering from above with angles up to 15° from vertical position that can damage interior component of motor(Fig. 4.3).

这种类型的电动机带有排气口,以防止固体和液体异物从与垂直位置成15°角以内的上方进落入,从而损坏电动机内部部件(图4.3)。

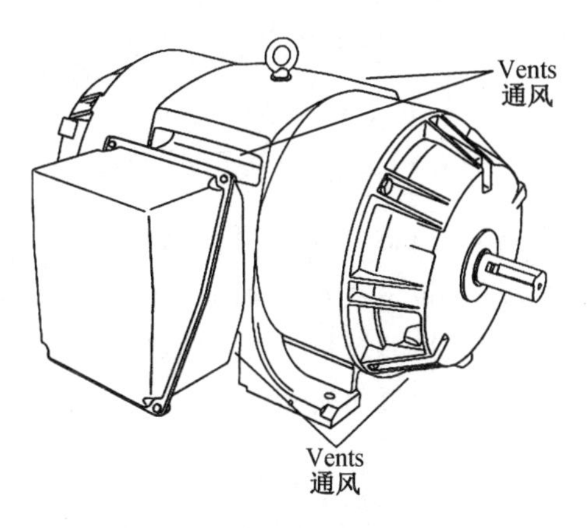

Fig. 4.3 Open drip proof motor

图4.3 开式防滴型电动机

Open ventilated drip proof motors areused where the risk of liquid leaking from overhead pipes and valves may be a problem. Air is drawn into the machine by an internal fan to provide cooling. The ventilation ducts are fitted with mesh screens to prevent any objects rom entering the motor and causing samage. These screens must always be kept clean and free from dust otherwise the motor will overheat due to inadequate ventilation.

开式防滴型电动机用于可能存在液体从架空管道和阀门泄漏风险的处所。内置风扇将空气吸入机器以提供冷却。通风管道安装有筛网,以防止任何物体进入电动机并造成堵塞。这些滤网必须始终保持清洁,无灰尘,否则电动机将因通风不足而过热。

If motor is not installed in the horizontal position, we need to make a additional cover to protect the motor.

如果电动机没有安装在水平位置,我们需要做一个额外的罩子来保护电动机。

2. Totally Enclosed Non-Ventilated (TENV)全封闭无通风型

This types is designed with totally enclosed to blocked the exchange of air between surrounded area and inside of the motor. But it is not fully enclosed because contaminated from outside could entering inside of the motor through the seal of shaft(Fig. 4. 4).

这种电动机为全封闭的,以阻止周围区域和电动机内部之间的空气交换。但它不是绝对封闭的,来自外部的污染可能通过轴的密封进入电动机内部(图 4. 4)。

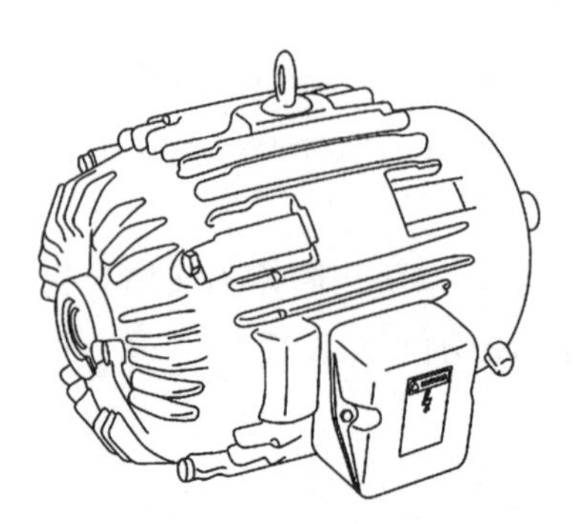

Fig. 4. 4　TENV motor

图 4. 4　全封闭无通风型电动机

The motor heat exchange through the enclosed by conduction process for small size. But for bigger size, to improve heat transfer the motor casing is finned to increase the surface area.

这种体积较小的电动机的热交换通过封闭的传导过程进行。但对于更大的尺寸,为了改善热传递,电动机外壳带有翅片,以增加表面积。

Motors located outside on weather decks have deck watertight enclosures but the external fan is omitted because of the possibility of ice formation.

位于露天甲板上的电动机具有甲板水密外壳,但由于可能结冰,省略了外部风扇。

3. Totally Enclosed Fan Ventilated (TEFV)全封闭风扇冷却型

This type is similar to the TENV type except it have external fan mounted at the end drive of motor and airflow across the fins is achieved by means of an external fan and cowl arrangement, so heat discharge can be more quickly(Fig. 4. 5).

该类型电动机类似于全封闭无通风型,但其在电动机的端部驱动器上安装了外部风扇,通过外部风扇和整流罩使翅片上产生气流,所以能实现更迅速的散热(图 4.5)。

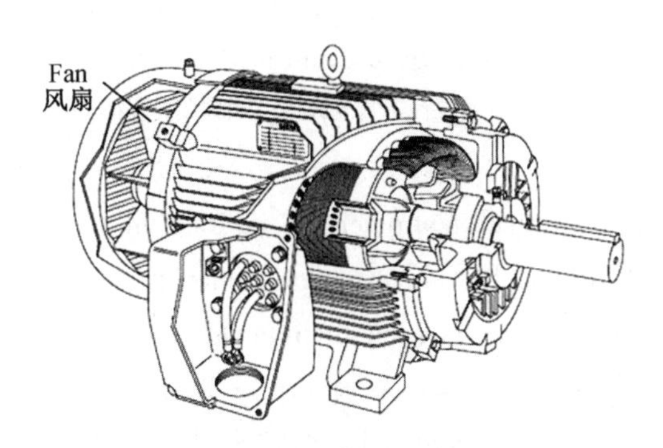

Fig 4.5　TEFV motor

图 4.5　全封闭风扇冷却型电动机

The design of the fan cover is to prevent form touching hazard and for safety reason. This type suitable for corrosive, dirty or moist surrounding area. TEFV motor are common used for industrial and domestic application.

风罩的设计是为了防止触碰危险。该类型电动机适用于周围有腐蚀性、肮脏或潮湿的区域,常用于工业生产和家用。

4. Explosion Proof (EXP)防爆型

This type of motor enclosure is similar design and appearence with the TEFV type but for explosion proof enclosures are made from cast iron material to stand from hazardous impacts(Fig. 4.6).

此类电动机外壳的设计和外观与全封闭风扇冷却型电动机类似,但防爆外壳由铸铁材料制成,以防冲击损坏(图 4.6)。

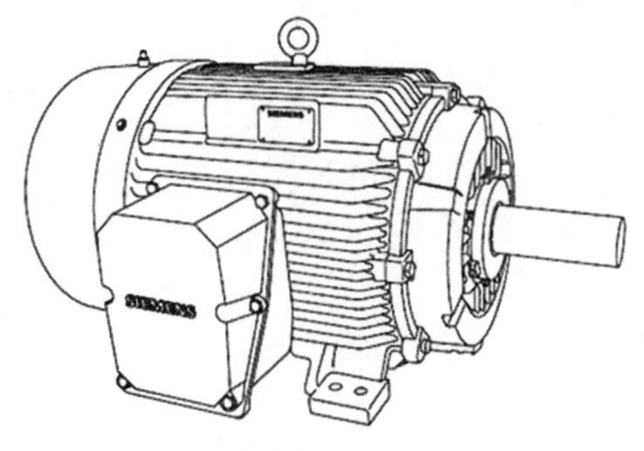

Fig. 4.6　Explosion proof motor

图 4.6　防爆型电动机

Deck motors for tankers must have a flameproof enclosure if they are within 3 m (4.5 m for some ships) of an tank outlet.

如果油轮的甲板电动机位于油柜出口 3 m(某些船舶为 4.5 m)范围内,则必须配备防爆外壳。

Before we select a motor enclosures for our application, please review about location, types of environment impact and ambient temperature to avoid any mistaken.

在为电动机选择机壳之前,需先查看位置、环境影响类型和环境温度,以避免弄错。

Enclosure protection for electrical equipment is defined in terms of its opposition to the ingress of solid particles and liquids. The enclosure protection is defined by the ingress protection (IP) code where a two-figure number is used to indicate the degree of protection against the ingress of solids and liquids as shown below. As shown in Table 4.1.

电动机外壳的防护等级是根据其防止固体颗粒和液体进入的程度来定义的。外壳防护由入侵防护(IP)代码表示,其中使用两位数表示防止固体和液体进入的防护等级,如表4.1所示。

Table 4.1 Intrusion prevention code description

表4.1 入侵防护代码说明

1st digi 第一位数字	Degree of protection of persons against contact with live or moving parts inside the enclosure and protection of equipment against ingress of solid bodies 对人体接近危险部分以及对外部固态物体的防护等级	2nd digi 第二位数字	Degree of protection against ingress of liquids 防水等级
0	No protection 无防护电动机	0	No protection 无防护电动机
1	Protection against accidental or inadvertent contact with live or moving parts inside the enclosure by a large surface of the human body, for example, hand but not protection against deliberate access to such parts 防止人体大面积(例如手)意外或无意地接触外壳内的带电或转动部件,但不防止故意接触此类部件 Protection against ingress of solid ≥ 50 mm foreign bodies 直径≥50 mm的固态物体不能侵入电动机内部	1	Protection against drops of condensed water: Drops of condensed water falling on the enclosure shall have no harmful effect 冷凝水滴落防护:垂直落下的水滴不会对设备造成损害

Table 4.1(Continued 1)

表 4.1(续 1)

1st digi 第一位数字	Degree of protection of persons against contact with live or moving parts inside the enclosure and protection of equipment against ingress of solid bodies 对人体接近危险部分以及对外部固态物体的防护等级	2nd digi 第二位数字	Degree of protection against ingress of liquids 防水等级
2	Protection against contact with live or moving parts inside the enclosure by fingers 手指(直径在 12 mm 以内)不会误碰到设备内部带电部分或转动部分 Protection against ingress of solid ≥12.5 mm foreign bodies 直径≥12.5 mm 的固态物体不能侵入设备内部	2	Protection against drops of liquid: Drops of falling liquid shall have no harmful effect when the enclosure is tilted at any angle up to 15° from the vertical 水滴防护:当设备的各垂直面倾斜 15°以内时,垂直落下的水滴应不对设备造成损害
3	Protection against contact with live or moving parts inside the enclosure by tools, wires or such objects of thickness greater than 2.5 mm 防止工具、电线或厚度大于 2.5 mm 的类似物体接触到设备内部带电部分 Protection against ingress of solid ≥2.5 mm foreign bodies 直径及厚度≥2.5 mm 及以上的固态物不可侵入设备内部	3	Protection against rain: Water falling in rain at an angle up to 60° with respect to the vertical shall have no harmful effect 防淋水:设备各垂直面在 60°范围内淋水不对设备造成损害
4	Protection against contact with live or moving parts inside the enclosure by tools, wires or such objects of thickness greater than 1 mm 防止工具、电线或厚度大于 1 mm 的类似物体接触到设备内部带电部分 Protection against ingress of solid ≥ 1 mm foreign bodies 直径及厚度≥1 mm 的固态物不可侵入设备内部	4	Protection against splashing: Liquid splashed from any direction shall have no harmful effect 防溅水:从设备任意方向溅水都不会对设备产生损害

Table 4. 1(Continued 2)

表 4. 1(续 2)

<table>
<tr><th>1st digi
第一位数字</th><th>Degree of protection of persons against contact with live or moving parts inside the enclosure and protection of equipment against ingress of solid bodies
对人体接近危险部分以及对外部固态物体的防护等级</th><th>2nd digi
第二位数字</th><th>Degree of protection against ingress of liquids
防水等级</th></tr>
<tr><td>5</td><td>Complete protection against contact with live or moving parts inside the enclosure
完全防止物体接触到设备内部带电部分
Protection against harmful deposits of dust ≥ 1 mm
防止直径≥1 mm 的有害粉尘侵入设备外壳
The ingress of dust is not totally prevented, but dust cannot enter in an amount sufficient to interfere with satisfactory operation of the equipment enclosed
不能完全防止尘埃进入设备内部,但是进入的尘埃不会影响设备的正常安全运行</td><td>5</td><td>Protection again water-jets: Water projected by a nozzle from any direction under stated conditions shall have no harmful effect
防喷流:从设备任意方向喷水都不会对设备产生损害</td></tr>
<tr><td>6</td><td>Complete protection against contact with live or moving parts inside the enclosure. Protection against ingress of dust≥1 mm
完全防止接触外壳内的带电或转动部件。防止直径≥1 mm 的灰尘进入</td><td>6</td><td>Protection against conditions on ships' decks (deck watertight equipment): Water from heavy seas shall not enter the enclosure under prescribed conditions
防强喷流:从设备任意方向进行强喷水都不会对设备产生损害</td></tr>
<tr><td colspan="2" rowspan="2">Note that the higher the numeral of the 1st and 2nd characteristic, the greater degree of protection the enclosure offers
注意两位数字越大,外壳防护等级越高
e. g. Jet-proof IP55 meets all the less onerous degrees such as IP22, IP23, IP34 and IP54
例如:防喷流等级 IP55 满足所有低等级防护,如 IP22、IP23、IP34 和 IP54</td><td>7</td><td>Protection against immersion in water: It must not be possible for water to enter the enclosure under stated conditions of pressure and time
防短时间浸水:在规定的压力和时间条件下,水不会浸入设备内部</td></tr>
<tr><td>8</td><td>Protection against indefinite immersion in water under specified pressure: It must not be possible for water to enter the enclosure
防特定压力下的持续潜水:既设备可长时间浸入水中而不会有水侵入设备内部</td></tr>
</table>

Deck watertight motors (IP56) have sealed bearings and a watertight terminal box. They can be completely immersed in shallow water for short periods. Sealing washers are fitted under all screws and a coat of special corrosion resisting paint is generally applied to all external and internal surfaces.

甲板水密电动机(IP56)具有密封轴承和水密接线盒,它可以在短时间内完全浸入浅水中。密封垫圈安装在所有螺钉下方,所有外表面和内表面通常涂上一层特殊的耐腐蚀涂料。

4.2.2　Motor Ratings 电动机额定参数

The motor converts electrical energy taken from the electric power supply into rotational mechanical energy at the rotor shaft. Power losses occur during the energy conversion which results in the production of heat in the motor. These losses increase when the load on the motor increases because the motor takes more current from the supply.

电动机将从电源获取的电能转换为转轴的旋转机械能。能量转换过程中会出现功率损耗,导致电动机发热。当电动机上的负载增加时,这些损耗会增加,因为电动机会从电源获取更大的电流。

The life of the insulating materials used on motor windings depends on the temperature at which it is operated, insulating materials are selected for marine practice based on an ambient temperature of 45 ℃. An adequate life-span for the insulation is based on the assumption that the maximum temperature limit is not exceeded(Table 4.2).

电动机绕组使用的绝缘材料的寿命取决于其运行温度,海上实践中绝缘材料的选择基于45 ℃的环境温度。绝缘材料设计寿命基于假设不超过最大温度限制(表4.2)。

Table 4.2　Motor insulation materials

表4.2　电动机绝缘材料

Insulation class 绝缘等级	Maximum temp. 最高温度/℃	Typical materials 典型材料
A	105	Cotton, natural silk, synthetic silk, presspan 棉、天然丝、合成丝、层压材料
E	120	Wire enamels with a base of polyvinyl acetyl, epoxy or polyamide resins 聚乙烯乙酰基、环氧树脂或聚酰胺树脂基漆包线
B	130	Mica products, wire enamels with a base of polyterephthalate, laminated glass-fibre materials 云母制品、以聚对苯二甲酸酯为基材的漆包线、夹层玻璃纤维材料

Table 4.2(Continued)
表4.2(续)

Insulation class 绝缘等级	Maximum temp. 最高温度/℃	Typical materials 典型材料
F	155	Mica products, glass fibre, wire enamels with a base of imide-polyester 云母制品、玻璃纤维、以聚酯亚胺为基材的漆包线
H	180	Mica products, glass fibre, wire enamels with a base of pure polyimide 云母制品、玻璃纤维、以纯聚酰亚胺为基材的漆包线

1. Rated Full Load Current (FLC) 额定满载电流

Maximum value of current-hat the motor can continuously supply power without exceeding the temperature limit for the insulating materials used.

电动机在不超过所用绝缘材料的温度限制的情况下,可连续供电的最大电流值即额定满载电流。

2. Rated Voltage 额定电压

The motor has been designed to operate successfully when connected to this value of supply voltage. If the rated voltage is not applied, overheating, stalling and burn-out can result.

电动机设计为在连接到额定电压时正常运行。如果未施加额定电压,可能导致电动机过热、失速和烧坏。

3. Rated Frequency 额定频率

The motor speed is directly affected by the supply frequency, so are the motor losses. If the motor is operated at other than rated frequency overheating can occur.

电动机转速直接受供电频率的影响,电动机损耗也是如此。如果电动机在额定频率以外的频率下运行,可能会发生过热。

4. Power Rating 额定功率

This is the shaft power output of the motor when it is connected to rated voltage and frequency when drawing its rated current from the supply.

电动机连接到额定电压和频率并从电源汲取额定电流时,轴的输出功率即额定功率。

5. Rated Speed 额定转速

This is the full load speed of the motor when connected to rated voltage and frequency.

额定转速是连接到额定电压和频率时电动机的满载转速。

6. IP Number 入侵防护等级

Indicates the degree of protection given by the motor enclosure.

入侵防护等级指示电动机外壳提供的保护程度。

The motor rating details are shown on the motor nameplate as in the example in Fig. 4. 7.
如图 4. 7 所示,电动机铭牌上显示了电动机额定参数详情。

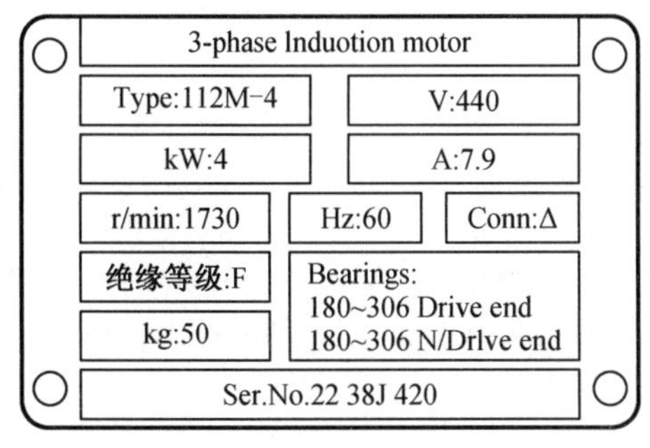

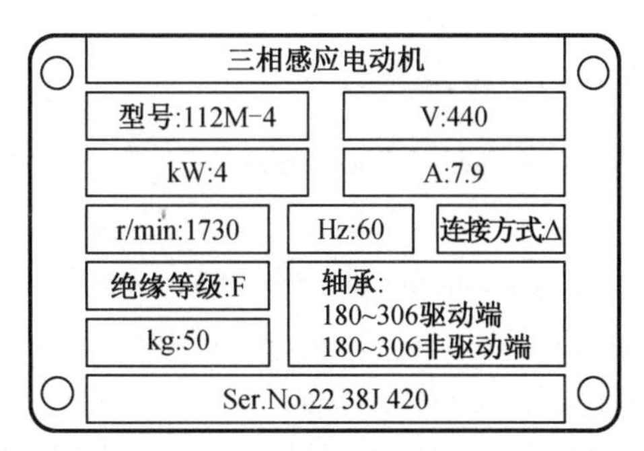

Fig. 4. 7 Motor name plate
图 4. 7 电动机铭牌

Standard three-phase AC induction motors are manufactured in about 60 frame sizes with power ratings from 0. 37-500 kW. A sample selection of output power ratings and their average FLC for 4-pole 440 V motors are listed below.

标准三相交流感应电动机大约有 60 种机架尺寸,额定功率为 0. 37~500 kW。表 4. 3 列出了 4 极 440 V 电动机的输出功率额定值及其平均满载电流的样本选择。

Table 4. 3 Output power ratings of 4-pole 440 V motors and their average FLC
表 4. 3 4 极 440 V 电动机输出功率额定值及其平均满载电流

P/kW	0. 55	1. 5	4. 0	11	22	37	55	75	100	200	500
I/A	1. 4	3. 1	7. 9	20. 1	39	64	90	125	162	321	780

4. 3 Induction Motor Operation 感应电动机的原理

When the three-phase AC power supply is connected to the stator phase windings, the resulting phase currents produce a multi-pole magnetic flux (Φ). This flux is physically rotated around the stator core by the switched sequence of the R-S-T currents at a speed called synchronous speed (n_s). The value of synchronous speed depends on how many magnetic pole-pairs (p) fixed by the stator winding arrangement and by the frequency (f) of the voltage supply connected to the stator winding.

当三相交流电源连接到定子相绕组时,相电流将产生多极磁通量 Φ。该磁通量通过相 R-S-T 的电流切换序列以同步转速(n_s)绕定子铁芯旋转。同步转速的大小取决于定子绕组的固定的磁极对数(p)以及连接到定子绕组的电源的频率(f)。

$$n_s = 60f/p(\text{r/min}) \text{ or(或) } N_s = f/p(\text{r/s})$$

Question 思考题

What is the synchronous speed of a 6-pole motor supplied at 60 Hz?
60 Hz 时,6 极电动机的同步转速是多少?

Answer 答案

20 r/s or(或) 1 200 r/min.

The stator rotating magnetic flux cuts through the rotor conductors to induce an alternating emf into them. Since the rotor conductors are connected together at the ends, the induced e. m. f. s set up rotor currents.

定子的旋转磁通量切割转子导体,在其中感应出交流电动势。由于转子导体的两端连接在一起,感应电动势会产生转子电流。

The rotor currents also produce a magnetic flux which interacts with the stator rotating flux which produces a torque (T) on the rotor conductor bars as shown in Fig. 4. 8.

转子电流还产生磁通量,该磁通量与定子旋转磁通量相互作用,从而在转子导条上产生转矩(T),如图 4. 8 所示。

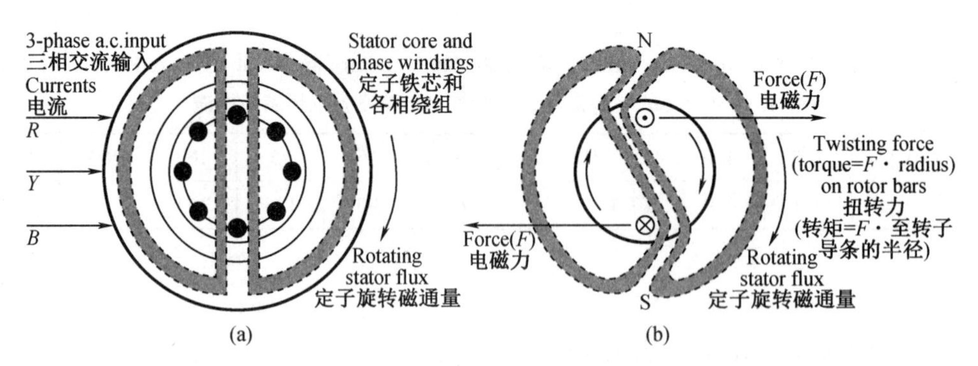

Fig. 4. 8 Induction motor action

图 4. 8 电动机的工作原理

Rotor torque size is determined as: $T \propto \Phi \cdot I_R \cdot \cos\varphi$ where Φ is the stator flux, I_R is the rotor current and φ is the angle between Φ and I_R. The rotor reactance varies with the rate of cutting flux which depends on the rotor speed. Hence $\cos\varphi$ (power factor) will vary during motor start-up as it accelerates up to its rated speed. If $\cos\varphi$ is ignored (for simplicity) then the shaft torque is approximately given by: $T \propto U^2$(as $\Phi \propto U$ and $I_R \propto \Phi$).

转子的转矩取决于 $T \propto \Phi \cdot I_R \cdot \cos\varphi$,其中 Φ 是定子磁通量,I_R 是转子电流,φ 是 Φ 和 I_R 之间的夹角。转子电抗随磁通量切割速率的变化而变化,磁通量切割速率取决于转子的转速。因此,当电动机加速至其额定转速时,$\cos\varphi$(功率因数)将在电动机启动期间发生变化。如果忽略 $\cos\varphi$(简单起见),则轴的转矩近似为 $T\propto U^2$(也写作 $\Phi\propto U$ 和 $I_R\propto\Phi$).

The direction of the rotor torque causes the rotor to rotate in the same direction as the rotating magnetic field.

转子转矩的方向使转子沿与旋转磁场相同的方向旋转。

Question 思考题

How is the rotor direction reversed?

如何使转子反向?

Answer 答案

Simply by swapping over any two supply line connections at the stator terminal box. This reverses the direction of the rotating magnetic field.

只需在定子接线盒处交换任意两个电源线的连接即可。这使旋转磁场的方向反向。

An induction motor cannot run at synchronous speed. This is because the rotor conductors would then be stationary with respect to the rotating magnetic field. No e. m. f. would be induced in the rotor and there would be no rotor current and no torque developed. Even when the motor is on no-load the rotor speed has to be slightly less than the synchronous speed, so that current can be induced into the rotor conductors to produce the torque to overcome the mechanical rotational losses of friction and windage.

感应电动机不能以同步转速正常运行。这是因为转子导体相对于旋转磁场静止。转子中不会产生感应电动势,也不会产生转子电流和转矩。即使在电动机空载时,转子转速也必须略低于同步转速,以便能够在转子导体中产生感应电流,从而产生转矩,以克服摩擦和风阻等机械损耗。

Slip speed is the difference between the synchronous speed (n_s) of the rotating magnetic flux and actual rotor speed (n_r).

转速差是旋转磁通量的同步速度(n_s)与实际转子速度(n_r)之间的差。

Slip is usually expressed as a percentage of the synchronous speed:

转差率通常表示为同步速度的百分比:

$$s=\left(\frac{n_s-n_r}{n_s}\right)\times 100\%$$

Question 思考题

If a 6-pole motor is supplied at 60 Hz and runs with a slip of 5%, what is the actual rotor speed?

如果 6 极电动机以 60 Hz 供电，并且以 5%的转差率运行，则实际转子转速是多少？

Answer 答案

The synchronous speed is 1,200 r/min, and the rotor slips by 5% of 1,200, i. e. by 60 r/min so the rotor runs at 1,140 r/min.

同步转速为 1 200 r/min，转差率为 5%，即 1 200×5% = 60 r/min，因此转子以 1 140 r/min 运行。

If the load torque on the motor shaft is increased, the rotor will tend to slow down (increasing the slip) which allows the rotor conductors to cut the flux at an increased rate. This causes more current to flow in the rotor which is matched by more stator supply current to meet the increased shaft torque demand. The motor will now run at this new, slightly reduced, speed. The fall of motor speed between no-load and full-load is very small (between 1% and 5%), so induction motors are considered to be almost constant speed machines.

如果电动机轴上的负载转矩增加，转子将减速（增加转差率），这使转子导体切割磁通的速率增加。导致感应出更多的电流流入转子，使定子供电增加与之相匹配，以满足增加的转矩需求。电动机现在将以这种新的略微降低的转速运行。空载和满载之间的电动机转速降非常小（1%～5%），因此感应电动机被视为近乎恒定转速的电动机。

The characteristic in Fig. 4. 9 shows the variation of torque with slip for a standard cage type induction motor. Also shown is a typical load characteristic which indicates the torque necessary to drive the load at different speeds.

图 4. 9 中的特性曲线展示了标准笼型感应电动机的转矩随转差率的变化，还表示出典型的负载特性，即不同转速下对应的负载转矩。

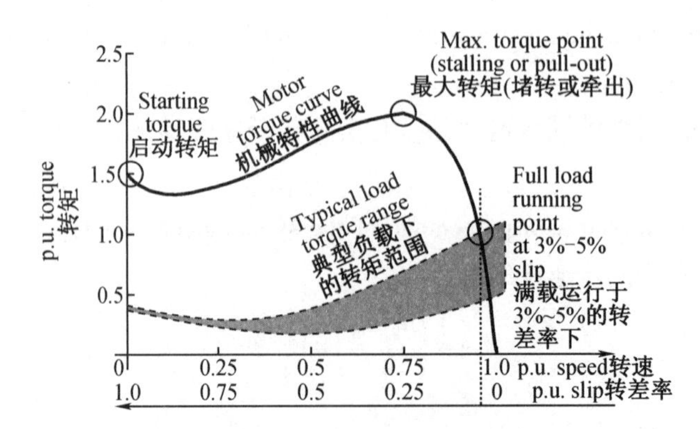

Fig. 4. 9 Motor torque-speed curve

图 4. 9 电动机转矩–转速曲线

Example 例如：

A 4 pole 60 Hz motor has a stator flux speed of: $n_s = f/p = 60/2 = 30$ r/s or 1,800 r/min.

一个 4 极 60 Hz 的电动机，其同步转速为 $n_s = f/p = 60/2 = 30$ r/s 或者 1 800 r/min。

On full load with a typical slip of 4%, the actual rotor speed will be 96% of n_s which is 1,728 r/min.

满载时的转差率通常为 4%，转子的实际转速为同步转速的 96%，即 1 728 r/min。

On light load the slip is typically 1% so the rotor speed rises to 1,782 r/min.

轻载时转差率通常为 1%，所以转子的实际转速升高到 1 782 r/min。

Hence, over the load range the shaft speed is almost constant.

因此，在负载范围内，轴转速几乎恒定。

At start-up, the motor develops more torque than is necessary to turn the load so the motor and load accelerate. The speed increases until, at the intersection of the two characteristics, the torque developed by the motor is the same as the torque required by the load at that speed. The motor and load will then run at this steady speed as the torque supplied exactly matches the demand.

启动时，电动机产生的扭矩超过转动负载所需的转矩，因此电动机和负载一起加速。随着转速增加，直到在两个特性曲线的交叉点处，电动机产生的转矩与该转速下负载所需的转矩相等。然后，电动机和负载将以该转速稳定运行，因为所提供的转矩与负载需求完全匹配。

4.4 Control Equipment 控制设备

When an induction motor is connected directly to its three-phase AC supply, a very large stator current of 5–8×full load current (FLC) is taken. This is due to the maximum rate of flux cutting ($s = 100\%$) in the rotor, creating large induced rotor currents.

当感应电动机直接连接到三相交流电源时，会产生非常大的定子电流，为满载电流(FLC)的 5~8 倍。这是由于转子以最大速率($s = 100\%$)切割磁通量，在转子中产生了较大的感应电流。

The corresponding supply power factor at start-up is very low, typically about 0.2 lagging; which rises to about 0.5 lagging on no-load then to about 0.85 lagging on full-load.

启动时相应的电源功率因数非常低，通常约为 0.2 滞后；它在空载时上升到大约 0.5 滞后，然后在满载时上升到约 0.85 滞后。

This starting surge current reduces as the motor accelerates up to its running speed.
当电动机加速到其运行速度时,启动浪涌电流减小。

Operating on light loads at low power factor is inefficient as the supply current is relatively high causing significant I^2R resistive (copper) losses. The only way to improve the power factor of the motor on light loads is to reduce the supply voltage. This can be achieved with an electronic voltage controller called a soft-starter and/or energy manager which can match the supply voltage to the start-up and load conditions. Such a controller aims to maintain the operating power factor as high as possible to minimise supply current and power losses. Note, this type of voltage controller does not control shaftspeed (which is controlled by frequency).
在轻载低功率因数下运行是低效的,因为电源电流相对较高,导致的 I^2R 电阻(铜)损耗显著。提高轻载电动机功率因数的唯一方法是降低电源电压。这可以通过软启动器电子式电压控制器和/或功率管理器来实现,它可以将电源电压与启动及负载条件相匹配。这种控制器旨在尽可能地保持较高运行功率因数,以使电源电流和功率损耗最小化。注意,这种类型的电压控制器不控制转速(转速由频率控制)。

Most induction motors are Direct-on-Line (DOL) switch-started because such starters are inexpensive and simple to operate and maintain. The high starting current surge will not cause serious heating damage to the motor unless the motor is repeatedly started and stopped in a short time period.
大多数感应电动机是直接(DOL)启动的,因为这种启动器价格低廉,操作和维护简单。其高启动电流冲击不会对电动机造成严重的过热损坏,除非电动机在短时间内反复启动和停止。

When very large motors are started DOL they cause a significant disturbance of voltage (voltage dip) on the supply lines due to the large starting current surge. This voltage disturbance may result in the malfunction of other electrical equipment connected tothe supply e. g. lighting dip and flickering effects.
当非常大的电动机直接启动时,大的启动电流会在电源线上引起电压的明显波动(电压降)。该电压波动可能导致连接到电源的其他电气设备发生故障,例如照明变暗和闪烁。

To limit the starting current some large induction motors are started at reduced voltage and then have the full supply voltage reconnected when they have accelerated close to their rated speeds. Reduced voltage starting is used for large motors driving loads like cargo pumps and bow thrusters. Two methods of reduced voltage starting are called star-delta starting and autotransformer starting, but an electronic "soft" starting option is also used.
为了限制启动电流,一些大型感应电动机在降压下启动,然后在加速到接近额定转速时重新接入全压运行。降压启动用于驱动货泵和船首侧推器等负载的大型电动机。两种降压启动方式分别为星形-三角形启动和自耦变压器启动,但也使用电子式“软”启动。

Contactors, as shown in Fig. 4. 10, perform the switching action in starters to connect and disconnect the power supply to the motor.

如图 4.10 所示,接触器在启动器中执行通断动作,以接通和断开电动机电源。

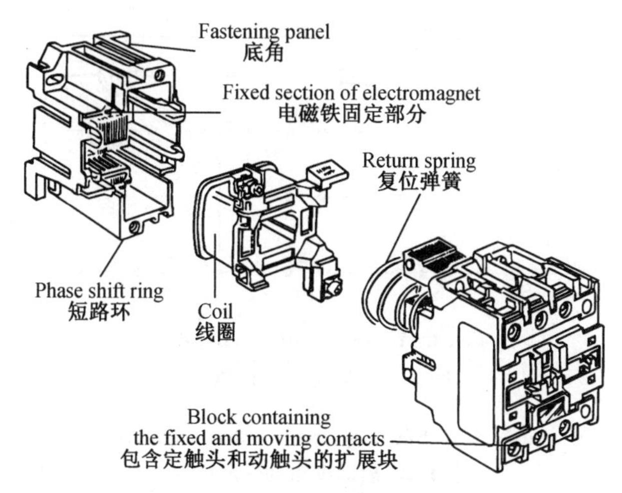

Fig. 4. 10 Contactor construction

图 4. 10 接触器的结构

The contactor is an electro-magnetically operated three-pole switch initiated from local and/or remote stop/start push buttons. If the current goes above the rated current for the motor, its contactor will be tripped out automatically by an overcurrent relay (OCR) to disconnect the motor from the supply.

接触器是由本地和/或远程停止/启动按钮启动的电磁操作三极开关。如果电流超过电动机的额定电流,其接触器将通过过电流继电器(OCR)自动跳闸,以断开电动机与电源的连接。

4.5 Direct-on-Line Starting 直接启动

In the example circuit shown in Fig. 4. 11, the induction motor is directly switched onto the three-phase AC power supply lines. This is a very simple starting arrangement which is used for the majority of induction motor drives.

在图 4.11 所示的示例电路中,感应电动机直接接入三相交流电源。这是一种非常简单的启动装置,用于大多数感应电动机驱动器。

The switching sequence for this starter circuit is asshown the Table 4. 4.

该启动器电路的动作顺序如表 4.4 所示。

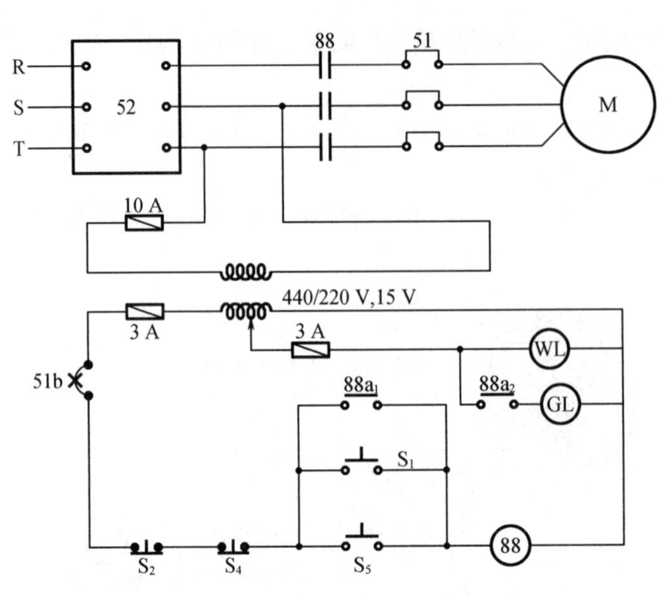

Fig. 4. 11 DOL starter circuit

图 4. 11 直接启动电路

Table 4. 4 Starting circuit action sequence

表 4. 4 启动电路动作顺序

Power circuit operation 动力电路操作	Control circuit operation 控制电路操作
Manual closing of breaker 52 手动闭合空开 52 Closing of line contactor 88, and 88 holds-in, motor starts 接触器 88 闭合,并保持闭合,电动机启动 88 contactor drops out, motor stops 接触器 88 断开,电动机停止	Control circuit voltage available (220 V from control transformer) 控制电路得电(220 V 来自控制变压器) Press start button S_1 or S_5(local or remote) 按下启动按钮 S_1 或 S_5(当地或远程) Auxiliary contact $88a_1$ and $88a_2$ close, GL on 辅助触头 $88a_1$ 和 $88a_2$ 闭合,灯 GL 亮 Press stop button S_2 or S_4(local or remote) on 按下停止按钮 S_2 或 S_4(当地或远程) On overload the OCR 51 trips out the circuit, OCR must be manually reset(after thermal time delay) 过载时,过电流继电器 51 会断开电路,过电流继电器必须手动复位(热延时后)

Further circuit additions can be made for remote control (e. g. by liquid level switch) and motor reversing (with an extra contactor).

可为远程控制(例如通过液位开关)和电动机换向(使用额外接触器)添加额外电路。

DOL switching demands a short duration (a few seconds) but large starting current, typically 5×FLC fixed by the motor impedance. This is generally acceptable to the supply generator as long as the corresponding voltage dip is not greater than 10%–15% within the run-up period. For large motor drives this starting surge will cause an un acceptable voltage dip at the supply bus-bars with likely malfunctions of other consumers e. g. lighting flicker and possible drop-out of supply contactors. The voltage dip is further compounded as all the other connected motors compensate by demanding an increased current to maintain their original power output. If prolonged, this sudden current loading may cause supply line and generator protection to trip. Hence large motors (e. g. bow and stern thrusters) require a more complicated starting nethod to limit the size of starting current and so protect the generator supply and other consumers. This means applying a reduced voltage at start-up.

直接启动需要持续时间短(几秒)且大的启动电流,通常为5倍满载电流,由电动机阻抗确定。只要相应的电压降在运行期内不大于10%~15%,供电发电机通常可以承受。对于大型电动机驱动装置,这种启动浪涌将在电源母线上造成不可接受的电压降,并可能导致其他用电设备出现故障,如照明闪烁和电源接触器断开。当所有其他连接的电动机通过要求增加电流以补偿其原始功率输出时,电压下降进一步加剧。如果持续下去,这种突然的电流负荷可能导致供电线路和发电机保护跳闸。因此,大型电动机(如船首和船尾侧推器)需要更复杂的启动方法,以限制启动电流的大小,从而保护发电机电源和其他用电设备。这意味着在启动时降低启动电压。

4.6 Reduced Voltage Starting 降压启动

During the run-up period the size of motor starting current can be limited by applying a reduced supply voltage or inserting some additional circuit impedance. The most common arrangement is to apply reduced voltage which is sub-divided into the methods of star-delta starting, autotransformer starting and "soft" starting.

在启动期间,可以通过施加降低的电源电压或接入一些额外的电路阻抗来限制电动机启动电流的大小。最常见的安排是降压启动,分为星形-三角形启动、自耦变压器启动和"软"启动。

4.6.1 Star-Delta Starting 星形-三角形启动

If a motor is DOL started with the stator winding star connected, it will only take one-third of the starting current that it would take if the windings were delta connected. The starting current of a motor which is designed to run delta connected can be reduced in this way.

如果电动机在定子绕组星形连接的情况下直接启动,则只需要绕组三角形连接时启动电流的三分之一。采用这种启动方式可以减小设计成三角形启动的电动机的启动电流。

Star-delta starters for motors, the phase windings are automatically switched using contactors controlled by a timing relay as shown in Fig. 4. 12. A choice of time delay relays are available whose action is governed by thermal, pneumatic, mechanical or electronic control devices.

电动机的星形-三角形启动器,各相绕组使用由时间继电器控制的接触器自动切换,如图 4. 12 所示。可选择时间继电器,其动作由热、气动、机械或电子控制装置控制。

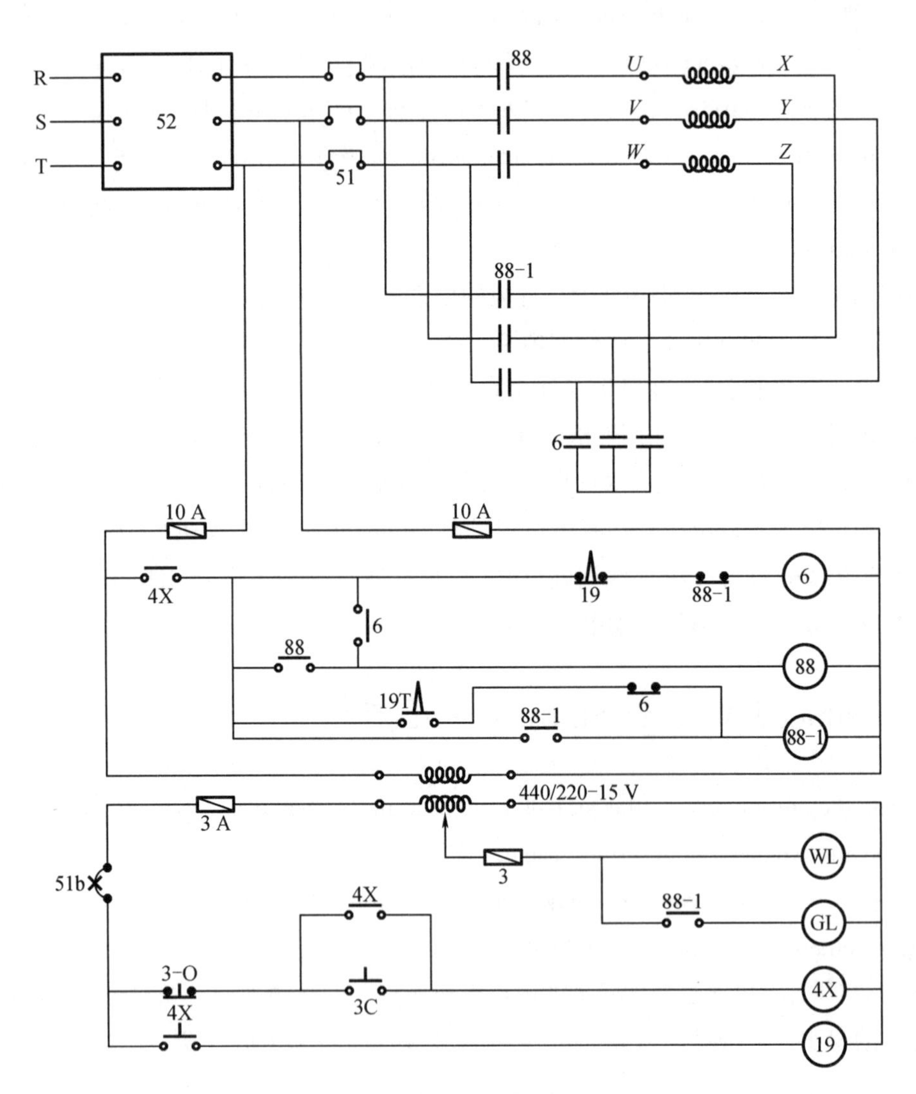

Fig. 4. 12 Star-delta starter circuit

图 4. 12 星形-三角形启动电路

Switching sequence for this starter circuit is as shown the Table 4. 5.

该启动器电路的动作顺序如表 4. 5 所示。

Table 4.5 Star-delta starting circuit action sequence

表 4.5 星形-三角形启动电路动作顺序

Power circuit operation 动力电路操作	Control circuit operation 控制电路操作
Manual closing of breaker 52 手动闭合断路器 52 Closing of contactor 6: Star connection 接触器 6 闭合:星形连接 Closing of 88: Motor supply 88 闭合:电动机通电 Opening of 6: Star connection opens 6 失电断开:星形连接断开 Closing of 88-1: Delta connection 88-1 闭合:三角形连接 88 & 88-1 contactors drops out, motor stops 88 和 88-1 失电断开,电动机停止	Control circuit voltage available(220 V from control transformer) 控制电路得电(来自控制变压器 220 V) Press start button 3C to close 4X 按下启动按钮 3C 使 4X 得电闭合 4X closes 19T,6 4X 使 19T 和 6 得电闭合 6 closes 88 6 使 88 得电闭合 "Hold-in" of 4X ,6 by 4X auxiliary 4X 和 6 由 4X 的辅助开关维持闭合 Opening of 6 by 19T auxiliary 19T 的辅助开关使 6 断开 Closing of 88-1 by 19T auxiliary 19T 的辅助开关使 88-1 闭合 Stop by 3-O button or OCR trip 51b 按下停止按钮 3-O 或 51b 动作跳闸

Note:19T has 2 pairs of auxiliary contacts with a time delay action (typically 40 ms) between the opening of the N/C and the closing of the N/O contacts.

注意:19T 有延时(40 ms)动作的 2 对触头,常闭的断开,常开的闭合。

Question 思考题

Why is the time delay necessary between the19T auxiliary contacts?

为什么 19T 的辅助开关需要延时?

Answer 答案

To provide an electrical interlock between contactors 6 and 88-1. This is to prevent a full short-circuit fault across the supply lines during the changeover from star to delta.

为接触器 6 和 88-1 提供锁闭,以防止星形-三角形转换时,供电线路完全短路。

At the instant of starting when the supply has just been switched on and the motor has not yet started to rotate, there is no mechanical output from the motor. The only factors which determine the current taken by the motor are the supply voltage (V) and the impedane of the motor phase windings(Z_{PH}).

在电源刚刚接通且电动机尚未开始旋转时的启动瞬间,电动机没有机械功率输出。决定电动机电流的唯一因素是电源电压(V)和电动机相绕组阻抗(Z_{PH})。

Compare the starting current when star connected to the starting current when delta connected as in Fig. 4. 13.

图 4. 13 中将星形连接的启动电流与三角形连接的启动电流进行比较。

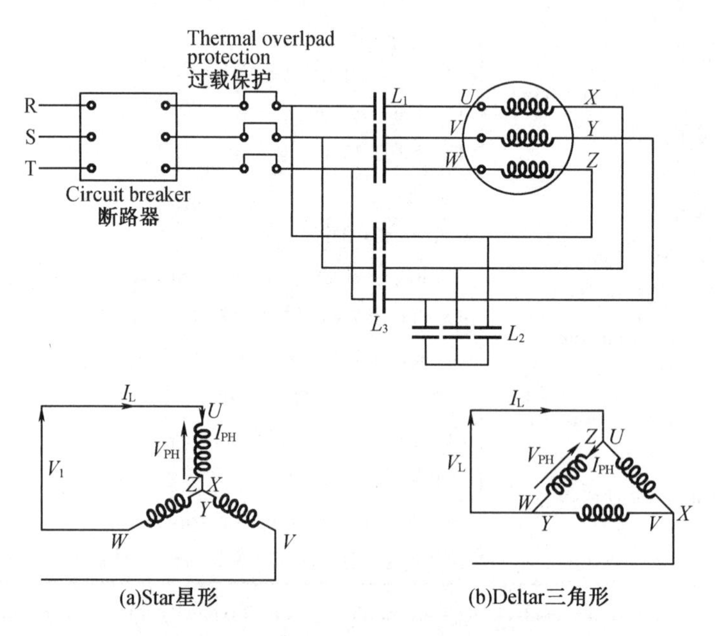

Fig. 4. 13　Star connected and delta connected

图 4. 13　星形连接和三角形连接

$$\text{Raito of: } \frac{I_L Y}{I_L \triangle}=\frac{V_L/\sqrt{3}\cdot Z}{\sqrt{3}\cdot V_L/Z}=\frac{1}{3}$$

This shows that the starting current of a delta connected motor can be reduced to one-third if the motor is star connected for starting. The shaft torque is also reduced to one-third which reduces the shaft acceleration and increases the run-up time for the drive but this is not usually a problem.

这表明,如果电动机星形连接用于启动,启动电流可以减少到三角形连接的三分之一,转矩也降低到三分之一,这降低了轴加速度并增加了驱动器的启动时间,但这通常不是问题。

When an induction motor is running on load it is converting electrical energy input to mechanical energy output. The input current is now determined by the load on the motor shaft.

当感应电动机带负载运行时,它将电能输入转换为机械能输出,此时输入电流由电动机轴带负载决定。

An induction motor will run at the same speed when it is star connected as when it is delta connected because the flux speed is the same in both cases being set by the supply frequency.

感应电动机在星形连接时将以与三角形连接时相同的转速运行,因为在两种情况下磁通量的转速相同,转速由电源频率设定。

This means that the power output from the motor is the same when the motor is star connected as when the motor is delta connected, so the power inputs and line currents must be the same when running in either connection.

这意味着,当电动机星形连接时,电动机输出的功率与三角形连接时相同,因此在任一连接中运行时,输入功率和线电流必定相同。

If the motor is designed to run in delta but is run as star connected, and on full load, then each stator phase winding will carrying an overcurrent of $\sqrt{3}$ ×rated phase current. This is because phase and line currents are equal in a star connection. This will cause overheating and eventual burnout unless tripped by the overcurrent relay. Remember that the motor copper losses are produced by the I^2R heating effect so the motor will run $(\sqrt{3})^2=3$ times hotter if left to run in the star connection when designed for delta running. This malfunction may occur the control timing sequence is not completed or the star contactor remains closed while a mechanical interlock prevents the delta contactor from closing.

如果电动机设计为三角形运行,但实际却以星形连接满载运行,则每个定子相绕组将承载$\sqrt{3}$倍额定相电流。这是因为星形连接中的相电流和线电流相等。这将导致电动机过热并最终烧毁,除非过电流继电器动作跳闸。记住,电动机铜损耗由 I^2R 发热效应产生,因此电动机如果在星形连接中运行将比设计用于三角形运行时的温度高$(\sqrt{3})^2=3$ 倍。如果时序控制未完成,或星形接触器保持闭合,而机械联锁阻止三角形接触器闭合,则可能发生此故障。

For correct overcurrent protection, the overcurrent relays must be fitted in phase connections and not in the line connections. Check the position of the overcurrent devices in the previous schematic diagram, Fig. 4. 12, for an automatic star-delta starter.

为使过电流保护正确动作,过电流继电器必须安装在相连接中,而不是线连接中。可查看图 4. 12 中的星形-三角形启动器的过电流保护装置的位置。

4. 6. 2 Autotransformer Starting 自耦变压器启动

Starting a large motor with a long run-up period will demand a very high current surge from the supply generator for a few seconds. This causes a severe voltage dip which affects all load on the system. Reduced voltage starting will limit the starting surge current. One way to reduce the initial voltage supplied to the motor is to step it down using a transformer. Then, when the motor has accelerated up to almost full speed, the reduced voltage is replaced by the full mains voltage.

The transformer used in this starter is not the usual type with separate primary and secondary windings. It is an autotransformer which uses only one winding for both input and output. This arrangement is cheaper, smaller and lighter than an equivalent double-wound transformer and it is only in operation during the short starting period. For induction motor starting, the autotransformer is a three-phase unit, and, because of expense, this method is only used with large motor drives, e. g. M/E L. O pumps.

启动时间长的大型电动机启动时需要供电发电机在几秒钟内产生非常高的电流浪涌。这会导致严重的电压降,影响系统上的所有负载。降压启动将限制启动浪涌电流。降低供给电动机初始电压的一种方法是使用变压器将其降压。然后,当电动机加速到几乎全速时,降低的电压被全压电源代替。该启动器中使用的变压器不像普通类型的变压器,具有独立的一次和二次绕组。它是一种仅使用一个绕组进行输入和输出的自耦变压器。这种布置比等效双绕组变压器更便宜、更小和更轻,并且仅在短时启动期间运行。对于感应电动机的启动,自耦变压器是一个三相装置,由于费用的原因,这种方法仅用于大型电动机驱动装置,例如主机的主滑油泵。

Fig. 4. 14 shows the supply voltage is connected across the complete transformer winding and the motor is connected to the reduced voltage tapping. A number of tappings are usually available on the transformer winding, giving voltage outputs ranging from about 50% to 80% of the mains supply voltage. e. g. a 60% tap on an autotransformer supplied at 440 V would provide a voltage output of 264 V(440×60%).

如图 4. 14 所示电源电压连接在整个变压器绕组上,电动机连接到降压抽头上。变压器绕组上通常有多个抽头,电压输出范围为电源电压的 50%~80%。例如,在 440 V 供电的自耦变压器上的 60%抽头将提供 264 V(440×60%)的输出电压。

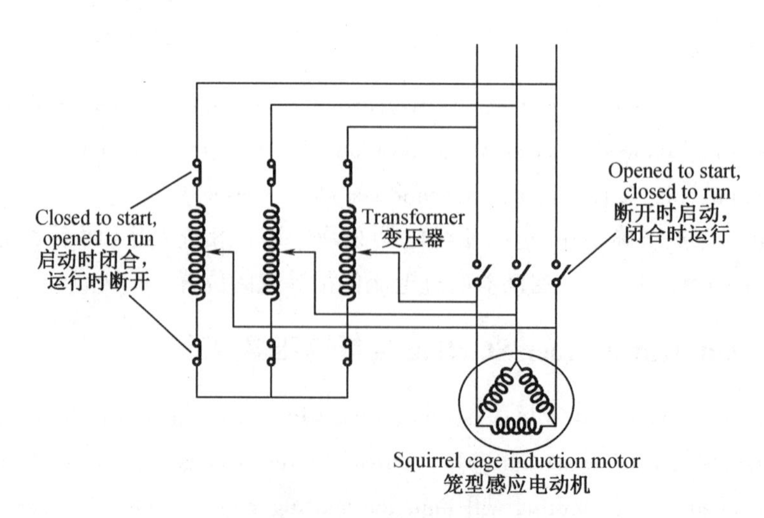

Fig. 4. 14 Autotransformer connection

图 4. 14 自耦变压器的连接

The autotransformer usually has a few tapping points to give a set of reduced voltages (e. g. 40%, 50% and 65%) which help to match the motor current demand to the supply capability.

自耦变压器通常具有抽头接点,以提供一组降低的电压(例如40%、50%和65%),这有助于使电动机的电流需求与供电能力相匹配。

As with the star-delta starter, the autotransformer may use what is called an open-transition switching sequence or a closed-transition switching sequence In the former, the reduced voltage is supplied to the motor at start then disconnected and the full supply voltage rapidly reconnected to the motor.

与星形-三角形启动器一样,自耦变压器可以使用所谓的断电换接程序或带电换接程序。在前者中,启动时降低电压提供给电动机,然后断开并且全压电源再快速接入电动机。

The problem with open-transition is that a very large surge current can flow after the transition from reduced to full voltage.

断电换接的问题是,在从降压过渡到全压后,会产生非常大的浪涌电流。

Question 思考题

What causes the large current surge in open transition starters when going from the start to the run condition?

从启动到运行状态时,是什么导致断电换接启动器中的大电流浪涌?

Answer 答案

All motors generate a back e. m. f. against the supply voltage when they are running. When the supply is removed from a running induction motor the magnetic field does not immediately collapse. The motor begins to slow down but still generates an e. m. f. When reconnected in open transition, the supply voltage and motor e. m. f. are not necessarily in phase (the condition is similar to synchronising a generator onto the bus-bars). An additional current surge is therefore likely at the changeover stage, causing further voltage dip and so affect other consumers. Closed transition starters overcome this because the motor is never actually disconnected from the supply during the starting cycle. Most autotransformer starters used the closed transition method.

所有电动机在运行时都会产生反电动势。当电源从运行的感应电动机中移除时,磁场不会立即瓦解。电动机会开始减速,但仍产生电动势。在断电换接中重新连接时,电源电压和电动机电动势不一定同相(类似于将发电机同步到母线上)。因此,在转换阶段可能会出现额外的电流浪涌,导致电压进一步下降,从而影响其他用电设备。带电换接启动器克服了这一问题,因为在启动周期,电动机电源从未实际断开过。大多数自耦变压器启动器使用带电换接方式。

A typical circuit closed transition starter circuit is shown in Fig. 4. 15.

图 4. 15 所示为典型的带电换接启动电路。

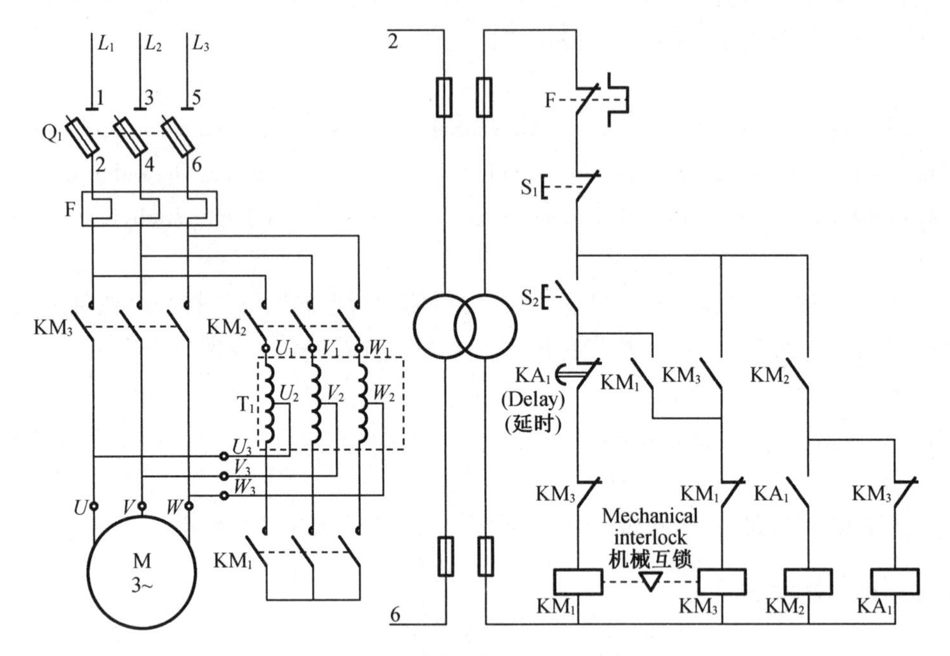

Fig. 4. 15 Autotransformer starter circuit

图 4. 15 自耦变压启动器电路

The switching sequence for this starter circuit is asshown the Table 4. 6.

该启动器电路的动作顺序如表 4. 6 所示。

4. 6. 3 Soft Starting 软启动

This method of supplying a gradually increasing AC voltage during start up generally refers to an efficient electronic switching technique.

这种在启动期间提供逐渐增大的交流电压的方法通常指的是高效的电子开关技术。

A basic method shown in Fig. 4. 16, is to use back-to-back connected thyristors in the supply lines which are "gated" to delay "turn-on" within each AC half cycle. This delayed switching applies a reduced average AC voltage to the motor.

图 4. 16 所示的基本方法是在电源线中使用背对背连接的晶闸管,这些晶闸管在每个交流半周期内"选通"以延迟"接通"电路。这种延迟切换将降低施加到电动机的平均交流电压。

Table 4.6　Autotransformer starter circuit action sequence

表 4.6　自耦变压启动器电路动作顺序

Power circuit operation 动力电路操作	Control circuit operation 控制电路操作
Manual closing of fused isolator Q_1 手动闭合熔断式隔离开关 Q_1 Closing of KM_1: Star connection of transformer 接触器 KM_1 闭合:变压器星形连接 Closing of KM_2: Motor supply from transformer KM_2 闭合:电动机通过变压器供电 Opening of KM_1: Star connection opens KM_1 断开:星形连接断开 Closing of KM_3: Direct supply to motor KM_3 闭合:直接向电动机供电 (Note the mechanical interlock of KM_1-KM_3) (注意 KM_1~KM_3 的机械连锁) KM_3 contactors drops out, motor stop 接触器 KM_3失电断开,电动机停止	Control circuit voltage available (220 V from control transformer) 控制电路得电(来自控制变压器的 220 V) Press start button S_2 to close KM_1 按下启动按钮 S_2使 KM_1 得电闭合 Inter locking of KM_3 by KM_1 KM_1 将 KM_3 锁闭 Closing of KA_1 by KM_1 KM_1 使 KA_1 闭合 Closing of KM_2 by KA_1 KA_1 使 KM_2 闭合 Hold-in of KM_2 KM_2 保持得电 Opening of KM_1 by KA_1(after time delay) 经过延时 KA_1 使 KM_1 断开 Closing of KM_3 by KM_1 KM_1 使 KM_3 闭合 Hold-in of KM_3 KM_3 保持得电 Opening of KM_2 by KA_1 KA_1 使 KM_2 断开 Stop by S_1 button or OCR trip F 通过 S_1 按钮或过流保护 F 停止

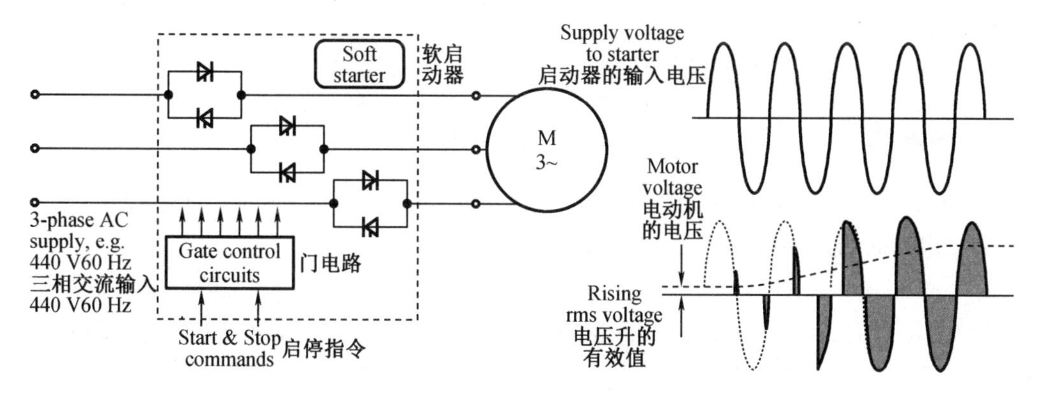

Fig. 4.16　Soft starter block diagram

图 4.16　软启动器框图

The applied motor voltage is gradually ramped up by the starter software program until the full voltage level is reached. To achieve maximum efficiency, the electronic switching circuit can be bypassed for normal running when the full voltage is reached.

通过启动机软件程序控制施加给电动机的电压逐渐升高,直到达到全电压。为了实现最高效率,达到全电压时可以旁通电子开关电路进行正常运行。

A soft starter may be further adapted to become a voltage controller over the motor operating load range. In this type of efficient "energy manager" application, the controller monitors the motor power factor which is a measure of the motor loading. On light load and full voltage, the power factor is low so the controller reduces the motor voltage which reduces current while improving power factor and efficiency. Note, this type of "softstart/energy manager" is not a speed controller. To electrically change the speed of an induction motor it is necessary to vary the applied frequency. Motor speed control methods are introduced in a later section.

软启动器可进一步作为电动机运行负载范围内的电压控制器。在这类高效"能量管理器"的应用中,控制器监控电动机功率因数,该功率因数是电动机负载的度量。在轻负载和全电压下,功率因数较低,因此控制器降低电动机电压,从而降低电流,同时提高功率因数和效率。注意,这种类型的"软启动/能量管理器"不是转速控制器。为了改变感应电动机的转速,必须改变所加的供电频率。电动机转速控制方法将在后面的章节中介绍。

Question 思考题

Estimate and compare the likely starting current surges for a motor that takes 200 A on full loadwhen started:

(a) DOL;

(b) Star-delta;

(c) Autotransformer with a 50% tapping.

估算并比较启动满载为 200 A 的电动机的可能启动电流:

(a) 直接启动;

(b) 星形-三角形启动;

(c) 自耦变压器带 50%抽头启动。

Answer 答案

(1) When starting DOL the initial surge current is about 5×FLC, i. e. 1,000 A.

直接启动时初始冲击电流约为 5×FLC=1 000 A。

(2) A star-delta starter reduces the initial starting surge to one-third of the equivalent DOL value, i. e. to about 330 A in this case.

星形-三角形启动时将启动电流降为直接启动的三分之一,约为 330 A。

(3) The autotransformer method reduces the initial starting surge to $(X)^2 \cdot I_{DOL}$ where $X =$ tapping point. In this example $X = 0.5$, so the surge current level is $0.5^2 \times 1,000 = 250$ A.

自耦变压器方式将启动电流降至 $X^2 \cdot I_{DOL}$，其中 X 为抽头结点。例题中 $X = 50\% = 0.5$，所以冲击电流大小为 $0.5^2 \times 1\ 000 = 250$ A。

The DOL starter is simple and cheap but causes a large starting surge. Star-delta starting reduces the surge but is somewhat more complex, requiring three contactors and a timer. The autotransformer method can be arranged to match the motor surge current and run-up period to meet the supply limitations by a suitable choice of voltage tapping. This starter is considerably more expensive than the other two starter types.

直接启动器简单且便宜，但会引起较大的启动冲击。星形-三角形启动减少了浪涌，但更复杂，需要三个接触器和一个时间继电器。自耦变压器方式可以使电动机浪涌电流和启动时间相匹配，通过选择适当的电压抽头来满足供电限制。这种启动器比其他两种启动器要贵得多。

4.7 Speed Control 转速控制

The standard cage-rotor AC induction motor operates as an almost constant speed drive over its load range. This feature is satisfactory for most of the ship's auxiliary services supplying power to ventilation fans and circulating pumps.

标准笼型转子交流感应电动机在其负载范围内几乎以恒速驱动运行。这一特点适用于风机和循环泵供电的大多数船舶辅助设施。

Variable speed control is necessary for cranes, winches, windlass, capstans, forced-draught fans etc. Ship's electric propulsion with electronic speed control may use DC motors or AC induction motors for low/medium power applications. Large power electric propulsion, e. g. for a passenger cruise ship, will use AC synchronous motors.

对于克令吊、绞车、起锚机、绞盘、强制通风机等，变速控制是必要的。具有电子转速控制的船舶电力推进系统，可使用低/中功率的直流电动机或交流感应电动机。大功率电力推进装置，例如客轮，将使用交流同步电动机。

Two main forms of speed control are available:

(1) Pole-changing for induction motors to give two or more fixed speeds, e. g. 2-speed forced-draught fans and 3-speed winches.

(2) Continuously variable speed control, e. g. smooth control of deck cranes, winches and electric ship propulsion using variable frequency.

转速控制有两种主要形式：

(1)改变感应电动机的极数,以提供两级或多级固定调速,例如 2 速强制通风机和 3 速绞车。

(2)无级变速,例如通过改变频率来平稳控制甲板起重机、绞车和电动船舶推进。

Fixed set speeds can be obtained from a cage-rotor induction motor by using a dual wound stator winding, each winding being designed to create adifferent number of magnetic poles.

通过使用双绕组定子,可以使笼型转子感应电动机获得有级调速,每个绕组都设计成不同数量的磁极。

Question 思考题

A dual-wound induction motor is arranged to create 6 pole and 10 pole stator magnetic fields. Estimate the rated speeds assuming that the rotor slips by 5% and the power supply is at a frequency of 60 Hz.

一台双绕组感应电动机用于产生 6 极和 10 极定子磁场。假设转差率为 5%,电源频率为 60 Hz,估算其额定转速。

Answer 答案

$n_s = 60f/p$ (n_s is the synchronous speed)

for 6 poles, $p=3$, so

$$n_s = 60f/p = 60\times60/3 = 1{,}200 \text{ r/min}$$

but the rated speed of rotor

$$n_r = n_s(1-5\%) = 0.95\times1{,}200 = 1{,}140 \text{ r/min}$$

for 10 poles, $p=5$, so

$$n_s = 60f/p = 60\times60/5 = 720 \text{ r/min}$$

but the rated speed of rotor

$$n_r = n_s(1-5\%) = 0.95\times720 = 684 \text{ r/min}$$

$$n_s = 60f/p \text{（} n_s \text{ 为同步转速）}$$

6 极时极对数为 3,故

$$n_s = 60f/p = 60\times60/3 = 1\ 200 \text{ r/min}$$

而转子的额定转速为

$$n_r = n_s(1-5\%) = 0.95\times1\ 200 = 1\ 140 \text{ r/min}$$

10 极时极对数为 5,故

$$n_s = 60f/p = 60\times60/5 = 720 \text{ r/min}$$

而转子的额定转速为

$$n_r = n_s(1-5\%) = 0.95\times720 = 684 \text{ r/min}$$

A 3-speed pole-change winch motor can be arranged that one stator winding (usually 24-pole) gives a low speed while the other is dual wound to give medium speed (8-pole) and high speed (4-pole) outputs.

3 速变极绞车的电动机可布局成由一个定子绕组(通常为 24 极)提供低速,而另一个为双绕组,提供中速(8 极)和高速(4 极)输出。

Speed control and drive direction are achieved by a set of switching and reversing contactors operated from the winch control pedestal. Remember that to reverse the rotation of an induction motor it is necessary to switch over two of the supply lines to the stator winding.

转速控制和转向由一组由绞车控制台操作的开关和换向接触器实现。记住,要使感应电动机反转,必须将接入定子绕组的两条电源线交换。

An alternative method giving two fixed speeds in a 2 : 1 ratio from a cage-rotor induction motor is to use a single stator winding which has centre-tap connections available on each phase. This method uses a starter with a set of contactors to switch the phase windings into either single-star (low speed) or double-star (high speed). The supply lines to the stator windings are shown in Fig. 4. 17.

另一种笼型转子感应电动机以 2:1的比例提供两级调速的方式,这是通过单个定子绕组实现的,每相绕组上都接有中心抽头。该方式使用带有一套接触器的启动器将各相绕组接为单星形(低速)或双星形(高速)。定子绕组的供电线路如图 4. 17 所示。

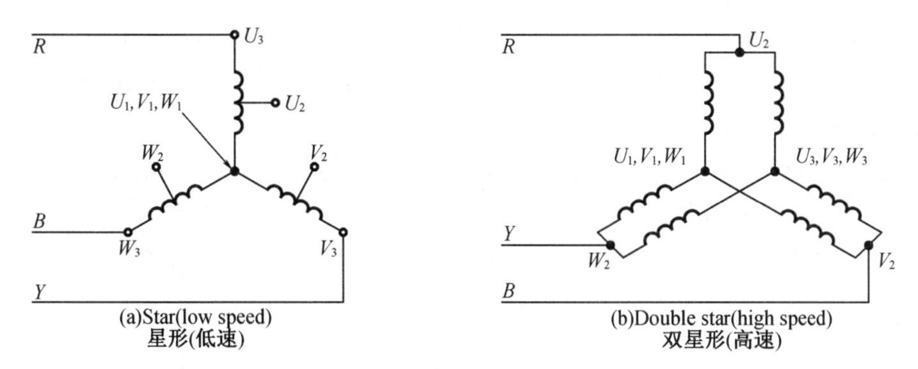

Fig. 4. 17 Star, double star connections

图 4. 17 星形、双星形连接

Note that two of the supply lines are interchanged in the double-star connection. This is to maintain the same direction of rotation as in the low speed connection.

请注意,在双星形连接中,两条电源线交换了。这是为了保持与低速连接时相同的转向。

A continuously variable speed range of motor control involves more complication and expense than that required to obtain a couple of set speeds. Various methods are available which include:

(1) Electro-hydraulic drive;

(2) Wound-rotor resistance control of induction motors;

(3) Ward Leonard DC motor drive;

(4) Variable-frequency induction or synchronous motor control.

电动机转速范围内的无级调速比两级调速的复杂度和费用更高。多种方法可用于调速,包括:

(1)电液驱动;

(2)绕线式感应电动机的转子电阻控制;

(3)沃德·伦纳德直流电动机驱动;

(4)感应电动机或同步电动机的变频调速控制。

The electro-hydraulic drive, often used for deck crane control, has a relatively simple electrical section. This is a constant single-speed induction motor supplied from a DOL or star-delta starter. The motor runs continuously to maintain oil pressure to the variable-speed hydraulic motors.

通常用于甲板克令吊控制的电液驱动装置具有相对简单的电气部分。这是一个由直接启动或星形-三角形启动器提供恒速的感应电动机。电动机持续运转,以维持变速液压马达的油压。

A crude form of speed control is provided by the wound rotor induction motor. The rotor has a three-phase winding (similar to its stator winding) which is connected to 3 sliprings mounted on the shaft as shown in Fig. 4. 18. An external three-phase resistor bank is connected to brushes on the rotor sliprings. A set of contactors or a sliding rheostat (for small motors) varies the amount of resistance added to the rotor circuit.

绕线感应电动机提供了一种简单的速度控制形式。转子有一个三相绕组(与其定子绕组类似),该绕组与安装在轴上的三个滑环相连,如图 4. 18 所示。外部三相电阻组与转子滑环上的电刷相连。一组接触器或滑动变阻器(适用于小型电动机)可改变转子电路的电阻值。

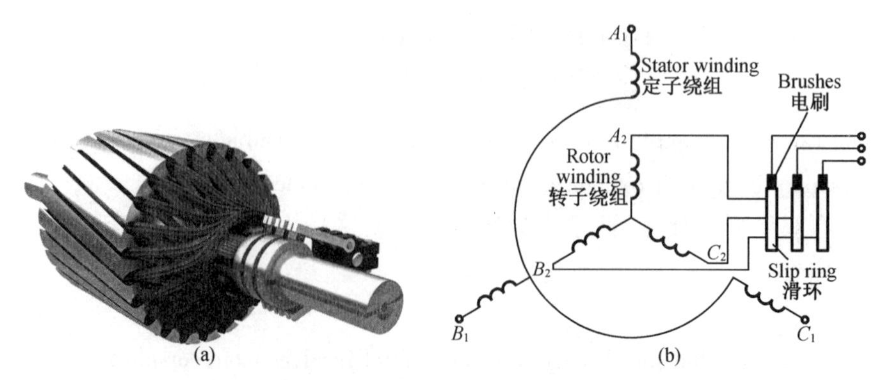

Fig. 4. 18 Wound rotor construction

图 4. 18 绕线式转子结构

Increasing the value of external resistance decreases the rotor speed. Generally, the starters of wound-rotor motors are interlocked to allow start-up only when maximum rotor resistance is in circuit, this has the benefits of reducing the starting current surge while providing a high starting torque.

增加外接电阻值会降低转子速度。通常绕线式转子电动机的启动器有连锁,仅当转子电路中接入最大电阻时才允许启动,这有利于减少启动电流冲击,同时提供高启动转矩。

The wound-rotor arrangement is more expensive than an equivalent cage-rotor machine. It requires more maintenance on account of the slip rings and the external resistor bank which may require special cooling facilities.

采用绕线式转子的电动机比等效笼型转子电动机更昂贵。由于其滑环和外接电阻器组可能需要专用的冷却设施,因此需要更多的维护。

Where continuously variable speed has to be combined with high torque, smooth acceleration, including inching control and regenerative braking, it is necessary to consider the merits of a DC motor drive. Speed and torque control of a DC motor is basically simple requiring the variation of armature voltage and field current.

当无级调速必须与高转矩、平稳加速,以及微动控制和再生制动相结合时,就需要考虑直流电动机驱动的优点了。直流电动机的转速和转矩控制比较容易,只需要改变电枢电压和励磁电流。

The problem is: where does the necessary DC power supply come from on a ship with an AC electrical system?

问题是:在配备交流电力系统的船舶上,需要的直流电源从哪里获得?

A traditional method for lifts, cranes and winches is found in the ward-leonard drive as shown in Fig. 4. 19. A constant speed induction motor drives a DC generator which in turn supplies one or more DC motors. The generator output voltage is controlled by adjusting its small excitation current via the speed regulator. The DC motor speed is directly controlled by the generator voltage.

如图 4. 19 所示,直流发电机电动机驱动装置是电梯、起重机和绞车采用的传统设备。一台恒速感应电动机驱动直流发电机,直流发电机继而为一台或多台直流电动机供电。发电机的输出电压由转速调节器调节小励磁电流来控制。直流电动机转速直接由发电机电压控制。

Obviously the motor-generator (M-G) set requires space and maintenance. An alternative is to replace the rotary M-G set with a static electronic thyristor controller which is supplied with constant AC voltage but delivers a variable DC output voltage to the drive motor as shown in Fig. 4. 20.

显然,电动发电机(M-G)组需要占用空间和维护。另一种选择是用静态电子晶闸管控制器代替电动发电机装置,该控制器由恒定的交流电压供电,但向电动机输出可变的直流电压,如图4.20所示。

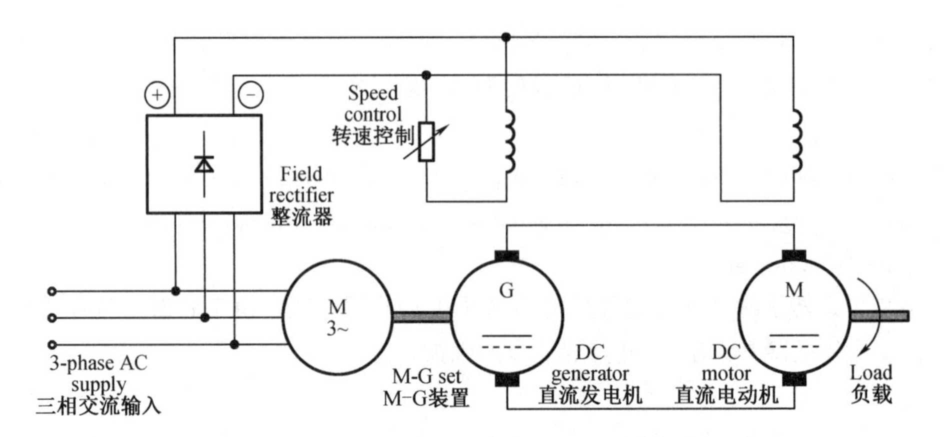

Fig. 4.19 Ward-leonard speed control method

图4.19 直流发电机电动机变速控制方式

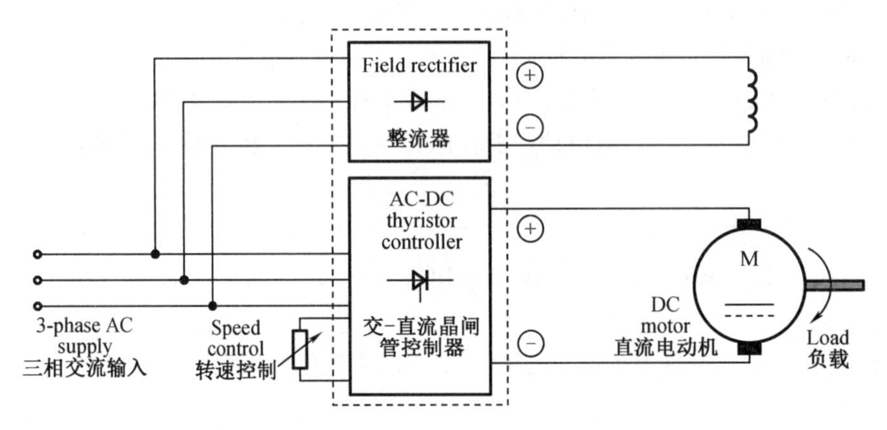

Fig. 4.20 Electronic control for a DC motor

图4.20 直流电动机的电子控制

Although the ward-leonard scheme provides an excellent power drive, practical commutators are limited to about 750 V DC maximum which also limits the upper power range. The commutators on the DC machines also demand an increased maintenance requirement.

尽管直流发电机方案的功率驱动极好,但实际上换向器的最大直流电压限制在750 V左右,这也限制了功率范围的上限。直流电动机换向器的维护要求也更多。

To eliminate these problems means returning to the simplicity of the cage-rotor induction motor. However, the only way to achieve a continuously variable speed output by electrical control is to vary the supply frequency to the motor. A static electronic transistor or thyristor (high power) controller can be used to generate such a variable frequency output to directly control the speed of the motor as in the example diagram in Fig. 4.21.

消除这些问题意味着回到笼型转子感应电动机的简单性上。然而,通过电气控制实现无级变速输出的唯一方法是改变电动机的供电频率。静态电子晶体管或晶闸管(大功率)控制器可用于产生如图 4.21 所示的变频输出,以直接控制电动机的转速。

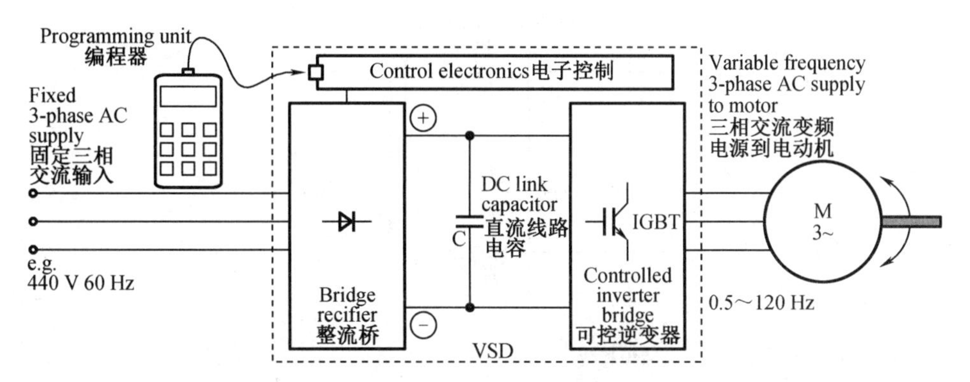

Fig. 4.21　Electronicvariable-speed drive controller

图 4.21　电子变速驱动控器

In an electronic variable speed drive (VSD), the fixed AC input is rectified and smoothed by a capacitor to a steady DC link voltage (about 600 V DC from a 440 V AC supply). The DC voltage is then chopped into variable-width, but constant level, voltage pulses in the computer controlled inverter section using insulated gate bipolar transistors(IGBTs). This process is called pulse width modulation or PWM, see Fig. 4.22. By varying the pulse widths and polarity of the DC voltage it is possible to generate an averaged sinusoidal AC output over a wide range of frequencies. Due to the smoothing effect of the motor inductance, the motor currents appear to be approximately sinusoidal in shape. By directing the currents in sequence into the three stator winding a reversible rotating magnetic field is produced at a frequency set by the PWM modulator.

在电子变速驱动器(VSD)中,恒定的交流输入经过整流并由电容器滤波至稳定的直流母线电压(从 440 V 交流电源得到约 600 V 直流)。然后,在计算机控制的绝缘栅双极型晶体管(IGBT)逆变器中,将直流电压斩波为宽度可变但幅值恒定的电压脉冲。这个过程称为脉宽调制(PWM),如图 4.22 所示。通过改变直流电压的脉冲宽度和极性,可以在宽频率范围内产生平均值为正弦的交流输出。由于电动机电感的平滑效应,电动机电流的形状近似正弦。通过将电流按顺序通入三个定子绕组中,能产生频率按脉宽调制器设定的可逆旋转磁场。

Accurate control of shaft torque, acceleration time and braking are a few of the many operational parameters that can be programmed into the VSD, usually via a hand-held unit. The VSD can be closely tuned to the connected motor drive to achieve optimum control and protection features for the overall drive. Speed regulation against load changes is very good and can be made very precise by the addition of feedback from a shaft speed encoder.

轴转矩、加速时间和制动是许多运行参数中的一部分,对它们的精确控制是可编程到电子变速驱动器中的,通常使用手持式编程装置。电子变速驱动器可与连接的电动机驱动器紧密协调,以实现对整个驱动器的最佳控制和保护。根据负载的变化调节转速非常好,并且可以添加轴转速编码器的反馈信号,使调速非常精确。

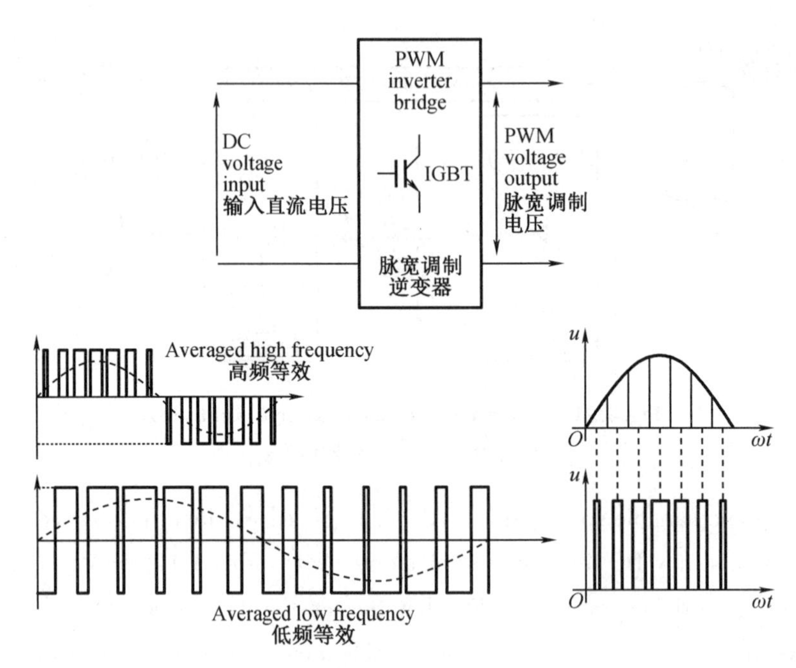

Fig. 4. 22　PMW control

图 4. 22　脉宽调制

VSDs, being digitally controlled, can be easily networked to other computer devices e. g. programmable logic controllers (PLCs) for the overall control of a complex process. A disadvantage of chopping large currents with such a drive creates harmonic voltages back into the power supply network. A harmonic voltage waveform is a distorted sinusoidal waveshape.

数字控制的电子变速驱动器便于连接网络上的其他计算机设备,例如可编程逻辑控制器(PLC),用于对复杂过程进行总体控制。用这种驱动器对大电流斩波的缺点是会产生谐波电压回馈到供电网络中。谐波电压波形是失真的正弦波形。

The analysis (not covered here) of a distorted waveshape reveals a set of sinusoidal harmonic voltages super imposed upon the base (or fundamental) frequency. Harmonic frequencies are integer (whole number) multiples of the fundamental frequency. In an AC system, even numbered harmonics are conveniently self-cancelling as are multiples of three in a three-phase network. This leaves harmonic numbered frequencies of 5, 7, 11, 13, 17, 19 etc. Fortunately, the higher the harmonic number the lower is the amplitude of the harmonic voltage. For a 60 Hz fundamental (1st harmonic), a 5th harmonic would be at a frequency of 300 Hz and a 7th harmonic would be at 420 Hz. The amplitude of a 5th harmonic may be up to about 20% of the fundamental while the 7th will be down to about 14% and so on.

对失真波形的分析(此处未涉及)揭示了在基频(或基频)上叠加了一组正弦谐波电压。谐波频率是基频的整数倍。在交流电系统中,偶次谐波可以容易地自抵消,就像三相网络中的三次谐波一样。这使得谐波编号频率为 5、7、11、13、17、19 等。幸运的是,谐波编号越高,谐波电压的幅值越低。对于 60 Hz 基波(1 次谐波),5 次谐波频率将处于 300 Hz,7 次谐波将处于 420 Hz。5 次谐波的幅值大约可达基波的 20%,而 7 次谐波的幅值大约可以低至基波的 14%,以此类推。

Such harmonic voltage disturbances caused by current switching can interfere with other equipment connected to the power system, e. g. progressive insulation breakdown due to high voltage spikes, flickering of the lighting, malfunction of low current devices such as electronic computers and instrumentation/control circuits.

这种由电流转换引起的谐波电压干扰会干扰连接到电力系统的其他设备,例如,由于高电压峰值、照明闪烁、电子计算机和仪表/控制电路等低电流设备故障而导致的绝缘逐步击穿。

Minimising harmonic disturbance involves good circuit design and the fitting of harmonic filters adjacent to the VSD drive. A harmonic filter is a combination of inductance and capacitance units tuned to absorb the unwanted frequencies.

将谐波干扰降至最低需要良好的电路设计以及在电子变速驱动器附近安装谐波滤波器。谐波滤波器是电感和电容单元的组合,被调整好以吸收不需要的频率。

Be guided by the manufacturers' installation notes regarding the need for filters, acceptable cable rating and length, earthing and bonding etc. before fitting such a drive.

在安装此类驱动器之前,应遵循制造商关于滤波器、可接受的电缆额定参数和长度、接地和接续等的安装说明。

Very large drives use thyristor converters and synchronous motors, e. g. for ship's electric propulsion as outlined in Chapter 8.

超大型驱动器使用晶闸管变换器和同步电动机,如第 8 章所述,用于船舶电力推进。

4.8　Motor Protection 电动机的保护

The circuits in Fig. 4. 23 show typical motor protection circuits on LV and HV supplies.

图 4. 23 中的电路展示了低压和高压供电的典型电动机保护电路。

In the HV motor protection scheme above, the back-up fuses are the trigger type. This type of fuse releases a trigger actuated by a spring held in tension until the element melts. When released, the trigger may be used to indicate a blown fuse or to trip a circuit breaker or contactor.

Trigger fuses are an additional protection against a single-phasing fault so that the motor is definitely tripped out when a single fuse blows.

在上述高压电动机保护方案中,备用熔断器为触发型。这种类型的熔断器释放触发器的弹簧,弹簧的张力保持到熔断器熔断。弹簧释放时,触发器可用于指示熔断器已熔断或使断路器或接触器跳闸。触发型熔断器是防止单相故障的附加保护,因此当单个熔断器熔断时,电动机肯定会跳闸。

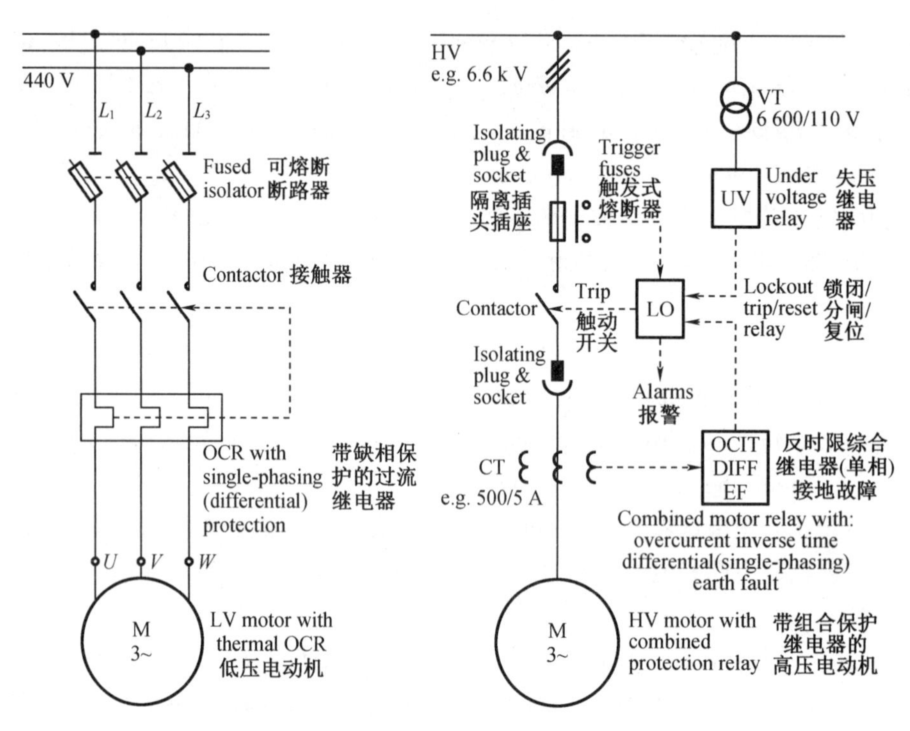

Fig. 4. 23 LV and HV motor protection circuit

图 4. 23 低压和高压电动机保护电路

Protecting an electric motor is basically preventing the motor from getting too hot. Remember, every 10 ℃ above the maximum recommended temperature of the insulation can reduce its working life by half. Obviously, the best way to protect a motor against overheating is to directly monitor the temperature of the motor windings. If the temperature exceeds the maximum set value for the motor insulation its contactor is tripped to stop the motor and allow it to cool down.

电动机的保护基本上就是防止电动机过热。记住,绝缘材料的温度比最高允许温度每高 10 ℃,其工作寿命就会缩短一半。显然,防止电动机过热的最佳方式是直接监测电动机绕组的温度。如果温度超过电动机绝缘的最大设定值,其接触器将跳闸,以停止电动机并使其冷却。

Three main types of direct temperature sensors can be used. These are: Thermocouple, resistance temperature device (RTD), thermistor.

可以使用三种主要类型的直接式温度传感器:热电偶、电阻温度检测器、热敏电阻。

The thermistor sensor is probably the most common as its thermal characteristic more closely matches that of a motor than the other types. Thermistors are small pellets of semiconductor material which are embedded into the insulation of all three motor stator windings during manufacture. When a thermistor gets hot its resistance changes dramatically. They are connected so that if the motor temperature gets too high the starter contactor will be tripped by an electronic protection relay to stop the motor.

热敏电阻传感器可能是最常见的,因为它的热特性比其他类型更接近电动机的热特性。热敏电阻是半导体材料的小颗粒,在制造过程中嵌入电动机定子的全部三个绕组的绝缘中。当热敏电阻变热时,其电阻会急剧变化。它们被接入后,如果电动机温度过高,电子保护继电器将使启动器中的接触器跳闸,以停止电动机。

Direct thermistor protection is usually only fitted to large motors, e. g. bow thrusters, FD fans, air conditioning compressors, etc.

直接式热敏电阻保护通常只安装在大型电动机上,如船首侧推器、FD 风机、空调压缩机等。

Most motors are protected by monitoring the temperature indirectly by measuring the current flowing in the supply lines. This method uses electronic, thermal or electromagnetic time-delayed overcurrent relays (OCRs) in the motor starter. The system is designed so that if the motor takes too much current because it is mechanically overloaded, the OCR will trip out the contactor coil, after a pre-set time delay, before severe overheating can occur.

大多数电动机是通过测量电源线中的电流间接监测其温度来进行保护的。该方法在电动机启动器中使用电子、热或电磁式延时过流继电器(OCR)。该系统设计为,如果电动机由于机械过载而产生过大电流,过流继电器将在预设时间延迟后,严重过热发生之前,使接触器线圈断电。

The largest overcurrent possible is the current taken when the motor has stalled. This, of course, is the starting current of the motor which will be about five times the full load current. The contactor is capable of tripping this stalled current quickly and safely.

可能的最大过电流是电动机堵转时的电流。当然,这是电动机的启动电流,约为满载电流的 5 倍。接触器能够快速且安全地分断该堵转电流。

If a short-circuit occurs in the motor, the starter, or the supply cable, then a huge fault current will flow. If the contactor tries to open under short-circuit conditions, serious arcing will occur at its contacts such that it may fail to interrupt the fault current. The prolonged short-circuit current will cause serious damage to the motor, starter and cable with the attendant risk of an electrical fire. To prevent this, a set of fuses or a circuit breaker is fitted upstream of the contactor which will trip out almost instantaneously thereby protecting the contactor during a short-circuit fault.

如果电动机、启动器或电源电缆发生短路,则将产生巨大的故障电流。如果接触器试图在短路条件下断开,其触点间将发生严重的电弧,从而可能无法中断故障电流。短路电流长时间存在将对电动机、启动器和电缆造成严重损坏,并伴随电气火灾的风险。为了防止这种情况,在接触器上游安装一组熔断器或断路器,该熔断器或断路器几乎能瞬时跳闸,从而在短路故障期间保护接触器。

It is important that the tripping characteristics, as shown in Fig. 4. 24, of the OCR and fuses/circuit breaker are coordinated so that the contactor trips on overcurrent while the fuses/circuit breaker interrupt shortcircuit fault currents. This contactor plus fuse arrangement is usually called back-up protection.

重要的是,如图 4. 24 所示,过流继电器和熔断器/断路器的跳闸特性应协调一致,以便在熔断器/断路器中切断短路故障电流时,接触器在过电流下跳闸。这种接触器+保险丝的形式通常称为备用保护。

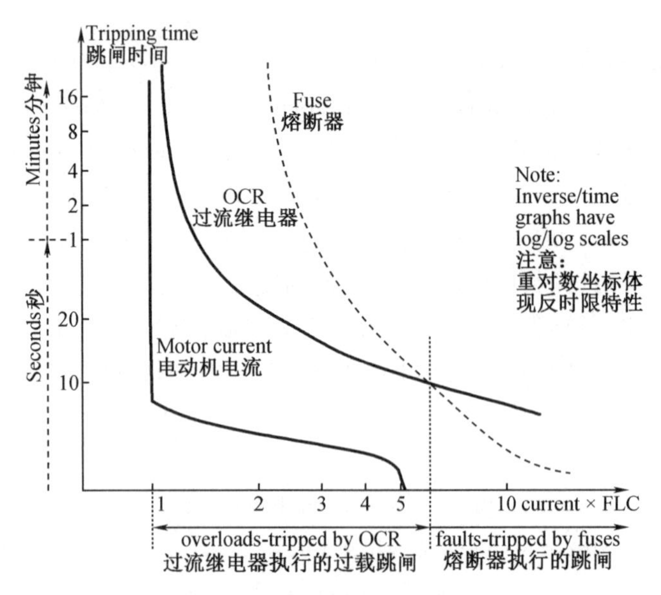

Fig. 4. 24　Motor protection curves

图 4. 24　电动机保护曲线图

Question 思考题

At what value of current should the OCR be set?

过流继电器的动作电流设定值应该为多少?

Answer 答案

To protect a modern continuous maximum rating(CMR) motor the thermal OCR should be set at the FLC rating of the motor. This will ensure that tripping will not occur within 2 h at 105% FLC. At 120% FLC tripping will occur within 2 h.

为了保护现代连续最大额定值(CMR)电动机,应将热过流继电器设置为电动机的额定满载电流值。这将确保在105%的满载额定电流下,2 h 内不会发生跳闸。在120%的满载额定电流时,跳闸将在2 h 内发生。

It must be emphasised that the motor fuses are not chosen for their rated current but for their inverse current-time (*I-t*) characteristic. This means that the current rating of fuses used to protect a motor does not appear to have any direct relationship to the FLC rating of the motor.

必须强调的是,电动机熔断器不是根据其额定电流选择的,而是根据其反向电流-时间(*I*-*t*)特性选择的。这意味着用于保护电动机的熔断器的额定电流似乎与电动机的满载额定电流没有任何直接关系。

Fuses used for back-up protection for motor circuits have a special time-current characteristic. They are generally carrying steady currents well below their rated capacity to allow for short duration DOL starting currents without blowing. Consequently they do not protect against normal overloads but do protect the motor and supply system against a short circuit fault. Fuses designed for motor circuit back-up protection have a restricted continuous current rating (called "M" rating) as compared with their fusing characteristic.

用于电动机电路后备保护的熔断器具有特殊的时间-电流特性。它们通常承载远低于其额定容量的稳定电流,以允许短时间的直接启动电流而不发生熔断。因此,它们不能防止普通过载,但能保护电动机和供电系统免受短路故障的损坏。与熔断特性相比,为电动机电路备用保护设计的熔断器具有受限的持续电流额定值(称为"M"额定值)。

Hence a typical fuse designation for motor circuits could be "32M63" which indicates a continuous rating of 32 A but a rating of 63 A for the starting period.

因此,电动机电路的典型熔断器名称可能为"32M63",表示持续电流额定值为32A,但启动期间的电流额定值为63 A。

Question 思考题

A motor is protected by a thermal OCR and back up fuses. Can the motor exceed its rated temperature without being tripped by the protection?

电动机由热继电器和备用熔断器保护。电动机是否能够在不被保护跳闸的情况下超过其额定允许温度?

Answer 答案

Yes. Although overheating is usually indicated by the current drawn by the motor rising above its rated value, a number of other situations can cause the motor overheating. For example: Very high ambient temperature; inadequate ventilation; a star-delta starter stuck in the star connection; stopping and starting too often; worn or dry shaft bearings. The motor windings can only be protected against these conditions by using direct thermal protection.

会。虽然过热通常由电动机汲取的电流上升到其额定值以上表示,但许多其他情况可能导致电动机过热。例如:非常高的环境温度;通风不足;星形-三角形启动器卡在星形连接位置;启停太频繁;轴承磨损或干燥。电动机绕组只能通过使用直接式热保护来防止这些情况发生。

There are three types of OCR used for motor protection:Electronic,thermal,electromagnetic.

用于电动机保护的过流继电器有三种类型:电子保护、热保护、电磁保护。

Electronic OCR relays have largely superseded electromagnetic types as they have no moving parts (except for their output trip relay) and their very reliable tripping characteristics can be closely matched to the motor circuit. Such relays are robust, smaller and lighter than the equivalent electromagnetic type.

电子式反时限过流继电器在很大程度上取代了电磁式继电器,因为它们没有活动部件(输出跳闸继电器除外),其非常可靠的跳闸特性可以与电动机电路高度匹配。这种继电器比同规格的电磁式继电器更坚固、更小、更轻。

A block diagram of such an electronic OCR is shown in Fig. 4. 25.

这种电子式反时限过流继电器框图如图 4. 25 所示。

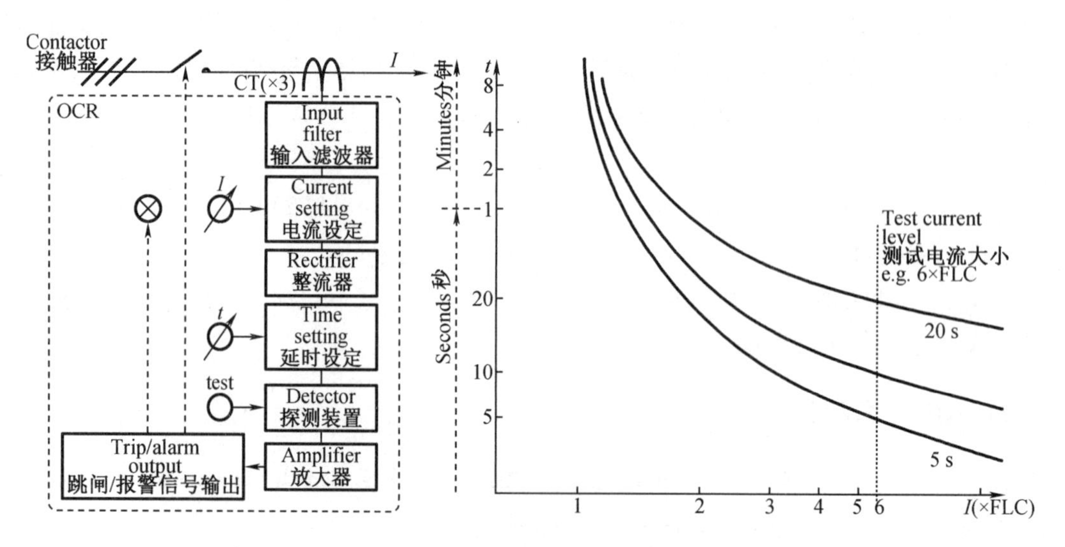

Fig. 4. 25　Electronic OCR

图 4. 25　电子式反时限过流继电器

The block diagram of the electronic OCR relay shows that the current and time settings can be adjusted over a limited range to match the motor FLC and run-up time. A self test of the OCR performance can usually be applied with a fixed setting of, typically, 6×FLC and the tripping-time can be measured and compared against the manufacturers current-time characteristics.

电子式反时限过流继电器的方框图显示,电流和时间设置可在一定范围内调整,以匹配电动机的满载额定电流和运行时间。过流继电器性能的自检通常采用固定设置,一般为6倍的 FLC,并且可以测量跳闸时间,并与制造商提供的电流-时间特性进行比较。

Although electromagnetic devices with time delays can give adequate protection against large, sustained overloads to motors which are operated well below their maximum output and temperature, they have been found to be inadequate for continuous maximum rated (CMR) motors.

尽管具有延时的电磁装置可以为在远低于其最大输出和温度下运行的电动机提供足够的保护,以防止过大的、持续的过载,但已发现它们不适用于持续最大额定(CMR)电动机。

Most LV motors are protected by less expensive thermal OCRs. Inverse-time thermal OCRs usually work with bi-metal strips as shown in Fig. 4. 26. The strips are heated by the motor current and bend depending on the temperature. If the motor takes an overload current, the strips open a normally-closed (NC) contact which trips out the line contactor to stop the motor.

大多数低压电动机由较便宜的热继电器保护。如图 4. 26 所示,反时限热继电器通常使用双金属片。金属片由电动机电流加热,并随温度弯曲。如果电动机承受过载电流,则金属片会断开常闭(NC)触点,使线路接触器跳闸以停止电动机。

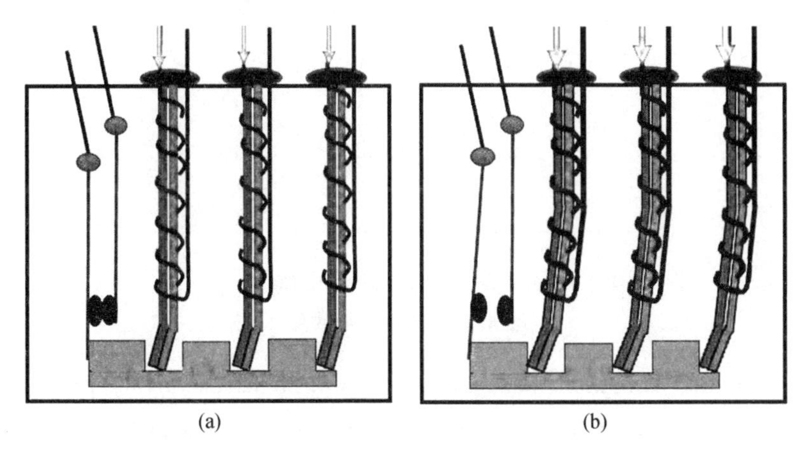

Fig. 4. 26 Bi-metal strips overcurrent action

图 4. 26 双金属片过流动作

The minimum tripping current of such a device can be adjusted over a small range. This adjustment alters the distance the strips have to bend before operating the trip contact.

这种装置的最小跳闸电流可在小范围内调节。该调整改变了跳闸触点动作之前金属片须弯曲的距离。

For larger motors, the heaters do not carry the motor current. They are supplied from CTs which proportionally step-down the motor current so that smaller heater components may be used.

对于大型电动机,其加热器不承载电动机电流。它们由电流互感器供电,电流互感器按比例降低电动机电流,因此可以使用较小的加热器组件。

To operate correctly, induction motors must be connected to a three-phase AC supply. Once started they may continue to run even if one of the three supply lines becomes disconnected. This is called single-phasing and can result in motor burn-out.

为了正常运行,感应电动机必须连接到三相交流电源。电动机一旦启动,即使三相电源线中的一相断开,它们也可以继续运行。这称为单相运行,可能导致电动机烧毁。

Single-phasing, as shown in Fig. 4. 27, is usually caused when one of the three back-up fuses blows or if one of the contactor contacts is open-circuited. The effect of single-phasing is to increase the current in the two remaining lines and cause the motor to become very noisy due to the uneven torque produced in the rotor.

单相运行,如图 4. 27 所示,通常由三个后备熔断器之一熔断或接触器触点之一开路引起。单相运行会增大剩余两条线路中的电流,并由于转子中产生的不平衡转矩,导致电动机噪声很大。

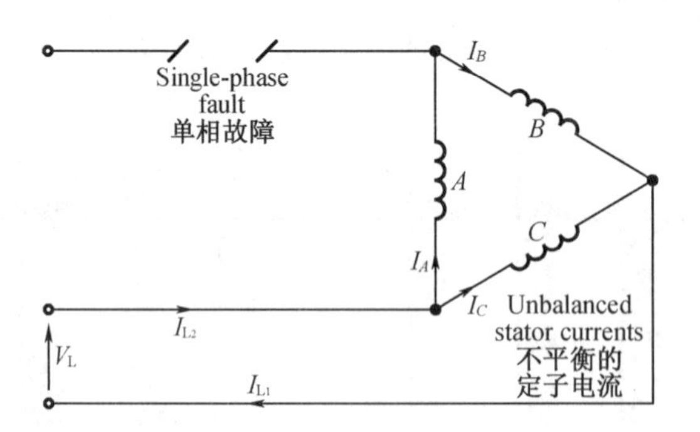

Fig. 4. 27 Single phasing fault

图 4. 27 单相运行故障

An increase in line current due to single-phasing will be detected by the protective OCR. The three thermal elements of an OCR are arranged in such a way that unequal heating of the bi-metal strips causes a differential switch contacts to trip out the motor contactor.

单相运行引起线电流的增大会被保护过流继电器检测到。过流继电器的三个热元件将使双金属片发热不均,导致差动开关触点动作,使电动机接触器跳闸。

For large HV machines a separate device, called a negative phase sequence (NPS) relay, is used to measure the amount of unbalance in the motor currents.

对于大型高压电动机,使用称为负序(NPS)继电器的独立装置测量电动机电流的不平衡量。

For star connected motor windings the phase and line currents are equal so the line connected OCR is correctly sensing the winding current. If the overcurrent setting is exceeded during a single-phase fault the motor will be tripped off.

对于星形连接的电动机绕组,相电流和线电流相等,因此线电路连接的过流继电器能正确感应绕组的电流。如果在单相运行故障期间的电流超过过流设定值,电动机将跳闸。

The situation is not so simple with a delta connected motor. Normally the line current dividesphasorally between two phases of the motor windings.

对于三角形连接的电动机,情况并非如此简单。通常,线电流在电动机两相绕组之间分相。

The phase current is as:

相电流为

$$I_{\mathrm{PH}}=\frac{I_{\mathrm{L}}}{\sqrt{3}}=0.577I_{\mathrm{L}}$$

When one of the lines becomes open-circuited a balanced three-phase condition no longer exists. Now the sets of line and phase currents are no longer balanced.

当其中一相线路开路时,三相平衡状态不再存在。现在,三相线电流和相电流不再平衡。

The Table 4. 6 shows typical values of line and phase currents at various levels of motor loading during a single-phasing fault as shown in Fig. 4. 27.

表 4. 7 显示了图 4. 27 所示单相运行故障期间电动机在不同负载状态下的线电流和相电流的典型值。

Table 4. 7 Typical values of line and phase currents at various levels of motor loading during a single-phasing

表 4. 7 单相运行故障期间电动机在不同负载状态下的线电流和相电流的典型值

Balanced (rated FLC %) 平衡态(占满载额定电流的百分数)	Unbalanced (rated FLC%) 非平衡态(占满载额定电流的百分数)		
	$I_{\mathrm{L}_2}, I_{\mathrm{L}_3}$	I_A, I_B	I_C
60	102	62	131
70	130	79	161
100	243	129	185

Particularly note that the current in winding C is considerably higher than that in the other two windings.

需要特别注意,C 相绕组中的电流明显高于其他两相绕组中的电流。

Look at the condition where the motor is at 60% of full load when single-phasing occurs: The line currents are 102% of the full load value but the current in winding C is 131% of its full load value. The 102% line current will probably not activate a line connected OCR and the motor remains connected. However, the local overheating in winding C of the motor will quickly result in motor damage.

请看单相运行故障发生时电动机处于60%满载额定电流的情况:线电流为满载额定电流值的102%,但绕组 C 中的电流为其满载额定电流的131%。102%的线电流可能不会触发线电路中的过流继电器,并且电动机保持通电。然而,电动机绕组 C 中局部过热将迅速导致电动机损伤。

Motors can he protected against this condition by using a differential type relay which trips out with unbalanced currents. In fact, most modern thermal OCRs for motors have this protection against single-phasing incorporated as a normal feature.

使用差动继电器可保护电动机免受这种情况的影响,该继电器在电流不平衡时跳闸。事实上,大多数用于电动机保护的现代热继电器都将这种单相运行保护作为普遍功能。

If single-phasing occurs when in operation on light load, the motor keeps on running unless the protection trips the contactor. If the motor is stopped, it will not restart. When the contactor is closed, the motor will take a large starting current but develop no rotating torque. The OCR is set to allow the starting current to flow long enough for the motor, under normal conditions, to run up to speed. With no ventilation on the stationary motor, this time delay will result in rapid and severe overheating. Worse still, if the operator makes several attempts to restart the motor, it will burn out. If a motor fails to start after two attempts, you must investigate the cause.

如果在轻载运行时发生缺相,电动机将继续运行,除非保护接触器跳闸。如果电动机停止了,则不会重新启动。当接触器闭合时,电动机将承受较大的启动电流,但不会产生旋转的转矩。过流继电器设置为允许启动电流存在足够长的时间,以便电动机在正常条件下运行到一定转速。在静止态电动机没有通风的情况下,延迟将迅速导致电动机严重过热。更糟的是,如果操作人员多次尝试重新启动电动机,电动机将烧毁。如果两次尝试后电动机都无法启动,则必须调查原因。

Undervoltage protection is necessary in a distribution system that supplies motors. If there is a total voltage loss or black-out, all the motors must be disconnected from the supply. This is to prevent all the motors restarting together which would result in a huge current surge, tripping out the generator again. Motors must be restarted in a controlled sequence after a supply failure.

在为电动机供电的配电系统中,欠压保护是必要的。如果发生失压或全船失电,则必须断开所有电动机的电源。这是为了防止所有电动机同时重新启动,导致巨大的电流冲击,使发电机再次跳电。电源故障解除后,必须按一定控制顺序重新启动电动机。

Undervoltage (UV) protection for LV motors is simply provided by the spring loaded motor contactor because it will drop out when the supply voltage is lost. For large HV motor the UV protection function will be covered by a relay separate from the OCR function or it may be part of a special motor relay which incorporates all of the necessary protection functions.

低压电动机的欠压(UV)保护仅由弹簧加载电动机接触器提供,因为当电源失压时,弹簧将释放。对于大型高压电动机,欠压保护功能将由独立于过流继电器功能的继电器覆盖,或者它可能是包含在具有所有必要保护功能的特殊电动机继电器中。

When the supply voltage becomes available, the motor will not restart until its contactor coil is energised. This will usually require the operator to press the stop/reset button before initiating the start sequence.

当电源电压恢复时,电动机将不会重新启动,直到其接触器线圈得电。这通常需要操作人员在执行启动程序之前按下停止/复位按钮。

For essential loads, the restart may be performed automatically by a sequence restart system. This system ensures that essential services are restarted automatically on restoration of supply following a blackout. Timer relays in the starters of essential motor circuits are set to initiate start-up in a controlled sequence.

对于必要负载,可通过顺序启动系统自动执行重启。该系统确保在失电后恢复供电时自动重启必要设施。在必要设施的电动机电路的启动器中,时间继电器设置为按一定顺序控制启动。

4.9 Single Phase Motors 单相电动机

Low power motors for power tools, refrigerators, vacuum cleaners etc. are typically supplied at 220 V AC 50/60 Hz.

电动工具、冰箱、真空吸尘器等的低功率电动机通常以 220 V,50/60 Hz 交流电供电。

With a single phase stator the magnetic field is purely alternating so no rotating magnetic field is set up. Any clockwise torque is opposed by an equal and opposite anti clockwise torque. Once the rotor moves it will accelerate in the direction started, but it will not self start.

对于单相定子,磁场是纯交变的,因此没有建立旋转磁场。任何时刻顺时针转矩都与逆时针转矩大小相等方向相反。一旦转子转动,它将沿转动方向加速,但不会自动启动。

Common types are: Split-phase induction motor, capacitor start/run induction motor, shaded pole induction motor.

单相电动机常见类型有分相式感应电动机、电容启动/运转感应电动机、罩极式感应电动机。

4.9.1 Split-phase Induction Motor 分相式感应电动机

A single phase motor has a cage rotor similar to that used in a three phase type. A single stator winding produces a pulsating magnetic field when energised with single phase AC current. This field cannot exert a rotating force on the cage rotor.

单相电动机具有与三相电动机中使用的笼型转子类似的转子。通入单相交流电时,单个定子绕组将产生脉动的磁场。该磁场不能在笼型转子上施加转动力矩。

One method used to produce a rotational force is to employ two stator windings fitted 90° to each other with both connected across the same supply, use a capacitor in series with the start winding. To get the effect of a rotating magnetic field (and hence induce a rotating force into the rotor), one winding is electrically phase-shifted by adding capacitance in series with one of the windings. when the machine speed reaches 75%, the start winding should be switched off, this may be done automatically using a centrifugal switch(Fig. 4. 28).

用于产生转动力矩的一种方法是采用两个定子绕组相互成 90°,两个绕组都连接在相同的电源上。为了获得旋转磁场的效果(从而在转子中感应出转动力矩),通过将其中一个绕组与电容串联,使其移相。当设备转速达到 75%时,切断启动绕组,这可以通过离心开关自动完成(图 4.28)。

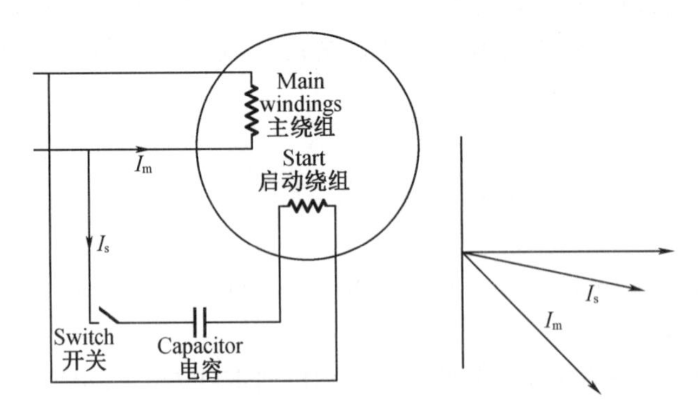

Fig. 4. 28 Split-phase induction motor circuit

图 4.28 分相式感应电动机电路

4.9.2 Capacitor Start/Run Induction Motor 电容启动/运转感应电动机

When the motor has started to run, the additional phase winding circuit may be disconnected and the rotor will continue to be pulsed around by the magnetic flux. This is called a capacitor start motor which is only useful for driving a very light load.

当电动机开始运转时,可断开附加相绕组电路,转子周围将继续产生脉振磁通量。这种电动机被称为电容启动电动机，仅用于驱动非常小的负载。

For starting and running, two capacitors are used in circuit as shown in Fig. 4. 29.

为了启动和运行，电路中使用两个电容器，如图 4. 29 所示。

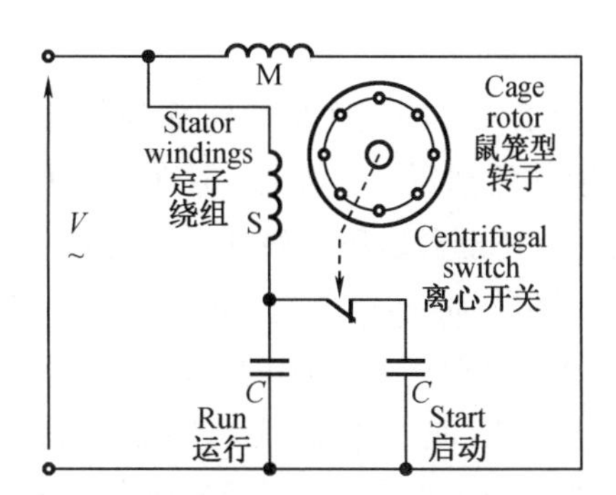

Fig. 4. 29　Capacitor start/run induction motor circuit

图 4. 29　电容启动/运转感应电动机电路

During the starting period the two paralleled capacitors create a large phase angle to the "S" winding current. As the rotor runs up to speed a switch cuts out one of the capacitors. The switch may be a centrifugal type on the rotor shaft or a current-operated time-delay relay in the motor terminal box. This type of motor gives good starting and running torque with reasonable power factor. Most split phase motors are arranged for a 4-pole stator winding so at 50 Hz its synchronous (flux) speed will be 1,500 r/min. As with all induction motors, the rotor will slip causing the shaft speed to be about 1,440 r/min on no-load. On-load, a single-phase motor will run with greater slip and operate with less efficiency, than a three-phase version.

在启动期间，两个并联电容器使"S"绕组电流产生较大的角位移。当转子加速运行时，开关切断其中一个电容器。开关可以是转子轴带的离心式开关，也可以是电动机接线盒中的通电延时继电器。这种类型的电动机具有良好的启动和运行转矩以及合理的功率因数。大多数分相电动机为 4 极定子绕组，因此在 50 Hz 时，其同步(磁通量)速度为 1 500 r/min。与所有感应电动机一样，转子有转差速，导致空载时轴转速约为 1 440 r/min。在负载状态下，单相电动机将比三相电动机产生更大的转速差，运行效率更低。

4. 9. 3　Shaded Pole Induction Motor 罩极式感应电动机

This is a low torque machine useful for low power drives such as small cooling fans in ovens and electronic equipment.

这是一种低扭矩装置，适用于低功率驱动器，如烤箱和电子设备中的小型冷却风扇。

Fig. 4. 30 shows how the face of each salient stator pole is partially split with one side carrying a thick copper ring called a shading ring. The pulsating AC flux divides into each half of the pole but is time delayed in the part with the shading ring. This is due to an induced current in the ring which opposes flux change in the shaded part. To the rotor, this delay appears as a flux shift across the overall pole face which drags the rotor with it by the normal induction motor action. Obviously, the developed torque is small and the machine is not very efficient but is an inexpensive drive for very low power applications. As with all induction motors the shaft base speed is fixed by the supply frequency, so at 50 Hz the maximum speed is 3,000 r/min and shaft loading will cause the rotor to slip below this value.

图 4.30 展示了每个凸极定子磁极的表面是如何部分分开的,其中一侧带有粗铜环,称为短路环。脉振的交流磁通量分配到每一半磁极,但在具有短路环的部分中有时间延迟。这是由于环中的感应电流与短路环部分磁极的磁通量变化相反。对于转子而言,这种延迟表现为磁通量在整个磁极面上的移动,通过普通感应电动机力矩作用拖动转子。显然,产生的转矩很小,设备的效率不高,但对于非常小的功率应用来说这是一种廉价的驱动器。与所有感应电动机一样,轴基础转速由电源频率固定,因此在 50 Hz 时,最大速度为 3 000 r/min,轴带负载将导致转子存在转速差,转子转速会小于该值。

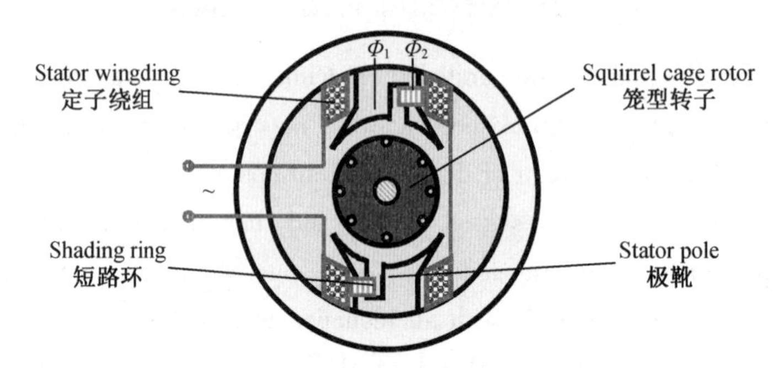

Fig. 4.30 Shaded pole induction motor

图 4.30 罩极式感应电动机

4.10 Maintenance 维护

The maintenance requirements for cage-rotor induction motors are very simple:

(1) Keep insulation resistance high and contact resistance low;

(2) Lubricate correctly and maintain a uniform air gap;

(3) Ensure both the interior and exterior are always clean and dry.

笼型转子感应电动机的维护要求非常简单:

(1) 保持绝缘电阻高,且接触电阻低;

(2) 正确润滑,并保持气隙均匀一致;

(3) 确保内部和外部始终清洁干燥。

Providedthese requirements are met, an induction motor should give trouble free service during its long life.

只要满足这些要求,感应电动机能在其较长的寿命内无故障运行。

Question 思考题

Whatis the most common cause induction motor failure?
感应电动机故障最常见的原因是什么?

Answer 答案

Failure of stator insulation due to dampness is a major problem with marine motors.
潮湿导致定子绝缘失效是船用电动机故障的主要原因。

Open ventilated motors are most at risk, particularly when they are used for long periods.
开放式通风电动机的风险最大,尤其是长时间使用时。

Anti-condensation heaters should be regularly checked to see that they are actually working and keeping the motor dry.
应定期检查防冷凝加热器,以确保它在正常工作并保持电动机干燥。

For all motors, cleanliness is most important. A regular cleaning routine is required to remove harmful deposits of dust, dirt, grease and oil from both inside and outside the motor. The cleaning of the external surface is especially important for totally enclosed motor which run continuously. The heat generated in this motors is removed through the external surface. A thick layer of dust will reduce the heat dissipation and result in very high temperatures. Internal dust and dirt in opened ventilated motors must be regularly removed by blowing or extraction and ventilation screens and ducts cleared out.
对于所有的电动机来说,清洁最重要。需要定期清洁,以清除电动机内外的有害灰尘、污垢、油脂和油类沉积物。外表面的清洁对于连续运行的全封闭电动机尤为重要。电动机中产生的热量通过外表面去除。厚厚的灰尘层会减少散热量,并导致电动机高温。开放式通风电动机内部的灰尘和污垢必须通过吹扫或抽气定期清除,并清理风筛和风道。

If motors are to be blown out, the air used must be absolutely dry and the pressure should not be more than 1.75 bar①. If the pressure is higher than this it forces the dust into the winding insulation rather than removing it.
如果要吹洗电动机,所用空气必须绝对干燥,压力不得超过 1.75 bar。如果压力高于此值,则会迫使灰尘进入绕组绝缘层,而不是将其清除。

When blowing out a motor remember to cover up other machines in the area to protect them from flying dust. Suction cleaning is better than blowing out.

---

① 1 bar = 100 kPa。

当吹洗电动机时,记得遮盖该区域内的其他机器,以保护它们不受扬尘的影响。吸洗比吹洗更好。

Question 思考题

How often should a motor be cleaned?
电动机应该多久清洁一次?

Answer 答案

Basically this will be determined by the local conditions and the type of ventilation. Only the external surfaces of totally enclosed motors will require regular cleaning. But both the outside and inside of open ventilated motors will require routine attention. The inside of a totally enclosed motor can be cleaned if the motor has been dismantled for bearing replacement. Motors in areas where considerable amounts of air-borne dust are expected, for example, hatch cover motors, will obviously require more frequent cleaning.

这将取决于当地条件和通风类型。全封闭电动机的外表面需要定期清洁。开放式通风电动机的外部和内部都需要日常注意。如果为了更换轴承而拆解了全封闭电动机,则可以一并清洁其内部。在预计有大量空气粉尘的区域内的电动机,例如舱盖电动机,显然需要更频繁的清洁。

Contamination by oil and grease from motor bearings is often a cause of insulation failure. The insulation should be cleaned by brushing or spraying with one of the many proprietary brands of cleaning fluid which are available. Badly contaminated motors may require total immersion of the stator windings in cleaning fluid.

电动机轴承油和润滑脂污染通常是绝缘失效的诱因。绝缘层应通过刷洗或喷涂多种专有品牌的清洁剂进行清洁。被严重污染的电动机可能需要将其定子绕组完全浸泡清洗液中清洁。

Broken or missing bearing covers must be repaired or replaced to prevent grease escaping.

轴承盖损坏或丢失必须及时修理或更换,以防止润滑脂溢出。

When a motor has been dismantled for cleaning and overhaul, it should be thoroughly inspected. In this way, faults can be detected before they evolve into a major breakdown.

拆解电动机进行清洁和检修时,应进行彻底检查。这样,可以在故障演变为重大事故之前被发现。

4.10.1 Stator 定子

Look at the stator windings for damaged insulation caused by careless replacement of the rotor into the stator. Discoloured insulation is an indication that the winding has been overheated. The cause of overheating must be found and corrected before allowing the motor back into service.

检查定子绕组是否因将转子放入定子过程中的疏忽而存在绝缘损坏。绝缘变色表明绕组有过热现象。在允许电动机重新投入使用之前,必须找到并修正过热原因。

Carefully examine the stator core for signs of rubbing with the rotor, usually caused by a worn bearing. Even slight rubbing of the rotor against the stator will generate enough heat to destroy the stator insulation. Replace the bearings before putting the motor back into service.

仔细检查定子铁芯是否与转子间有摩擦迹象,这通常是由轴承磨损引起的。即使转子与定子的轻微摩擦也会产生足够的热量,从而破坏定子绝缘。电动机重新投入使用前,要更换轴承。

Laminated steel core plates which have been badly scored may cause a local hot spot to be generated when the motor is running. This is because the iron(Fe) losses will increase in the damaged area. After the motor has been put back into service with new bearings, check the motor running temperature. After a short period of service dismantle the motor and check for discolouration at the core damage which will indicate local heating. If you suspect core hot spots then the motor core will need to be dismantled for the laminations to be cleaned and reinsulated—definitely a shore job.

已严重刻痕的硅钢叠层铁芯可能导致电动机运行时产生局部发热点。这是因为受损区域的铁(Fe)损会增加。电动机采用新轴承重新投入使用后,检查其运行温度。短时间运行后,拆下电动机,检查铁芯损坏处是否变色,这表明局部是否发热。如果怀疑铁芯有发热点,则需要拆卸电动机铁芯,以便清洁和再绝缘化——这绝对是一项岸修工作。

The insulation resistance reading is the best indication as to the presence of moisture in the motor windings. Breakdowns due to insulation failure usually result in an earth fault, short-circuited turns in a phase or phase-to-phase faults.

绝缘电阻读数是电动机绕组中是否存在水分的最佳指示。绝缘失效通常会导致接地故障、匝间短路或相间故障。

Question 思考题

How do you check the insulation resistance between phases on an induction motor?

如何检查感应电动机各相之间的绝缘电阻?

Answer 答案

Larger motors are usually six-terminal, which means that all six ends of the stator windings are brought out to the terminal block. Links between the terminals are used to star or delta connect the motor. Disconnect the supply leads and remove the links. Test between phases with an insulation resistance tester as shown in Fig. 2. 9.

大型电动机通常有六个端子,这意味着定子绕组的所有六个端部都连接到接线排上。端子之间的连接用星形或三角形连接。断开电源线接头并拆下连接线。如图 2. 9 所示,用兆欧表进行相间绝缘测试。

A problem can arise on small, three terminal motors where the star or delta connection is made inside the motor. Only one end of each winding is available at the terminal block. Phase-to-phase insulation resistance cannot be checked. If a three terminal motor is to be rewound, ask the repairer to convert it to a six terminal arrangement.

在小型三端子电动机中,如果在电动机内部进行星形或三角形连接,则可能会出现一个问题——接线端子上只有每个绕组的一端可用,无法检查相间绝缘电阻。如果三端子电动机需要重绕,请维修人员将其转接为六端子形式。

4.10.2 Bearings 轴承

Induction motors are fitted with ball and/or roller bearings. These bearings are robust and reliable and should give very little trouble provided they are properly fitted, kept clean and lubricated correctly. Many engineers argue that if a bearing seems to be operating correctly it should not be tampered with.

感应电动机配有滚珠和/或滚柱轴承。这些轴承坚固可靠,只要正确安装、保持正确的清洁和润滑,应不会产生任何问题。许多工程人员认为,如果轴承运行正常,就不应该对其摆弄。

Portable vibration detection results, sampled periodically and analysed can be a very useful way to recognise the onset of a bearing failure. Bearing temperature, e. g. using embedded detectors or with portable Infra Red (IR) spot checks, is another indicator for the general health of a shaft bearing.

对便携式振动测试结果定期采样和分析,是监测轴承故障的非常有用的方法。轴承温度,例如使用嵌入式探测器或便携式红外点温(IR)测量,是轴承总体健康状况的另一个指标。

Otherwise, it is not easy to predict the unexpired life of bearings that have already run for some time. Also, inspection may not show damage to raceways and rolling elements in areas hidden from view. The best way is to renew the bearings as part of a planned maintenance programme. If this is not possible because of cost or a shortage of replacements, then bearings should be removed, cleaned and inspected for signs of damage before a decision to refit or renew is taken.

否则,很难预测已经运行一段时间的轴承的有效寿命。此外,检查可能不会指示隐藏区域的滚道和滚动元件损坏。最佳方式是将更换轴承作为维护计划的一部分。如果由于成本或更换件短缺而无法进行更换,则在决定重新安装或更换之前,应拆下、清洁并检查轴承是否有损坏迹象。

Before opening up a bearing, make sure that the complete area around the housing is clean and dry. Manufacturers recommend that bearings should be removed from the shaft as seldom as possible, but cleaning and inspection is best done with the bearing off the shaft. If the correct size of wedges or pullers is used, then removal should not cause any damage. Bearings should be cleaned by immersion in a solvent such as clean white spirit, then thoroughly dried in a jet of clean, dry compressed air. Bearings should not be spun by the air jet because skidding can damage the rolling elements and raceways.

打开轴承之前,确保壳体周围的整个区域清洁干燥。制造商建议应尽可能少地从轴上拆下轴承,但最好在轴承与轴分离的情况下进行清洁和检查。如果使用了正确尺寸的楔子或拉马,则拆卸时不应造成任何损坏。轴承应浸入溶剂如清洁的溶剂油中进行清洁,然后再用清洁、干燥的压缩空气彻底干燥。由于打滑会损坏滚动元件和滚道,因此轴承不应通过空气喷射使其旋转。

Once dry, the bearing must be lightly oiled. Any traces of metal particles, such as brass, indicate cage wear and the bearing must be replaced. If there is no evidence of metal particles, carefully examine the raceways and rolling elements for signs of wear or damage. Hold the inner race in one hand and slowly turn the outer race. Any sticking or unevenness in the rotation requires a rewash of the bearing and rotation in the cleaning fluid. If the sticking persists the bearing must be rejected. Similarly, bearings with visible signs of corrosion, overheating or damage, and those with a noticeable degree of roughness in rotation should also be replaced.

干燥后,必须对轴承进行轻微润滑。任何金属颗粒痕迹,如黄铜,表明轴承罩磨损,必须更换轴承。如果没有金属颗粒的迹象,仔细检查滚道和滚动元件是否有磨损或损坏的迹象。用一只手握住内圈,然后慢慢转动外圈。旋转中存在任何黏滞或不均匀都需要重新清洗轴承,并在清洗液中转动。如果卡滞现象持续存在,则该轴承不能使用。同样,有明显腐蚀、过热或损坏迹象的轴承以及旋转粗糙度明显的轴承也应更换。

When fitting a bearing to a shaft, first clean the shaft and apply a thin film of light oil. Set the bearing square on the shaft end, with a tubular drift (pipe), force the bearing against the shaft shoulder. The drift should bear on the inner race as close to the shaft as possible. Large bearings can be heated for 10 – 15 min in clean mineral oil up to 80 ℃ to facilitate fitting. Lubricate the bearings with the correct type and quantity of grease as recommended by the manufacturer. Fill the bearing about one third to one half full with grease. Over greasing causes churning and friction which results in heating, oxidation of the grease and possible leakage through the seals.

将轴承安装到轴上时,先将轴清洁并涂抹一薄层轻油。将轴端放置好轴承,并使用管状冲头(管)将轴承压在轴肩上。冲头应尽可能靠近轴并压在轴承内圈上。大型轴承可在高达 80 ℃的清洁矿物油中加热 10~15 min,以便安装。按照制造商的建议,使用正确类型和用量的润滑脂润滑轴承。向轴承加注约三分之一至一半的润滑脂。过度润滑会导致搅拌和摩擦,从而导致润滑脂发热、氧化,并可能从密封件中泄漏。

On account of the high ambient temperature and excessive vibration which many marine motors endure, grease life can be short and fresh grease should be applied at regular intervals. Unless the bearing housing has a vent hole to allow excess grease to escape, it will be necessary to clean out the bearing housing before charging it with fresh grease. Because of the vibration on ships, bearings can be damaged when the motor is not running.

由于许多船用电动机持续承受高温环境和过度振动,润滑脂寿命可能很短,应定期注入新鲜润滑脂。除非轴承箱有通风孔,允许多余的润滑脂逸出,否则在向轴承箱注入新润滑脂之前,必须清理轴承箱。由于船上的振动,当电动机没有运行时,轴承也可能会损坏。

The shafts of stationary motors should be periodically rotated a quarter turn to minimise vibration damage to the bearings.

固定式电动机的轴应定期旋转四分之一圈,以尽量减少轴承因振动而损坏。

4.10.3 Rotor 转子

Maintenance of cage-rotor induction motors tends to mainly involve the stator windings and bearings. Cage-rotors require little or no special care in normal service. Inspect for signs of damage and overheating in the cage winding and its laminated steel core. Make sure that all core ventilating ducts are clean and clear. If an internal fan is fitted it must be in good condition if it is to provide adequate cooling.

笼型转子感应电动机的维护主要涉及定子绕组和轴承。笼型转子在正常使用中几乎不需要特别护理。检查笼型转子绕组及其叠层铁芯有无损坏和过热迹象。确保所有铁芯通风槽清洁干净。如果安装了内部风扇,则其必须处于良好状态,才能提供足够的冷却。

Question 思考题

A cage-rotor induction motor has been flooded with sea water and its insulation resistance is down to 0 MΩ. What is the procedure for putting the motor back into service?

笼型转子感应电动机已被海水淹没,其绝缘电阻降至 0 MΩ。将电动机重新投入使用要经过什么程序?

Answer 答案

The main problem is to restore the insulation resistance of the stator winding to a high value. This is achieved in three stages: Cleaning, drying, re-varnishing.

主要问题是将定子绕组的绝缘电阻恢复到高值。这可通过三个阶段实现:清洁、干燥、重新上漆。

Salt contamination can be removed by washing with clean, fresh water. Any grease or oil on the windings has to be removed using a degreasant liquid.

用干净的淡水清洗可以去除盐污染。绕组上的任何油脂或油必须使用脱脂液体清除。

Dry the stator windings with low power electric heaters or lamps and plenty of ventilation to allow the dampness to escape. Alternatively, the windings can be heated by current injection from a welding set or from a special injection transformer. Be sure to keep the injected current level well below the motor's full load rating.

用低功率电加热器或烤灯干燥定子绕组,以及充足的通风,以排出湿气。或者绕组可以通过焊接装置或专用注入变压器注入电流进行加热。确保注入电流等级应远低于电动机的满载额定值。

With the windings clean and dry, and if the IR test remains high over a few hours, apply a couple of coats of good quality air-drying insulating varnish.

在绕组清洁干燥的情况下,如果红外点温测试结果持续较高数小时以上,则应涂上两层质量良好的空气干燥绝缘清漆。

The motor starter and other control equipment should be regularly inspected to check and maintain the following items.

应定期检查电动机启动器和其他控制设备,以检查和维护以下项目。

4.10.4　Enclosure 外壳

Check for accumulations of dirt and rust. Any corroded parts must be cleaned and repainted. Examine the starter fixing bolts and its earth bonding connection — particularly where high vibration is present, e. g. in the steering flat and the forecastle.

检查有无污垢和铁锈堆积。任何被腐蚀的部件必须清洗并重新上漆。检查启动器固定螺栓及其接地连接,尤其是存在高振动的情况下,例如在舵机平台和艏甲板上。

4.10.5　Contactors and Relays 接触器和继电器

Check for any signs of overheating and loose connections. Remove any dust and grease from insulating components to prevent voltage breakdown by surface tracking. Ensure that the magnet armature of contactors moves freely. Remove any dirt or rust from magnet faces which may prevent correct closing.

检查有无过热和连接松动的迹象。清除绝缘部件上的灰尘和油脂,以防止表面爬电导致电压击穿。确保接触器的电枢能够自由移动。清除磁铁表面可能妨碍其正确闭合的污垢或铁锈。

4.10.6　Contacts 触头

Examine for excessive pitting and roughness due to burning. Copper contacts may be smoothed using a fine file. Copper oxide, which acts as a high resistance, can be removed using glass-paper. Do not file silver alloy contacts or remove silver oxide as it acts as a good conductor. A thin smear of electrical contact lubrication helps to prolong the life of all contacts. When contacts have to be replaced, always replace both fixed and moving contacts in pairs.

检查因灼烧而产生的过度点蚀和粗糙度。铜触头可以使用细锉刀磨平。高阻氧化铜可以使用玻璃砂纸去除。不要锉削银合金触头或去除氧化银,因为氧化银是良导体。触头上涂抹润滑薄层有助于延长所有触头的寿命。当必须更换触头时,始终成对更换定触头和动触头。

Check contact spring pressure and compare adjacent contact sets for equal pressure. Examine power and control fuse contacts for signs of overheating — lubricate the contact blades on fuseholders.

检查触头弹簧压力,与相邻触头组的压力比较是否相等。检查电源和控制电路保险丝触点有无过热迹象——检查润滑保险丝座上的触点弹片。

4.10.7 Connections 连接

Examine all power and control connections for tightness and signs of overheating. Check flexible leads for fraying and brittleness.

检查所有电源和控制线路连接是否紧固和有过热迹象。检查柔性接头是否磨损和变脆。

4.10.8 Overcurrent Relays 过流继电器

Check for proper settings (relate to motor FLC).

检查设置是否正确(与电动机满载额定电流相关)。

Inspect for dirt, grease and corrosion and for freedom of movement (not possible with an electronic type Of OCR).

检查有无污垢、油脂、腐蚀以及移动的可能(电子式过流继电器无法检查)。

A thorough OCR performance test can only be carried out by calibrated current injection.

只有通过校准电流注入装置才能进行全面的过流继电器性能测试。

4.10.9 Control Operation 控制操作

Observe the sequence of operation during a normal start-up, control and shut-down of the motor. Particularly look for excessive contact sparking (only possible with open-type contactors). Remember to check the operation of emergency stop and auto-restart functions.

观察电动机正常启动、控制和停止期间的操作过程。特别要注意是否有过多的接触火花(仅在开放式接触器可见)。记得检查紧急停止和自动重启功能的运行情况。

Chapter 5　Generators and Main Circuit Breakers
第5章　发电机及其主开关

5.0　Introduction 介绍

The electrical power demand aboard ship will vary according to the ship type (tanker, bulk carrier, ro-ro, container, ferry, cruise liner, offshore support etc.) and its day-to-day operational needs (at sea or in port). To meet the power demand, two or more main generators are used which are backed up by an emergency generator and an emergency battery service.

根据船舶类型(油轮、散货船、滚装船、集装箱船、渡轮、邮轮、近海支援船等)及其日常操作的需要(海上或港口),船上的电力需求会有所不同。为满足电力需求,一般使用两台或两台以上的主发电机,并由一台应急发电机和应急蓄电池作为备用。

The construction, operation, protection and maintenance of generators is described together with a review of main circuit breakers and the main switch board.

本章综合介绍了发电机的结构、运行、保护和维护保养,并对主断路器和主配电板进行了回顾。

5.1　AC Generator Operation 交流发电机的原理

Main generator power ratings range from, typically, 100 kW–2 MW at 440 V, 60 Hz AC or 380 V, 50 Hz AC driven by diesel, steam turbine, gas turbine or propulsion shaft-driven prime movers. As the demand for increased electrical power installations arise (e. g. for specialist offshore vessels and cruise liners) it is necessary to generate at HV with voltages typically at 6.6 kV, 60Hz, but 3.3 kV and 11 kv are also used.

典型主发电机额定功率一般为 100 kW ~ 2 MW,交流 440 V, 60 Hz 或交流 380 V, 50 Hz,由柴油、蒸汽轮机、燃气轮机或推进轴驱动的原动机驱动。由于对电力装置的需求增加(例如专门的近海船只和邮轮),需要发高压电,一般电压为 6.6 kV,60 Hz,也有使用 3.3 kV 和 11 kV 的情况。

An emergency generator, typically 20–200 kW at 440 V or 220 V, will bediesel driven and fitted with an automatic start facility.

应急发电机的电压一般为 440 V 或 220 V,功率为 20~200 kW,采用柴油机驱动,并配备自动启动装置。

Battery supplies from lead-acid or alkaline cells, usually rated at 24 V DC, provide sufficient power for the emergency alarm and communication systems together with some lighting and power essential for safety during a main power failure.

电池用铅酸电池或碱性电池,通常额定电压为 24 V 直流,在主电源失效时,为紧急报警和通信系统及照明提供足够的电力以保证船舶安全。

As the vast majority of ships use alternating current (AC) generators (some times called alternators), the principles and operational features will cover this type only, and ignore the direct current (DC) type.

由于绝大多数船舶使用的是交流发电机,本章将只介绍交流发电机的工作原理和运行特点,忽略直流发电机。

The basic principle of an AC generator is: Pairs of electromagnetic poles are driven (by the prime mover) past fixed coils of wire on the stator as shown in Fig. 5. 1.

交流发电机的基本工作原理是:成对的磁极被驱动(通过原动机),切割定子的线圈,如图 5.1 所示。

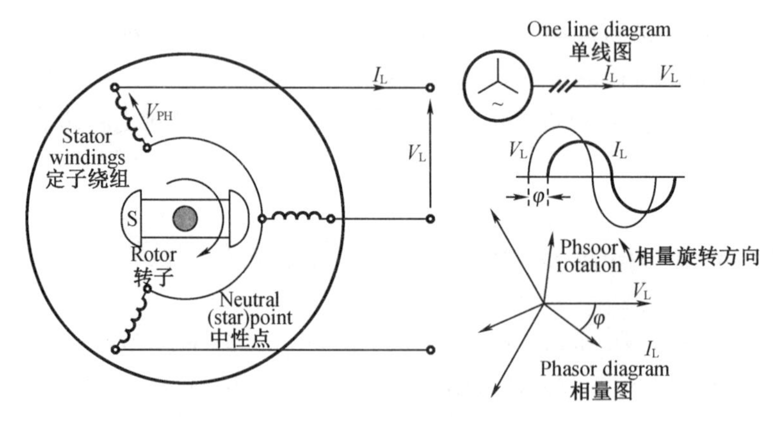

Fig. 5. 1 Principle of AC generator operation

图 5. 1 交流发电机工作原理

An alternating e. m. f. which, ideally, has a sinusoidal waveform, is induced into each stator phase winding.

交变电动势的理想状态为正弦波形,被感应到每相定子绕组中。

The useful e. m. f. level (E) is called the root mean square (rms) value and all equipment is rated in rms terms. A peak, or maximum, level is 1. 414 ($\sqrt{2}$) times larger than the rms level. e. g. if E is 440 V, then $E_{max}=1.414\times440=622$ V.

电动势的有效值 (E)为均方根值,所有设备的额定值都以均方根计算。峰值或幅值比均方根大 1. 414 倍($\sqrt{2}$)。例如,如果 E 为 440 V,那么 $E_{max}=1.414\times440=622$ V。

The size of e. m. f. generated depends on the strength of magnetic flux (Φ) and the rate at which this flux cuts the coils, so where n is the rotational speed of the rotor poles in r/min. The voltage available at the generator terminals is $V=E-I\cdot Z$ (phasor calculation) where I is the load current flowing in the stator phase windings. An internal phase volt-drop of ($I\cdot Z$) occurs due to the impedance Z of a phase winding which is made up from its resistance and reactance.

电磁场产生的电动势的大小取决于磁通量的大小(Φ)和该磁通切割线圈的速率,所以在这里电动势 E 与 n 和 Φ 成正比,其中 n 是旋转磁极的转速,单位为 r/min。发电机的端电压 $V=E-I\cdot Z$(矢量运算),I 是通过定子绕组的负载电流。电流流过由各相绕组的电阻和电抗组成的阻抗 Z,在内部各相产生了电压降($I\cdot Z$)。

The frequency f (measured in Hz) of the emf is the number of wave form cycles per second. This obviously depends on the rotational speed and the number of poles, so $n=60\,f/p$ where $n=$ speed in r/min, $p=$ pairs of poles. Related speeds and frequencies with the number of pole-pairs are given in the Table 5. 1.

电动势的频率 f(以 Hz 为单位)是每秒的波形周期数。显然这取决于转速和磁极对数,所以 $n=60f/p$。其中 n 为每分钟的转数,p 为极对数。对应的转速、频率与极对数如表 5. 1 所示。

Table 5. 1　Speeds and frequencies with the number of pole-pairs

表 5. 1　转速、频率与极对数

Pole-pairs 极对数	Speeds 转速/(r/min)	
	60 Hz	50 Hz
1	3 600	3 000
2	1 800	1 500
3	1 200	1 200
4	900	750

These two basic relationships for emf and frequency dictate how to control the voltage and frequency output of a generator. In practice the speed is maintained practically constant by the generator's prime-mover which fixes the output frequency. The constant speed then allows the size of generated emf to be directly controlled by the size of pole flux (excitation).

电动势和频率的这两个基本关系决定了如何控制发电机的电压和频率输出。实际上,保持发电机的原动机转速的恒定就能使发电机输出频率恒定。由于转速恒定,因此产生的电动势的大小直接受控于磁通量(励磁)的大小。

A practical AC generator has three sets of coils, called phase windings, located in slots in the stator surrounding the rotating magnetic poles. The emf induced in each phase is 120° out of phase with the other two phases. Three-phase windings are labelled as $U-V-W$ with colour coding of red, yellow and blue used on terminals and bus-bars. One end of each of the three phase windings are joined together to form the neutral point of a star connection.

实物交流发电机有三组线圈,称为相绕组,位于旋转磁极周围的定子槽中。每一相感应出的电动势与其他两相相差 120°。三相绕组用 $U-V-W$ 标记,并在端子和母排上用红、黄、蓝三色编码。每个三相绕组的一端连接在一起作为中性点,形成星形连接。

The other ends of the phase windings are connected to outgoing conductors called lines.

相绕组的另一端与称为“线”的输出导体相连。

The three output line voltages (represented by V_L) and the 3 output line currents (represented by I_L) combine to create the three-phase electrical power output of:

三个输出线电压(V_L)和三个输出线电流(I_L)组合,得到三相输出功率:

$$P=\sqrt{3}\cdot V_L\cdot I_L\cdot \cos\varphi(\mathrm{W})$$

In a star connection, any line voltage V_L, is made up from two phase voltages, where $V_L=\sqrt{3}\cdot V_{PH}$. The $\sqrt{3}$ factor is due to the 120° displacement between phase voltages. e. g. if $V_L=440$ V, then $V_{PH}=254$ V.

在星形连接中,任意线路电压 V_L 由两相电压组成,其中 $V_L=\sqrt{3}\cdot V_{PH}$。$\sqrt{3}$因数是由于各相电压之间的相位差为 120°。例如,如果 $V_L=440$ V,那么 $V_{PH}=440/\sqrt{3}\approx 254$ V。

The rated values of a machine always refer to line conditions (as stated on rating plate).

设备的额定值总是参考线参数(如铭牌上所述)。

Angle φ, is the phase angle between V_{PH} and I_{PH} which is determined by the types of electrical load on the generator (e. g. lighting, motors, galley equipment etc.).

角度 φ 是 V_{PH}和 I_{PH} 之间的相位角,由发电机上的电气负载类型决定(如照明、电动机、厨房设备等)。

$\cos\varphi$ is the power factor of the electrical load and is typically about 0. 8 lagging which means that the current waveform lags about 37° behind the voltage.

$\cos\varphi$ 是负载的功率因数,通常滞后 0. 8 左右,这意味着电流波形滞后于电压约 37°。

Question 思考题

The power factor meter shown in Fig. 5. 2 has its scale divided into four segments—each calibrated 0−1.0. What is the significance of each segment?

图 5.2 所示的功率因数计将其刻度分为四段,每段都经过校准,分别为 0~1.0。每段的意义是什么?

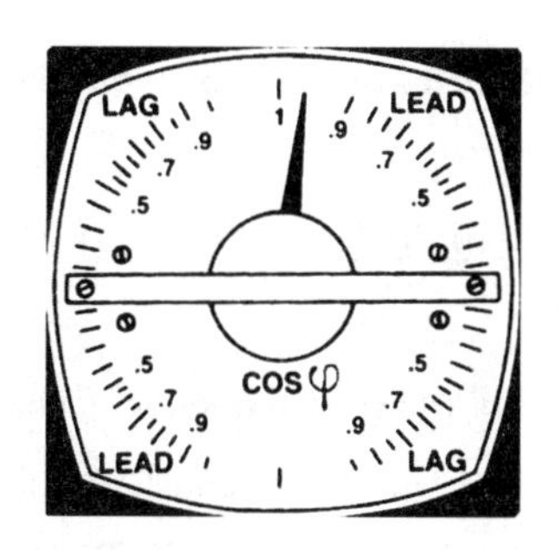

Fig. 5.2　Power factor meter

图 5.2　功率因数计

Answer 答案

An indication in the top half of the scale shows that the machine is generating. The bottom half of the scale indicates that the generator is motoring. Both top and bottom halves are further split into lagging and leading power factor sections.

刻度盘的上半部分显示机器正在发电机模式输出电力。刻度盘的下半部分表示发电机正在运行于电动机模式。上半部分和下半部分进一步分为滞后和超前功率因数部分。

A three-phase AC generator rated at 600 kW, 440 V at 0.83 lag will deliver a full load line current of:

额定功率为 600 kW,额定电压为 440 V 的三相交流发电机在 0.83 滞后时,将提供以下满载线电流:

$$I_L = \frac{P}{\sqrt{3}V_L \cdot \cos\varphi} = \frac{600\ 000}{\sqrt{3}\times 400\times 0.83} = 948.6\ \text{A}$$

This means that the phase windings, cable conductors and generator circuit breaker must be capable of carrying this full load current (FLC) continuously without exceeding their temperature Limits.

这意味着各相绕组、电缆导体和发电机断路器必须能够持续承载满载电流,而不超过其温度限制。

Question 思考题

If the above 600 kW generator circuit breaker is protected by an OCR setting of 125% what will be the actual minimum tripping current level?

如果600 kW以上的发电机断路器由125%的过流继电器保护,则实际最小跳闸电流等级是多少?

Answer 答案

The full load line current is 948.6 A, so the generator overcurrent relay will trip at: 125%×948.6=948.6 A.

满载线电流为948.6 A,因此发电机过流继电器将在125%×948.6=948.6 A跳闸。

The speed of an auxiliary diesel driven generator (DG) is accurately managed by an electronic fuel governor which maintains an almost constant output frequency over its load range.

辅助柴油驱动发电机(DG)的转速是由一个电子调速器来管理并保持在发电机负荷范围内,始终输出一个近乎恒定的频率。

A propulsion-shaft driven (SG) generator can be an efficient method for extracting electric power from the ship's main engine as the power is derived from lower cost fuel than that used for an auxiliary DG unit. The SC may be fitted directly in-line with the slow speed propulsion shaft or, more commonly, be gear-driven up to a higher speed.

推进轴驱动发电机(轴带发电机,SG)是一种可以从船舶的主机提取电力的有效设备,因为电力来自主机的燃料成本相比用于辅机单元更低。同步补偿器可以直接安装在低速推进轴上,更常见的方法是通过齿轮驱动达到更高的转速。

Also, by using a shaft generator as the main source of electric power during long sea passages, the DG units operate for short periods only with a reduced maintenance requirement.

此外,通过使用轴带发电机作为长途海上航行的主要电力来源,辅机机组只需在短时间内运行,减少了维护需求。

An apparent disadvantage of a shaft generator is that it has no direct frequency control as this is determined by the main engine speed which is set for the ship's full-away speed range (e.g. 70%-100%). This means that the frequency must be separately regulated at the output of the shaft generator to maintain a constant 60 Hz to the ship's electric power consumers. Such a frequency regulator utilizes an electric AC-DC-AC. converter as shown in Fig. 5.3.

轴带发电机的一个明显的缺点是,它没有直接的频率控制,而是由主机转速决定,为船舶的全速范围(例如70%~100%)。这意味着必须单独调节轴带发电机的输出频率,以保持对船舶的电力负载以恒定的60 Hz频率输出。该频率调节器采用如图5.3所示的交流-直流-交流变换器。

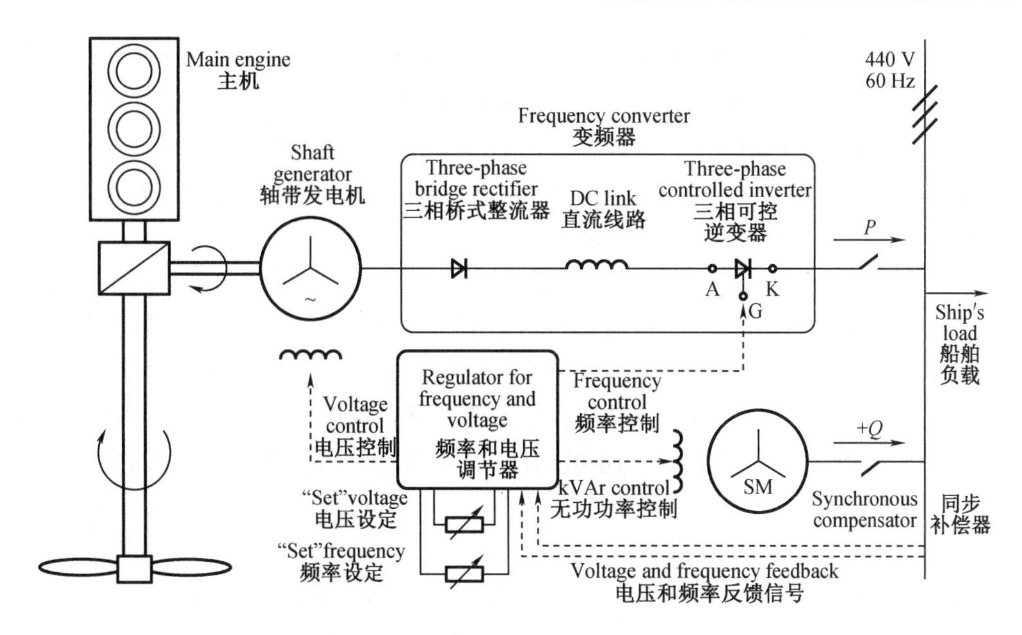

Fig. 5.3　Shaft generator control circuit

图 5.3　轴带发电机控制电路

At the three-phase rectifier stage, the AC generator voltage is converted to a DC voltage. The three-phase controlled inverter converts the DC back to a fixed output frequency by sequenced thyristor switching. A DC link inductor coil is interposed between the rectifier and inverter to smooth the normal current flow and act as a current-limiter in the event of a short circuit fault.

在三相整流阶段,交流发电机的交流电压被转换成直流电压。三相可控逆变器通过按一定顺序通断的闸管将直流电转换成固定的交流输出频率。在整流器和逆变器之间插入一个直流电感线圈,以使正常电流输出平滑,并在短路故障时作为限流器。

An inverter thyristor switch is turned on by a positive current pulse to its gate when its anode is positive with respect to its cathode. The thyristor is only turned-off when its current is reduced to (approximately) zero. This is a problem for the inverter thyristors when driving into the ship's inductive load (typically about 0.8 power factor lagging). In this case the current continues to flow in a thyristor after its voltage has gone through a zeropoint causing disruption of the inverter switching sequence.

当晶闸管的阳极为正、阴极为负,栅极接收正向电流脉冲时逆变器晶闸管导通。晶闸管只有在其通过的电流降至(近似)零时才会断开;当接入船舶的感性负载时(通常约 0.8 功率因数滞后)为逆变晶闸管带来问题。在这种情况下,晶闸管的电压经过零点后,电流继续在晶闸管中流动,从而导致逆变器导通顺序中断。

To overcome this problem, it is necessary to have the thyristor current in-phase with its voltage so that turn off is automatically achieved (line commutation) at the end of each AC half-cycle. The addition of leading kVAr compensation to the power system to create an overall unity power factor solves the problem. Hence, the SG/converter must only supply true power P (kW). At every instant the leading kVAr($+Q$) must exactly match the lagging kVAr($-Q$) of the ship's load so the compensation must be automatically controlled. The practical solution is to include a synchronous motor, operating as a synchronous compensator, whose operating power factor is controlled by regulating its d. c. field current.

为了克服这个问题,必须使晶闸管的电流与其电压同相,以便在每个交流半周期结束时自动实现关断(换向)。在电力系统中加入超前的无功补偿,以创造一个单位的功率因数,解决了这个问题。因此,SG/变换器必须只提供真正的有功功率 P (kW)。在每一时刻,超前的无功功率 ($+Q$)必须精确匹配船舶负载的滞后无功功率($-Q$),因此补偿必须被自动控制。实际的解决方案是增加一个同步电动机,作为同步补偿器,其运行功率因数是通过调节其直流磁场电流来控制的。

Overall, the bus-bar voltage is fixed by the field flux in the shaft generator and the bus-bar frequency is regulated by the controlled inverter.

总而言之,轴带发电机的磁场磁通量使母线电压恒定,用可控的逆变器调节母线频率。

5.2 Generator Construction and Cooling 发电机结构及其冷却

5.2.1 Construction 结构

The two main parts of any rotating AC machine are its stator and rotor.

旋转交流发电机的两个主要部件是定子和转子。

The fabricated steel stator frame supports the stator core and its three-phase windings as shown in Fig. 5.4.

装配式定子钢架支撑定子铁芯及其三相绕组,如图 5.4 所示。

The stator core is assembled from laminated steel with the windings housed in slots around the inner periphery of the cylindrical core.

定子铁芯由叠层钢组装而成,绕组被封装在围绕圆柱形铁芯的内部外围的槽中。

The stator coils are interconnected (in the end-winding regions) to form three separate phase windings with six ends. These phase ends are found in the stator terminal box as shown in Fig. 5.5.

定子线圈相互连接(在绕组末端区域),形成三个独立的六端相绕组。这些相端在定子接线盒中,如图 5.5 所示。

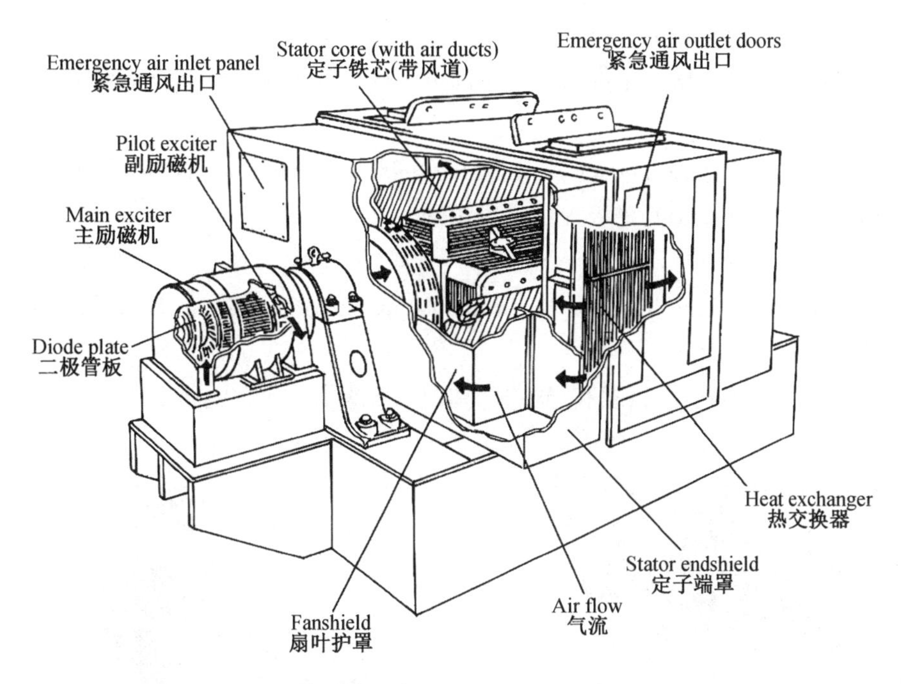

Fig. 5. 4　Generator construction

图 5. 4　发电机结构

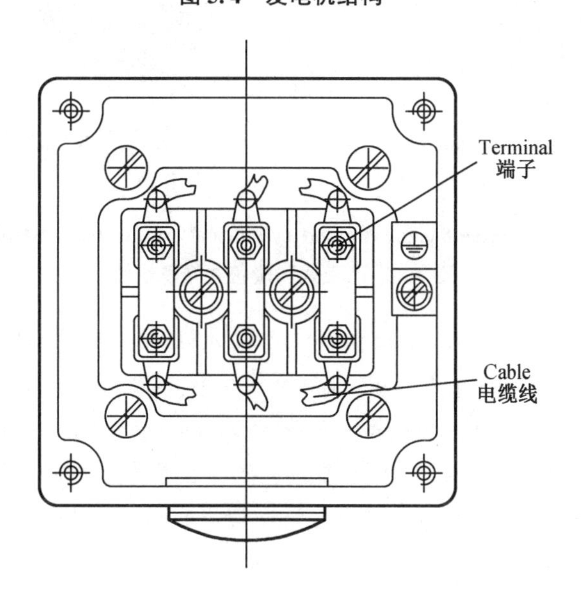

Fig. 5. 5　Generator terminal box

图 5. 5　发电机接线盒

In some cases only three terminals are available in the terminal box. In this case, the neutral or star point connection is an internal part of the stator winding arrangement.

在某些情况下,接线盒中只有三个端子可用。在这种情况下,中性点或星形连接点是定子绕组内部的部分。

The main outgoing cables connected to the seterminals conduct the generator's electric power to its circuit-breaker at the main switchboard.

连接到这些端子的主输出电缆将发电机的电力传导到主配电板上的断路器。

The rotor of a main AC generator provides the field excitation from its electromagneticpoles.

主交流发电机的转子由其磁极提供磁场激励。

Two constructional forms of rotor are available as shown in Fig. 5. 6: salient pole type, cylindrical type.

转子有两种结构形式:凸极式和隐极式,如图 5. 6 所示。

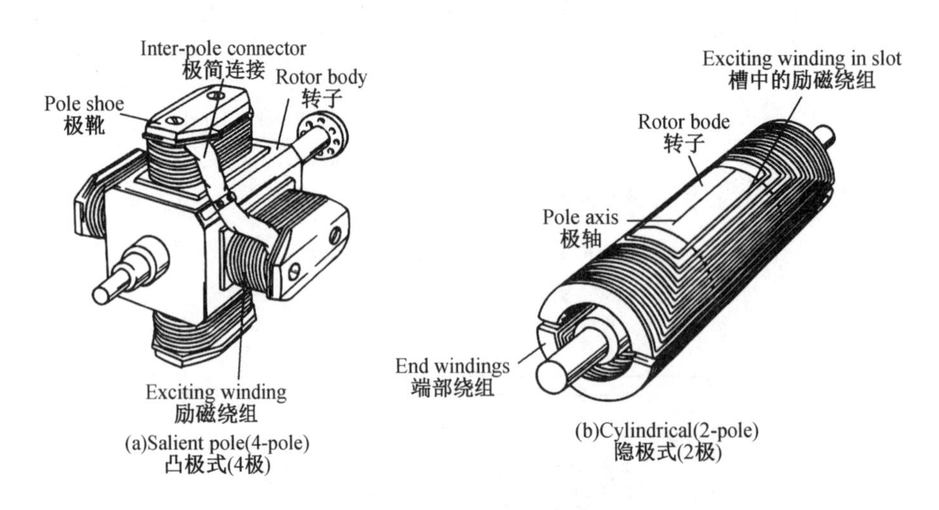

Fig. 5. 6 Salient pole type and cylindrical type rotor construction

图 5. 6 凸极式和隐极式转子结构

The salient pole type has projecting poles bolted or keyed onto the shaft hub. Field excitation windings are fitted around each pole. This type of rotor is used with medium and low shaft speeds (1,800 r/min and below) and is the most common arrangement for marine generators.

凸极式转子具有通过螺栓或键接在轴毂上的突出极靴。励磁线圈安装在每个磁极周围。这种类型的转子用于中低转速(1 800 r/min 以下)下是船用发电机最常见的形式。

Cylindrical type rotors are generally used with large power, high speed (1,500-3,600 r/min) steam/gas turbine drives. The excitation windings are wedged into axial slots around the steel rotor. Unwound sections of the rotor form the pole faces between the winding slots.

隐极式转子通常用于大功率,高速(1 500~3 600 r/min)蒸汽/燃气轮机驱动中。励磁绕组嵌入转子周围的轴向槽中。转子未嵌绕组部分形成绕组槽之间的极面。

The shaft bearings of large generators (and motors) are usually insulated to prevent stray currents from circulating through. Unbalanced (stray) end-winding magnetic flux induces an

e. m. f. along the steel shaft. This will cause a current to circulate through the shaft, bearings and bedplate to produce arcing across the bearing surfaces and degradation of the oillayer. Under generator unbalanced fault conditions the bearing problem it may be severe.

大型发电机(和电动机)的轴和轴承通常是绝缘的,以防止杂散电流通过。不平衡的(杂散的)端绕组磁通量会沿钢轴产生电动势。这将导致电流通过轴、轴承和机座闭环,在轴承表面产生电弧和油层退化。在发电机不平衡故障情况下,轴承问题可能会很严重。

To prevent the flow of shaft current, one bearing (usually the non-drive end) is electrically isolated from earth by a thin layer of insulating material beneath the bearing pedestal. The pedestal holding-down bolts must also be insulated by suitable sleeving.

为了防止轴电流通路,一个轴承(通常是非驱动端)通过在轴承座下面的一薄层绝缘材料与大地绝缘。底座固定螺栓也必须用合适的套管绝缘。

In normal operation the effectiveness of the pedestal insulation can be checked by measuring its voltage to earth which may show as a few volts.

在正常运行中,可以通过测量对地电压来检查基座绝缘的有效性,对地电压可能显示为几伏。

The rotor poles are supplied with direct current (DC) from an exciter. If the exciter equipment is a conventional DC generator or is static (see section on excitation methods), the DC excitation current is fed into the field windings via carbon brushes on a pair of shaftmounted slip-rings.

转子磁极由励磁机提供直流电。如果励磁设备是传统的直流发电机或静态的设备(见励磁方式部分),则直流励磁电流通过轴上安装了滑环的一对碳刷馈送到励磁绕组。

To eliminate the maintenance problems associated with rotating contacts, a brushless arrangement is usual for marine generators. All brush gear, commutators and slip rings are eliminated by using an AC exciter with its output being rectified by shaft-mounted silicon diodes as shown in Fig. 5. 7. The diodes are connected as a three phase AC/DC bridge circuit.

为了消除与旋转触点有关的维护问题,船用发电机通常采用无刷的形式。所有的电刷齿轮、换向器采用交流励磁器而取消滑环,励磁器的输出由轴装硅二极管整流,如图 5. 7 所示。这两个二极管连接成三相交流电/直流电桥式电路。

The six diodes, mounted on the shaft, convert the AC exciter output to DC which is then fed directly into the main generator rotor field windings.

六个二极管安装在轴上,将交流励磁器的输出转换为直流,然后直接馈送到主发电机的转子励磁绕组。

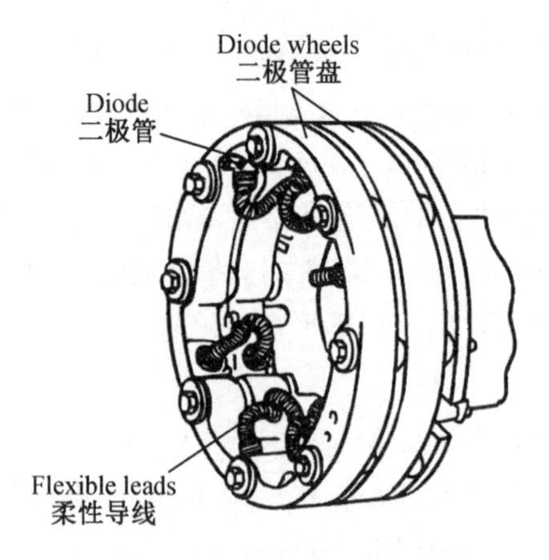

Fig. 5.7 Rotor diode plate

图 5.7 转子二极管板

Note, the AC exciter has its own DC field poles fitted on its stator while the rotor carries its three-phase AC exciter output windings. This construction layout is inverted compared with that of the main generator.

注意,交流励磁机有自己的直流励磁磁极安装在其定子上,而转子携带三相交流励磁机输出绕组,这与主发电机的结构布置相反。

5.2.2 Cooling 冷却

Power losses, typically 10% of the generator rating, cause internal heating in the windings and magnetic cores of both rotor and stator. This heat must be continuously transferred out of the generator to prevent excessive temperature rise causing breakdown of winding insulation.

功率损耗通常占发电机额定功率的 10%,它导致转子和定子的绕组及铁芯内部发热。这种热量必须不断地传递出发电机,以防止过高的温升造成绕组绝缘击穿。

Forced air circulation in a closed circuit (to prevent ingress of dirt) via an air cooler is pressurised by a fan on the rotor shaft: Cooling air is forced through ventilation ducts in the stator core, between rotor poles and through the air gap (a few millimetres) between stator and rotor.

封闭回路中的强制空气循环(以防止污物进入),空气冷却器由转子轴上的风扇加压,冷却空气被强迫通过定子铁芯、转子磁极之间的风道,以及定子和转子之间的气隙(几毫米)。

Water cooling of the circulating air may also be used for generators with a large power rating. Temperature detectors (resistance type, thermistors or thermocouples) are used to monitor the temperature of stator windings, bearings and the cooling air/water of the generator. Single or grouped temperature alarms are activated at the main watchkeeping position.

额定功率较大的发电机也可用水冷的循环空气进行冷却。温度探测器(电阻型,热敏电阻或热电偶)用于监测定子绕组、轴承和发电机的冷却空气/水的温度,可在主值班地点激活单个或分组温度报警。

While the generator is stopped during standby or maintenance periods, low power electric heaters within the machine prevent internal condensation forming on the winding insulation. These heaters may be switched on manually or automatically from auxiliary contacts on the generator circuit-breaker. Heater power supplies are normally 220 V AC single-phase supplied from a distribution box local to the generator.

当发电机在待机或维护期间停止时,机器内部的低功率电加热器防止绕组绝缘上形成内部冷凝水。这些加热器可以手动打开或通过发电机断路器上的辅助触点自动打开。加热器电源通常为 220 V 单相交流,由机旁配电箱供电。

Question 思考题

The water cooling system on a large generator is out of service due to a faulty inlet valve. How will this affect the generator operation?

某大型发电机的水冷却系统因进水阀故障而无法使用。这将对发电机的运行产生怎样的影响?

Answer 答案

The generator can only be used to supply a much reduced electrical power output to keep the machine temperatures below their maximum permitted levels. External emergency doors in the generator's air cooling ducts may be opened in such cases. The penalty is that the normally closed air circuit of the generator is now open to the engine room atmosphere.

发电机电力输出供应将大大减少,以保持机器温度低于最大允许等级。在这种情况下,可以打开发电机风冷管道的外部应急通道。其缺点是,发电机通常封闭的空气回路现在对机舱大气敞开。

5.3 Excitation Methods 励磁的方式

The two factors essential for the production of a generated e. m. f. in an AC generator are rotational speed (n) and magnetic flux(Φ). Field windings on the rotor create strong magnetic field poles when direct current is passed through them. Various methods have been devised to supply the correct DC field (excitation) current to produce the required AC output voltage from the stator terminals. The excitation must be continually regulated to maintain the generator output voltage as the load power demand fluctuates.

在交流发电机中产生电动势的两个重要因素是转速(n)和磁通量(Φ)。当直流电通过转子绕组时,转子上的励磁绕组会产生强磁场。已经设计了各种方法来提供合适的直流磁场(励磁)电流,以产生定子端电压所需的交流输出。励磁必须持续调节,使发电机输出电压在负载波动时维持稳定。

Broadly, the excitation methods are either rotary or static. A rotary method utilises an AC or DC exciter which is shaft-mounted and rotates with the main generator rotor. Traditionally, rotary exciters were DC generators with stationary field poles, rotating armature, commutator and brushgear. Now the most common arrangement is to use a shaft mounted AC exciter.

广义地说,励磁方式要么是旋转的,要么是静态的。旋转方式利用一个轴带的交流或直流励磁机,并与主发电机转子一起旋转。传统的转子发电机励磁机是由固定磁极、旋转电枢、换向器和电刷组成的直流电动机。现在最常见的形式是使用安装在轴上的交流励磁机。

In some applications, a small additional rotary pilot exciter may be used to supply current to the main exciter field. A pilot exciter is a small permanent magnet AC generator which is driven from the generator shaft. Its output voltage is generally at a high frequency (e. g. 1,000 Hz) but this is rectified to DC before being fed into the main exciter field.

在某些应用中,一个小型的附加旋转引导励磁机可用于向主励磁场提供电流。引导励磁机是一种小型的永磁交流发电机,由发电机轴驱动。它的输出电压通常是高频的(例如 1 000 Hz),但在馈送到主励磁机之前,它被整流为直流。

A "brushless" excitation scheme is shown in Fig. 5. 8. The absence of brushes, brushgear and carbon dust improves reliability and considerably reduces generator maintenance. Exciter voltage is achieved by six shaft-mounted silicon diodes. The suppression resistor connected across the main generator field protects the diodes against voltage surges arising from sudden changes in excitation current.

无刷励磁方案如图 5. 8 所示。没有电刷、齿轮和碳尘,提高了可靠性,大大减少了发电机的维护。励磁器电压由六个安装在轴上的硅二极管实现。连接在主发电机磁场上的抑制电阻保护二极管免受励磁电流突然变化引起的电涌。

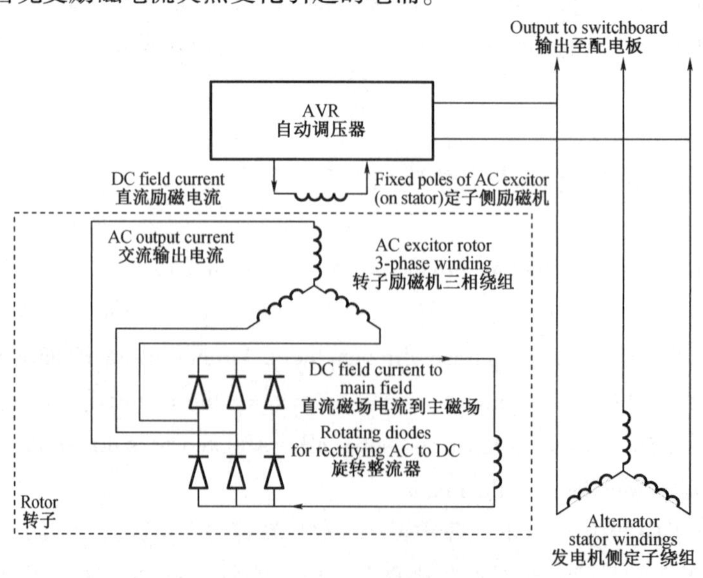

Fig. 5. 8　Brushless excitation scheme

图 5. 8　无刷励磁方案

Question 思考题

What is likely to happen if one of the rotating diodes fails, and becomes:

(a) An open circuit;

(b) A short-circuit.

如果其中一个旋转二极管失效,并发生如下故障,可能会发生什么?

(a)开路;

(b)短路。

Answer 答案

(a) The remaining healthy diodes would continue to supply the main field. In manual (hand) control the total field current, and hence generator voltage, will be slightly reduced. Under AVR control, the exciter field current would be automatically boosted to maintain the correct generator voltage while the diode failure would probably be undetected. The exciter will gradually overheat.

(a) 其余健康的二极管将继续向主磁场供电。手动控制总磁场电流时,发电机电压将略有降低。在自动调压器控制下,励磁机的励磁电流将自动提高,以保持合适的发电机电压,而二极管故障可能不会被检测到。励磁机会逐渐过热。

(b) A short-circuited diode is more serious as it leads to a short-circuited exciter. Rapid overheating of the exciter will occur.

(b) 二极管短路会导致励磁器短路,情况更为严重。励磁机会迅速过热。

Although diode failures are rare, some generator field systems are fitted with an electronic detector relay to give an alarm and/or trip signal when such a fault occur. Usually, the detector monitors the exciter field current whose size and shape are noticeably affected by a diode failure.

二极管故障很少见,一些发电机励磁系统安装了电子检测继电器,如果发生这种故障,可以发出警报和/或跳闸信号。通常探测器会监测励磁机的励磁电流,其大小和波形受到二极管失效的影响明显。

Generators with rotary exciters, conventional or brushless, have a relatively sluggish response to sudden load changes. For example, it may take typically up to 1.5 s to correct a 15% voltage dip caused by the start-up of a large pump motor.

带有旋转励磁器的发电机,无论是传统的还是无刷的,对负载的突然变化的响应都相对缓慢。例如,通常需要 1.5 s 来修正由大型电动机启动引起的 15%的电压降。

Question 思考题

What factors govern the overall voltage response of a generator to sudden (transient) load changes?

什么因素控制发电机对突然(瞬态)负载变化的整体电压响应?

Answer 答案

The main opposition to changes in the field current required to correct the generator output voltage are:

(1) Inductance of main rotor field winding;

(2) Inductance of exciter field winding;

(3) Regulator (manualor automatic) response.

修正发电机输出电压所需的励磁电流变化的主要阻碍是:

(1)主转子磁场绕组的电感;

(2)励磁机励磁绕组的电感;

(3)调节器(手动或自动)的响应。

The transient voltage response of a generator can be improved by eliminating the rotary exciter in favour of a static excitation method. In this arrangement, the generator field draws its d. c. current via a static excitation transformer/rectifier unit fed directly from the generator voltage and current output. This arrangement is known as compounding as it is controlled by voltage (shunt effect) and current (series effect) feedback.

发电机的瞬态电压响应可以通过取消旋转励磁机而采用静态励磁方式来改善。在这种形式中,发电机磁场通过静态励磁变压器/整流单元直接从发电机的电压和电流输出端获得直流电流。这种安排被称为复励,因为它是由电压(分流效应)和电流(串联效应)反馈控制的。

Response time as low as 0. 1 s to correct a 15% voltage dip are common with static excited compound generators. This fast response is most desirable on general/bulk cargo ships where heavy and frequent load surges arise from deck cranes and winch gear.

静态励磁复励发电机修正15%的电压降的响应时间低至0. 1 s是常见的。这种快速响应最适合一般货船/散货船,因为甲板克令吊和缆机装置会引起负荷频繁波动。

Such static excitation equipment may be located within the generator casing or inside the main switchboard. This type of generator has two shaft slip-rings and brushgear to connect the static excitation equipment to the rotor field winding.

这种静态励磁设备可以安装在发电机外壳内或主配电板内。这种发电机有两个轴滑环和电刷,它们可将静态励磁设备连接到转子磁场绕组上。

The basic scheme of a self-excited compounded generator is shown in Fig. 5. 9 (single-phase operation is shown for simplicity).

自励复合发电机的基本方案如图 5.9 所示(简单起见,单相运行)。

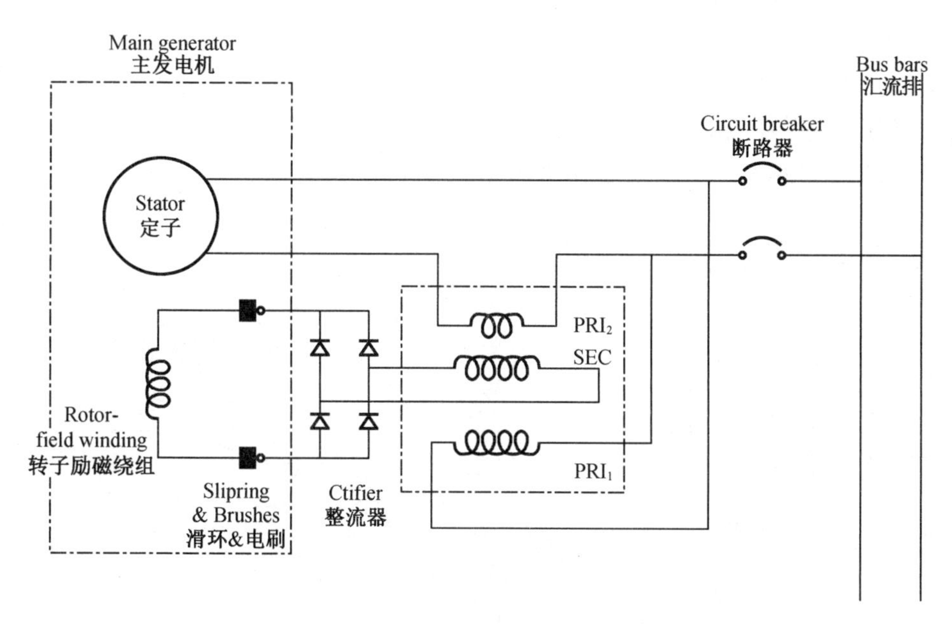

Fig. 5.9　Singal phase compound excetation circuit

图 5.9　单相励磁电路

Note, compounded means that the excitation is derived from the generator output voltage and its current.

注意,复合的意思是励磁来自发电机输出的电压和电流。

On no-load, the generator excitation is provided by the PRI_1 winding of the excitation transformer. On load, the generator current injects an additional excitation current via PRI_2 of the transformer to maintain a constant output voltage. If the excitation components are carefully designed, the generator voltage of a compounded generator can be closely maintained at all loads without the use of an AVR or manual voltage trimmer. However, some generator manufacturers do include an AVR and a manual trimmer rheostat in such a compounded static excitation scheme. This addition may provide closer voltage regulation over the load range and allow manual control of the generator voltage, e. g. for synchronising and kVAr load balancing between generators.

在空载时,发电机励磁由励磁变压器的 PRI_1 绕组提供。在负载情况下,发电机电流通过变压器的 PRI_2 注入额外的励磁电流,以保持恒定的输出电压。如果励磁元件经过精心设计,复励发电机的电压可以在不使用自动调节器或手动电压微调器的情况下,密切维护所有负载。然而,一些发电机制造商确实将自动调节器和手动微调变阻器加在这样的复合静态激励设计中。这样可以提供更紧密的电压调节,并允许手动控制发电机电压,例如发电机之间的同步和无功功率负载平衡。

A practical three-phase static excitation scheme has additional components such as reactors and capacitors. The circuit in Fig. 5. 10 has no AVR or manual trimmer regulator. A load current surge will automatically feed back an adjustment to the field excitation to correct the resulting voltage surge so quickly that the output voltage remains practically constant.

实际应用中三相静态励磁方式有额外的组件,如电抗器和电容器。图 5. 10 所示的电路没有自动调压器或手动微调调节器。负载电流的冲击将自动反馈到励磁调整,以修正由此产生的电压冲击,其调节之迅速,使输出电压几乎维持恒定。

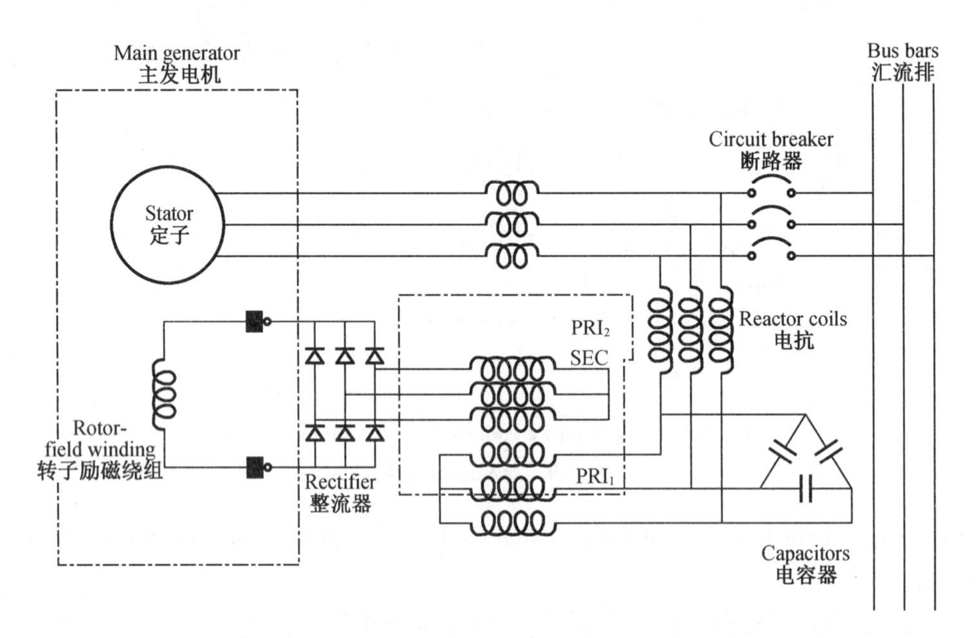

Fig. 5. 10 Three-phase compound excetation circuit

图 5. 10 三相励磁电路

Compound excitation systems require the static components to be designed to closely match its associated generator.

复合励磁系统要求静态元件要与相关发电机紧密匹配。

5. 4 Automatic Voltage Regulation 电压自动调节

Sudden load current surges (e. g. due to motor starting) on a genetator cause a corresponding change in its output voltage. This is due to an internal voltage drop in the generator windings and the effect is usually called voltage dip. Similarly, load shedding will produce an overvoltage at the bus-bars. An unregulated or non-compounded generator excitation system would not be realistic on board ship due to the varying voltage caused by the fluctuating load demand. AVR equipment is necessary to rapidly correct such voltage changes. See Fig. 5. 11.

发电机上突然产生的负载浪涌电流(例如由于电动机启动)导致其输出电压相应的变化。发电机内部绕组的电压降通常称为电压暂降。类似地,负载切除将使母线上产生过电压。由于负荷需求的波动会引起电压的变化,非调节或非复合发电机励磁系统在船上应用是不现实的。自动电压调节设备是必要的,以迅速修正这种电压变化。如图 5.11 所示。

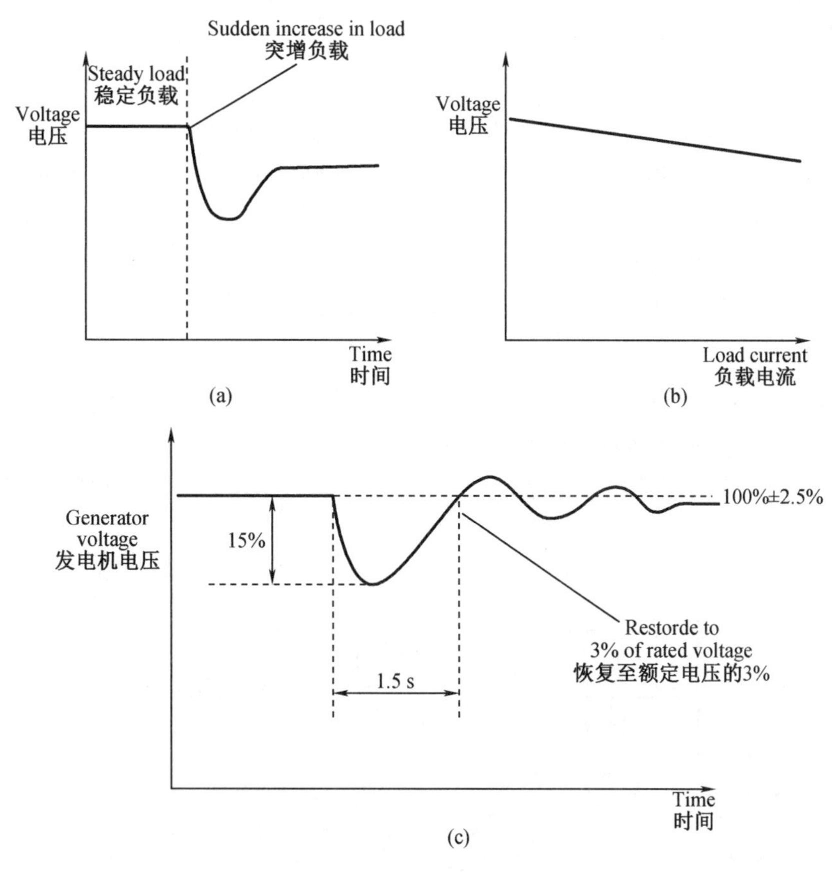

Fig. 5.11　AVR voltage response

图 5.11　自动调压器的电压调节响应

An AVR will control the generator's voltage to ±2. 5% (or better) of its set value over the full load range. This is its steady-state voltage regulation. Transient voltage dip is usually limited to 15% for a specified sudden load change with recovery back to rated voltage within 1. 5 s. In special cases where unusually large surges are expected (e. g. from heavy-duty cargo cranes) the generator/AVR performance limits may be extended.

自动调压器将在全负荷范围内将发电机电压控制在其设定值的±2. 5%以内(或更好)。这是它的稳态电压调整率。对于指定的突然负载变化,瞬态电压降通常限制在 15%以内,并能在 1. 5 s 内恢复到额定电压。在一些特殊情况下,发电机/自动调压器的性能要求可能会扩大(例如来自重型货物起重机的要求)。

The AVR senses the generator output voltage and acts to alter the field current to maintain the voltage at its set value. A manual trimmer regulator may be fitted on the generator control panel to set the voltage level e. g. 440 V. More usually, the voltage trimmer potentiometer is on the control card of the AVR so is not accessible to an operator.

自动调压器感应发电机输出电压,改变励磁电流,维持电压在设定值。手动微调调节器可安装在发电机控制面板上,以设置电压等级,如440 V。更常见的是,电压微调电位计在自动调压器的控制板上,因此操作人员不易访问。

The control circuit for a modern AVR consists of transformers, rectifiers, zener diodes, transistors and thyristors. These are mounted on one or more circuit cards fitted either within the switchboard or local to the generator.

现代化的自动调压器控制电路由变压器、整流器、稳压二极管、晶体管和晶闸管组成。这些都安装在配电板或发电机旁的一个或多个电路板上。

Although the AVR control circuit design varies with the manufacturer the basic scheme contains the following elements shown in Fig. 5. 12.

虽然不同制造商的自动调压器电路设计不同,但基础方案包含的元件如图5. 12所示。

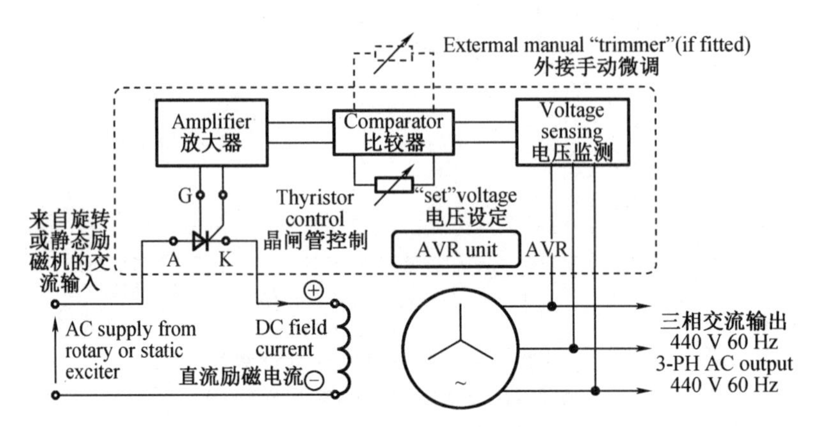

Fig. 5. 12 AVR block diagram

图5. 12 自动调压器系统框图

The voltage sensing unit transforms down, rectifies and smooths the generator output voltage, This produces a low voltage DC signal that is proportional to the AC generator voltage. This actual DC signal is compared with a set DC value produced by a reference circuit of zener diodes and resistors. An error signal output from the comparator is then amplified and made suitable for driving the field circuit regulating thyristor(s).

电压感应单元对发电机输出电压进行降压、整流和滤波处理,产生与交流发电机电压成正比的低压直流信号。此实际的直流信号与一个由稳压二极管和电阻组成的参考电路的直流设定值相比较。然后将比较器输出的偏差信号放大,使之适于驱动励磁电路的晶闸管调节。

A thyristor is a fast-acting electronic switch controlled by a voltage signal at its gate terminal. This device rectifies and regulates the generator field current.

晶闸管是一种由栅极电压信号控制的快速动作的电子开关。其可对发电机励磁电流进行整流和调节。

Additional components and sub-circuits are included in the AVR to ensure:

(1) Rapid response time with voltage stability;

(2) Fair current (and kVAr) sharing when generators are to be operated in parallel;

(3) Quick voltage build-up during generator run-up;

(4) Overvoltage/undervoltage alarm/trip protection.

自动调压器中还包括其他组件和子电路,以确保:

(1)响应时间短,电压稳定;

(2)当发电机并网运行时,电流(和无功功率)分配平衡;

(3)发电机启动过程中快速建立电压;

(4)过压、欠压报警、跳闸保护。

The complete AVR circuit is fairly complex and includes a few pre-set variable resistors for the control of sensitivity, offset-error and stability (proportional, integral and differential control). These are adjusted and set during generator trials to achieve an optimum and stable performance. It is recommended that you resist the temptation to fiddle with such pre-set controls unless fully competent with such a feedback control system.

完整的自动调压器电路相当复杂,包括几个预设的可变电阻,用于控制灵敏度、偏差和稳定性(比例、积分和微分控制)。这些调整和设置在发电机试验期间进行,以实现最佳且稳定的性能。切勿乱动预设控制参数,除非能完全掌握这种反馈控制系统。

AVR running checks, as guided by the manufacturer, consist of AC and DC voltage measurements at installed test points. These are compared with values found acceptable during previous generator trials. The test voltmeter type and its range are usually specified for each test.

在制造商的指导下,自动调压器运行检查包括在预装测试点位的交流和直流电压检测。将这些测量值与之前的发电机试验中正常值进行比较。检测电压表的类型及其量程通常在每次试验时都有明确规定。

Most ships will carry a spare AVR unit or spare cards which may be interchanged after a suspected failure. An AVR changeover should only be attempted when its generator is stopped and locked off. Checks at the test points on the new AVR excitation field current level and the manual regulator operation (if fitted) should be proven with the generator running on no-load before attempting to synchronise on to the bus-bars.

大多数船舶只携带一个备用自动调压器单元或备用电路板,在怀疑其故障后可以互换。自动调压器更换只能在发电机停机并锁定时进行。在测试点位对新自动调压器励磁电流大小的检查和手动调节器操作功能(如果安装),应在发电机空载运行时进行验证,然后再尝试同步并到母线上。

When generators are load sharing in parallel, check for approximately equal current (or kVar) sharing between the machines. This will indicate correct operation of their AVRs.

当发电机并联运行时,检查两台机器之间的电流(或无功功率)分配是否近似相等。这表示自动调压器在正常工作。

Question 思考题

What precaution must be taken when testing the insulation of generator cables and wiring connected to an AVR unit?

当对连接到自动调压器装置的发电机电缆和接线进行绝缘测试时,必须采取什么预防措施?

Answer 答案

Electronic components such as transistors, integrated circuit chips, thyristors, etc. are likely to be damaged during a high voltage (500 V) megger test. To test the generator and its cables to earth and protect the electronic parts, either:

(1) Short-circuit all outgoing cable terminals during the IR test;

(2) Remove electronic card(s);

(3) Disconnect all cables at both ends and test separately.

电子元件如晶体管、集成电路芯片、晶闸管等在高压(500 V)兆欧表测试电压下很可能损坏。测试发电机及其接地电缆,并保护电子部件,措施包括:

(1)测试时,将所有出线端子短路;

(2)移除电路板;

(3)断开所有电缆的两端,分别测试。

5.5 Generators in Parallel 发电机的并联运行

Main generator units (gas-turbine, steam turbine or diesel drives) have to be run in parallel to share a total load that exceeds the capacity of a single machine. Changeover of main and standby generator units requires a brief parallel running period to achieve a smooth transition without blackout. For simplicity and security it is not normally possible to run a main generator in parallel with either the emergency generator or a shore supply. Circuit breaker interlocks arc used to prevent such an arrangement.

主发电机组(燃气轮机、蒸汽轮机或柴油机)必须并联运行,以分担超过单机容量的总负荷。主发电机和备用发电机的转换需要并联运行一段时间,以实现平稳过渡而不失电。为了简单和安全,通常不能将主发电机与应急发电机或岸电并联运行。断路器联锁装置用于防止这种情况。

Essentially, parallel running is achieved in the two stages of: Synchronising then load sharing. Both operations are, of course, usually carried out automatically but manual control is still in common use and is generally provided as a back-up to the auto control.

并联运行基本可分为以下两个阶段实现:先同步再转移负载。当然,这两种操作通常都是自动执行的,但手动控制仍然常用,通常作为自动控制的备用。

The generator already on-the-bars is called the running machine and the generator to be brought into service is the incoming machine (Fig. 5. 13). To smoothly parallel the incoming generator, it must be synchronised with the live bus-bars.

已经在网的发电机称为运行机组,而要投入使用的发电机则是待并发电机(图 5. 13)。为了顺利并联待并发电机,它必须与主电网同步。

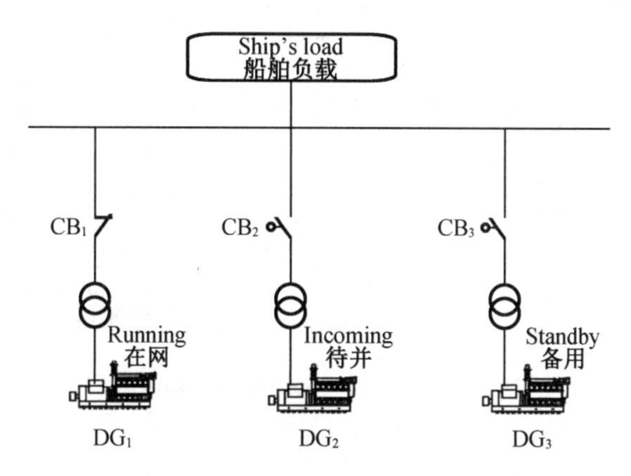

Fig. 5. 13　Two DG to be synchronised

图 5. 13　两台发电机准备并网

Question 思考题

What are the likely consequences of attempting to close the incomer's circuit breaker when the generator voltages are not in synchronism?

当发电机电压不同步时,试图闭合待并发电机主开关的可能后果是什么?

Answer 答案

Voltage phase difference causes a large circulating current between the machines which produces a large magnetic force to pull the generator voltages (and field poles) into synchronism. This means rapid acceleration of one rotor and deceleration of the other. The large forces may physically damage the generators and their prime-movers and the large circulating current may trip each generator breaker, lead to blackout, danger and embarrassment.

电压相位差会在发电机之间产生较大的环流,从而产生较大的励磁,将发电机电压(和磁极)拉入同步状态。这意味着要使一个转子快速加速,另一个转子减速。较大的作用力可能会对发电机及其原动机造成物理损伤，并且较大的环流可能会使每台发电机断路器跳闸，导致全船失电、危险和困境。

To achieve smooth manual synchronising, the incomer must be brought upto speed to obtain approximitely the same frequency as shown on the bus-bar frequency meter e. g. 60 Hz(Fig. 5. 14).

为了实现平稳的手动同步，必须将待并发电机转速提高使其频率接近电网频率表所示的频率，例如 60 Hz(图 5. 14)。

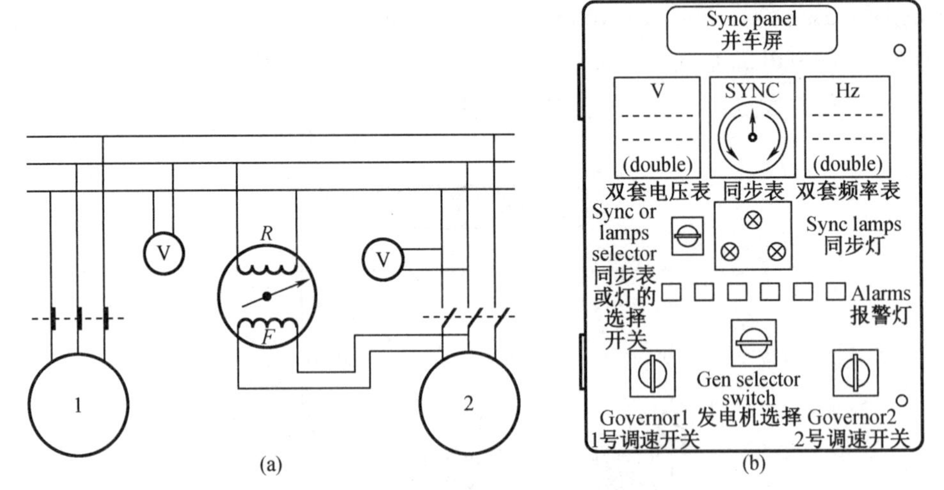

Fig. 5. 14 Synchronising instruments

图 5. 14 并车仪表

The incoming generator voltage is set by its AVR or manually trimmed (if available) to be equal to the bus-bar voltage.

待并发电机的电压通过自动调压器设定或手动调整(如果可用)，使其等于母线电压。

Fine tuning of the speed can now be observed on the synchroscope or synchronising lamps. The incomer is adjusted so that the synchroscope indicator rotates slowly clockwise (fast direction) at 3−5 s per indicator revolution.

现在可以在同步表或同步灯上观察到转速的微调。调节待并发电机，使同步表指针以每转一圈 3～5 s 的速度顺时针缓慢旋转(快速方向)。

The circuit-breaker should be closed as the indicator approaches the 12 o'clock (in-phase) position. Breaker closing between 5−to the 12 o'clock synchroscope position is satisfactory as long as the pointer rotation is fairly slow.

当指针接近 12 点钟(同相)位置时，断路器应合闸。如果指针旋转相当缓慢，断路器在同步表差 5 分钟 12 点的位置合闸是合适的。

Question 思考题

What indication is available to show the optimum synchronised condition?
从什么指示参数可以看出已达到良好的同步状态?

Answer 答案

The incoming generator ammeter pointer will show very little kick when correctly synchronised.

正常同步时,并入发电机的电流表指针将显示非常小的跳动。

A traditional pointer-type synchroscope is usually short-time rated (e. g. up to 20 min) to avoid overheating do not forget to switch it off after a paralleling procedure.

传统的指针式同步表通常额定工作时间短(例如最多 20 min),为避免过热,在并车程序完成后不要忘记将其关闭。

Modern synchroscope indicators use a circular set of LED's (light emitting diodes) which sequentially light up to show the phase difference between the generator voltages.

现代的同步表指示器使用一组圆形发光二极管,依次点亮以显示发电机电压之间的相位差。

As a back-up, or alternative, to the synchroscope a set of lamps may be used. The correct synchronised position may be shown by either of the following methods:

(1) Lamps dark method(2 lamps);

(2) Lamps bright method (2 lamps);

(3) Sequence method(3 lamps).

作为同步表的备用或替代,可使用一组灯。可通过以下任一方法显示正确的同步点:

(1)灯光明暗法(2 灯灭);

(2)灯光明暗法(2 灯亮);

(3)灯光旋转法(3 灯)。

In each case the lamps are connected between the incoming generator and the bus-bars. The sequence method, as shown in Fig. 5. 15, is preferred as it displays a rotation of lamp brightness which indicates whether the incoming machine is running fast (clockwise) or slow (anti-clockwise). As with the synchroscope, the lamp sequence must appear to rotate slowly clockwise. Correct synchronisation occurs when the top or key lamp is dark and the two bottom lamps are equally bright.

在任一种方式下,灯都连接在进线发电机和母线之间。如图 5. 15 所示,灯光旋转法是首选方法,因为它显示灯亮度的旋转,指示输入机器是快速(顺时针)还是慢速(逆时针)。

与同步示波器一样,灯序列必须显示为顺时针缓慢旋转。当顶灯或钥匙灯暗而两个底灯亮时,会发生准确的同步。

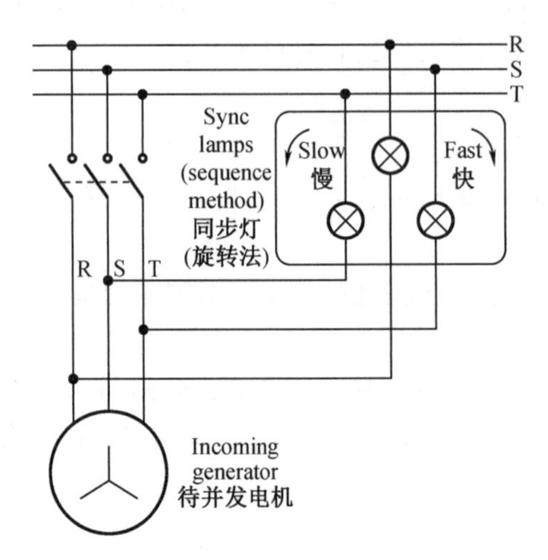

Fig. 5. 15　Synchronising with sequence method

图 5. 15　灯光旋转法同步

Question 思考题

How could you monitor the correct instant for synchronising without the aid of a synchroscope or synchronising lamps?

如果没有同步表或同步灯的帮助,如何监测准确同步的瞬间?

Answer 答案

Connect a voltmeter asshown in Fig. 5. 16 (expect up to 500 V on a 440 V system), across one pole of the open incoming generator circuit breaker. This procedure is more easily (and safely) performed at the synchroscope terminals behind the door of the synchronising panel at the front of the main switchboard. Check the circuit diagrams before such testing.

如图 5. 16 所示,在断路器的一极两端连接电压表(440 V 系统的量程要达到 500 V)。在主配电板并车屏的同步表接线端子上进行此程序更容易(更安全)。在进行此类测试之前,请先核查电路图。

Adjust the generator speed until the voltmeter very slowly fluctuates from zero to maximum.

调整发电机的转速,直到电压表缓慢地由零向最大值变动。

Close the breaker when the voltmeter indication passes through zero. Note, for this operation, an analogue (pointer and scale) meter is easier to follow than a digital type.

当电压表指示通过零点时,闭合断路器。注:对于这种操作,模拟(有指针和刻度)电压表比数字电压表更容易跟随。

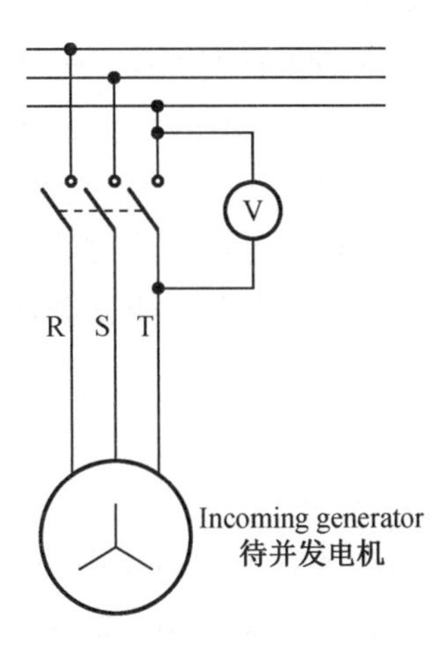

Fig. 5.16　Synchronising with a voltmeter

图 5.16　电压表同步

A check-synchronising unit has an electronic circuit to monitor the voltage, phase angle and frequency of the incoming generator with respect to the bus-bars. Circuit breaker operation is initiated by the watchkeeper but the check-synchronising monitor only allows a permit-to-close signal when all the synchronising conditions are within acceptable limits. This method provides a useful safeguard against operator error but retains overall watchkeeper control for adjusting the voltage and frequency.

同步监测装置具有用于监测待并发电机相对于母线的电压、相位角和频率的电路。断路器操作由值班人员进行,但同步监视器仅允许在所有同步参数均在可接受范围内时发出“允许合闸”信号。该方式可有效防止操作人员的误操作,且保留了用于调整电压和频率的整体看守控制。

Auto-synchronising of an incoming generator does everything an operator would do: Senses and controls the voltage and frequency then initiates a circuit-breaker close signal at the correct instant. The auto-synchronising equipment uses electronic circuits to monitor the size of voltage, frequency and phase angle difference, then acts to regulate them until they are equal to the existing bus-bar conditions.

待并发电机的自动同步功能完成了操作人员要做的所有并网操作:监测并控制电压和频率,然后在正确的瞬间发出断路器合闸信号。自动同步装置使用电子电路监测电压、频率和相位角差的大小,然后对其进行调节,直到它们等于现有母线对应参数。

Usually, the check for auto synchroniser units are switched between a set of generators as and when required. When an incoming generator has been successfully synchronised the synchronising equipment should be switched off.

通常,自动同步单元的检查会根据需要在发电机组之间切换。当待并发电机已成功同步时,同步装置应关闭。

The total bus-bar load can now be shared between generators or totally transferred to one machine. In parallel operation, a generator governor directly controls power (kW) while its AVR trimmer or manual voltage regulator controls Reactive volt amps (kVAr) or power factor.

母线总负载现在可以由发电机之间共同承担或完全转移到一台机器上。在并联运行中,发电机调速器直接控制有功功率,而其自动调压微调器或手动电压调节器控制无功功率或功率因数。

Manual kW load sharing is achieved by raising the governor setting of the incoming machine while lowering the setting on the running machine. The balance of power sharing is dictated by the governor (speed) droop of each generator prime mover. Current (or kVAr) sharing is set by the voltage droop of each generator AVR. See Fig. 5. 17.

通过升高待并发电机的调速器设定,同时降低在网发电机的调速器设定,可以实现手动有功功率分配。功率的平均分配由每个发电机原动机的调速器(转速)降决定。电流(或无功功率)分配由每个发电机的自动调压器的电压降设置。如图 5. 17 所示。

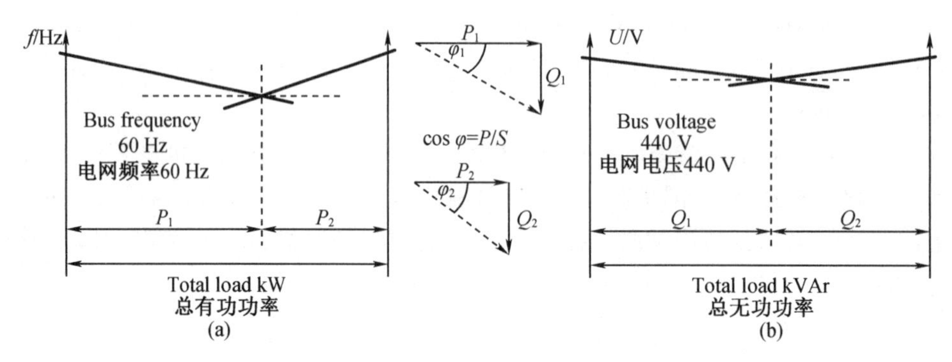

Fig. 5. 17 Generarator load sharing

图 5. 17 发电机的负载转移

For equal load sharing of kW and kVAr, each machine must have similar droop characteristics which are typically 2%-4% between no-load and full-load values.

对于有功和无功功率的平均分配,每台机器必须具有相似的下垂特性,调差系数通常在空载和满载之间,为 2%~4%。

An overall balance of load sharing for kW and kVAr can be seen by comparing the power factor (cos φ) meters of each generator.

通过比较每台发电机的功率因数(cos φ)表,可以看出有功和无功功率分配的总体平衡情况。

Question 思考题

Two generators are load sharing in parallel: Generator 1 delivers 500 kW at 0. 8 power factor lag, and Generator 2 delivers 400 kW and 350 kW/(kVAr) lag. Calculate:

(a)The kVAr loading of Generator 1;

(b)The power factor of Generator 2;

(c)The total bus-bar loading in kW, kVAr and power factor.

两台发电机并联运行进行功率分配:1 号发电机承担 500 kW 的功率,功率因数 0.8 滞后,而 2 号发电机承担 400 kW 有功功率和 350 kW 滞后的无功功率。计算:

(a)1 号发电机的无功功率;

(b)2 号发电机的功率因数;

(c)母线的总有功功率、无功功率和功率因数。

Answer 答案

(a) $\cos\varphi_1 = 0.8$, $\varphi_1 = 36.9°$, from PQS power triangle(根据功率三角形):

$$Q_1 = P_1 \cdot \tan\varphi_1 = 500 \times \tan 36.9° = 375 \text{ kW}$$

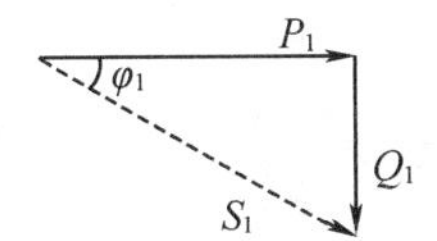

(b) $\tan\varphi_2 = \dfrac{Q_2}{P_2} = \dfrac{350}{400} = 0.875$, $\varphi_2 = 41.2°$, power factor $= \cos\varphi_2 = \cos 41.2° = 0.75$;

(c) $P = 500 + 400 = 900$ kW; $Q = Q_1 + Q_2 = 375 + 350 = 725$ kW; $\tan\varphi = \dfrac{Q}{P} = \dfrac{725}{900} = 0.81$, $\varphi = 38.9°$; power factor $= \cos\varphi = \cos 38.9° = 0.78$。

Auto-load sharing equipment is yet more black-box electronics. The circuits compare the kW loading of each generator (via CTs and VTs) and any difference is used to provide an error signal to raise, lower the governor setting of each prime mover as necessary. Such equipment is usually trouble-free, requiring little maintenance other than an occasional visual inspection, cleaning and checking the tightness of connections. Manual load sharing is the obvious fallback if the auto-control equipment fails.

自动负载分配设备是类似黑匣子的电子产品。电路比较每个发电机的有功功率(通过电流互感器和电压互感器),任何差异都用来提供偏差信号,以根据需要提高或降低每个原动机的调速器设定。这种设备通常无故障,除了偶尔进行目视检查、清洁和连接的紧密性检查外,几乎不需要维护。如果自动控制设备出现故障,显然手动负载分配是备选方案。

Question 思考题

Two generators are load sharing equally in parallel when a total loss of excitation occurs in No. 2 machine. What is the likely outcome?

两台发电机并联运行并且负载平均分配,当 2 号发电机发生完全失磁时,可能的结果是什么?

Answer 答案

Generator No. 2 will run as an induction generator drawing its excitation kVAr from No. 1. Both generator currents will rise rapidly with No. 1 becoming more lagging while No. 2 runs with a leading power factor (indicated on cos φ meter). A loss of excitation trip (if fitted) or the overcurrent relay should trip No. 2 generator probably causing an overload on No. 1. Alternatively, No. 1 trips on overcurrent which deprives No. 2 of excitation and its breaker trips out on undervoltage. Result — total power failure.

2号发电机将作为感性电动机运行,从1号发电机汲取其无功励磁。两台发电机的电流将迅速上升,1号发电机变得更加滞后,而2号发电机则以超前的功率因数(如用cos φ表所示)运行。失磁跳闸(如安装)或过电流继电器保护应使2号发电机跳闸,可能导致1号发电机过载。或者,1号发电机因过电流跳闸,使2号发电机失去励磁,其断路器因欠压跳闸。结果就是彻底停电。

5.6 Emergency Generators 应急发电机

The power rating of an emergency generator is determined by the size and role of the ship. On some small vessels a few kW will suffice for emergency lighting only. Larger and more complicated vessels, e. g. LPG carriers, passenger liners, etc., may require hundreds of kW for emergency lighting, re-starting of the main engine auxiliaries and to supply fire-fighting pumps.

应急发电机的额定功率由船舶的大小和作用决定。在一些小型船舶上,仅几千瓦就足以用于应急照明。大型和更复杂的船舶,如液化石油气运输船、客轮等,可能需要数百千瓦的功率用于应急照明、主机辅助设备的重新启动和消防泵的供电。

The construction and operation of an emergency generator is similar to that of a main generator. Excitation supplies, either static or rotary, will usually be governed by an automatic voltage regulator. In some cases where a static compounded exciter provides a reasonably constant generator voltage, the AVR may be omitted.

应急发电机的结构和运行原理与主发电机类似。静态或旋转励磁电源通常由自动电压调节器控制。在静态复合励磁机提供合适且恒定的发电机电压的某些情况下,可以省略自动调节器。

Generally, the emergency generator output voltage is at the same level as that of the main generators, e. g. 440 V, 60 Hz, three-phase AC. In an HV/LV system e. g. 6.6 kV/440 V, the emergency generator will usually operate at 440 V and the emergency switchboard will be interconnected with the engine room 440 V switchboard in normal operation.

通常,应急发电机输出电压与主发电机相同,例如440 V,60 Hz,三相交流。在6.6 kV/

440 V 的高压/低压系统中,应急发电机通常在 440 V 下运行,应急配电板将在正常运行时与机舱 440 V 配电板互连。

However, smaller emergency generator sets may deliver power at 220 V three-phase AC or even single-phase AC for lighting and essential navigation aids only. An emergency generator is connected to its own emergency switchboard and they are located together in a compartment above the water-line, e. g. on the boat deck. In normal operation the emergency board is supplied from the main board by a cable called the interconnector.

然而,较小的应急发电机组可能是仅为照明和基本导航设备提供 220 V 三相交流甚至单相交流电力的。应急发电机连接到其自身的应急配电板,它们一起位于水线上方的隔间中,例如甲板上。在正常操作中,应急配电板通过内部连接装置的电缆从主配电屏供电。

It is not normally possible to synchronise the emergency and main generators. Special interlocks in the control circuits of the circuit-breakers, at each end of the interconnector, prevent parallel running.

通常不可能使应急发电机和主发电机同步。断路器控制电路中内部连接装置两端的特殊连锁防止并联运行。

Starting of the emergency generator prime mover is generally automatic. The run-up is initiated by an electrical relay which monitors the normal voltage supply (e. g. 440 V).

应急发电机原动机的启动通常是自动的。加速由监测正常供电电压(例如 440 V)的电气继电器启动。

Falling mains frequency or voltage causes the start-up relay to operate the engine starting equipment. The prime mover may be electrically cranked from its own 24 V battery and starter motor or hydraulic started from its manual charged local to the generator engine.

电源频率或电压下降导致启动继电器动作启动设备。原动机可通过其自身的 24 V 电池和启动电动机进行电启动,或通过其自身安装在发电机机体上的手动充能装置进行液压启动。

A manual start-up may be initiated by push buttons in the main control room and in the emergency generator room. Small generator prime movers can usually be manually cranked with a starting handle.

手动启动可通过主控制室和应急发电机室内的按钮进行。小型发电机原动机通常可以通过启动手柄手摇启动。

Correct functioning of the auto-start equipment is obviously vital to the production of emergency power. Weekly testing of the emergency generator should include simulation of the loss of normal power. The start-up equipment may provide a switch to interrupt the normal voltage supply to the control panel which then triggers the start-up sequence. Loss of main power supply can easily be simulated by pulling a fuse in the auto start panel which supplies the under-voltage or under-frequency relay.

自动启动设备的正确运行显然对应急电源的产生至关重要。应急发电机每周的测试应包括正常供电的失电模拟。启动设备可以提供一个开关以中断向控制面板的正常电压供应,然后控制面板触发启动程序。通过拉动自动启动面板中的保险丝(为欠压或欠频继电器供电),可以很容易地模拟主电源的失电状态。

Emergency generators should be regularly checked and run up to speed for short test runs to comply with safety regulations. These no-load running checks should, when practicable, be supplemented occasionally by an actual load test. This requires the disconnection of normal mains power from the emergency board while the emergency generator is loaded up to near its rated value. Only proper load test will prove the performance of the emergency generator, its prime-movern and the circuit-breaker operation.

应定期检查应急发电机,并进行运行至设定转速的短时测试,以符合安全规范。如果可行,这些空载运行检查应偶尔通过实际的带负荷测试进行补充。这需要断开应急配电板的正常电源,再将应急发电机加载到接近其额定负载。只有适当的负载测试才能检验应急发电机、原动机和断路器的工作性能。

5.7 Generator Protection 发电机的保护

Apart from direct temperature measurement of the stator windings and the internal air, the protection of a generator is largely based on the sensing of current and voltage from CTs and VTs, the number and type of protective relay functions increases with the generator kVAr rating and voltage level, protective relays are electromagnetic (traditional) or electronic (increasingly more common) which are mounted on the generator front panel of the main switch hoard. Some protective-functions may be grouped together within a single relay Case. Settings for level and time-delay must be periodically checked by injecting currents-and/or voltages directly into the relay (usually via a special multi-pole socket adjacent to the relay and internally wired to it). Also see Chapter 3 for general circuit protection methods. Some typical relay types employed for generator protection are outlined in Fig. 5. 18.

除了定子绕组和内部空气的直接温度测量外,发电机的保护主要基于电流互感器和电压互感器的电流和电压监测,继电器保护功能的数量和类型随着发电机无功功率额定值和电压等级而增加,继电器保护是电磁式(传统)或电子式(越来越常见)的,安装在主配电板的发电机屏前面板上。某些保护功能可在单个继电器箱中组合在一起。必须定期通过直接向继电器注入电流和/或电压(通常通过继电器附近的特殊多极插座和内部接线)来检查上限和延时设置。一般电路保护方式见第 3 章。用于发电机保护的一些典型继电器类型如图 5. 18 所示。

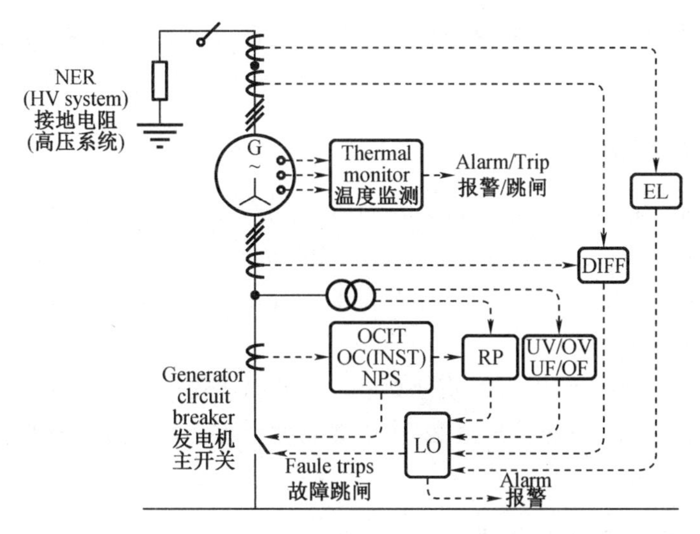

Fig. 5. 18　Generator protection system

图 5. 18　发电机的保护系统

5. 7. 1　OCIT 反时限过流继电器

The over corrent inverse time (OCIT) relay function monitors general balanced load for overloading and has current/time setting determined by the overall protective discrimination scheme.

反时限过电流继电器(OCIT)功能:监控一般平衡的负载是否过载,并具有由整体保护识别方案确定的电流/时间的设置。

Typical setting ranges for current (I) and time (t) are: $I>(0.7-2)I_n$ (I_n = normal or rated generator current), $t=1-10$ s.

电流和时间的典型设定范围如下:电流大于额定电流的 0. 7~2 倍,时间为 1~10 s。

5. 7. 2　OC(INST) 瞬时过流继电器

"Instantaneous" trip to protect against extremely high overcurrent caused by a short-circuit fault. Typical setting ranges are: $I\gg(2-10)I_n$, $t=0.1-1$ s.

"瞬时"跳闸,以防止短路故障引起的极高的过电流。典型设置范围为:电流远大于 2~10 倍的额定电流,时间为 0. 1~1 s。

5. 7. 3　NPS 负序继电器

A negative phase sequence (NPS) relay determines the amount of unbalance in the stator currents which is an indirect measure of the generator stator and rotor temperature. A relatively small degree of unbalance causes a significantly increased temperature rise so the NPS current setting is low at around 0. 2 I_n.

负序继电器(NPS)可确认定子不平衡电流的大小,这是对发电机定子和转子温度的一种间接测量。相对较小程度的不平衡电流会导致温度显著升高,因此 NPS 电流设定值较低,约为额定电流的 0.2 倍。

5.7.4 DIFF 差动保护

This is a differential measurement of current at each end of a stator phase winding. This comparison of current is to detect an internal fault in the stator windings which may be caused by partially short-circuited coil turns and/or earth faults. Current settings for this serious fault are very low e. g. about 0.1 I_n.

这是对定子各相绕组两端电流的差分测量。该电流比较用于检测定子绕组中的内部故障,该故障可能由线圈部分匝数短路和/或接地故障引起。此严重故障的电流设定值非常低,约为额定电流的 0.1 倍。

5.7.5 EL 漏电保护继电器

An earth leakage(EL) relay (sometimes called zero phase sequence) detects an earth fault current returning back through the earthed neutral connection. In a ship's HV generator system the earth fault current is limited by a high impedance neutral earthing resistor (NER) or earthing transformer so the pick-up current setting is very low, e. g. 1–5 A with a time delay of 0.1–0.5 s.

漏电保护继电器(EL,有时称为零序继电器)可检测返回到接地中性点的接地故障电流。在船舶的高压发电系统中,接地故障电流受到高阻抗中性点接地电阻(NER)或接地变压器的限制,因此拾取电流设定值非常低,为 1~5 A,其延时为 0.1~0.5 s。

5.7.6 UV/OV 欠电压/过电压保护

Under voltage and over voltage (UV/OV) functions are monitored by these relays with settings of around 0.8U_n and 1.2U_n respectively (U_n— rated voltage) with time delays of about 2 s. An overvoltage function may not be required in many protection schemes.

欠电压/过电压(UV/OV)保护功能由这些继电器监控,设置分别为 0.8U_n 和 1.2U_n(U_n 为额定电压),延时约为 2 s。在许多保护方案中可能不需要过电压保护功能。

5.7.7 UF/OF 欠频率/过频率保护

Under and over frequency (UF/OF) settings are typically 58 Hz and 62 Hz for a 60 Hz system.

在额定频率 60 Hz 的系统中,欠频率/过频率(UF/OF)保护的典型设定值为 58 Hz 和 62 Hz。

5.7.8 LO 锁闭继电器

This is the master lock out (LO) or trip/hand-reset relay responsible for tripping the generator circuit breaker. Its action is instantaneous when triggered by a protective relay. It can also be used to trip the generator prime-mover and initiate generator field suppression together with the signalling of an alarm.

这是主闭锁(LD)或跳闸/手动复位继电器,负责使发电机断路器跳闸。当由保护继电器触发时,其动作是瞬时的。它还可用于使发电机原动机跳闸,并启动发电机磁场抑制,发出报警信号。

5.7.9　RP 逆功率保护

Generators intended to operate in parallel must have reverse power protection(RP).

拟并联运行的发电机必须具有逆功率保护(RP)。

A reverse power(RP) relay monitors the direction of power flowing between the generator and the load. If a prime-mover failure occurred the generator would act as a motor. The reverse power relay detects this fault and acts to trip the generator circuit-breaker.

逆功率继电器(RP)监控发电机和负载之间的功率流动方向。如果原动机发生故障,发电机将成为电动机。逆功率继电器检测到该故障,并动作使发电机断路器跳闸。

The pick-up power level setting and time-delay setting are adjustable and are pre-set to suit the prime-mover. If the prime mover is a turbine, very little power is absorbed when motoring and a reverse-power pick-up setting of 2%-3% is usual. If the prime mover is a diesel then a setting range of 5%-15% is usually adopted with a time delay range of about 0.5-3 s is usual.

拾取功率设定值和延时设定值是可调的,并且是为适配原动机预先设置好的。如果原动机是涡轮机,则在驱动时吸收的功率非常小,逆功率拾取设置通常为2%~3%。如果原动机是柴油机,则通常采用5%~15%的设定范围,约0.5~3 s的时间延迟范围。

The RP relay operation is easily checked during a generator changeover. The outgoing generator is gradually throttled down so that it motors causing the reverse power relay to trip its generator circuit-breaker.

在发电机转换过程中,逆功率继电器的功能很容易检查。输出发电机逐渐减速,以便电动化,逆功率继电器将其发电机断路器跳闸。

5.8　Generator Maintenance 发电机的维护

Regular inspection and the correct maintenance of generators and their associated control gear is essential to prevent failure and inefficient operation.

发电机及其相关控制装置的定期检查和正确维护对于故障预防和低效运行至关重要。

Caution: Always ensure that the generator prime-mover is shut down and locked off before you begin any maintenancc; also ensure that the generator circuit breaker is locked off, auto-start circuits are disabled and electric heaters are switched off and isolated; all wiring to the generator should be inspected for damage or frayed insulation and tightness of terminal connections; particularly check for signs of oil and water contamination of cable insulation within terminal boxes; check that the cooling air intake and exhaust openings are not blocked and are free of dirt and dust.

注意:在开始任何维护之前,始终确保发电机原动机已关闭并锁闭;还应确保发电机断路器已锁定,自动启动电路已禁用,电加热器已关闭并隔离;应检查发电机的所有接线是否损坏或绝缘是否磨损以及端子连接的紧固性,特别要检查接线盒内电缆绝缘是否有进油和进水迹象;检查冷却空气进气口和排气口是否堵塞,有无污垢和灰尘。

Inspect and clean the generator rotor and stator windings by removing dust with a dry lint-free cloth. Low pressure, dry compressed air may be used to dislodge heavier dirt but be careful not to drive the dirt deeper into the windings. An industrial type vacuum cleaner is very effective for removing dirt from the windings. Use a rubber or plastic coated nozzle on the vacuum cleaner tube to prevent abrasive damage to the sensitive winding insulation. Oil on the surface of winding insulation will reduce the insulation resistance and shorten its life. The oily deposits can be removed by washing the windings with special degreasant liquids. Minor abrasions to winding insulation can be repaired, after cleaning, by the application of a suitable air-drying varnish.

检查并清洁发电机转子和定子绕组,方法是用干燥无绒布清除灰尘。低压、干燥的压缩空气可用于清除较重的污垢,但注意不要将污垢更深地推入绕组。工业型真空吸尘器对于清除绕组中的污垢非常有效。在真空吸尘器管上使用橡胶或塑料涂层喷嘴,以防对敏感绕组绝缘层造成磨损。绕组绝缘表面的油会降低绝缘电阻并缩短其寿命。可通过使用特殊脱脂液清洗绕组来去除油性沉积物。清洁后,可使用适当的风干清漆修复绕组绝缘层的轻微磨损。

Rotor sliprings must be checked for uniform(even) wear and that the carbon brushes have free movement in their boxes. Correct brush pressure can be checked using a pull-type spring balance instructions. A pull of around 1-1.5 kg is usual. If the brushes become too short (below about 2 cm) the reduced spring pressure will cause sparking at the slipring contact. Replace brushes with the correct type and bed them to the curvature of the slip rings. This can be done by placing a thin strip of glass paper (not emery paper) over the slip ring with its cutting surface under the carbon brush. Pull the glass paper around the slip ring until the brush surface has the same contour as the ring. The last few passes of the glass paper should be made in the same direction as the normal rotor direction. Remove all traces of carbon dust with a vacuum cleaner.

必须检查转子滑环磨损情况是否一致(均匀),碳刷是否在其箱内自由移动。碳刷压力可以使用拉力式弹簧进行检查。通常拉力约为1~1.5 kg。如果电刷变得太短(少于约2 cm),弹簧压力降低将导致滑环接触处产生火花。更换正确类型的电刷,并将其固定在滑环的曲面上。这可以通过在滑环上放置一条薄的玻璃纸(不是砂纸)来完成,滑环的切割表面在碳刷下方。拉动滑环周围的玻璃纸,直到刷子表面具有与滑环相同的轮廓。玻璃纸的最后几道应沿与正常转子方向相同的方向拉动。用真空吸尘器清除所有碳尘痕迹。

Generator excitation transformers, AVR components and rotating diodes must be kept free of dirt, oil and dampness. A special contact grease is used between the diode connections to prevent electrolytic action occurring between dissimilar metals. Check such contacts for tightness but do not disturb them unnecessarily.

发电机励磁变压器、自动调压器部件和旋转整流器必须无污垢、油和湿气。二极管连接之间使用特殊的接触润滑脂,以防止不同金属之间发生电解作用。检查此类触点的紧固性,但非必要时不要触动它们。

Measure the insulation of the stator and rotor windings to earth and between stator phases (assuming that the neutral point is available for disconnection at the terminal box).

测量定子和转子绕组对地及定子各相之间的绝缘(假设中性点可在接线盒处断开)。

Remember to disconnect or short-circuit any electronic circuit components which are likely to be damaged by a high voltage insulation test. Consult the wiring diagrams and the manufacturer's instructions before testing. Record the IR values and note the prevailing temperature and humidity. Compare with previous test results. A minimum IR value is usually taken to be 1 MΩ but a lower value may be acceptable to a surveyor based on 1 kΩ/V, e. g. 450 kΩ or 0. 45 MΩ for a 450 V generator. However, it is the historical trend of the machine IR values which will give a better picture of the insulation condition.

记住断开或短路任何可能因高压绝缘测试而损坏的电子电路部件。测试前,请参阅接线图和制造商说明书。记录 IR 值并记录当前温度和湿度。与之前的测试结果进行比较。最小 IR 值通常为 1 MΩ,但基于 1 kΩ/V,船检可以接受更低的值,例如 450 V 发电机为 450 kΩ 或 0. 45 MΩ。然而,设备 IR 值的历史记录趋势将更好地展现绝缘状况。

Generators with very low IR values (less than 0. 5 MΩ) should be given a thorough cleaning then dried out. If the IR has recovered to a reasonable value a-hich has become steady during the drying period, its windings should be covered with high-quality air-drying insulating varnish. Should the IR value remain low during a dry-out, the machine insulation needs to be completely reimpregnated or rewound (generally by a specialist contractor).

IR 值非常低(小于 0. 5 MΩ)的发电机应进行彻底清洁,然后干燥。如果 IR 已恢复到合理值,且在干燥期间已变得稳定,则其绕组应覆盖优质干燥的绝缘清漆。如果在干燥过程中 IR 值较低,则需要对机器绝缘进行完全重新浸渍或重绕(通常由专业承包商操作)。

After maintenance, no-load running checks should precede synchronising and loading. On load, particularly check excess temperature rise and load sharing stability when running in parallel.

维护过后，应在同步和加载之前进行空载运行检查。带负荷时，特别要检查并联运行时的过度温升和负荷分配稳定性。

Finally, if a generator is to be left idle or a long time, make sure that its winding is suitably heated to prevent internal condensation forming on its insulation. As with all electrical equipment — dirt, overheating and dampness are the "enemy".

最后，如果发电机要闲置或长时间闲置，请确保适当加热其绕组，以防止在绝缘层上形成内部冷凝。与所有电气设备一样，污垢、过热和潮湿是"敌人"。

5.9 Main Switchboard 主配电板

A typical layout of a ship's main switchboard is shown in Fig. 5. 19.

船舶主配电板的典型布局如图 5. 19 所示。

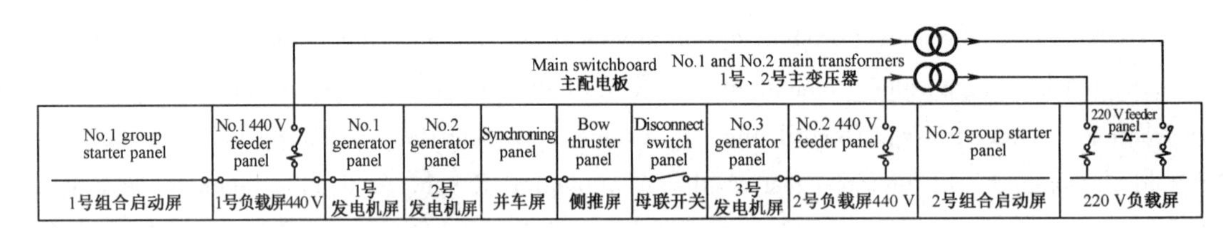

Fig. 5. 19　Main switchboard layout

图 5. 19　主配电板布局

The central section of the main switchboard is used for the control of the main generators. The switchgear cubicles on either side of the generator panels are used for essential services and flanking these are the grouped motor starter panels.

主配电板的中央部分用于控制主发电机。发电机屏两侧的开关柜为基本设施，这些开关柜的旁边是组合启动屏。

Handles for opening the doors on switchboard cubicles are usually linked (or interlocked) to an isolating switch. This ensures that supplies to components in the cubicle are switched off before the door can be opened.

开关柜上开门的把手通常与隔离开关相连（或互锁）。这可确保在门打开之前关闭机柜内部件的电源。

Fused isolators areisolating switches that incorporate fuses. The action of opening the switch isolates the fuses so that they can be replaced safely. Fused isolators can also be interlocked with the cubicle door handle. Motor starters frequently incorporate this arrangement. One type of interlocked fused isolator can be completely withdrawn and removed to ensure complete safety when carrying out maintenance on equipment.

熔断隔离器是配合熔断器的隔离开关。开关的断开动作会隔离保险丝,以便安全更换保险丝。熔断隔离器也可与隔间门把手连锁。电动机启动器经常采用这种设置。一种类型的连锁熔断隔离器可以完全抽出和移除,以确保在对设备进行维护时的绝对安全。

Maintenance on fused isolators consists of periodically checking the operating mechanism. Contacts must be inspected for damage and lightly greased with an electrical lubricant. The interlock mechanism (if fitted) should also be examined for correct and safe operation.

熔断隔离器的维护包括定期检查操作机构。必须检查触点是否损坏,并用电气润滑剂轻量润滑。还应检查连锁机构(如安装)是否能正确和安全地运行。

A separate section switches the three phase to 220 V AC low power and lighting services. Check the switchboard and particularly note the controls and instruments on the generator panels, the link to the emergency switchboard, steering gear supplies (duplicated), other essential services to the engine-room, navigation equipment supplies and section board feeders.

配电板的单独区域将三相电转换后供给 220 V 交流低功率设备和照明设施。检查配电板,要特别注意发电机面板上的控制和仪表、与应急配电板的连接、舵机电源(双套)、机舱的其他基本设施,以及导航设备供电和区域配电板馈线。

Note the alarms and insulation resistance (earth fault) monitors on both the 440 V and the 220 V sections.

注意:440 V 和 220 V 区域上的报警及绝缘电阻(接地故障)监视器。

The 440/220 V lighting transformers may be located inside the main switchboard or, more likely, will be separately mounted nearby.

440/220 V 照明变压器可能位于主配电板内,或可能单独安装在附近。

The main generator supply cables are connected directly to their respective circuit-breakers. Short copper bars from each generator circuit breaker connect it to the three bus-bars which run through the length of the switchboard. The bus-bars may be seen if the rear doors of the switchboard cubicle are opened, but they may be in a special enclosed busbar duct acting as an internal fire barrier.

主发电机供电电缆直接连接到各自的断路器上。每个发电机断路器的短铜排将其连接到贯穿配电板总长的三条母线上。如果配电板柜的后门打开,可以看到母线,但它们可能位于用作内部防火屏障的特殊封闭母线管道中。

Take care when opening doors on switchboards, live parts are exposed: You are in danger.

打开配电板柜门时,如果有裸露的带电部件,你就有危险。

The ship's electrical diagrams will include drawings of the front, and perhaps the rear of the main switchboard showing the as fitted equipment. The electrical distribution diagrams will follow the physical arrangement of the main switchboard layout.

船舶的电路图将包括主配电板的前部和后部的图纸,展示已安装的设备。配电图将遵循主配电板的物理布局。

You should study the electrical circuit and layout diagrams for your ship to identify, locate and appreciate the role of each key component in the scheme. Efficient fault-finding on a distribution network can only be achieved by a thorough understanding of the scheme and its normal operation.

应研究船舶的电路图和布局图,以识别、定位和了解方案中每个关键部件的作用。只有彻底了解该方案及其正常运行情况,才能实现配电网络的有效故障查找。

Switchboard instruments and controls for particular functions are grouped together. For example, the generator synchronising panel has all the instruments, relays and switches necessary for generator paralleling; each generator panel has all the instruments, relays, switches, controls and status lamps necessary for control of the generators; the instruments on panels of outgoing circuits are usually limited to an ammeter, status lamps, function switches (e. g. manual/off/auto) and push buttons.

用于特定功能的配电板仪表和控制器组合在一起。例如,发电机并车屏具有发电机并联所需的所有仪表、继电器和开关;每个发电机面板具有控制发电机所需的所有仪表、继电器、开关、控制器和状态灯;面板上输出电路的仪表通常仅限于电流表、状态灯、功能开关(如手动/关闭/自动)和按钮。

Low power control and instrument wiring is of relatively small crosssection, with multicoloured plastic insulation which is clearly identified against the larger main power cables.

低功率控制电路和仪表接线的截面相对较小,带有多色塑料绝缘层,与较大的主电源电缆相比可以清楚地鉴别。

The instrumentation and control wiring is supplied from fuses which are located behind the appropriate panel. Green and yellow striped earth wiring from instruments and panel doors etc., is connected to a common copper earthbonding bar running the length of the switchboard at its rear. This earth bar is electrically bonded to the ship's steel hull.

仪表和控制接线通过位于相应面板后面的保险丝供电。仪表和柜门等的绿黄相间条纹接地线连接到一根公共铜接地排,该接地排沿配电板后部的长度延伸。该接地排与船舶的钢质船体电气连接。

5.10 Main Circuit Breakers 主开关

LV generator circuit-breakers and other large distribution circuit-breakers (600-6,000 A) on board ship are traditionally of the air break type called ACB (air circuit breaker). This means that the circuit-breaker contacts separate in air. An ACB outline is shown in Fig. 5.20.

船上的低压发电机断路器和其他大型配电断路器(600~6 000 A)是传统的空气断路器类型,称为ACB(空气断路器)。这意味着断路器触点能在空气中分离。ACB轮廓如图5.20所示。

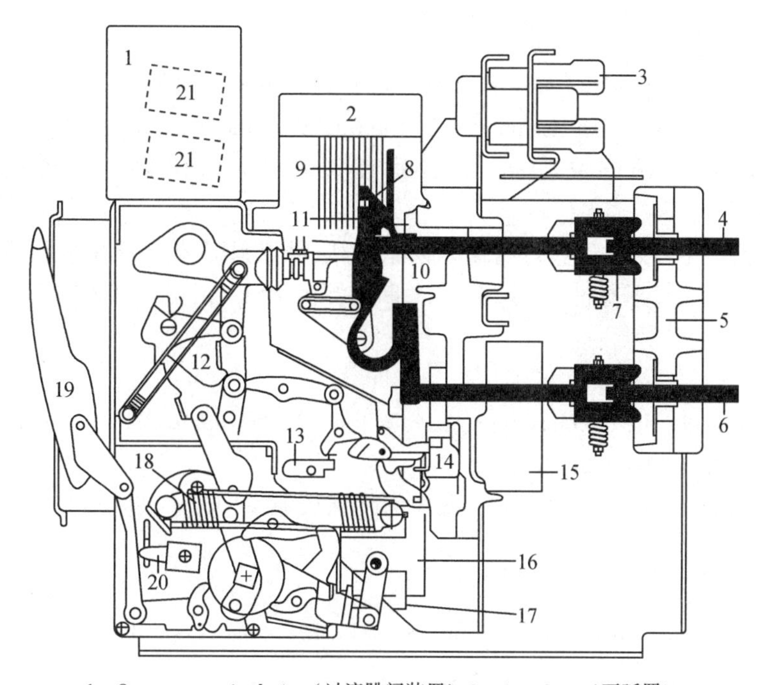

1—Overcurrent trip device (过流跳闸装置);2—Arc chutes(灭弧罩);
3—Isolating contacts of control circuits(控制电路隔离触头);4—Line-side main circuit terminals(电网侧主接线端);
5—Draw-out moulded base(抽出式模压底座);6—Load-side main circuit terminals(负载侧主接线端);
7—Isolating contacts of main circuits(主电路隔离触头);8—Fixed arcing contacts(定弧触头);
9—Moving arcing contacts(动弧触头);10—Fixed main contacts(定主触头);11—Moving main contacts(动主触头);
12—Closing mechanism(合闸机构);13—Trip bar(分闸杆);14—Inst. trip devices(for marine use)[瞬时跳闸装置(船用)];
15—CT (for overcurrent trip device)[电流互感器(过流跳闸元件)];16—Charging motor(储能电动机);
17—Closing latch release(合闸钩爪释放装置);18—Closing spring(合闸弹簧);19—Charging handle(储能手柄);
20—Quick close/slow close selector lever (快/慢合闸转换手柄);21—Auxiliary switches(辅助开关)。

Fig. 5.20 Circuit breaker components (stored energy type)

图5.20 断路器元件(储能型)

HV installations e. g. at 6.6 kV and 11 kV generally use the vacuum interrupter type or gas-filled (sulphur hexafluoride, SF_6) breakers. Outlines shown in Fig. 5.21.

高压电装置,例如6.6 kV和11 kV,通常使用真空灭弧断路器类型或气体填充(六氟化硫,SF_6)断路器。轮廓如图5.21所示。

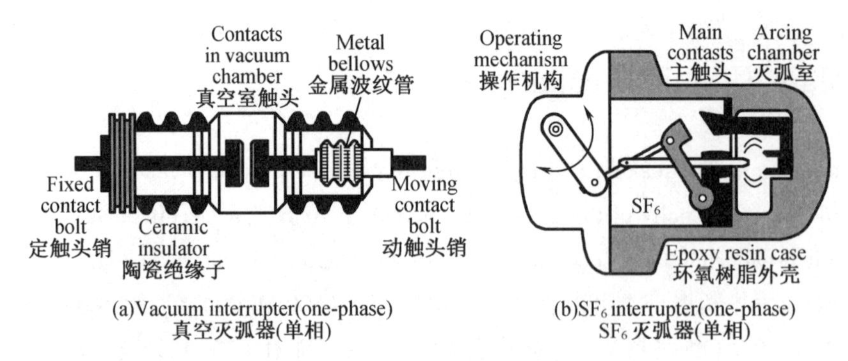

Fig. 5. 21　Vacuum and SF_6 interrupter

图 5.21　真空和 SF_6 灭弧器

In a vacuum interrupter the contacts only need to be separated by a few millimetres as the insulation level of a vacuum is extremely high. The quality of the vacuum in the sealed interrupter chamber is checked by applying a short duration HV pulse (e. g. 10 kV for a 6. 6 kV breaker) across the open contacts.

在真空断路器中,由于真空的绝缘等级非常高,触点只需要分开几毫米即可。通过在断开触点上施加短时高压脉冲(例如 6. 6 kV 断路器为 10 kV),可检查密封灭弧室中的真空质量。

In the gas breaker the contacts separate in a special interrupter chamber containing SF_6 gas typically at 500 kPa (5 bar) at 20 ℃.

在气体断路器中,触点在含有 SF_6 气体的特殊灭弧室中分离,通常在 20 ℃下,压力为 500 kPa(5 bar)。

The operating mechanism for vacuum and SF_6 breakers is similar to that employed for an ACB.

真空断路器和 SF_6 断路器的操作机构与 ACB 的操作机构类似。

Fig. 5. 22 shows how each main circuit breaker is mounted on guide rails inside a main switchboard cubicle from which it must be withdrawn and isolated from the bus-bars for maintenance and testing.

图 5. 22 展示了每个主断路器如何安装在主配电板柜内的导轨上,为了维护和测试,必须将主断路器从配电板柜中抽出并与母线隔离。

The breaker and its guide rails are usually mounted in a special cassette bolted into the switchboard cubicle and electrically connected to the bus-bars. If repair work demands that the breaker is to be completely removed from its cassette then usually a special hoist or fork-lift is required for large, heavy-duty units.

断路器及其导轨通常安装在一个特殊盒中,其用螺栓固定在配电板柜中并与母线电气连接。如果维修工作需要将断路器从其盒中完全取出,则大重型装置通常需要专用起重机或叉车。

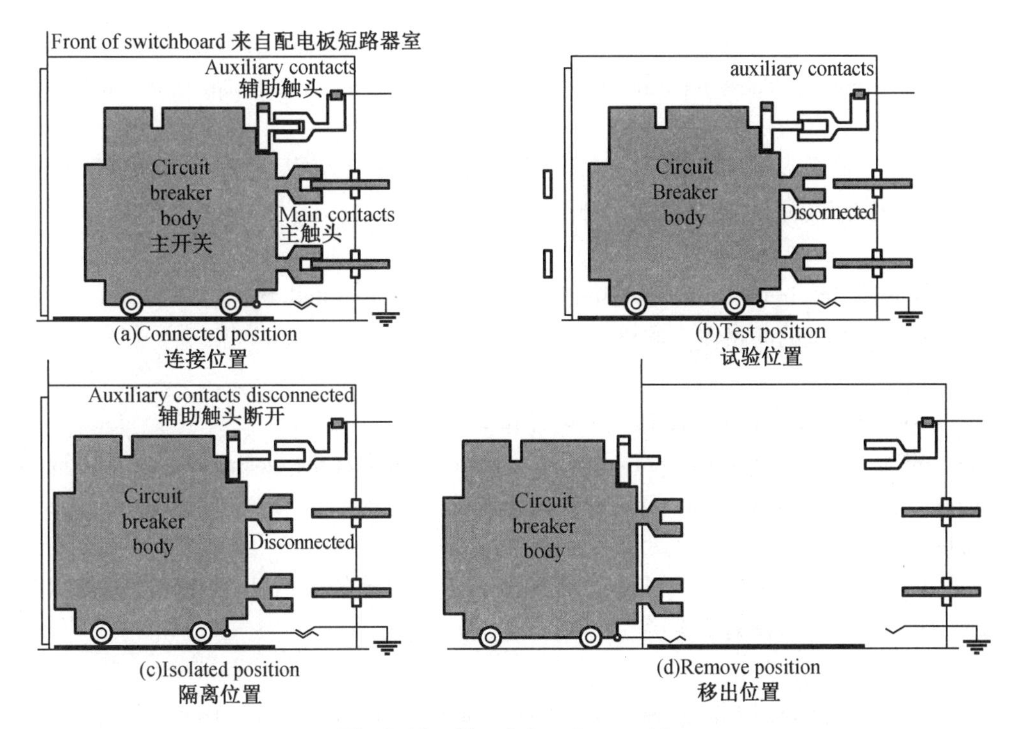

Fig. 5. 22　Circuit breaker position

图 5. 22　断路器位置

The actionof withdrawing the circuit breaker causes a safety shutter to cover the live bus-bar contacts at the rear of its cubicle. The mechanical linkage in a circuitbreaker is quite complex and should not be interfered with except for maintenance and lubrication as specified by the manufacturer.

抽出断路器的动作会导致安全挡板覆盖其开关柜后部的带电母线触头。断路器中的机械连接非常复杂,除制造商规定的维护和润滑外,不应干预。

The main fixed and moving contacts are of copper (sometimes of special arc-resistant alloy or silver tipped) and usually silver-alloy coated. Main contacts should not be scraped or filed. If the main contacts suffer severe burning they will probably require realignment as specified by the manufacturer.

主要的固定和移动触头是铜(有时是特殊的抗电弧合金或镀银),通常再镀上银合金。主触头不应被刮擦或锉削。如果主触头严重烧损,则可能需要按照制造商的规定重新校准。

Arcing contacts normally suffer burning and may be dressed by a smooth file as recommended by the manufacturer. Carborundum and emery should not be used — the hard particles can embed themselves in the soft contacts and cause future trouble.

弧触头通常承受燃烧,并可按照制造商的建议用光滑锉刀修整。不应使用金刚砂——

硬颗粒会嵌入软触头,并带来后患。

The arc chutes or arc splitter boxes confine and control the inevitable arc to rapidly accelerate its extinction. These must be removed and inspected for broken parts and erosion of the splitter plates.

灭弧罩或分弧盒限制和控制不可避免的电弧,以加速其熄灭过程。必须拆除这些部件,并检查其是否有破损和栅板的腐蚀。

Various types of circuit breaker closing mechanism may be fitted.

可安装各种类型的断路器合闸机构。

1. Independent Manual Spring 独立手动弹簧式

The spring charge is directly applied by manual depression of the closing handle. The last few centimetres of handle movement releases the spring to close the breaker. Closing speed is independent of the operator.

通过手动按下合闸手柄直接施加弹簧充能。手柄移动的最后几厘米释放弹簧以闭合断路器。闭合速度与操作人员无关。

2. Motor Driven Stored Charge Spring (Most Common Type for Marine Applications) 电动机驱动储能弹簧式(最常用于船舶应用)

Closing springs are charged by a motor-gearbox unit. Spring recharging is automatic following closure of the breaker which is initiated by a pushbutton. This may be a direct mechanical release of the charged spring, or more usually, it will be released electrically via a solenoid latch.

合闸弹簧由电动机齿轮箱单元充能。弹簧充能在断路器闭合后自动进行,由按钮触发。这是储能弹簧的直接机械释放,或者更通常地,它将通过线圈控制闩锁释放。

3. Manual Wound Stored Charge Spring 手动盘绕储能弹簧式

This is similar to above method but with manually charged closing springs.

这与上述方法类似,但合闸弹簧使用手动充能。

4. Solenoid 线圈式

The breaker is closed by a d. c. solenoid energised from the generator or bus-bars via a transformer/rectifier unit, contactor, push button and, sometimes, a timing relay.

断路器由直流线圈闭合,该线圈由发电机或母线通过变压器/整流器单元、接触器、按钮和实际继电器供电。

Warning: Circuit breakers store energy in their springs for

(1) Store-charge mechanisms in the closing springs;

(2) Contact and kick-off springs.

警告:断路器在弹簧中储存能量,用于

(1)在合闸弹簧中储存机械能;

(2)接触和分闸弹簧。

Extremely care must be exercised when handling circuit breakers with the closing springs charged, or when the circuit breaker is in the ON position. Isolated circuit-breakers racked out for maintenance should be left with the closing springs discharged and in the OFF position. Circuit-breakers are held in the closed or ON position by a mechanical latch. The breaker is tripped by releasing this latch allowing the kick-off springs and contact pressure to force the contacts open.

当操作合闸弹簧已储能的断路器时,或当断路器处于接通位置时,必须格外小心。维护已隔离的断路器应处于断开位置并保持合闸弹簧释放。断路器通过机械闩锁保持在闭合或接通位置。通过释放该闩锁,断路器跳闸,允许分闸弹簧和触点压力迫使触头断开。

Tripping can be initiated:

(1) Manually — a push button with mechanical linkage trips the latch;

(2) Undervoltage trip coil or relay (trips when de-energised);

(3) Overcurrent/short-circuit trip device or relay (trips when energised);

(4) Solenoid trip coil — when energised by a remote push-button or relay (such as an electronic overcurrent relay).

跳闸可通过以下方式触发:

(1)手动——带有机械联动装置的按钮会使闩锁跳闸;

(2)失压跳闸线圈或继电器(断电时跳闸);

(3)过电流/短路跳闸装置或继电器(通电时跳闸);

(4)电磁跳闸线圈——由远程按钮或继电器(如电子过电流继电器)通电时。

Mechanical interlocks are fitted to main circuit breakers to prevent racking-out if still in the ON position. Care must be taken not to exert undue force if the breaker will not move, otherwise damage may be caused to the interlocks and other mechanical parts.

机械联锁装置安装在主断路器上,以防止在仍然处于"闭合"位置的情况下抽出。如果断路器不动作,必须注意不要施加过大的力,否则可能损坏连锁装置和其他机械部件。

Electrical interlock switches are connected into circuit-breaker control circuits to prevent incorrect sequence operation, e. g. when a shore-supply breaker is closed.

电气联锁开关连接到断路器控制电路中,以防止不正确的操作程序,例如当岸电断路器闭合时。

The ship's generator breakers are usually interlocked OFF to prevent parallel running of a ship's generator and the shore supply. But newly disigned ship's mian generators already can be parallelled with the shore supply for smooth changeover.

船舶发电机断路器通常与岸电互锁,以防止船舶发电机和岸上电源并联运行。但是新设计的船舶主发电机已经可以与岸电并网运行以实现无扰动切换。

Chapter 6 Ancillary Electrical Services
第 6 章 辅助电气设施

6.0 Introduction 介绍

To ensure a safe working environment, together with off duty comfort in the accommodation quarters on board your ship, a considerable proportion of the generated electric power is absorbed in the ancillary services.

为了保证船上工作环境安全,以及生活区舒适,相当比例的电力供应被用于辅助服务系统。

Lighting of the ship's deck areas, engine room and accommodation to meet specified levels of illumination is provided by various light fittings (luminaires) designed to work safely in their particular locations.

各种照明设备使甲板区域、机舱和生活区的照明满足在特定工作区域安全工作的设计要求。

The hotel services for food storage, preparation and cooking, together with accommodation air-conditioning and laundry services, are essential for the general maintenance of the mariner.

船上食物的储存、准备和烹饪以及生活区的空调及洗衣服务对船员的日常生活来说是必不可少的。

This chapter will examine ships' lighting and refrigeration/air conditioning together with galley and laundry services. Additionally, hull protection by the impressed current cathodic protection method and battery supplies are also included.

本章将研究船舶照明和厨房洗衣服务及冷藏、空调用电,另外也将包括船体电流阴极保护方式和蓄电池供电。

6.1 Ships' Lighting 船舶照明

Historically, the original application of electricity in ships was for lighting. Oil lanterns were a definite fire risk and the ship's lamp trimmer had great difficulty in maintaining his navigation lights in stormy weather.

历史上,早期的船舶电力是用于照明的。油提灯的火灾风险显著,船灯工在暴风雨天气保持航行灯正常工作也有很大的难度。

To meet the safety and comfort levels of illumination required throughout your ship a wide range of lighting fittings (luminaires) are used. The power ratings of the lamps used will vary from a few watts for alarm indicator lamps to a few kW for deck floodlights and searchlights (e. g. a Suez Canal Projector Light).

用大范围照明设备(灯具)来满足全船照明所需的安全等级和舒适度,灯的功率从几瓦的报警指示灯到几千瓦的甲板泛光灯和探照灯(如苏伊士运河射灯)。

The amount of light falling on a particular area can be checked with a luminance meter which is calibrated in lux (lx). 1 lx is the illumination of 1 lm/m^2 where a lumen is the unit of luminous flux. For example, container loading requires a minimum illumination level of 50 lx while a main engine control room may be illuminated to a level of 500 lx. The minimum illumination standards for crew spaces in UK registered ships are specified in "*The Merchant Shipping (Crew Accommodation) Regulations*".

特定区域的光照度可以用一个以勒克斯(lx)为单位的亮度计来测量。1 lx 就是 1 lm/m^2 的照明,流明(lm)是光通量的国际单位。例如,集装箱的装载需要最低 50 lx 的照度,集控室可能要 500 lx 的照度。《商船(船员生活区)条例》规定了在英国注册的船舶上船员生活区的最低照明标准。

The luminous efficiency of a light fitting is defined as the ratio of lumens/watt. This efficiency reduces in time mainly because the lamp deteriorates as the lumens emitted gradually get less while the watts input remains constant. Dirt on the lamp reflector and lamp-glass will also reduce its luminous efficiency.

灯具的发光效率是光通量与功率的比值。发光效率的降低主要是由于灯泡的老化造成灯泡功率不变时光通量减小。灯具反光器和玻璃灯罩上的灰尘也会降低发光效率。

Group replacement of lamps is often considered by shipping companies to be more economic and convenient than individual replacement following lamp failure. Cleaning of the fittings can also be carried out during group lamp replacement so maintaining a high luminous efficiency.

航运公司认为灯具成组更换比单独更换故障灯具更经济方便。灯具配件的清洁也可以在成组更换灯具时进行,这样可以保持较高的发光效率。

Lamp end caps are many and various but the most common types are screw and bayonet fittings. The old names, e. g. Goliath Edison Screw (GES) and Bayonet Cap (BC) are now re-designated to indicate the cap type and its dimensions.

灯头多种多样,最常用的形式有螺口式和卡口式。旧型号例如格莱斯爱迪生螺口(GES)和卡口(BC),现在已重新设计型号来表示灯头的种类和尺寸。

A selection of old names and the current codes are listedin the Table 6.1.

旧型号和当前型号灯头的选择如表 6.1 所示。

Table 6.1　A selection of old names and the current codes

表 6.1　旧型号和当前型号灯头的选择

Old Code 旧型号	Description 描述	Current Code 当前型号
ES	Edison Screw 爱迪生螺口	E27/27
GES	Goliath Edison Screw 格莱斯爱迪生螺口	E40/45
SES	Small Edison Screw 小爱迪生螺口	E14/23x15
MES	Miniature Edison Screw 微型爱迪生螺口	E10/13
LES	Lilliput Edison Screw 螺口米泡	E5/9
BC	Bayonet Cap 卡口	B22/25x26
SBC	Small Bayonet Cap 小型卡口	B15/24x17
MCC	Miniature Centre Contact 微型卡口	BA9s/14

Broadly, the luminaires employ one of two general lamp types classified as: incandescent, discharge.

一般来说,灯具采用以下两种普通灯泡类型中的一种:白炽灯、放电灯。

6.2　Incandescent Lamps 白炽灯

The most common lamp used for general lighting is the simple filament type as shown in Fig. 6.1. A current is passed through the thin tungsten wire filament which raises its temperature to around 3,000 ℃ when it becomes incandescent (it glows).

最常见的普通灯泡是简单灯丝类型的,如图 6.1 所示。电流通过细钨丝,当钨丝温度升到 3 000 ℃左右时就会变得炽热(发光)。

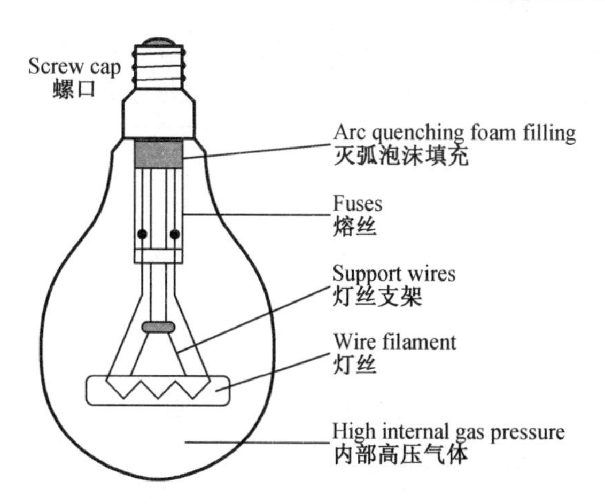

Fig. 6. 1 Incandescent lamp construction

图 6. 1 白炽灯结构

The glass bulb is filled with an inert gas such as nitrogen or argon which helps to reduce filament evaporation to allow an operating life expectancy of about 1,000 h. Lamp power ratings are available from 15 ~1,000 W.

玻璃灯泡内充满惰性气体(如氮气和氩气)有助于减少灯丝的蒸发,使灯泡的预期工作寿命可达约 1 000 h。灯泡的功率为 15~1 000 W。

The ordinary filament lamp is called a general lighting service(GLS) lamp. One variation of the basic lamp design has a special coiled-coil filament which increases the life expectancy of low power (up to 150 W) lamps and are referred to as double-life lamps. Specially reinforced construction lamps (called rough-service) have a tough filament for use in areas where shock and vibration are expected — this type is useful with portable handlamps. Other variations include: clear glass bulb, inside frosted glass bulb (pearl) to reduce glare, tubular construction, internal reflector lamps, decorative lamps (e. g. candle shape) and heating lamps.

一般的白炽灯被称作普通照明灯(GLS)。基础灯泡设计的一种类型是有一个特殊的复绕卷曲灯丝,它可以延长小功率(高达 150 W)灯的预期工作寿命,这种灯又被称作双寿命灯。特别是有加强结构(亦称恶劣服务)的灯具拥有更加坚固的灯丝,这种灯被用在有冲击和振动的地方,该种类型的灯泡对便携式手提灯很适用。其他类型包括无色玻璃灯泡、可降低刺眼强光的内磨砂玻璃灯泡(珍珠状)、其他管状灯泡、内反射镜灯、装饰灯(如烛形)和加热灯。

Typical lamp power ratings and light outputs as shown in Table 6. 2.

典型灯具的额定功率和平均光照输出如表 6. 2 所示。

Table 6.2 Typical lamp power ratings and average light outputs (for a 240 V supply)

表 6.2 典型灯具的额定功率和平均光照输出(240 V 供电)

<table>
<tr><th colspan="2">Single-coil type 单绕型</th><th colspan="2">double-coil type 复绕型</th></tr>
<tr><th>Power
功率/W</th><th>Light
光通量/lm</th><th>Power
功率/W</th><th>Light
光通量/lm</th></tr>
<tr><td>15</td><td>150</td><td></td><td></td></tr>
<tr><td>25</td><td>200</td><td></td><td></td></tr>
<tr><td>40</td><td>325</td><td>40</td><td>390</td></tr>
<tr><td>60</td><td>575</td><td>60</td><td>665</td></tr>
<tr><td></td><td></td><td>75</td><td>885</td></tr>
<tr><td>100</td><td>1 160</td><td>100</td><td>1 260</td></tr>
<tr><td>150</td><td>1 960</td><td>150</td><td>2 075</td></tr>
<tr><td>200</td><td>2 720</td><td colspan="2" rowspan="5">For high vibration areas, single-coil lamps are preferred as they are more robust than the double-coil type
在震动大的区域,选用单绕型灯丝比复绕型灯丝更多,因为它更耐用</td></tr>
<tr><td></td><td>4 300</td></tr>
<tr><td>500</td><td>7 700</td></tr>
<tr><td>750</td><td>12 400</td></tr>
<tr><td>1 000</td><td>17 300</td></tr>
</table>

Question 思考题

Estimate the luminous efficiency of 100 W single-coil and double-coil lamps.

估算 100 W 单绕型和复绕型灯丝的发光效率。

Answer 答案

Efficiency = Output lumens/input watts = 1 160/100 = 11.6 lm/W and 12.6 lm/W.

效率=输出光通量/输入功率=1 160/100=11.6 lm/W。同理复绕型灯丝为 12.6 lm/W。

A popular variation of the incandescent lamp is the tungsten-halogen type, This lamp construction has a gas-filled quartz tube or bulb which also includes a halogen vapour such as iodine or bromine. When the filament is heated, evaporated tungsten particles combine with the halogen vapour to form a tungsten-halide. At the high filament temperature, the tungsten vapour reforms onto the filament. This regenerative process continues repeatedly creating a self-cleaning action on the inner surface of the glass tube or bulb. In an ordinary GLS lamp the tungsten evaporation from the filament causes an internal blackening of the glass bulb which is eliminated in the tungsten-halogen lamp.

一种流行的白炽灯是钨卤素型,这种灯具有充满气体的石英管或灯泡,其中包含卤素蒸气,如碘或溴。当灯丝被加热时,蒸发的钨颗粒与卤素蒸气结合形成钨卤化物。在灯丝高温时,钨蒸气重新附着在灯丝上。该再生过程持续不断地在玻璃管或灯泡的内表面上产生自清洁作用。在普通照明灯中,灯丝中的钨蒸发会导致玻璃灯泡内部发黑,这种现象在卤钨灯中不存在。

Two basic lamp forms for the tungsten halogen design are the linear double-ended lamp (K class) and the single-ended lamp (M class) as shown in Fig. 6. 2.

钨卤素灯设计的两种基本灯具形式是线性双端灯(K 类)和单端灯(M 类),如图 6.2 所示。

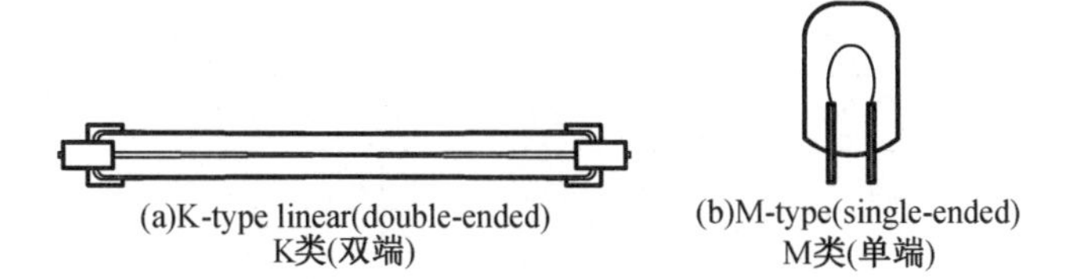

Fig. 6. 2　K & M lamp construction

图 6. 2　K 类和 M 类灯泡结构

Linear tungsten-halogen lamps must be used in the horizontal position otherwise the halogen vapour will concentrate at its lower end which results in rapid blackening of the tube and a reduced operating life. Both the linear and bulb type are particularly useful for display, floodlighting and spotlighting.

线性钨卤素灯必须用于水平位置,否则卤化蒸气会集中在其下端,导致管子迅速发黑且使用寿命缩短。线性型和灯泡型钨卤素灯对于显示、泛光和聚光灯都特别适用。

Examples of tungsten-halogen lamp details(Table 6. 3,Table 6. 4).

钨卤素灯详情示例如表 6. 3 和表 6. 4 所示。

Table 6. 3　Linear double-ended (240 V rated and life expectancy of 2,000 h)

表 6. 3　线性双端(240 V 额定值和 2 000 h 的预期寿命)

Type 型号	Power 功率/W	Light output 输出光通量/lm
K9	300	5 000
K1	500	9 500
K2, K3	750	15 000
K4	1 000	21 000
K5	1 500	33 000
K6 & K8	2 000	44 000

Table 6.4 Single-ended
表 6.4 单端

Type 型号	Voltage 电压/V	Power 功率/W	Life 寿命/h	Light output/lm 输出光通量/lm
M29	6	10	100	210
M30	6	20	100	420
M34	6	20	2 000	350
M28	12	100	2 000	2 150
M32	12	50	2 000	900
M35	12	20	250	450
M36	24	250	2 000	5 750
M38	240	300	2 000	5 000
M40	240	300	2 000	8 500

Tungsten-halogen lamps must be carefully handled when being fitted. If the outside surface of the quartz tube or bulb is touched with dirty or greasy hands, premature failure can occur due to fine surface cracks in the glass. Handle the tube by its ends only, or use a paper sleeve over the lamp during fitting. If accidentally handled, the lamp glass may be cleaned with a spirit solvent, carbon tetrachloride or trichlorethylene.

安装钨卤素灯时必须小心操作。如果用脏手或油腻手触摸石英管或灯泡的外表面,则可能会产生细微的玻璃表面裂纹而过早发生故障。在安装过程中,请仅握住灯管的末端,或在灯管上使用纸套。处理意外情况时,可使用酒精溶剂、四氯化碳或三氯乙烯清洁灯泡玻璃罩。

6.3 Discharge Lamps 放电灯

The light output from a discharge lamp is generated by the flow of current in an electric arc between two electrodes through a gas and metal vapour inside a sealed glass bulb or tube. The most common metal vapour employed in discharge lamps are: Mercury (as used in a fluorescent tube) and Sodium. Low and high-pressure types of mercury and sodium lamps are available.

放电灯的光输出是由两个电极之间的电弧电流通过密封玻璃灯泡或管内的气体和金属蒸气所产生的。放电灯中最常见的金属蒸气有汞和钠蒸气,可提供低压和高压类型的汞灯和钠灯。

A suitable voltage applied between the electrodes of a discharge lamp causes an arc discharge through the gas. This ionisation of the gas either creates visible light directly or by secondary emission from a phosphor coating on the inside wall of the lamp glass.

在放电灯电极之间施加适当的电压,可使气体产生电弧放电。这种气体电离要么直接产生可见光,要么通过灯玻璃内壁上磷光体涂层的二次发射产生可见光。

The discharge lamp current must be carefully controlled to maintain the desired light output and some form of current limiting ballast is required. This ballast is often an iron-cored inductor (choke coil) but special transformers and electronic regulator ballast circuits are also used. The ballast must match the lamp (e. g. a 20 W fluorescent tube must have a matching 20 W ballast unit) to ensure correct lamp operation for high luminous efficiency and long life.

必须小心控制放电灯电流,以保持所需的光输出,并且需要某种形式的限流镇流器。这种镇流器通常是铁芯电感(扼流线圈),但也使用特殊的变压器和电子调节器镇流器电路。镇流器必须与灯具匹配(例如,20 W 荧光灯管必须具有匹配的 20 W 镇流器装置),以确保灯具正确运行,从而实现高发光效率和长的使用寿命。

6.3.1　Mercury Fluorescent 汞荧光灯

Mercury fluorescent are manufactured as low pressure and high pressure lamp types. Low-pressure mercury fluorescent type the most obvious example of this type is the popular fluorescent tube as shown in Fig. 6.3. It is classified as an MCF lamp (M = mercury, C = low pressure, F = fluorescent coating). The inside surface of the glass tube is coated with a fluorescent phosphor which emits white light. Variations of phosphor material create different light colours of which the most common are called: Warm White Colour 29, Warm White de luxe Colour 32, Daylight Colour 33, and White Colour 35.

汞荧光灯是作为低压和高压灯类型制造的。其中低压汞荧光灯最常见的应用是流行的荧光管型,如图 6.3 所示。它被归类为 MCF 灯(M 表示水银,C 表示低压,F 表示荧光涂层)。其玻璃管的内表面涂覆有能发射白色荧光的磷光体。磷光体材料的变化会产生不同的光色,其中最常见的是暖白色 29、暖白色奢华色彩 32、日光颜色 33、白色 35。

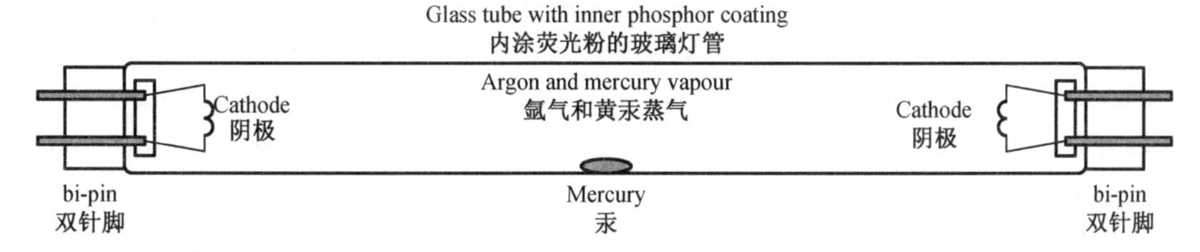

Fig. 6.3　Fluorescent lamp construction

图 6.3　荧光灯结构

Fluorescent tubes are available in lengths from 150–2,400 mm with power ratings from 4–125 W. The tube ends are usually fitted with bi-pin lamp caps or miniature bi-pin for the small tubes. Typical luminous efficiency for a fluorescent tube is about 70 lm/W with an average operating life of 5,000 h.

荧光灯管的长度为 150~2 400 mm,额定功率为 4~125 W。灯管末端通常配有双针灯头或小型双针灯管。荧光灯管的典型发光效率约为 70 lm/W,平均工作寿命为 5 000 h。

To strike a fluorescent tube, its gas filling (usually argon or krypton) must be ionised by a voltage between its cathodes that is slightly higher than that required to maintain the normal discharge. Two common methods are used to strike the tube: The switch-start circuit, the transformer quick-start circuit. The circuit in Fig. 6. 4 shows a typical switch-start circuit.

为了撞击荧光管,其充气(通常为氩或氪)必须通过阴极之间的电压进行电离,该电压略高于维持正常放电所需的电压。通常有两种方法用于激发灯管:开关启动电路、变压器快速启动电路。图 6. 4 所示电路为典型的开关启动电路。

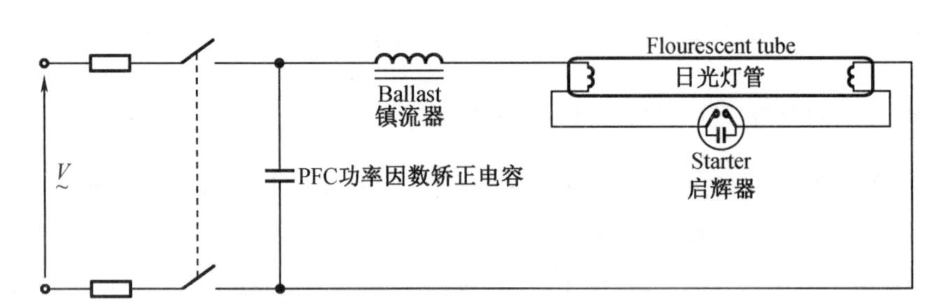

Fig. 6. 4　Fluorescent lamp circuit and glow starter

图 6. 4　荧光灯电路和辉光启动器

The starting action is initiated by a glow type starter switch which is connected between opposite ends of the tube.

启动动作由与两管脚连接的启辉器开关启动。

When the supply voltage is applied to the circuit, the full mains voltage appears across the starter switch. A glow discharge occurs between the starter contacts which quickly heat up, bend and touch each other. This allows current to flow through the lamp cathodes which will cause the tube ends to heat up and glow before the tube actually strikes. The tube strikes when the starter switch re-opens as it cools down during its closed (non-glow) period. When the starter switch opens it interrupts an inductive coil (choke) circuit which produces a surge voltage across the tube which then strikes.

当给电路施加电源电压时,整个电源电压会加在启辉器开关上。快速加热、受热弯曲并相互接触的启辉器触点之间会产生辉光放电。这允许电流流过灯的阴极,使灯脚在灯管实际激发之前加热并发光。当启辉器开关在关闭(非辉光)期间冷却而再次打开时,灯丝发出的电子会撞击灯管使其激发。当启辉器开关打开时,它会中断感应线圈(扼流线圈)电路,每次启辉器开关关闭时,一个大电流通过扼流线圈,使其温度升高。

The tube is now full-away and the reduced arc voltage across it is not sufficient to re-start the glow discharge in the starter so its contacts remain open. In fact, in the normal running condition, the starter switch can be unplugged from its bayonet cap base and the lamp will function normally. The tube will not, of course, re-strike after switch off without the starter action.

现在灯管已完全激发,其上降低的电弧电压不足以重新启动启辉器中的辉光放电,因此其触点保持打开状态。事实上,在正常运行条件下,启辉器开关可以从卡口盖底座上拔下,指示灯将正常工作。当然,在没有启辉器动作的情况下,灯管在关闭后不会再次激发。

Two or three strikes may be required to get the lamp running normally as the starter contacts may open before the cathodes are sufficiently heated. Such cold-striking reduces the lamp life by erosion of the cathode material which causes irregular lamp flashing.

可能需要两次或三次激发才能使灯管正常工作,因为在阴极充分加热之前,启辉器触点可能会断开。这种冷激发会腐蚀阴极材料,导致灯管不规则地闪烁,从而缩短灯管的使用寿命。

In normal operation the choke coil acts as a series reactance to limit the lamp discharge current. Severe blackening at the tube ends is a sure sign that its useful life is finished.

在正常操作中,扼流线圈充当串联电抗,以限制灯管的放电电流。灯管末端严重发黑是其使用寿命结束的确定表现。

Each time the starter switch closes, a large current surges through the choke coil which increases its temperature. So, excessive lamp flickering must be corrected by lamp or starter replacement. Most choke coils are potted in a thermosetting polyester compound within a steel case.

每次启辉器开关闭合时,一个大的冲击电流流经扼流线圈,使其温度升高。因此,灯管过度闪烁的现象,必须通过更换灯管或启辉器迅速排除。大多数扼流线圈都封装在钢制外壳内的热固性聚酯化合物中。

While an earth fault is unlikely to occur within a choke an open circuit is possible and can be simply checked using an ohmmeter. No repair of a choke-coil is feasible so it must be completely replaced with an identically rated unit. Similarly, glow starters should only be replaced with an equivalent which matches the size of tube it is to be used with.

虽然扼流线圈内不太可能发生接地故障,但可能存在开路,可使用欧姆表简单地检查。扼流线圈的维修是不可行的,因此必须用相同额定值的扼流线圈进行更换。类似地,辉光启辉器只能用与其所用灯管容量相匹配的启辉器进行更换。

An example of a transformer quick-start circuit is shown in Fig. 6. 5. The lamp discharge begins as soon as the cathodes reach their operating temperature. A capacitive effect between the cathodes and the earthed metalwork of the fitting ionises the gas and the tube strikes very quickly.

变压器快速启动电路的示例如图 6.5 所示。阴极一旦达到工作温度,灯丝就开始放电。阴极和配件接地金属件之间的电容效应会使气体电离,管子会很快激发。

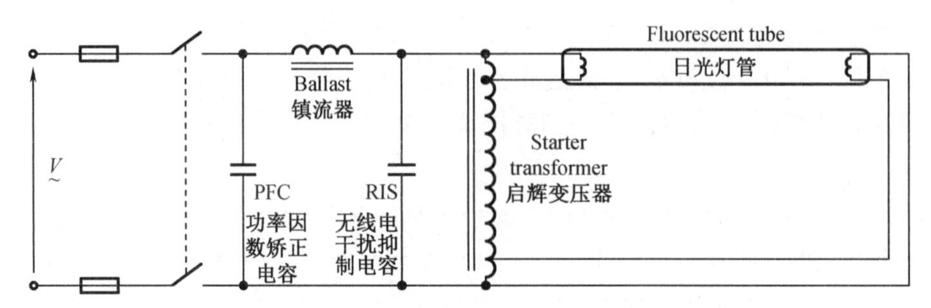

Fig. 6.5 Transformer-start fluorescent lamp circuit

图 6.5 变压器启动荧光灯电路

Most tubes have a conducting path through the phosphor coating or alternatively, a special metal earth strip running between the end caps which assists the starting process. The transformer ballast gives an immediate start but some difficulty can occur with low ambient temperatures, low supply voltage and poor earthing. Many other variations of quick-start circuits using transformers and resonant effects are used.

大多数灯管都有一条穿过磷光体涂层的导电路径,或者在端盖之间有一条特殊的金属接地带,这有助于启动。变压器镇流器可迅速启动,但在环境温度低、电源电压低和接地不良的情况下可能会出现启动困难。许多其他快速启动电路利用变压器和谐振效应。

Capacitors are used with discharge tubes for power factor correction (PFC) and radio interference suppression (RIS).

电容器与放电管一起使用,用于功率因数校正(PFC)和无线电干扰抑制(RIS)。

The PFC capacitor is used to raise the supply power factor to around 0. 9 lagging. Without this capacitor the power factor may be as low as 0. 2 lagging due to the high choke-coil inductance to cause the supply current to be 4-5 times larger than normal. For a 125 W tube a PFC value of about 7. 2 μF is typical.

功率因数矫正电容用于将电源功率因数提高到约 0. 9 滞后。若没有该电容,由于扼流线圈电感性高,导致电源电流比正常值大 4~5 倍,因此功率因数可能低至 0. 2 滞后。对于 125 W 的灯管,典型的功率因数矫正电容约为 7. 2 μF。

Radio interference from discharge tubes is caused by the ionisation process of the discharge through the tube. This is suppressed by a capacitor fitted across the tube ends. In glow-switch circuits, the RIS capacitor is actually fitted within the starter. Typical RIS capacitor values are around 0. 000 5 μF.

放电灯管的无线电干扰是由放电灯管的放电电离过程引起的。该干扰由安装在灯管端的电容器抑制。在启辉器开关电路中,功率因数矫正电容实际上安装在启辉器中。典型的功率因数矫正电容约为 0.000 5 μF。

Starter switches with an electronic time-delay can be used to eliminate flicker at switch on.
带有电子延时的启动器开关可用于消除接通时灯管的闪烁。

An electronic ballast circuit can be used to improve luminaire efficiency and supply power factor by increasing the lamp frequency to around 30 kHz.
电子镇流器电路可将灯具频率增加至约 30 kHz 来提高灯具效率和电源功率因数。

Question 思考题

What would happen if the RIS capacitor in a glow-switch failed to a short-circuit?
如果启辉器开关中的功率因数矫正电容发生短路故障,会发生什么情况?

Answer 答案

The tube would not strike but would glow at its ends while the choke may overheat and eventually fail. A similar result would occur if the bi-metal strips of the starter welded together.

灯管不会激发,但其末端会发光,而扼流线圈可能过热并最终失效。如果启辉器的双金属条焊接在一起,也会出现类似的结果。

High-pressure mercury fluorescent type A typical high-pressure lamp and its circuit is shown in Fig. 6. 6. This type of lamp is coded as MBF (M = Mercury, B = high pressure, F fluorescent coating). An additional suffix to lamp codes may be/U or /V meaning that the lamp is designed for fitting in a Universal or Vertical position respectively, e. g. MBF/U.

高压汞荧光 A 型典型高压灯及其电路如图 6. 6 所示。这种灯的代码为 MBF(M 表示汞,B 表示高压,F 表示荧光涂层)。灯代码的附加后缀可以是/U 或/V,分别代表灯被设计为安装在通用或垂直位置,例如 MBF/U。

The high-pressure mercury lamp comes in sizes ranging from 50 to 1,000 W and is fitted with Edison screw or Goliath Edison screw lamp caps. Its luminous efficiency is in the range of 40-60 lm/W with an average life of around 7,500 h. The lamp takes several minutes to reach full brightness. It will not immediately re-strike when rapidly switched off then back on because the vapour pressure prevents this happening. Re-striking will occur when the discharge tube has sufficiently cooled down.

高压汞灯的规格从 50 W 到 1 000 W 不等,并配有爱迪生螺口或格莱斯爱迪生螺口灯头。其发光效率为 40~60 lm/W,平均寿命约为 7 500 h。灯泡需要几分钟才能达到最大亮度。当快速关闭然后再打开时,它不会立即重新启动,因为蒸气压力阻止了这种情况的发生。当放电灯管充分冷却时,将发生再激发。

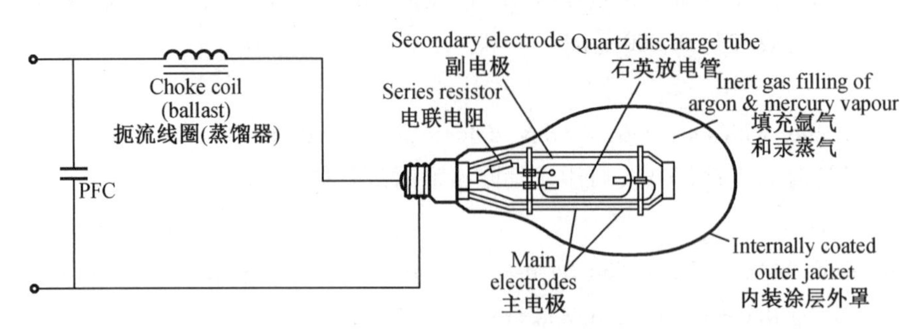

Fig. 6. 6　High-pressure lamp and its circuit

图 6. 6　高压汞灯电路

Lamp gas ionisation is obtained between a secondary electrode fitted close to one of the main electrodes which warrms up the tube and an arc strikes between the main electrodes. Mercury, which was condensed on the tube will now vaporise and the main arc passes through it. The secondary electrode ceases operation as the lamp pressure builds up.

灯内气体电离是在靠近一个主电极的副电极之间实现的,该电极使灯管升温,并使主电极之间产生电弧。在管子上凝结的水银将蒸发,并维持主电弧。当灯内压力增大时,副电极停止工作。

6. 3. 2　Sodium Vapor 钠蒸气灯

Sodium vapor lamps like the mercury lamps, come in low-pressure and high-pressure versions.

钠蒸气灯像汞灯一样,有低压和高压两种。

1. Low-pressure Sodium Vapor Type 低压钠蒸气灯

A low-pressure sodium lamp is coded as SOX (SO = sodium vapor, X = standard single-ended lamp of integral construction). A typical lamp shape and its circuit is shown in Fig. 6. 7. The lamp has a U-shaped arc tube containing metallic sodium and an inert gas such as neon. Common lamp power ratings are 35 W, 55 W, 90 W, 135 W and 180 W with luminous efficiencies in the range of 120−175 lm/W with an average operating life of 6,000 h. The low-pressure sodium lamp needs a high voltage (480 − 650 V) which requires a special transformer ballast or electronic ballast circuit.

低压钠蒸气灯编码为SOX(SO 表示钠蒸气,X 表示整体结构的标准单端灯)。图 6. 7 所示为典型的灯具外形及其电路。该灯有一个 U 形电弧管,其中含有金属钠和氖气等惰性气体。普通灯的额定功率为 35 W、55 W、90 W、135 W 和 180 W,发光效率为 120~175 lm/W,平均工作寿命为 6 000 h。低压钠蒸气灯需要高电压(480~650 V),这需要特殊的变压镇流器或电子镇流器电路。

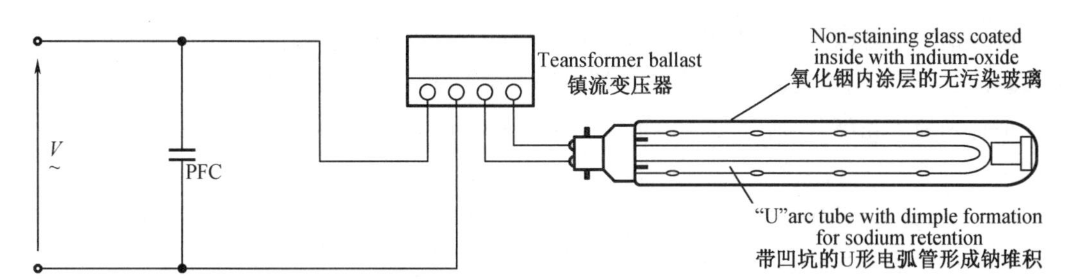

Fig. 6. 7　SOX lamp and circuit

图 6. 7　低压钠蒸气灯电路

When first ignited the SOX lamp gives a red glow as the discharge is initially through the neon gas. As the lamp warms up the sodium begins to evaporate to take over the discharge from the neon causing the lamp colour to change from red to yellow. The time taken to reach full brightness is between 6−15 min.

当首次点火时,低压钠蒸气灯发出红光,因为放电最初是通过氖气进行的。当灯升温时,钠开始蒸发,代替氖气的放电,导致灯的颜色从红色变为黄色。到达满亮度所需的时间为 6~15 min。

2. High-pressure Sodium Vapor Type 高压钠蒸气灯

A typical lamp and its circuit is shown in Fig. 6. 8. The basic lamp type is coded as SON (SO = sodium vapour, N = high pressure), but two other variations are labelled as SON−T (a tubular clear glass type) and SON−TD (a tubular doubleended clear quartz type).

图 6. 8 所示为典型的灯具形式及其电路。基本灯类型编码为 SON(SO 表示钠蒸气,N 表示高压),但其他两种类型标记为 SON−T(管状透明玻璃类型)和 SON−TD(管状双端透明石英类型)。

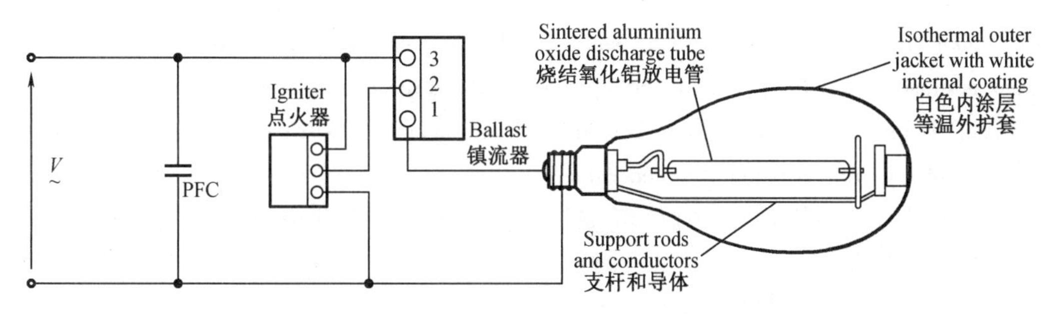

Fig. 6. 8　SON lamp and circuit

图 6. 8　高压钠蒸气灯电路

The SON lamp gives a wide spread of illumination with a golden-white light. Lamp starting is achieved by a high voltage pulse from an electronic igniter circuit which ceases to function once the main arc has been struck. A start-up delay of about 5 min is required for the lamp to reach full brightness but will usually re-strike within 1 min of extinction from the hot condition.

高压钠蒸气灯以金白光提供广泛的照明。灯的启动是通过电子点火器电路的高压脉冲实现的,一旦主电弧被击中,电子点火器电路就会停止工作。灯需要大约 5 min 的启动延迟才能达到最大亮度,但通常会在热条件熄灭后 1 min 内重新点亮。

SON lamp power ratings range between 70 and 1,000 W with corresponding luminous efficiencies being between 80 and 120 lm/W.

高压钠蒸气灯的额定功率为 70~1 000 W,相应的发光效率为 80~120 lm/W。

6.4 Voltage Effects on Lighting 电压对照明的影响

Naturally, all lamps are designed to produce their rated luminous output at their rated voltage. An overvoltage on an incandescent lamp produces a brighter and whiter light because the filament temperature is increased. Its operating life is, however, drastically reduced. A 5% increase over its rated voltage will reduce the lamp life by 50%.

理所当然,所有灯具都设计为在其额定电压下产生其额定发光输出。白炽灯上的过电压会使其产生更亮、更白的光,因为灯丝温度会升高。然而,其使用寿命大大会缩短。超过额定电压 5%时,灯泡寿命将缩短 50%。

Conversely, a supply voltage reduction will increase the operating life of a GLS lamp but it produces a duller, reddish light. Lamps rated at 240 V are often used in a ship's lighting system operating at 220 V. This under-running should more than double the lamp life.

相反,电源电压降低会延长普通照明灯的工作寿命,但会产生更暗的红光。额定电压为 240 V 的灯具通常用于 220 V 下运行的船舶照明系统。这种不足运行会使灯具寿命延长一倍以上。

Similar effects on light output and operating life apply to discharge lamps but if the supply voltage is drastically reduced (below 50%) the arc discharge ceases and will not re-strike until the voltage is raised to nearly its normal value. A fluorescent tube will begin to flicker noticeably as the voltage is reduced below its rated value.

对光的输出和工作寿命的类似影响也适用于放电灯,但如果电源电压大幅降低(低于 50%),电弧放电将停止,并且在电压升高到接近其正常值之前不会重新激发。当电压降至额定值以下时,荧光灯管将开始明显闪烁。

The normal sinusoidal AC voltage waveform causes discharge lamps to extinguish at the end of every half cycle, i. e. every 10 ms at 50 Hz or every 6.7 ms at 60 Hz. Although this rapid light fluctuation is not detectable by the human eye, it can cause a stroboscopic effect whereby rotating shafts in the vicinity of discharge lamps may appear stationary or rotating slowly which could be a dangerous illusion to operators.

正常正弦交流电压波形使放电灯在每半个周期结束时熄灭,即在 50 Hz 时每 10 ms 或在 60 Hz 时每 6.7 ms 熄灭一次。尽管人眼无法检测到这种快速的光波动,但它会导致频闪效应,因此放电灯照明范围内的转动轴可能会给人静止或缓慢旋转的感觉,这对操作员来说可能是一种危险的错觉。

Question 思考题

Give three methods to alleviate a stroboscopic problem.
列出三种解决频闪问题的方法。

Answer 答案

(1) Use a combination of incandescent and discharge lighting in the same area.
在同一区域使用白炽灯和放电灯的组合。

(2) Use twin discharge lamp fittings with each lamp wired as a lead-lag circuit, i. e. the lamp currents are phase displaced so that they go through zero at different times, hence the overall light output is never fully extinguished.

使用双放电灯配件,每个灯作为超前-滞后电路连接,即灯电流相移,使其在不同时间过零,因此总光输出永远不会完全熄灭。

(3) Where a three-phase supply is available, connect adjacent discharge luminaires to different phases (red, yellow, blue) so the light in a given area is never extinguished.

如果有三相电源,则将相邻的放电灯具连接到不同的相位(红色、黄色、蓝色),以便给定区域的灯光永远不会熄灭。

6.5 Navigation and Signal Lights 航行灯和信号灯

The number, position and visible range of navigation lights aboard ships are prescribed by the IMO in their "*International Regulations for Preventing Collisions at Sea*". In the UK, the national authority for maintaining marine safety standards is the Maritime and Coastguard Authority (MCA).

国际海事组织在其《国际海上避碰规则》中规定了船舶航行灯的数量、位置和可见范围。在英国,维护海上安全标准的国家机构是海事和海岸警卫队管理局(MCA)。

By far the most common arrangement is to have five specially designed navigation running lights referred to as foremast, mainmast (or aftmast), port, starboard and stern. See Fig. 6.9.

到目前为止,最常见的方式是设计 5 个航行灯,分别为前桅灯、主桅(或后桅)灯、左舷灯、右舷灯和艉灯,如图 6.9 所示。

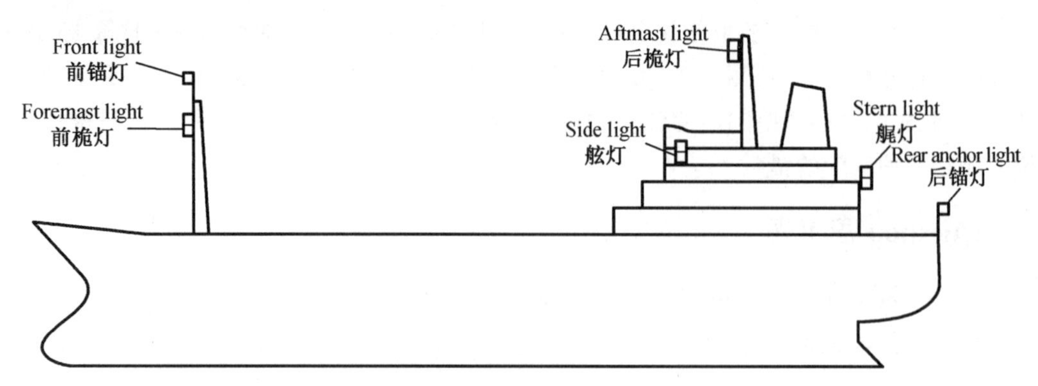

Fig. 6. 9 Ship navigation lights arrangement

图 6. 9 船舶航行灯布局

Two anchor lights, fitted forward and aft, may also be switched from the navigation light panel on the bridge. The side lights are red for port and green for starboard while the other lights are white.

前后安装的两个锚灯也可从驾驶台上的导航灯面板切换。左舷的侧灯为红色,右舷的侧灯为绿色,而其他灯为白色。

For vessels length more than 50 metres, the masthead light(s) must be visible from a range of 6 n mile and the other navigation lights from 3 n mile.

对于长度超过 50 m 的船舶,桅顶灯必须在 6 n mile 范围内可见,其他航行灯必须在 3 n mile 范围内可见。

To achieve such visibility, special incandescent filament lamps are used each with a typical power rating of 65 W but 60 W and 40 W ratings are also permitted in some cases.

为了实现这种可视性,使用特殊白炽灯,每个白炽灯的典型额定功率为 65 W,但在某些情况下也允许使用 60 W 和 40 W 的额定功率。

Due to the essential safety requirement for navigation lights it is common practice to have two fittings at each position, or two lamps and lampholders within a special dual fitting.

由于导航灯的基本安全要求,通常在每个位置安装两个配件,或在特殊的双配件内安装两个灯具和灯座。

Each light is separately supplied, switched, fused and monitored from a navigation light panel in the wheelhouse. The electric power is provided usually at 220 V AC with a main supply fed from the essential services section of the main switchboard. An alternative or standby power supply is fed from the emergency switchboard. A changeover switch on the navigation light panel selects the main or standby power supply.

每盏灯分别独立由驾驶室中的航行灯面板供电、开关、熔断和监控。电源通常为 220 V

交流电,主电源由主配电板的必要设备供电部分提供。备用或备用电源由应急配电板供电。通过导航灯面板上的转换开关来选择主电源或备用电源。

The navigation light panel has indicator lamps and an audible alarm to warn of any lamp or lamp-circuit failure. Each lamp circuit has an alarm relay which monitors the lamp current. The relay may be electromagnetic or electronic. A basic double navigation light scheme with alternative power supplies is shown in Fig. 6. 10.

导航灯面板具有指示灯和声音报警器,用于警告任何灯或灯电路故障。每个灯电路都有一个监控灯电流的报警继电器。继电器是电磁式或电子式的。图 6. 10 所示为带有备用电源的基本双导航灯方案。

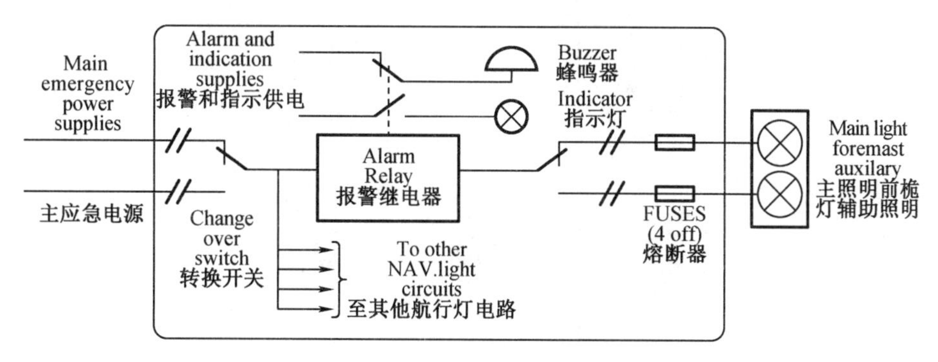

Fig. 6. 10　Navigation light panel

图 6. 10　航行灯控制屏

Various signal lights with red, green, white and blue colours are arranged on the signal mast as shown in Fig. 6. 11. These lights are switched to give particular combinations to signal states relating to various international and national regulations. Pilotage requirements, health, dangerous cargo conditions, etc. , are signalled with these lights.

信号桅上布置有红、绿、白、蓝等多种颜色的信号灯,如图 6. 11 所示。这些灯按与各种国际和国家法规相关的信号状态提供特定的组合开启。引航要求、健康状态、危险货物状况等由这些灯发出相应的信号。

The not under command (NUC) state is signalled using two all-round red lights vertically mounted at least 2 m apart. Such important lights are fed from the 24 V DC emergency supply but some ships may also have an additional NUC light-pair fed from the 220 V AC emergency power supply.

失控(NUC)状态通过两个全方位红灯发出信号,垂直安装,相距至少 2 m。这些重要的灯由 24 V 直流应急电源供电,但一些船舶也可能有一对额外的失控灯由 220 V 交流应急电源供电。

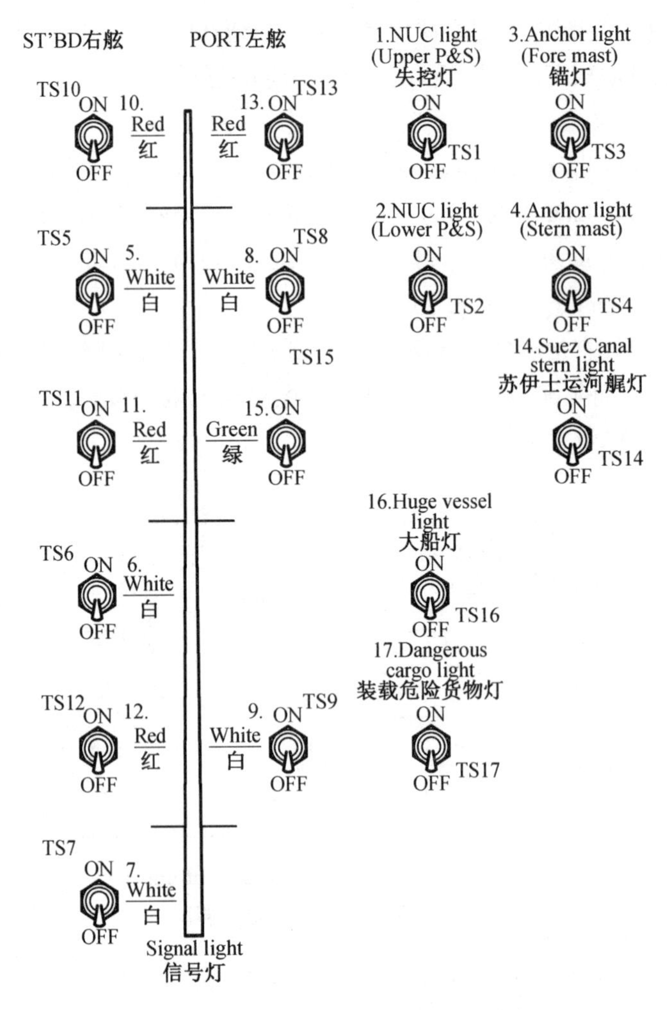

Fig. 6.11 Signal lights arrangement and control panel

图 6.11 信号灯布局和控制屏

6.6 Emergency Lighting 应急照明

Depending on the ship's classification, e. g. ferry, ro-ro, gas carrier, etc. , and tonnage the "*Safety of Life at Sea*" (SOLAS) convention prescribes minimum requirements for emergency lighting throughout the vessel.

《国际海上人命安全公约》(SOLAS)规定了全船应急照明的最低要求,具体取决于船舶的分类,如轮渡、滚装船、气体运输船等,以及吨位。

Emergency light fittings are specially identified, often with a red disc, to indicate their function. Most of the emergency lighting is continuallv powered from the ship's emergency switchboard at 220 V AC.

应急灯配件经过特殊标识,通常带有红色圆盘,以指示其特性。大多数应急照明由船舶应急配电板以 220 V 交流电压持续供电。

A few emergency lights may be supplied from the ship's 24 V DC battery, e. g. at the radio-telephone position in the wheelhouse, the main machinery spaces and the steering flat.

一些应急灯可由船舶的 24 V 直流电池供电,例如在驾驶室、主机舱和操舵台的无线电话位置。

Some shipping companies now fit special battery-supported light fittings along main escape routes in the engine room, accommodation and at the lifeboat positions on deck. Generally, such emergency lights in the accommodation are arranged to produce light immediately on mains failure.

一些航运公司在机舱、生活区和甲板上的救生艇位置沿主要逃生路线安装有特殊的电池照明装置。一般而言,生活区内的应急灯在电源故障时应能立即发光。

Boat station emergency lights are switched on when required. Inside the fitting a maintenance-free battery, usually nickel-cadmium, is continually trickle charged from the normal main supply via a transformer/rectifier circuit. The battery is then available to supply the lamp via a DC to AC inverter when the main power is absent. Usually the battery will only function for a few hours. This power supply arrangement is called an uninterruptible power supply or UPS. Such battery supported light fittings can be simply tested by switching off the normal mains power supply or, in some cases, by a test switch on the actual fitting. Periodic inspection and testing of all emergency lights is an essential requirement on all ships. A visible, illuminated escape route reduces uncertainty and assists orderly evacuation.

艇甲板应急灯在需要时打开。在应急灯内部,免维护电池(通常为镍镉电池)通过变压器/整流器电路从正常电源持续涓流充电。当主电源失效时,蓄电池可通过直流转交流逆变器向应急灯供电。通常电池只能工作几个小时。这种电源装置称为不间断电源(UPS)。这种电池支持的灯具可以通过关闭正常电源或在某些情况下,通过实际电源上的测试开关进行简单测试。定期检查和测试所有应急灯是所有船舶的基本要求。一条可见的、有照明的逃生路线减少了逃生的不确定性,有助于有序疏散。

Passenger ships carrying more than 36 passengers are required by IMO resolution A752(18) to be fitted with low location lighting (LLL) to identify escape routes where normal emergency lighting is less effective due to the presence of smoke. An LLL system must function for at least 60 min after activation and it should indicate a line along the corridors of an escape route.

国际海事组织第 A752(18)号决议要求载客超过 36 人的客船安装低位置照明(LLL),以确定因烟雾而导致正常应急照明效果不佳的逃生路线。低位置照明系统必须在激活后至少运行 60 min,并应指示走廊沿线的逃生路线。

The installation of LLL should be on at least one side of the corridor, either on the bulkhead within 300 mm of the deck or on the deck within 150 mm of the bulkhead. In corridors more than 2 m wide, it should be installed on both sides.

低位置照明设备的安装应至少位于走廊的一侧,位于甲板 300 mm 范围内的舱壁上或舱壁 150 mm 范围内的甲板上。在宽度超过 2 m 的走廊中,应在两侧安装。

The LLL light sources may be low power LED's, incandescent lamps or a photoluminescent material containing a chemical that stores energy when illuminated by visible light. Of these sources, the LED and incandescent lamp are the most effective. For hazardous areas such as car decks on a ferry, an intrinsically safe (Exia) version can be installed.

低位置照明光源可以是低功率 LED、白炽灯或光致发光材料,其中含有在可见光照射下储存能量的化学物质。在这些光源中,LED 和白炽灯是最有效的。对于危险区域,如渡轮上的汽车甲板,可安装本质安全型(Exia)光源。

Fig. 6. 12 indicates the main components of an LLL system where the LED's are wired onto a printed circuit board within a clear polycarbonate rectangular tube with connectors at each end. A similar arrangement is available using low power incandescent lamps.

图 6. 12 显示了低位置照明系统的主要部件,其中 LED 被连接到透明聚碳酸酯矩形管内的印刷电路板上,每端带有连接器。使用低功率白炽灯也有类似的布置。

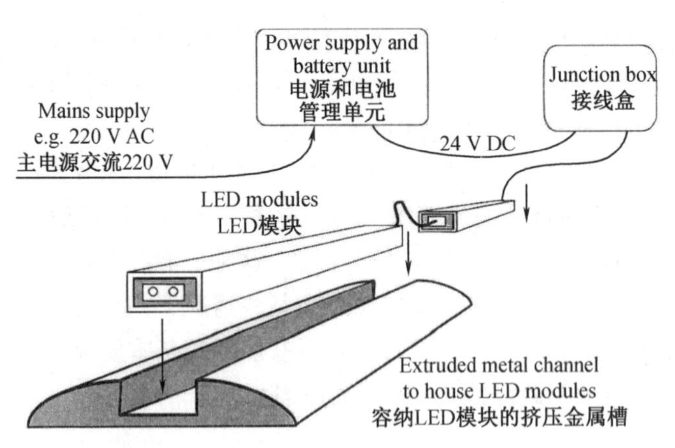

Fig. 6. 12 Low location lighting (LLL)

图 6. 12 低位置照明装置

6. 7 Maintenance of Lighting Fittings 灯具的维护

The performance of electric lamps will deteriorate with time. Eventually they fail and the lamps must be replaced. Simple lamp replacement becomes the most obvious maintenance task. When a luminaire fails to light-up when switched on, it is natural to suspect lamp failure. If this does not solve the problem, checks on the lamp control equipment and power supply must follow.

电灯的性能会随着时间的推移而恶化。最终,它们会出现故障,此时必须更换灯具。简单的灯具更换成为最明显的维护任务。当灯具在打开时无法点亮,我们自然会怀疑灯具有故障。如果这不能解决问题,则必须随后检查灯的控制设备和电源。

An incandescent lamp may be checked (out of circuit) for low-ohm continuity using a multimeter. If the lamp appears intact then the fault must lie in the supply or its connections. Voltage and continuity checks of the supply, fuse/MCB and ballast circuit must be applied. Remember that a single earth fault on an insulated two-wire lighting supply will not blow a fuse. However, a similar earth fault on an earthed supply system (as used for a 110 V transformer supply to deck sockets for portable tools and handlamps) will blow a fuse.

可使用万用表检查白炽灯(电路故障)的低阻连续性。如果指示灯看起来完好无损,则故障必定位于电源或其连接中。必须对电源、熔断器/MCB 和镇流器电路进行电压和连续性检查。请记住,绝缘双线照明电源上的单个接地故障不会熔断保险丝。然而,已接地供电系统上的类似接地故障(如用于便携式工具和手灯甲板插座的 110 V 变压器电源)将熔断保险丝。

Question 思考题

Why will a single earth fault blow a fuse in an earthed supply system?
为什么单一接地故障会使接地供电系统中的保险丝熔断?

Answer 答案

The single E/F completes a low resistance path back to the neutral or centre point of the supply with a resulting large fault current to rupture the fuse(Fig. 6. 13).

单个 E/F 完成返回电源中性点或中心点的低电阻路径,产生大故障电流,使保险丝熔断(图 6. 13)。

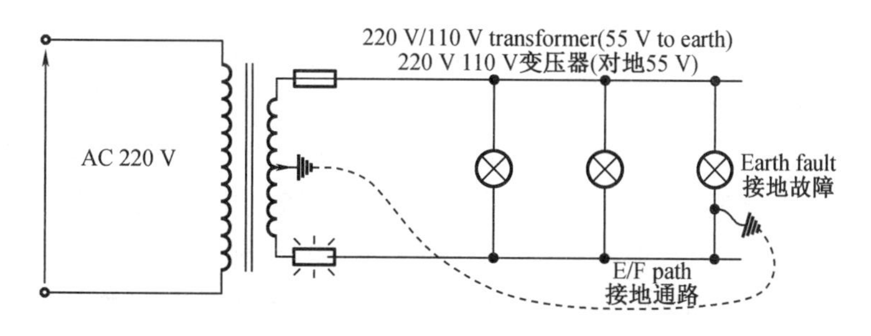

Fig. 6. 13 Earth fault effect in an earthed supply system

图 6. 13 接地故障对供电系统的影响

A maintenance check list:

(1) Remember that it is good practice to replace both fuses after clearing a fault which has

ruptured only one of them.

(2) When replacing a lamp, ensure that the circuit is dead and isolated while removing the old lamp and inserting the new one. The glass bulb or tube of an old and corroded fitting may break loose from its end-cap while attempting to remove the lamp. If the supply is still connected, it is relatively easy to cause an accidental short circuit during the removal process and the corresponding arc flash may cause blindness, burns and fire.

(3) Always replace a lamp with the correct size, voltage and power rating for the fitting it is housed in. Overheating and fire can easily result by using a higher powered incandescent lamp than the fitting was designed for. Check the lampholder wire connections behind the lampholder for signs of overheating (hard, brittle insulation on the wires) and replace if necessary.

(4) Take care when disposing of lamps, particularly discharge tubes, which should be broken (outdoors) into a container (e. g. a strong plastic bag) to avoid handling the debris.

(5) Remember that in a fluorescent lamp circuit the capacitor may remain charged for a while after switch off unless fitted with a discharge resistor. Play safe, discharge the capacitor with a screwdriver blade before touching its terminals.

(6) Cleaning of the lamp glass and reflectors is essential for safety and necessary to maintain the luminous efficiency of the luminaire.

(7) Particular care should be paid to the maintenance of the watertight integritv of exposed luminaires (e. g. for navigation, signal and deck lighting) at their flanged joints and cable gland entry. Similarly, a regular inspection of all portable handlamps and portable cargo light fittings, together with their flexible cables and supply plugs, should be undertaken.

维护检查清单如下：

(1)请记住，在排除仅使其中一个熔断器断裂的故障后，最好更换两个熔断器。更换灯时，在拆卸旧灯和插入新灯的同时，确保电路已断开且已隔离。

(2)当试图拆卸车灯时，旧的腐蚀配件的玻璃灯泡或玻璃管可能会从其端盖上脱落。

(3)如果电源仍然接通，则在拆卸过程中相对容易造成意外短路，相应的电弧闪光可能导致失明、烧伤和火灾。

(4)处理灯具时要小心，尤其是放电管，放电管应(在室外)放入容器(如结实的塑料袋)中，以避免处理碎屑。

(5)请记住，在荧光灯电路中，电容器在关闭后可能会保持充电一段时间，除非安装了放电电阻器。为安全起见，在接触电容器端子之前，用螺丝刀对电容器放电。

(6)清洁灯具玻璃和反射器对于安全至关重要，也是保持灯具发光效率的必要条件。

(7)应特别注意在法兰接头和电缆密封套入口处维护外露灯具(例如用于导航、信号和甲板照明的灯具)的水密完整性。同样，应定期检查所有便携式手灯和便携式货灯配件及其软电缆和电源插头。

6.8 Refrigeration and Air Conditioning 制冷与空调

The basic electric power and control elements for refrigeration and airconditioning are outlined below.

制冷和空调的基本电力及控制元件概述如下。

6.8.1 Refrigeration 制冷

The safe storage of food necessitates that it is maintained at low temperatures which requires the process of refrigeration. For bulk foods one large industrial refrigeration plant will serve separate cold rooms for the storage of meat, fruit and vegetables, dairy products, etc. Smaller domestic sized refrigerators are used to meet the daily catering needs in the galley, pantries, duty messrooms and in cabins. The refrigeration process is also utilised in deep-freezers, water chillers and air-conditioning plant. Large scale cargo space refrigeration is also necessary for the transportation of foods and certain liquid chemicals and gases.

食品的安全储存要求其保持在低温下,这需要冷藏过程来实现。对于散装食品,一个大型工业制冷厂将提供单独的冷藏室,用于储存肉类、水果和蔬菜、乳制品等。小型家用冰箱用于满足厨房、食品储藏室、值班餐厅和舱室的日常餐饮需求。制冷过程也用于深度冷冻柜、冷水机和空调设备。大型货舱制冷对于运输食品和某些液体化学品及气体也是必要的。

Whatever the size or role of the ship's refrigerators, the basic principle is common to them all. Each will have an evaporator (cooling unit), a refrigerant compressor and a condenser.

无论船上冰箱的大小或作用如何,其基本原理是共通的,都包括一个蒸发器(冷却装置)、一个制冷剂压缩机和一个冷凝器。

The refrigerant is generally Freon-12 (CCl_2F_2) or Freon-22, but ammonia is also used in large systems. Freon refrigerants in general use are colourless and almost odourless, while also being non-toxic, non-corrosive and nonflammable. However, when exposed to an open flame, a highly toxic phosgene gas is produced.

制冷剂通常为氟利昂-12(CCl_2F_2)或氟利昂-22,但在大型系统中也使用氨。通常使用的氟利昂制冷剂无色无味,同时无毒、无腐蚀性和不易燃。然而,当暴露在明火中时,其会产生有剧毒的光气。

Additional components to the basic refrigerant cycle may include filter-driers, heat exchangers, accumulators and pre-coolers. Also required are the operating and protective controls such as thermostats, relays, defrost controls and over current trips.

基本制冷剂循环的其他部件可能包括过滤器干燥器、热交换器、蓄能器和预冷却器。

还需要操作和保护控制装置,如恒温器、继电器、除霜控制装置和过电流跳闸装置。

Above the domestic sized refrigerator, the compressor motor will invariably be a three-phase type driving a reciprocating compressor. The domestic version will usually be a single-phase motor driving a rotary compressor.

在家用冰箱上,压缩机电机将始终为三相,驱动往复式压缩机。国内版本通常是单相电动机驱动旋转式压缩机。

The basic refrigerant circuit of a direct (or primary) expansion system used for the cooling of meat and vegetable rooms is outlined in Fig. 6. 14.

图 6. 14 概述了用于冷却肉类和蔬菜室的直接(或一次)膨胀系统的基本制冷剂回路。

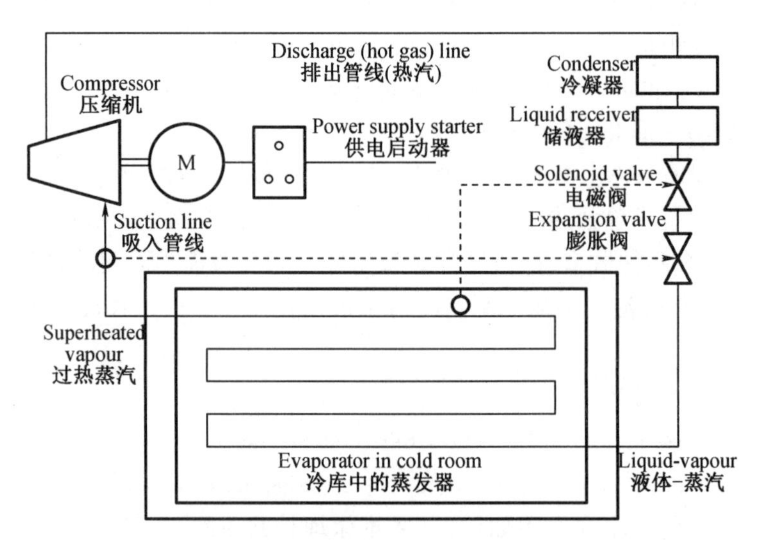

Fig. 6. 14 Refrigerator scheme and main components

图 6. 14 冰箱系统和主要元件

Each cold room is fitted with a thermostat which operates a solenoid valve between set temperature limits. The quantity of refrigerant flowing in the system is regulated by the expansion valve. This valve is controlled by a liquid phial connected by a capillary tube attached to the vapour return pipe at the outlet of the evaporator.

每个冷藏室都配有一个恒温器,该恒温器在设定的温度范围之间操作一个电磁阀。系统中的制冷剂流量由膨胀阀调节。该阀门由毛细管连接至蒸发器出口蒸汽回流管的液体温包控制。

When the room temperature falls to the pre-set level, the thermostat de-energises the solenoid valve to stop circulation of the refrigerant. The resulting pressure drop in the compressor suction line will operate a low-pressure cut-out valve and stop the compressor.

当室温降至预设水平时,节温器将使电磁阀断电,以停止制冷剂循环。压缩机吸入管路中产生的压降将操作低压切断阀并停止压缩机。

The rooms or compartments are cooled by natural air circulation through the evaporator coils or by forced-air from a fan blowing across a bank of cooling tubes.

房间或隔间通过蒸发器盘管的自然空气循环或通过风扇吹过冷却管组的强制空气进行冷却。

In a domestic refrigerator the cooling effort is controlled by using a control thermostat to switch the compressor on or off.

在家庭用冰箱中,通过使用温度控制器开或关压缩机来控制制冷效果。

The hermetically sealed compressor motor is the split-phase type having two separate windings start and run as shown in Fig. 6. 15.

密封压缩机电动机为分相式,具有两个独立绕组,启动和运行如图 6. 15 所示。

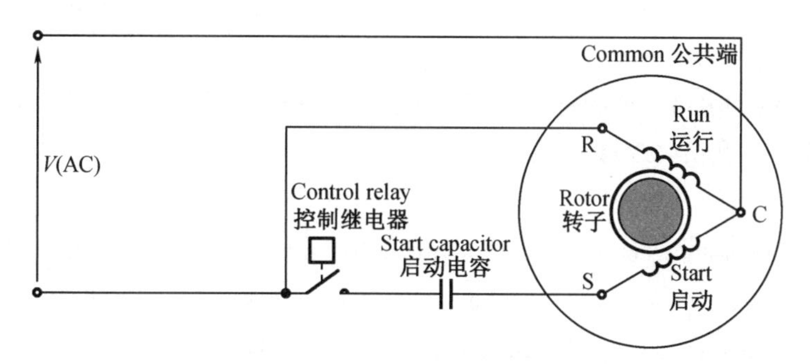

Fig. 6. 15　Split-phase type motor

图 6. 15　分相电动机

The motor is accelerated by connecting both start andrun phase windings to the supply. When the motor reaches about 80% of its rated speed, the start winding is tripped out of circuit. For compressor drives, this switch is usually in the form of a current-operated relay which is fitted adjacent to the compressor.

通过将启动和运行相绕组连接到电源,电动机加速。当电动机达到其额定转速的 80% 左右时,启动绕组脱离电路。对于压缩机驱动装置,该开关通常采用电流操作继电器的形式,该继电器安装在压缩机附近。

Question 思考题

If the motor terminal markings are unknown, how could you identify the start, run and common terminal connections?

如果电动机端子标记未知,如何识别启动、运行和公共终端连接?

Answer 答案

The start winding (being short-time rated) has a higher resistance than the run winding so a resistance check should identify the terminals as follows:

(1) Using a multimeter on the low resistance range, find the two terminals that have the highest resistance between them. These are the start and run terminals. The remaining terminal must be the "common".

(2) Connect one lead of the meter onto the common terminal and touch the other meter lead onto the other terminals in turn and note the readings.

(3) The highest reading indicates the start winding terminal. The other remaining terminal is the run connection. Typically, the run winding is 1.5-6 Ω and the start winding is 6-22 Ω.

启动绕组(短时额定)的电阻高于运行绕组,因此电阻检查应确定以下端子:

(1)使用万用表低电阻挡,找出电阻最高的两个端子。这些是启动和运行终端。其余端子必须是"公共"端子。

(2)将仪表的一根表笔连接到公共端子上,然后依次用另一根表笔接触其他端子,并记录读数。

(3)最高读数表示启动绕组端子。剩下的另一个终端是运行连接。通常,运行绕组为1.5~6 Ω,启动绕组为6~22 Ω。

The main temperature control device in the refrigerator is the thermostat which senses the evaporator temperature via a capillary tube. The set temperature is adjusted by a control knob which tensions the control spring against the pressure of the bellows.

冰箱中的主要温度控制装置为恒温器,其通过毛细管感应蒸发器温度。设定温度由一个控制旋钮调节,该旋钮使控制弹簧相对于波纹管压力张紧。

For motor protection a bimetallic overcurrent relay (OCR) trip is included as part of the control relay alongside the compressor. The motor supply current either passes directly through a bi-metal strip or disc or the bi-metal is heated indirectly from a small resistance heater alongside it. A motor overcurrent will cause the bi-metal to deflect and cause a snap-action switch to open.

对于电动机保护,双金属过电流继电器(OCR)跳闸是压缩机旁边控制继电器的一部分。电动机供电电流要么直接通过双金属条或圆盘,要么通过其旁边的小电阻加热器间接加热双金属。电动机过电流将导致双金属发热变形弯曲,使速动开关断开。

Fig. 6.16 shows the complete circuit of a simple domestic refrigerator (i. e. without timers, automatic defrost or air-circulation fans).

图6.16显示了简单家用冰箱的完整电路(即没有定时器、自动除霜或空气循环风扇)。

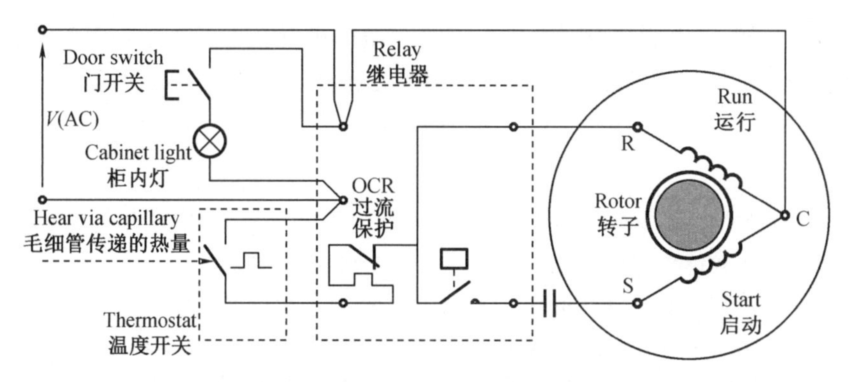

Fig. 6. 16 The complete circuit of a simple domestic refrigerator

图 6. 16 简易冰箱电路

When the evaporator temperature rises, the thermostat switch closes allowing current to flow through the motor run winding and the relay solenoid coil. This current is initially high causing the solenoid to close the relay switch to allow current into the start winding.

当蒸发器温度升高时,节温器开关闭合,使电流流过电动机运行绕组和继电器电磁线圈。该电流最初较高,导致电磁阀闭合继电器开关,以允许电流进入启动绕组。

The motor will now begin to accelerate from standstill causing its run winding current to reduce to a level where the start-relay will drop off. The motor will now run continuously on the run-phase only. When the evaporator reaches its set temperature the thermostat resets and the motor is switched off.

电动机现在将开始从静止状态加速,导致其运行绕组电流降低到可使启动继电器下降的水平。此时电动机仅在运行阶段连续运行。当蒸发器达到设定温度时,恒温器复位,电动机关闭。

The most common way to achieve automatic defrosting of the evaporator is to use a time-switch to cut out the refrigeration circuit and initiate a defrost heater circuit. The timer may be a small motor with a cam driven changeover switch or an electronic timer with relay changeover contacts.

实现蒸发器自动除霜的最常见方法是使用时间开关切断制冷电路,并启动除霜加热器电路。计时器可以是带有凸轮驱动转换开关的小型电动机,也可以是带有继电器转换触点的电子计时器。

A bimetallic defrost thermostat controls the defrost heater in or below the evaporator. Most defrost thermostats close at 20 °F① ±5 °F and open at 55 °F±5 °F. Defrost periods may vary from 15 to 45 min with up to four defrost cycles in 24 h depending on the fridge/freezer design.

---

① 华氏温度与摄氏温度的换算公式为摄氏温度=(华氏温度-32 °F)/1.8。

双金属除霜恒温器控制蒸发器内或下方的除霜加热器。大多数除霜恒温器在 20 °F±5 °F 时关闭,在 55 °F±5 °F 时打开。除霜周期可能从 15 min 到 45 min 不等,24 h 内最多可进行四次除霜循环,具体取决于冰箱/冷冻柜的设计。

Some refrigerators and freezers may have electric heaters fitted for various duties such as a dewpoint heater (to prevent sweating on the cabinet in the freezer area) and a compartment divider panel or stile heater (to prevent sweating on the panel). Additionally there may be condenser and evaporator fans which are driven by single-phase shaded-pole type motors.

一些冰机和冷冻机可能安装有用于各种用途的电加热器,如露点加热器(防止冷冻柜区域的机柜结水滴)和隔间隔板或梯架加热器(防止面板结水滴)。此外,还可能有冷凝器和蒸发器风扇,由单相罩极式电动机驱动。

6.8.2 Air Conditioning 空调

Air conditioning is a process' which heats, cools, cleans and circulates air together with the control of its moisture content. The air must be delivered to a room with a definite temperature and specified relative humidity.

空调可加热、冷却、清洁和循环空气,并控制空气中的水分含量。空气必须输送到具有一定温度和规定相对湿度的房间。

For summer duty, the usual method is to cool the incoming air to a temperature below the dew point to allow condensation to occur until the mixture has the desired specific humidity then heating the air to the required delivery temperature and relative humidity. In winter, the incoming air may have to be heated and have water added to achieve the correct inlet conditions. In most plants the bulk of the mixture is re-circulating air with fresh air intake forming about one third of the total required. The amount of make-up air is a statutory requirement which is typically between 17 m^3/h and 28 m^3/h.

对于夏季工作,通常的方法是将进入的空气冷却至低于露点的温度,以允许发生冷凝,直到混合物具有所需的特定湿度,然后将空气加热至所需的输送温度和相对湿度。在冬季,可能需要对进入的空气进行加热并添加水分,以达到正确的进气条件。在大多数电厂中,大部分混合物是再循环空气,新鲜空气进气口约占所需总空气量的三分之一。补充空气量是法定要求,流量通常为 17~28 m^3/h。

The electrical aspects of accommodation air conditioning (A/C) comprises the power equipment of motors and starters for the compressor(s), fans and sea-water cooling pumps. Associated control equipment will include electric solenoid valves, high and low-pressure and temperature switches together with safety cut-outs for overcurrent, loss of refrigerant, low compressor oil pressure, etc.

住宿空调(A/C)的电气组成包括压缩机、风扇和海水冷却泵的电动机和启动器的动力设备。联合控制设备包括电动电磁阀、高低压和温度开关以及过电流、制冷剂损失、低压缩机油压力等安全断路器。

The usual air-conditioning system used for the accommodation spaces of cargo ships is the central single-duct type, shown in Fig. 6. 17. In its simplest form a single compressor serves the whole accommodation.

货船起居舱常用的空调系统为中央单风管式,如图 6. 17 所示。在其最简单的形式中,一台压缩机为整个舱室提供服务。

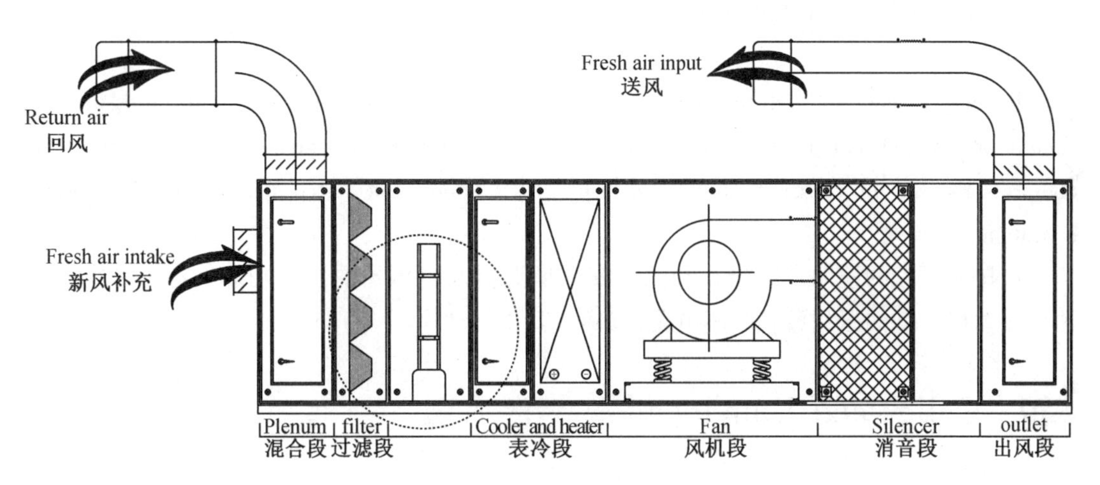

Fig. 6. 17　Air-conditioning scheme

图 6. 17　空调系统

The compressor is generally a multicylinder reciprocating type with a power rating in the range of 50–200 kW, although rotary-vane or screw-action compressors may also be encountered. Large passenger vessels may have a total power requirement of more than 5 MW for the AC compressor drives to maintain air delivery to the hotel and staff accommodation areas. Capacity control of the reciprocating compressor is by automatic unloading of cylinders by valve control using servo oil pressure.

压缩机通常为多缸往复式,额定功率为 50~200 kW,但也可能是旋转叶片式或螺杆式压缩机。大型客船的交流压缩机的驱动总功率可能超过 5 MW,以维持向酒店和员工住宿区的空气供应。往复式压缩机的容量控制是通过伺服油压阀门自动卸载气缸来实现的。

The compressor, air fan and sea water pump are driven by simple fixed speed, three-phase AC induction motors each with its own starter and supplied from a distribution board fitted in the air-conditioning plant room.

压缩机、风机和海水泵由简单的定速三相交流电动机驱动,每个电动机都有自己的启动器,并由安装在空调间内的配电板供电。

Routine electrical maintenance and fault finding on the motors and starters will involve cleaning, checking of connections, megger (IR)/continuity tests and running tests as described.

电动机和启动器的日常电气维护和故障查找将涉及清洁、检查连接处、绝缘(IR)/连续性测试和运行测试。

Inspection of connections and correct operation of any electric heaters must also be performed. Such heaters may be used for heating the compressor crankcase oil and for separating the refrigerant (Freon-12 or Freon-22) from the oil in an oil reservoir.

还必须检查所有电加热器的连接和正确运作。此类加热器可用于加热压缩机曲轴箱机油,并用于从储油器的机油中分离制冷剂(氟利昂-12 或氟利昂-22)。

Regular inspection and testing of controlfunction of safety thermostats and pressurestats should be carried out in accordance with the manufacturer's instructions. In particular the compressor's low oil pressure alarm and trip circuit should be tested periodically for correct operation.

应按照厂家的说明定期检查和测试安全恒温器及恒压器的控制功能。特别是应定期测试压缩机的低油压报警和跳闸电路,以确保其正常动作。

6.9 Galley and Laundry 厨房及洗衣房

The following section outlines the basic power and control units utilised for galley and laundry services.

本节概述了厨房和洗衣服务所用的基本电源及控制装置。

6.9.1 Galley 厨房

The electrical power in a galley is largely absorbed in producing heat. Ovens, deep fryer pans, water boilers and the hotplates on the galley range all employ resistive heating elements which are usually controlled by bimetallic thermostats. Other electrical galley equipment may include oven air circulating and range exhaust fans, meat slicers, food mixers and grinders, dishwashers, potato peelers and garbage disposal units. Most of this equipment will utilise small electric motors together with the necessary control switches, safety interlocks and indicator lamps.

厨房中消耗的电力大部分用来产生热量。烤箱、油炸锅、开水器和厨房炉灶上的加热板都采用电阻加热元件,这些元件通常由双金属恒温器控制。其他厨房电气设备可能包括烤箱空气循环和炉灶排气扇、切肉机、食品搅拌机和研磨机、洗碗机、马铃薯去皮机及垃圾处理装置。大多数设备会使用小型电动机以及必要的控制开关、安全联锁装置和指示灯。

Because of the large power requirement for food preparation and cooking, the major galley items are supplied from the three-phase AC 440 V system. Smaller galleys may be supplied from the lowvoltage 220 V AC system. The electrical equipment has to work safely in the usual galley atmosphere of high humidity and high temperature.

由于食品制备和烹饪需要大量电力,因此主要厨房设备由 440 V 三相交流系统供电。较小的厨房可由低压 220 V 交流系统供电。电气设备必须能在高湿度和高温的厨房环境中安全工作。

All in all, the galley electrics work in a tough area so be prepared for faults caused by the environmental hazards of grease, dust and dampness.

总而言之,厨房电气设备在恶劣的环境中运行,因此要做好预防油脂、灰尘和潮湿等环境危害引起的故障的准备。

Heating elements are usually formed from Nichrome-wire insulated with a magnesium-oxide (MgO) powder within an inconel tube which forms the outer sheath. Power ratings vary from 1 kW to about 4 kW and some elements are arranged to be switched to give varying levels of heat.

加热元件通常由镍铬合金线制成,镍铬合金线在铬镍铁合金管内用氧化镁(MgO)粉末绝缘,形成外护套。功率额定值从 1 kW 到约 4 kW 不等,一些元件被设置为可切换形式以提供不同程度的热量。

The simplest arrangement is obtained using a 3-heat, 4-position switch to control 2 elements within a single hotplate on a single-phase supply. The two resistance elements are interconnected by the switch to give a choice of OFF, LOW, MEDIUM and HIGH settings as shown in Fig. 6. 18.

最简单的配置是使用一个 3 挡加热、4 位开关控制单相电源上单个加热板内的 2 个电阻元件。如图 6. 18 所示,2 个电阻元件通过开关互连,以提供断开、低、中和高设置的选择。

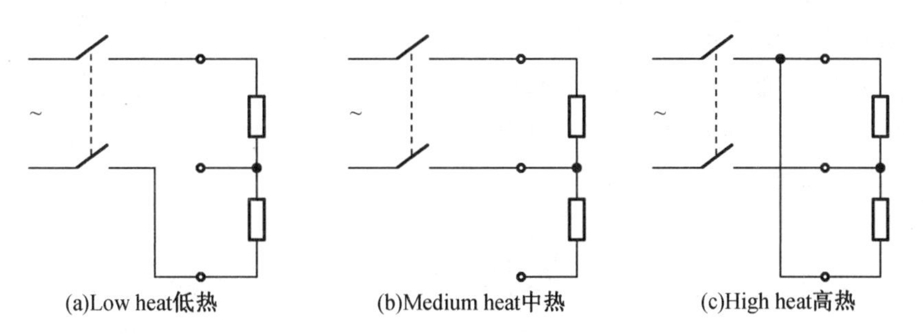

Fig. 6. 18 3-heat switching circuit

图 6. 18 三种加热转换电路

For larger heating power control using 440 V three-phase AC, three heating elements can be interconnected into star and delta connections.

对于使用 440 V 三相交流电的大功率加热控制,3 个加热元件可以成星形和三角形连接。

Closer control of heating elements is obtained by using thermostat switches and electronic switching. The thermostat switch type shown in Fig. 6. 19, houses a bi-metallic switch which cycles the heating element on and off at a rate determined by the switch setting. Average hot-plate temperature is fixed by the ratio of time that the element is on to the time it is off. Circuit current heats the bi-metal which operates the control switch.

通过使用恒温器开关和电子开关,可以更紧密地控制加热元件。图 6. 19 所示的恒温器开关类型包含一个双金属开关,该开关以开关设定的速率循环断开和闭合加热元件。热板的平均温度由元件断开和闭合的时间比例确定。电路电流通过双金属片使其发热来控制开关动作。

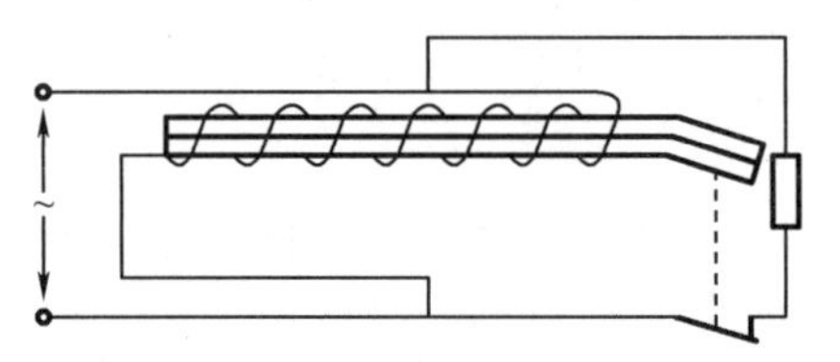

Fig. 6. 19　Thermostat switch circuit

图 6. 19　温度开关电路

Oven thermostat controls have a similar switching action but a temperature sensing capillary tube, located in the oven, deflects a diaphragm or bellows which activates the switch.

烘箱恒温器控制具有相似的开关动作,但位于烘箱内的温度传感器毛细管使膜片或波纹管偏转,从而使开关动作。

Electronic switching devices such as transistors, thyristors and triacs may also be used for temperature control of ovens and hot-plates. Be careful not to megget test low-voltage electronic components during maintenance and fault finding. Check the manufacturer's instructions and drawings before fault finding around electrical control circuits.

电子开关器件,如晶体管、晶闸管和可控硅也可用于烘箱和热板的温度控制。在维修和查找故障时,注意不要对低压电子元件进行绝缘测试。在查找电气控制电路故障前,先查阅制造商的说明书和图纸。

The most likely fault in a heating element is open-circuit. Earth faults within the element or on the wires supplying it are also possible. Loose wire connections cause localised overheating with the wire burning away to casue an open-circuit, but the possibility of a short-circuit or earth fault also arises.

加热元件最有可能的故障是开路。元件内部或元件的供电线路也可能发生接地故障。电线连接松动会导致局部过热,至少会烧坏电线,造成开路,但也有可能出现短路或接地故障。

The connecting wires lying close to heating elements should be covered with high-temperature silicone or fibre glass sleeving or with ceramic beads.

靠近加热元件的连接线应覆盖高温硅脂或玻璃纤维套管或陶瓷珠。

Question 思考题

What would be the resistance of a healthy 2 kW, 220 V heating elements?

一个正常的 2 kW,220 V 加热元件的电阻是多少?

Answer 答案

$I = P/V = 2\,000/220 = 9.1\ \text{A}$

$P = I^2R \rightarrow R = P/I^2 = 24.2\ \Omega$

When measured cold element, the resistance value may be lower than the calculated value. High power ovens and hotplate ranges are often supplied from the three-phase, 440 V AC supply. Thermostats control the on-off heating cycle. A simple oven circuit is shown in Fig. 6. 20 as an example of contactor control. Many and varied circuits occur in practice and the manufacturer's drawings must be checked in a particular case.

测冷态元件时,电阻值可能低于计算值。大功率烘箱和热板炉通常由 440 V 三相交流电源供电。温控器控制开关控制加热循环。图 6. 20 是一个简单的接触器控制的烘箱电路。在实际应用中会出现许多不同的电路,在特殊情况下必须查阅制造商的图纸。

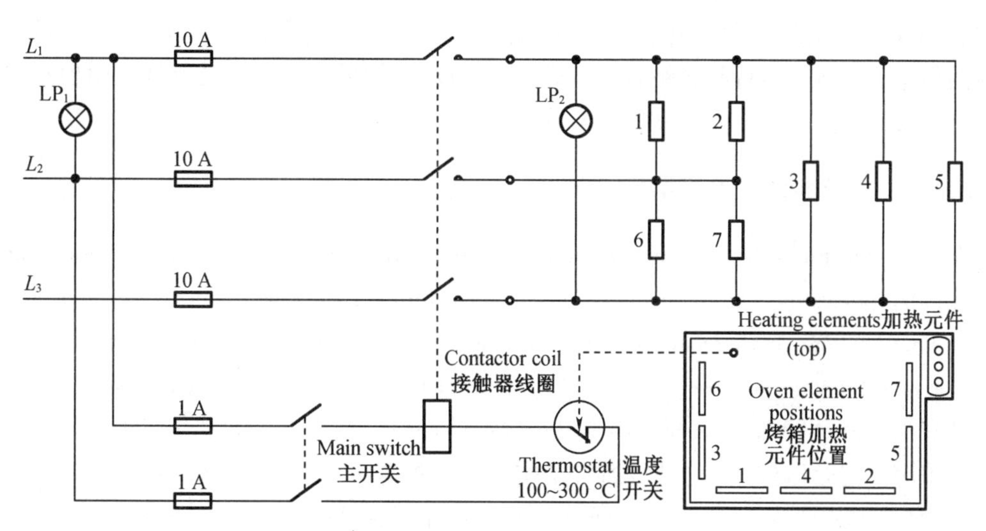

Fig. 6. 20 Simple oven circuit

图 6. 20 简易烤箱电路

Microwave ovens provide rapid defrosting and cooking of foods. The microwaves are produced by a special valve called a magnetron operating at around 4, 000 V with a frequency of 2,450 MHz. Specialised knowledge is required for the repair of this type of oven and internal fault finding is not recommended without the manufacturer's guidance.

微波炉可使食物迅速解冻和烹调。微波是由一种称为磁控管的特殊阀门产生的，其工作电压约为 4 000 V，频率为 2 450 MHz。此类烤箱的维修需要专业知识，未经制造商指导，不建议进行内部故障查找。

Inspection and maintenance of galley equipment is most important. The main objective is to keep the electrical parts clean and free of water, oil, dust and grease. Pay particular attention to all connection points in high current heating circuits where loose connections cause overheating and further problems. For operator safety, all enclosure metalwork must be earthed and regular checks of earthing wires must be given priority.

厨房设备的检查和维护是最重要的。其主要目的是保持电气部件清洁，无水、油、灰尘和油脂。特别注意大电流加热电路中的所有连接点，如果连接松动会导致过热和其他问题。为了操作人员的安全，所有外壳金属件必须接地，并且必须优先定期检查接地线。

Insulation resistance (IR) tests on heating elements, when cold, may reveal surprisingly low values (10 - 100 kΩ) even with new elements. This is because the element insulation (magnesium-oxide powder) is somewhat hygroscopic (absorbs moisture). The insulation resistance value of a healthy heating element should rise rapidly after being operated for a few minutes. Obviously, if the IR value of an element remains low when hot, it is defective and must be replaced.

加热元件的绝缘电阻(IR)测试，在冷态时，即使使用新元件，也可能显示出惊人的低阻值(10~100 kΩ)。这是因为元件绝缘(氧化镁粉)有一定的吸湿性(吸收水分)。正常电热元件的绝缘电阻值在运行几分钟后应迅速上升。显然，如果一个元件的绝缘电阻值在加热时仍然很低，那么它就是有故障的，必须更换。

6.9.2 Laundry 洗衣房

Washing machines, spin dryers and tumble dryers utilise heat and mechanical rotation during their laundry processes. The sequence of events is controlled by timers which are often simple electric timer motors driving cam-operated switches. Alternatively, electronic timers with relay switching or solid state electronic switching using thyristors or triacs may be employed.

洗衣机、旋转烘干机和滚筒式烘干机在洗衣过程中会有机械旋转和热量的使用。这些设备的工序由定时器控制，定时器通常是驱动凸轮操作开关的简单电动定时电动机。或者，可以使用具有继电器开关的电子计时器或使用晶闸管、三端双向晶闸管的固态电子开关。

Small washing machines operating on a single-phase supply have motors which are usually the split-phase type of the capacitor-start, capacitor-run. Larger washing machines operate from the three-phase AC power supply with a three-phase induction motor drive.

运行在单相电源上的小型洗衣机有一种电动机,它通常为分相式电容器启动,电容器运行。大型洗衣机使用三相交流电源和三相感应电动机驱动。

Control items in a washing machine include water level switches, temperature switches (bi-metallic) and solenoid valves in the inlet and outlet water lines. Lid and door switches interrupt the main power supply if operated after the washing sequence has begun.

洗衣机中的控制项目包括水位开关、温度开关(双金属)和进出水管线中的电磁阀。如果在清洗程序开始后操作盖和门,开关动作会中断主电源。

Spin dryers have a safety door interlock that prevents it being opened while the drum is still revolving. Tumble dryers often only have one motor with a doubleended shaft for drum and blower fan drives.

旋转烘干机有一个安全门连锁装置,防止滚筒仍在旋转时打开门。滚筒式烘干机通常只有一个电动机,带有用于驱动滚筒和鼓风机风扇的双端轴。

Lint and fluff collects on the motor and wiring which causes no trouble while it remains dry and in small quantities. Periodic removal of the fluff will help prevent faults arising where dampness may combine with the fluff to cause conductive tracking between live conductors and to earth. Small single-phase motors are sometimes protected by a thermal cut-out attached to the stator end windings.

若有棉绒和绒毛聚集在电动机和接线上,在保持干燥和少量的情况下不会造成麻烦。定期清除绒毛将有助于防止因潮湿和绒毛结合而导致带电导体和地之间漏电故障。小型单相电动机有时由连接到定子端部绕组的热断路器保护。

6.10 Cathodic Protection 阴极保护

The outer surface of a ship's hull subjected to electro-chemical attackby corrosive currents that flow between areas of the hull which are at slighly different electric potentials.

船体的外表面易受到腐蚀性电流的电化学侵蚀,腐蚀性电流在船体各区域之间流动,这些区域的电位相差很小。

Dissimilar metals, variations in structural and chemical uniformity in hull plates and welding, differences in paint thickness, quality, water temperature. Salinity and aeration all combine to cause areas of the hull to become either anodic (positive) or cathodic (negative).

不同金属制成的船体板的结构和化学均匀性不同,焊接也有差异,油漆厚度、质量、水温也不同。盐度和曝气共同作用导致船体区域变成阳极(正)或阴极(负)。

Fig. 6. 21 shows that in the hull, electrons flow from anode to cathode leaving positively charged iron ions at the anodic area. At the cathode the effect of the arrival of electrons is to produce negatively charged hydroxyl ions (OH^-) by electrolysis of the sea water. These negative ions flow through the sea to the anodic area where they combine with the positive iron ions to form ferrous hydroxide $Fe(OH)_2$. This ferrous hydroxide is further oxidised by dissolved oxygen to form ferric hydroxide $Fe(OH)_3$. Thus the anodic area is gradually corroded away whilst no corrosion takes place at the cathodic area.

图6.21显示,在船体中,电子从阳极流向阴极,在阳极区留下带正电的铁离子。在阴极,电子电解海水产生带负电荷的氢氧基离子(OH^-)。这些负离子通过海水流向阳极区,在那里它们与正离子结合,形成氢氧化铁亚铁[$Fe(OH)_2$]。这种氢氧化亚铁被溶解氧进一步氧化,形成氢氧化铁[$Fe(OH)_3$]。因此,阳极区逐渐被腐蚀掉,而阴极区则不发生腐蚀。

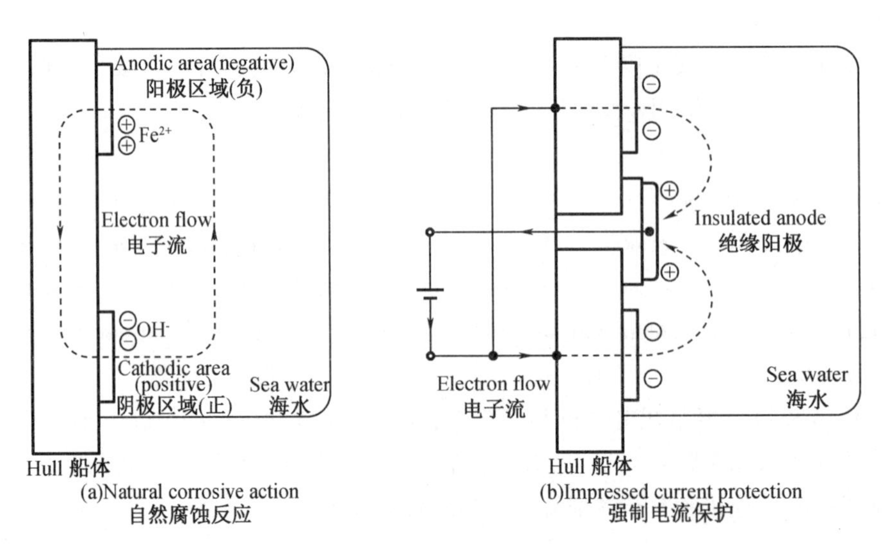

Fig. 6.21 Cathodic protection

图6.21 阴极保护

This naturally corrosive action can be overcome if the complete hull is made cathodic, i. e. electrons are allowed to arrive at the hull surface and produce negative hydroxyl ions but no electrons leave the hull to produce positive iron ions. This is achieved by fitting insulated lead or platinised titanium anodes to the hull and applying a positive d. c. potential to them with respect to the hull.

如果整个船体为阴极,则可以克服这种自然腐蚀作用,即允许电子到达船体表面并产生氢氧基离子,但没有电子离开船体产生正铁离子。这是通过在船体上安装绝缘铅或镀铂钛阳极,并对其施加与船体相关的正直流电位来实现的。

The negatively charged hydroxyl ions (OH^-) now pass to the insulated lead anodes causing the lead surface to change to lead peroxide (PbO_2).

带负电荷的氢氧基离子(OH^-)现在传递到绝缘的铅阳极,导致铅表面形成过氧化铅

(PbO_2)。

The potential is of such a value that it just overcomes the original corrosion current and gives rise to an impressed protection current which flows in the complete circuit. The value of protection current must be critically controlled to just prevent corrosion, as beyond this value the increase in the rate of release of hydroxyl ions will cause sponginess and flaking of the anti-fouling paint.

电位的作用是,它刚好克服了原始的腐蚀电流,并产生了在整个电路中流动的外加保护电流。保护电流的值必须严格控制,以防止腐蚀,因为超过这个值,氢氧基离子释放速度的增加将导致防污漆起泡和剥落。

Initially the electrolytic action will form PbO_2 on the surface of the anodes and when this skin is formed the action reduces. The anodes take on a rich brown appearance (positive lead-acid battery plate) and in service are expected to last 7-10 years.

最初,电解作用会在阳极表面形成过氧化铅,当这种表皮形成时,电解作用减弱。阳极呈现棕色外观(正铅酸电池极板),预计使用寿命为7~10年。

The correct value of protection current can be determined by reference electrodes. These are either of zinc or silver attached to the hull, but insulated from it, below the waterline.

保护电流的正确值可以通过参考电极来确定。附着在船体上的锌或银电极,在吃水线以下并与船体绝缘。

The voltage measured between the hull and reference electrodes of an unprotected ship with sea water as an electrolyte is:Zinc electrode (450 mV negative to hull),Silver electrode (600 mV positive to hull).

在未受保护的以海水作为电解质的船舶上,测量船体和参考电极之间的电压为:锌电极对船体为负450 mV,银电极对船体为正600 mV。

When satisfactorily protected, the protection current will make the hull 200 mV more negative, i. e. a zinc reference electrode will register 250 mV negative to hull and silver 800 mV positive to hull. The reference electrode voltage may, therefore, be used to monitor the protection, but more important, is used as the signal source to automatically regulate the value of protection current.

当得到满意的保护时,保护电流将使船体增加200 mV负电势,即锌参考电极将记录为对船体负250 mV,银参考电极记录为对船体正800 mV。因此,参考电极电压可以用来监测阴极保护,更重要的是它还被用作自动调节保护电流值的信号。

Cathodic protection systems fitted in ships consist of a number of anodes (lead or platinised titanium) fitted to the hull at selected places below the waterline, and control equipment which automatically regulates the anode current to the required value. Direct current is supplied to the anodes, which is transformed and rectified from the ship's 440 V, 60 Hz, three-phase AC distribution system. The control equipment comprises reference electrodes, an amplifier assembly and one or more transformer rectifier units.

安装在船舶上的阴极保护系统由安装在船体水线以下选定位置的若干阳极(铅或镀铂钛)和自动调节阳极电流到所需值的控制设备组成。船上的440 V, 60 Hz,三相交流配电系统经过变压整流后获得直流电供给阳极。控制设备包括参考电极、放大器组件和一个或多个变压器整流单元。

The anode current control is usually regulated by electronic thyristor controllers and the diagram in Fig. 6.23 outlines a typical scheme.

阳极电流控制通常是由电子晶闸管控制器来调节的,图6.23中的框图概括了一个典型的方案。

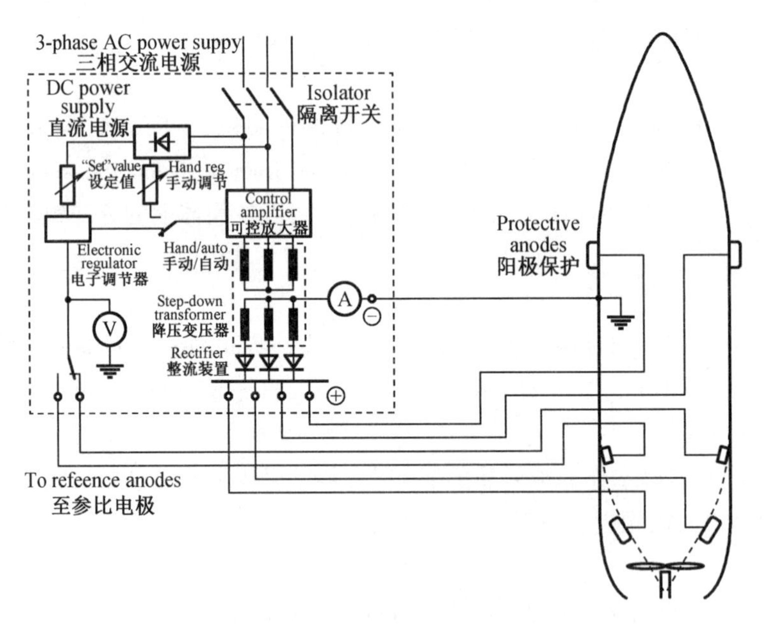

Fig. 6.23 Ship anodes and impressed current control system

图6.23 船体电极和阴极保护控制系统

The control equipment automatically monitors the size of anode current required which will vary with the ship's speed, water temperature and salinity, condition of paint work etc. Typical anode current densities range from 10 mA/m^2 to 40 mA/m^2 for the protection of painted surfaces and 100–150 mA/m^2 for bare steel surfaces.

该控制设备自动监测所需阳极电流的大小,它会随着船速、水温和盐度、油漆工作状况等的变化而变化。典型的阳极电流密度范围为10~40 mA/m^2,用于保护涂漆表面,100~150 mA/m^2 的用于裸钢表面。

The total impressed current for a hull in good condition may be as low as 20 A. Maximum controller outputs may be up to about 600 A at 8 V.

处于良好状态的船体的总外加电流可能低至 20 A。在 8 V 时,控制器的最大输出电流可能高达约 600 A。

Cathodic protection does not appear to deter molluscular growth on the shipshull, so a top coat of anti-foul (poisonous) paint is still necessary. Typical reference and main anode outlines are shown in Fig. 6. 24.

阴极保护似乎不能阻止软体动物在船体上的生长,所以在船底表面涂上一层防污(有毒)涂料仍然是必要的。典型的参考阳极结构和主电极结构如图 6. 24 所示。

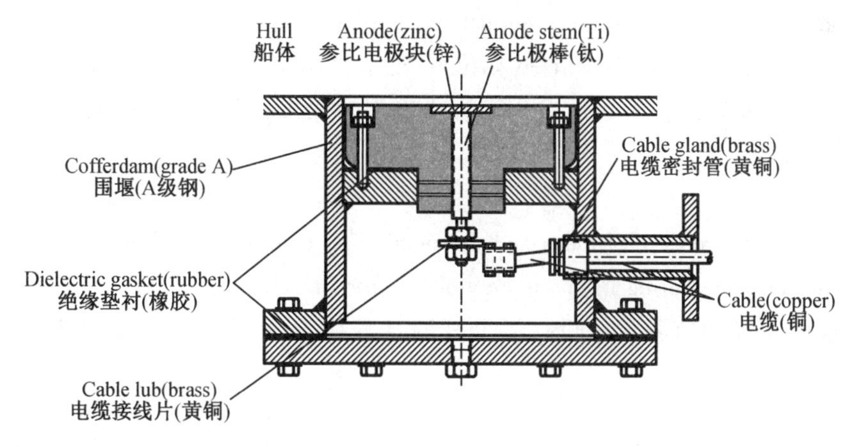

(a) Reference anode construction 参考阳极结构

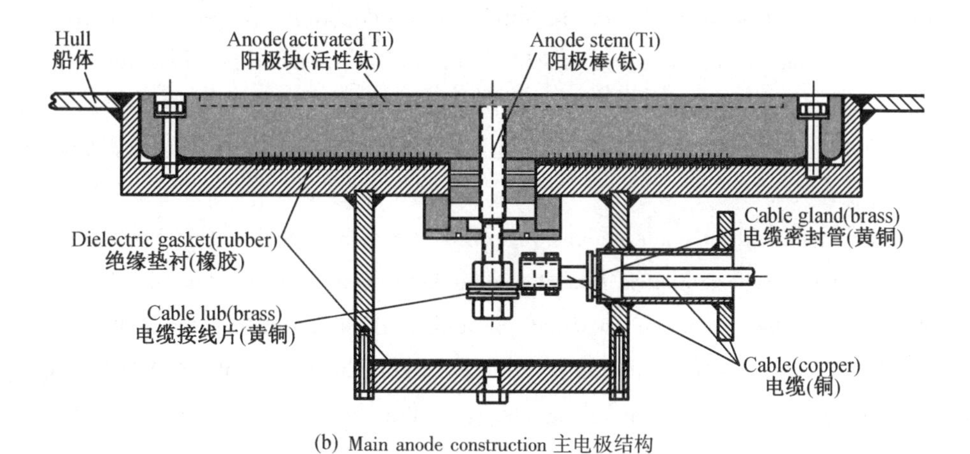

(b) Main anode construction 主电极结构

Fig. 6. 24 Reference anode construction and main anode construction

图 6. 24 典型的参考阳极结构和主电极结构

Monitoring facilities in the cathodic protection control cabinet may provide measurements of:

(1) Reference electrode voltage (hull potential);

(2) Amplifier output voltage;

(3) Total anode current;

(4) Individual anode current.

阴极保护控制柜内的监测设施可提供以下测量:

(1)参考电极电压(船体电位);

(2)放大器输出电压;

(3)总阳极电流;

(4)单个阳极电流。

Measurements should be regularly logged together with the ship operating conditions, e. g. location, draught, water tempreture, etc. Changes in underwater hull area, speed, water temprature/salinity and paint condition will cause the anode current to vary. But the hull protection should remain constant in a normal regulated system.

测量数据应定期与船舶操作条件(如位置、吃水、水温等)一起记录。水下船体面积、船速、水温/盐度和油漆条件的变化,会引起阳极电流的变化。但在正常的调节系统中,船体保护应该保持恒定。

Although the reference electrodes and the monitoring facilities give a reasonable day to day check they are only measuring in the vicinity of the fitted electrodes.

尽管参考电极和监测设施进行了合理的日常检查,但它们仅在安装电极附近进行测量。

When the ship is moored singly or stopped at sea, voltage readings can be taken between a portable silver or zinc test electrode and the ship's hull. This portable electrode is lowered 2-3 m below the water surface and as close as possible to the hull at specified positions around the ship.

当船舶单独系泊或停在海上时,可在便携式银或锌测试电极和船体之间读取电压读数。该便携式电极降低至水面以下 2~3 m 处,并尽可能靠近船舶周围指定位置处的船体。

Check the manufacturer's instructions regarding the storage and setting up of the portable electrode. Some have to be immersed in a plastic bucket of sea water for about 4 h before the hull test. With the cathodic protection switched on and working normally, the voltage measured between hull and a silver/silver chloride portable electrode should be 750-850 mV using a high resistance multimeter (e. g. analogue or digital type); the electrode being positive with respect to hull.

检查制造商关于便携式电极的储存和设置说明。在船体测试之前,有时便携式电极必须在装满海水的塑料桶中浸泡大约 4 h。当阴极保护打开并正常工作时,使用高阻万用表(模拟或数字型)测量船体和银/氯化银便携式电极之间的电压应为 750~850 mV;电极相对于船体的电位为正。

When dry docked, ensure that the main anodes and reference electrodes are covered with paper tape to prevent paint contamination.

当进干坞时,确保主阳极和参考电极用纸胶带覆盖,以防止被油漆污染。

To ensure that the rudder, propeller and stabiliser fins receive the same degree of cathodic protection as the hull it is necessary to electrically earth-bond these items to the hull. The rudder stock may be bonded by a wire braid linking the top of the stock to the deckhead directly above it. Carbon brushes rubbing on the rotating main propulsion shaft effectively bond the shaft to the hull. A periodic inspection of such earthing should be carried out as the brushes wear away and may occasionally stick in their brush holders.

为了确保舵、螺旋桨和减摇鳍收到与船体同样程度的阴极保护,有必要将这些部件与船体进行电气接地连接。舵杆可通过位于顶部的钢丝编织杆连接到其正上方的甲板上。在旋转的主推进轴上摩擦的碳刷有效地将推进轴与船体黏合在一起。应定期检查这种接地,因为电刷会磨损,有时可能会卡在刷座上。

6.11　Battery Supplies 电池供电

Properly maintained storage battery will instantly supply electric power when required. This feature makes a battery the key element in the provision of essential and emergency power supplies on board ships.

妥善维护的蓄电池可以在需要时立即供电。这种特性使电池成为船上必要和应急电源的关键部件。

Essential routine power supplies, e. g. for radio equipment, telephone exchange, fire detection, general alarm circuits etc., are often supplied from two sets of batteries worked on a regular charge/discharge cycle.

必要的常规电源,如无线电设备、电话交换机、火灾探测、通用报警电路等,通常由两组定期充电/放电循环的电池供电。

Emergency battery supplies, e. g. for emergency generator start-up and emergency lighting, are used in a standby role to give power when the mainsupply fails.

应急电池电源,例如,用于应急发电机启动和应急照明,在主电源发生故障时用作备用电源。

Ships' batteries are usually rated at a nominal voltage of 24 V DC. In some cases a battery system of 110 V or 220 V DC may be used where a large amount of emergency lighting and power is vital or where a battery is the only source of emergency power.

船舶蓄电池的额定电压通常为 24 V 直流。在某些情况下,如大量应急照明和电源至关重要或蓄电池是唯一应急电源的情况下,可使用 110 V 或 220 V 直流蓄电池系统。

The two main types of rechargeable battery cell are: Lead-acid and alkaline. The nominal cell voltages of each type are 2 V for lead-acid and 1.2 V for alkaline. Hence, twelve lead-acid cells or twenty alkaline cells must be connected in series to produce a nominal 24 V. More cells may be connected in parallel to increase the battery capacity which is rated in Ampere-hours (Ah). The battery capacity is usually rated in terms of its discharge at the 10 h rate. A 350 Ah battery would be expected to provide 35 A for 10 h. However, the battery will generally have a lower capacity at a shorter discharge rate. The manufacturer's discharge curves must be checked for such details. After a 10 h discharge a lead-acid cell voltage will have fallen to approximately 1.73 V. The equivalent figure for an alkaline cell is 1.14 V.

两种主要的可充电电池类型是铅酸电池和碱性电池。每种类型的标称电池单元的电压为铅酸 2 V,碱性 1.2 V。因此,12 个铅酸电池或 20 个碱性电池必须串联以产生标称 24 V 电压。可以并联更多的电池以增加以安培·小时(Ah)为单位的电池容量。电池容量通常根据 10 h 的放电率来确定。一个 350 Ah 的电池预计能提供 35 A 的电流,持续 10 h。然而,在较短的放电速率下,电池通常具有较低的容量。对于这些细节,必须检查制造商的放电曲线。放电 10 h 后,铅酸电池电压将降至约 1.73 V。碱性电池的等效值为 1.14 V。

Battery installations for both types of battery are similar in that the battery room should be well ventilated, clean and dry. Both types generate hydrogen gas during charging so smoking and naked flames must be prohibited in the vicinity of the batteries. Steelwork and decks adjacent to lead-acid batteries should be covered with acid-resisting paint and alkali-resisting paint. Acid cells must never be placed near alkaline cells otherwise rapid electrolytic corrosion to metalwork and damage to both batteries is certain For similar reasons, never use lead-acid batterv maintenance gear (e.g. hydrometer, topping up bottles, etc.) on an alkaline installation or vice-versa.

两种类型电池的安装相似,电瓶间应通风良好、清洁干燥。这两种类型的电池在充电过程中都会产生氢气,因此在蓄电池附近必须禁止吸烟和明火。与铅酸蓄电池相邻的钢结构和甲板应涂上耐酸漆和耐碱漆。不得将酸性电池放置在碱性电池附近,否则金属制品会快速受到电解腐蚀,两个电池都会受到损坏。出于类似原因,切勿在碱性装置上使用铅酸电池维护装置(如比重计、加液瓶等),反之亦然。

Battery maintenance includes keeping the cell tops clean and dry, checking the tightness of terminal nuts and applying a smear of petroleum jelly to such connections to prevent corrosion. Be most careful when handling the battery electrolyte (e.g. when using a hydrometer to check its specific gravity). Use protective rubber gloves and eye goggles when handling electrolyte. Insulated spanners should be available for use on cell connections to prevent accidental short-circuiting of battery terminals. Such a short-circuit across the terminals of just one cell of a battery will cause a blinding flash with the probability of the cell being seriously damaged.

电池维护包括保持电池顶部清洁和干燥,检查端子螺母的紧固性,并在此类连接上涂抹凡士林以防止腐蚀。处理蓄电池电解液时要格外小心(例如,使用比重计检查其比重时)。处理电解液时,请使用橡胶防护手套和护目镜。应提供绝缘扳手用于紧固电池连接,以防止电池端子意外短路。一个电池单元的端子间短路将产生电弧,发出炫目闪光,电池有可能受到严重损坏。

Question 思考题

An alkaline cell has an electrolyte of potassium hydroxide while a lead-acid cell uses sulphuric acid. Both are diluted with distilled water. What first aid treatment would you apply should you be splashed with either electrolyte?

碱性电池的电解液为氢氧化钾,而铅酸电池的电解液为硫酸。两者都用蒸馏水稀释。如果电解液溅到身上,需采取什么急救措施?

Answer 答案

In both cases rapidly wash eyes and skin with plenty of fresh water. The electrolyte of alkaline cells causes skin burns which should be treated with boracic powder and the eyes washed out with a solution of boracic power. Sulphuric acid splashes can be washed with a saline solution. For both types of battery first aid equipment should be in the battery compartment.

在这两种情况下,应用大量淡水迅速清洗眼睛和皮肤。碱性电池的电解液会导致皮肤灼伤,应使用硼粉进行治疗,并用硼粉溶液冲洗眼睛。硫酸溅出物可以用盐水清洗。对于这两种类型的蓄电池,急救设备应位于蓄电池间内。

The state of charge held by a lead-acid battery is best indicated by a test on the electrolyte specific gravity (SG) by using a hydrometer as shown in Fig. 6. 25. A fully charged lead-acid cell has an SG of about 1. 27-1. 285 (often written as 1,270-1,285) which falls to about 1. 1(or 1,100) when fully discharged. The cell voltage also falls during discharge and its value can also be used as an indication of the state of charge.

如图 6. 25 所示,用比重计对电解液比重(SG)进行测试,可以最好地表明铅酸电池所持有的电荷状态。一个充满电的铅酸电池的比重为 1. 27~1. 285(通常写成 1 270~1 285),当完全放电时,比重约为 1. 1(或 1 100)。电池电压在放电过程中也会下降,其值也可以作为电荷状态的指示。

A lead-acid battery may be safely discharged until the cell voltage drops to approximately 1. 73 V (measured while delivering load current).

铅酸电池在电池电压降至约 1. 73 V 前可以保持安全放电(在向负载输送电流时测量)。

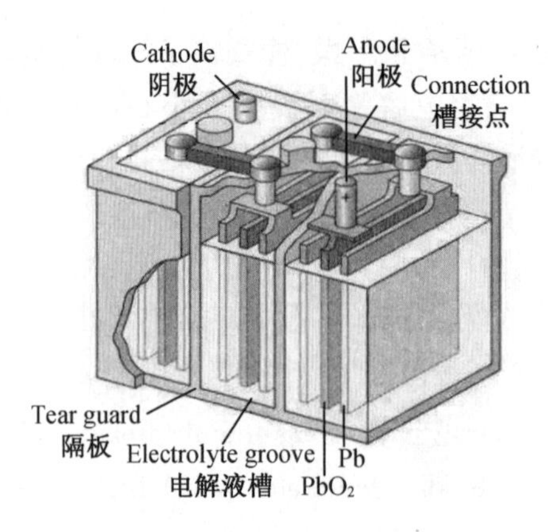

Fig. 6. 25 Outlines the principal features of a lead-acid cell

图 6. 25 铅酸电池单元的原理特性

The open-circuit (no-load) battery voltage readings can be misleading as a high value does not necessarily indicate that the cells are in a healthy chargedstate.

开路(空载)电池电压读数可能具有误导性,因为高值并不一定表明电池处于健康的充电状态。

Note, the SG values quoted above for lead-acid cells are based on an ambient temperature of 15 ℃. Corrections to the SG value at any other ambient temperature are as follows:

(1) Add 0. 007 to reading for each 10 ℃ above 15 ℃;

(2) Subtract 0. 007 from reading for each 10 ℃ below 15 ℃.

注意,上面引用的铅酸电池的比重值是基于 15 ℃的环境温度下的。在任何其他环境温度下,比重值的修正如下:

(1) 15 ℃以上每加 10 ℃加 0. 007;

(2) 15 ℃以下每减 10 ℃减去 0. 007。

e. g. a hydrometer reading taken during an ambient temperature of 25 ℃ is 1. 27. The equivalent SG value at 15 ℃ is 1. 27+0. 007 = 1. 277 (or 1,277).

例如,在环境温度为 25 ℃时比重计读数为 1. 27。15 ℃时的当量比重值为 1. 27+0. 007 = 1. 277 (或 1 277)。

The state of charge of an alkaline battery cell cannot be determined from its SG value. The electrolyte density does not change during charge/discharge cycles but gradually falls during the lifetime of the battery.

碱性电池的充电状态不能由其比重值来确定。电解液密度在电池充放电循环过程中不发生变化,但在电池的使用寿命中逐渐下降。

New alkaline cells have an SG of around 1,190. When this reduces to about 1,145 (which may take 5–10 years depending on the duty cycle) the electrolyte must be completely renewed or the battery replaced. Discharge of alkaline cells should be discontinued when the cell voltage has fallen to about 1.1 V.

新的碱性电池的比重约为 1 190。当这一数值降至 1 145(根据额定工作循环,可能需要 5~10 年)时,必须完全更换电解液或更换电池。当碱性电池电压降至 1.1 V 左右时,应停止放电。

Battery charging equipment uses a transformer/rectifier arrangement to supply the required DC voltage to the cells. The size of voltage depends on the battery type (lead-acid or alkaline) and the mode of charging, e.g. charge/discharge cycle, boost charge, trickle or float charge. Check the manufacturer's instructions for details of the required charging voltages. Do not allow electrolyte temperatures to exceed about 45 ℃ during charging.

电池充电设备使用变压器/整流装置为电池提供所需的直流电压。电压大小取决于电池类型(铅酸或碱性)和充电方式,如充放电循环、升压充电、涓流充电或浮充电。有关所需充电电压的详细说明,请参阅制造商的说明书。充电过程中电解液温度不能超过 45 ℃。

A lead-acid cell will gas freely when fully charged but an alkaline cell gases throughout the charging period. The only indication of a fully charged alkaline cell is when its voltage remains at a steady maximum value of about 1.6–1.8 V.

铅酸电池在充满电的时候无气体释放,而碱性电池在整个充电过程中都会释放气体。完全充满电的碱性电池的唯一标志是它的电压保持在一个稳定的最大值,即 1.6~1.8 V。

Generally, alkaline cells are more robust, mechanically and electrically, than lead acid cells. Nickel cadmium cells will hold their charge for long periods without recharging so are ideal for standby duties. Also they operate well with a float-charge to provide a reliable emergency supply when the main power fails.

一般来说,碱性电池在机械和电气方面都比铅酸电池更坚固。镍镉电池可以在不充电的情况下长时间保持充电状态,因此是备用任务的理想选择。此外,当主电源出现故障时,它们的浮动充电功能可以提供可靠的应急电源。

For all rechargeable batteries (other than the sealed type) it is essential to replace lost water (caused during gassing and by normal evaporation) with the addition of distilled water to the correct level above the plates. Exposure of the cell plates to air will rapidly reduce the life of the battery.

对于所有可充电电池(密封型除外),必须在极板上方的正确位置加入蒸馏水,以补充丢失的水分(在充气和正常蒸发过程中造成的)。电池极板暴露在空气中会迅速缩短电池的寿命。

On all ships and offshore platforms there are particular essential services which are vital during a complete loss of main power. Such services include switchgear operation, navigation lights, foghorns, fire and gas detection, internal communications, some radio communications, alarm systems. To avoid the loss of essential services they are supported by an uninterruptible power supply (UPS). These can be for battery supported DC supplies or AC supplies both of which can be configured as continuous UPS or standby UPS. Fig. 6. 26 shows an a. c. supported UPS arrangement.

在所有的船舶和海上平台上,都有一些特殊的基本服务,它们在主动力完全丧失时至关重要。这些服务包括开关柜操作、导航灯、雾笛、火灾和气体探测、内部通信、一些无线电通信、报警系统。为了避免基本服务的丧失,它们由不间断电源(UPS)支持。这些可以用于电池支持的直流电源或交流电源,都可以配置为在线式不间断电源或备用式不间断电源。图 6.26 所示为交流不间断电源配置。

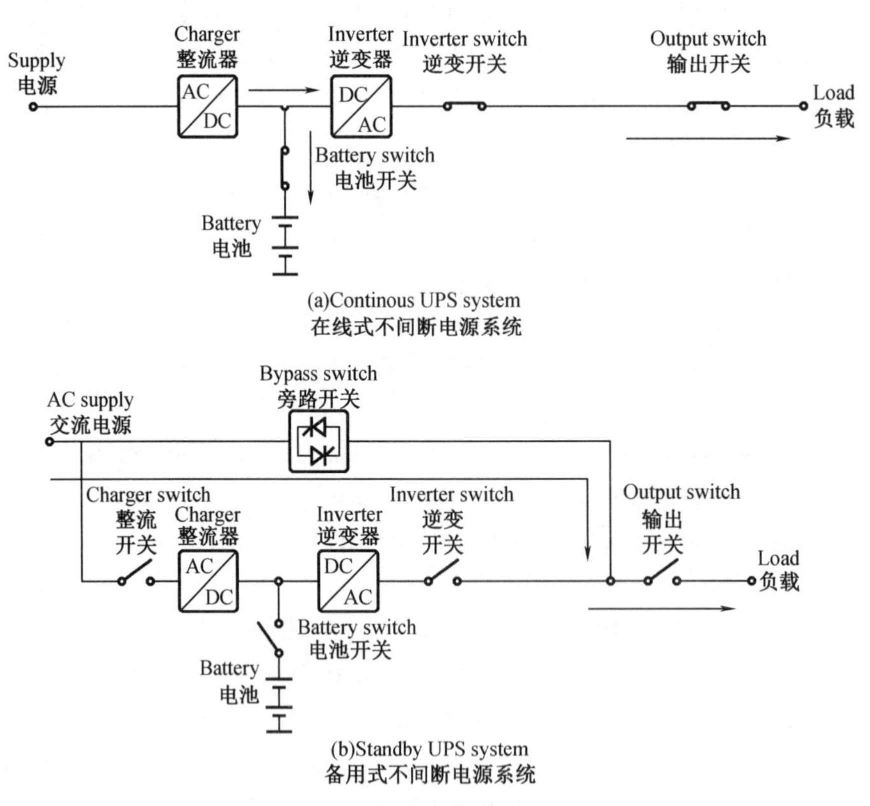

Fig. 6. 26 AC supported UPS arrangement

图 6. 26 交流输入的不间断电源系统

The arrangement shown in Fig. 6. 27 is typical of a continuous UPS dec. supported supply system. The essential DC services are normally supplied from the 440 V main power system through charger No. 1 which continuously trickle charges its battery. During a loss of main power, battery No. 1 maintains a transitional supply while the emergency generator restores power to the emergency board and hence to charger No. 2. Either battery is available for a few hours if both main and emergency generators are unavailable.

图 6.27 所示为典型的不间断直流供电系统。必要的直流服务通常由 440 V 的主电源系统通过 1 号充电器提供,它不断地对电池进行涓流充电。在主电源失效期间,1 号电池保持过渡供电,而应急发电机恢复供电到应急配电板和 2 号充电器。如果主发电机和应急发电机都不可用,这两种电池都可以使用几个小时。

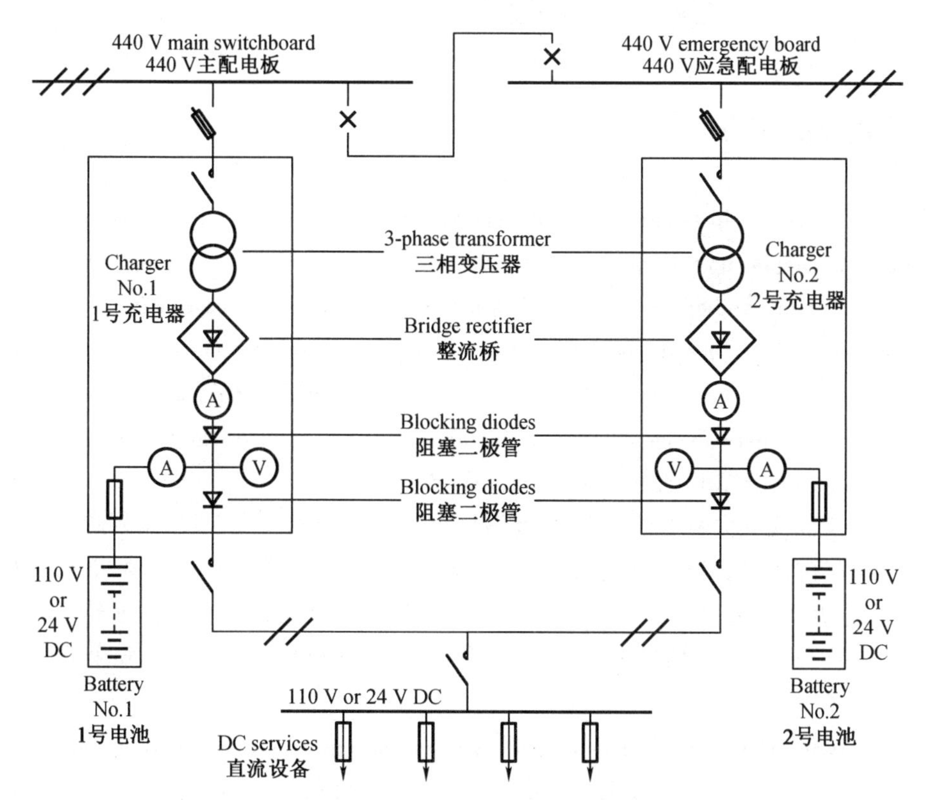

Fig. 6.27 UPS DC battery charger

图 6.27 不间断电源的直流充电器

Some critical emergency lights have an internal battery supported UPS within the luminaire where its battery charge is continuously maintained during nonemergency conditions.

一些重要的应急灯在灯具内部有一个电池支持的不间断电源,在非紧急情况下,它的电池可以持续充电。

Chapter 7 Special Electrical Practice for Oil, Gas and Chemical Tankers

第 7 章 油船、液化气船、化学品船的专用电气规程

7.0 Introduction 介绍

Ships and offshore installations that transport, process and store bulk quantities of oil, gas and liquid chemicals are subject to special codes of practice regarding their electrical installations. Statutory authorities and classification societies generally base their recommendations on Publication 92 of the International Electrotechnical Commission (IEC). The object of all such guidance is to prevent the hazards of fire and explosion occurring on board these tank ships. Spaces in tankers where explosive gas-air mixtures may be expected to be present are called dangerous or hazardous. All other areas being regarded as safe.

运输、加工和储存大量石油、天然气及液体化学品的船舶和海上设施,须遵守其电力设施的特殊作业守则。法定机构和船级社一般根据国际电工委员会(IEC)第 92 号文件提出建议。所有这些指导的目的是防止在这些船上发生火灾和爆炸的危险。油轮上可能存在爆炸性气体-空气混合物的空间称为危险或风险空间。其他区域被认为是安全的。

The best way to avoid explosions caused by electrical equipment is simply not to install such equipment in thehazardous areas. However, special electrical equipment is permitted and this chapter will provide a guide to the range and maintenance of such explosion (Ex) protected equipment.

避免电气设备引起爆炸的最好办法就是不要在危险地区安装这种设备。然而,特殊电气设备是允许的,本章将提供这类防爆(Ex)保护设备的使用范围和维护指南。

7.1 Tanker Classification 油轮分类

Shore practice for hazardous areas is to divide the areas into three zones (0,1,2) which recognises the degree of hazard by indicating the likelihood of an explosive gas-air mixture being present. This practice is not used on tankers. However, electrical equipment is manufactured on the basis of such zones.

在岸上常将危险区域划分为三类(0,1,2),以此表明存在爆炸性气体-空气混合物的可能性来识别危险程度。但这一做法不适用于油轮。但是,电气设备是根据这一区域划分制造的。

On tankers, areas are designated as either dangerous or normally-safe spaces. A dangerous space is defined as an area where flammable gas-air mixtures would normally be expected to occur. The degree of hazard or danger presented by a dangerous space is determined, initially, by the nature of the flammable cargo of the tanker.

在油轮上,区域被化分为危险的或通常安全的空间。危险空间是指通常预期会发生易燃气体-空气混合物的区域。危险空间的危险程度最初由油轮易燃货物的性质决定。

On this basis, four types of tankers are recognised as:

(1) Type A: Oil tankers intended for the carriage in bulk of non-boiling oil cargoes having a flash point (closed test) of 60 ℃ or less. These include crude oil carriers, gasoline carriers, etc.

(2) Type B: Oil tankers intended for carriage in bulk of non-boiling oil cargoes having a flash point (closed test) in excess of 60 ℃. These include tankers for carrying bituminous or asphalt products, or for carrying diesel or fuel oils.

(3) Type C: Gas carriers intended for the carriage in bulk of liquefied petroleum gas (LPG) or liquefied natural gas (LNG).

(4) Type D: Tankers for the carriage in bulk of other flammable liquid cargoes.

在此基础上,油轮被认定为四种类型:

(1) A 型:适用于运输大量非沸点石油货物的油轮,货物闪点(密闭试验)为 60 ℃或以下。这些船包括原油船、汽油船等。

(2) B 型:用于运输闪点(封闭试验)超过 60 ℃的散装非沸点油货物的油轮,包括载运沥青或沥青产品的油船,或载运柴油或燃料油的油船。

(3) C 型:散装运输液化石油气(LPG)或液化天然气(LNG)的气体运输船。

(4) D 型:散装运输其他易燃液体货物的油船。

This includes those cargoes which are potentially more dangerous than those conveyed by Type A and Type C tankers, and those products which exhibit chemical nstability.

还包括可能比 A 类和 C 类油轮运输的货物更危险的货物,以及具有化学不稳定性的产品。

7.1.1 Type A Tankers A 型油轮

Dangerous spaces:

(1) Cargo tanks.

(2) Cofferdams adjoining cargo tanks.

(3) Cargo pump rooms.

(4) Enclosed or semi-enclosed spaces immediately above cargo tanks, or having bulkheads above and in line with the cargo tank bulkheads.

(5) Enclosed or semi-enclosed spaces immediately above cargo pumprooms, or above vertical cofferdams adjoining cargo tanks, unless separated by a gastight deck and suitably mechanically

ventilated.

(6) Spaces, other than cofferdams, adjoining and below the top of the cargo tanks, e. g. trunks, passageways and holds.

(7) Areas on open deck, or semi-enclosed spaces on open deck, within at least 3 m of any cargo oil tank outlet or gas or vapour outlet.

(8) Areas on open deck over all cargo tanks, including all ballast tanks within the cargo tank block and to the full width of the vessel plus 3 m forward and aft on open deck, up to a height of 2.4 m above the deck.

(9) Compartments for cargo hoses.

(10) Enclosed or semi-enclosed spaces having a direct opening into any of the spaces or areas mentioned above.

危险空间:

(1)油舱。

(2)与货油舱相连的空隔舱。

(3)货油泵舱室。

(4)紧靠液货舱上方的封闭或半封闭空间,或在液货舱舱壁上方并与液货舱舱壁对齐的舱壁。

(5)紧邻货舱泵房上方的封闭或半封闭空间,或毗邻货舱的垂直空舱上方,除非有气密甲板隔开,并有适当的机械通风。

(6)除空舱外,毗连和低于货舱顶部的空间,如围阱、走廊和货舱。

(7)露天甲板上的区域或露天甲板上的半封闭空间,距离货油舱出口或气体或蒸气出口至少 3 m 以内。

(8)所有货舱上方的开放甲板区域,包括货舱体内的所有压载舱,以及整个船的宽度加上在开放甲板上的前后 3 m,最高高度达到甲板以上 2.4 m。

(9)液货软管舱室。

(10)有通往上述任何空间或区域的直接开口的封闭或半封闭空间。

Electrical equipment and cables should only be located in dangerous spaces when it is absolutely necessary. Only intrinsically safe (Exi) electrical equipment is allowed inside cargo tanks. Electric motors are not permitted in cargo pump rooms.

电气设备和电缆只有在绝对必要的情况下才应安装在危险空间。只有本质安全型(Exi)电气设备才被允许安装在液货舱内。货舱泵房不允许使用电动机。

Flameproof (Exd) or pressurised (Exp) luminaires may be used in pumprooms. The switches and fuses for the luminaires must be located in a normally safe space outside the pumproom. At least two independent circuits must be provided for the lighting. If maintenance is carried out on the luminaires of one circuit, this circuit must be de-energised while the other circuit provides sufficient light for the work to be safely completed.

隔爆型(Exd)或增压型(Exp)灯具可用于泵室。灯具的开关和保险丝必须放置在泵房外一个通常安全的地方。照明必须至少提供两个独立的回路。如果维修一个电路的灯具,则该电路必须断电,而另一个电路则提供足够的光照以安全完成工作。

Question 思考题

Tanker pumprooms require two separate lighting circuits. How can the circuits be arranged so that the luminaires can only be opened up when the correct circuit has been isolated?

货油舱泵房需要两个独立的照明电路。如何布置电路,使灯具只有在电路被正确隔离后才能被检修?

Answer 答案

Many tankers use the following arrangement:

(1) The luminaires on one of the circuits have bolts with a different size or type of head to those on the luminaires supplied by the other circuit. Typically, these would be two different types of triangular bolt head.

(2) The keys to remove the bolts are actually the operating handles of the circuit isolators. A key can only be removed from its trapped position on the switch after the circuit has been isolated. This key can only open up those luminaires connected to the circuit which has been isolated.

(3) Cable runs are permitted through most dangerous spaces except cargo tanks, provided they are continuously monitored for earth leakage.

(4) Flameproof (Exd) or pressurised (Exp) luminaires are permitted in enclosed or semi-enclosed spaces immediately above a cargo tank, above a cargo pump room and in compartments for storing cargo hoses. The switches and fuses must be located in a normally safe area and must switchover both lines of the circuit (i. e. double pole switching).

许多油轮采用以下措施:

(1)其中一种电路上的灯具与另一种电路上提供的灯具配有不同尺寸或类型的螺栓。一般来说,这是两种不同类型的三角形螺栓头。

(2)拆卸螺栓的钥匙实际上是电路隔离器的操作手柄。只有在电路被隔离后,才能将钥匙从开关上的锁住位置移开。这把钥匙只能打开那些连接到隔离电路上的灯具。

(3)电缆可以通过除货舱外的最危险的空间,前提是要对其对地漏电进行持续监测。

(4)隔爆型(Exd)或增压型(Exp)灯具允许安装在货舱正上方的封闭或半封闭空间、货泵房上方以及用于存放货舱软管的隔间内。开关和保险丝必须位于正常安全区域,并且可以自由切换电路的两条线路(即双极切换)。

7.1.2　Type B Tankers B 型油轮

Dangerous spaces are not defined for vessels of this type; but it is recommended that care to be exercised so that potential sources of ignition are reduced as far as possible. Also, the following practices should be followed:

(1) Use intrinsically safe (Exi) for any monitoring or instrumentation equipment which is in direct contact with oil in the cargo tanks or in the oil circuits;

(2) Cargo pump motors should be increased safety (Exe) type if they are located in the cargo pump room;

(3) All portable electrical equipment used in the cargo tanks must be suitably explosion protected (Ex).

这类船舶没有定义危险空间,但建议小心行事,以便尽可能减少潜在的火源。此外,还应遵循以下做法:

(1)对于任何与货舱或油路中的油直接接触的监控或仪表设备,使用本质安全型设备;

(2)如果货泵电动机位于货泵室,则应增加安全性(Exe)类型;

(3)所有用于货舱的便携式电气设备必须具有适当的防爆保护(Ex)。

7.1.3 Type C Tankers (Gas Carriers) C型油轮(气体运输)

Dangerous spaces:

(1) A space in the cargo area which is not equipped with approved arrangementsto ensure that its atmosphere is at all times maintained in a safe condition.

(2) An enclosed space outside the cargo area through which any piping terminates, unless approved arrangements are installed to prevent any escape of product vapour into the atmosphere of that space.

(3) A cargo containment system with cargo piping:

①A hold space where cargo is carried in a cargo containment system requiring a secondary barrier;

②A hold space where cargo is carried in a cargo containmentsystem not requiring a secondary barrier.

(4) A space separated from a hold space described in ① above by singlegastight steel boundary.

(5) A cargo pump room and cargo compressor room.

(6) A zone on open deck, or semienclosed space on open deck, within 3 m of any cargo tank outlet, gas or vapour outlet, cargo piped flange, cargo valve or of entrances and ventilation openings to a cargo pumproom and cargo compressor rooms.

(7) The open deck over the cargo area and 3 m forward and aft of the cargo area on open deck up to a height of 2.4 m above the weather deck.

(8) A zone within 2.4 m of the outer surface of a-cargo containment system where such surface is exposed to the weather.

(9) An enclosed or semi-enclosed space in which pipes containing products are located.

(10) A compartment for cargo hoses.

(11) An enclosed or semi-enclosed space having a direct opening into any dangerous space or area.

危险空间：

(1)货物区域内的空间未配备经批准的设施，以确保其大气始终处于安全状态。

(2)货舱外的封闭空间，任何管道不应通过该封闭空间，除非经授权已经采取合适的措施，以防止任何产品蒸气泄漏到该封闭空间。

(3)带有管道布置的货舱系统：

①在需要设置二级屏障的货物隔离系统内运载货物的货舱空间；

②在不需要设置二级屏障的货物隔离系统内运载货物的货舱空间。

(4)用单个气密钢垫圈将上述①中所述的舱位分隔开的空间。

(5)货油泵室和货舱压缩机室。

(6)这些区域包括任何货舱出口、气体或蒸气出口、货舱管路法兰、货舱阀门或通往液货泵室和液货压缩机室的入口及通风开口 3 m 内的露天甲板上的半封闭空间或露天甲板空间。

(7)位于货舱上方的开放式甲板，以及在开放式甲板上货舱前后 3 m 的高度，最高可高于露天甲板 2.4 m。

(8)货舱密封系统外表面 2.4 m 以内的区域，该区域的表面暴露在外界环境下。

(9)一种封闭或半封闭的空间，运载货物的管道就设在其中。

(10)带有运载货物的管道舱室。

(11)一个封闭或半封闭的空间，有一个直接通向任何危险空间或区域的开口。

The recommendations for the use of electrical equipment in dangerous spaces are the same for this type of vessel as they are for Type A tankers. There are, however, two important additional recommendations for gas carriers:

(1) Cargo Pump Motor—Submerged cargo pump motors andtheir cables are permitted in cargo tankssubject to the atmosphere of the tankeing controlled to prevent presence of a gas-air mixture when the motors are energized.

(2) Gas Compressor Motors—These motors are allowed, under certain circumstances, to be sited in the same space as the compressors. In these instances the motors are required to be pressurised (Exp) with air, inert gas or water

在 B 型危险空间使用电气设备的建议与 A 型油轮相同。不过，对天然气运输船还有两项重要的补充建议：

(1)货油泵电动机——全浸式货油泵电动机及其电缆允许置于货舱内，但应受储油环境控制，以防止马达运转时出现可燃气体-空气混合物。

(2)气体压缩机电动机——在某些情况下，这些电动机允许与压缩机位于同一空间内。在这些情况下，电动机需要用空气、惰性气体或水加压(Exp)。

Alternatively, an increased safety (Exe) motor within a flameproof (Exd) enclosure may be used and marked overall as Exe d.

另外,也可以在隔爆(Exd)外壳内使用增安型(Exe)电动机,并将其整体标记为隔爆型Exe d。

7.1.4 Type D Chemical Carriers D型化学品运输船

The products carried in these vessels may produce explosive gas-air mixtures and can also be intensely corrosive. In cases like this electrical equipment must not only be explosion protected but also designed to withstand corrosion.

这些油轮运载的产品可能产生爆炸性的气体-空气混合物,也可能具有强烈的腐蚀性。在这种情况下,电气设备不仅要有防爆保护,而且要设计得耐腐蚀。

These products are categorised as follows in order to give guidance on the electrical equipment which would be suitable:

(1) Products which have similar properties to those carried by vessel types A, B and C. The recommendations given for those vessels would apply.

(2) Products which are considered to be more hazardous than those above. The extent of dangerous areas is increased from 3 m to 4.5 m.

(3) Products which are susceptible to chemical instability which creates flammable gases. Special arrangements would be required for this type of product.

(4) Products which will damage any electrical equipment with which they come into contact. Materials and enclosures must resist the corrosive effect of these products.

这些化工产品被分类如下,以为布设适合的电气设备提供指导:

(1)与A、B和C型油轮运载的产品性能相似的产品。针对这些油轮提出的建议将适用于D型油轮。

(2)被认为比上述产品更危险的产品。危险区域范围由3 m增加到4.5 m。

(3)容易产生化学不稳定性的可燃气体的产品。这类产品需要特殊安排处理。

(4)会损坏与之接触的任何电器设备的产品。材料和外壳必须有效防止这些产品的腐蚀。

7.2 Hazardous Zones 危险区域

Hazardous areas ashore are classified into zones which indicate the probability of an explosive gas-air mixture being present and, therefore, the likelihood of an explosion occurring.

(1) Zone 0—In which an explosive gas-air mixture is continuously present, or present for long periods.

(2) Zone 1—In which an explosive gas-air mixture is likely to occur in normal operation.

(3) Zone 2—In which an explosive gas-air mixture is not likely to occur in normal operation and, if it occurs, will exist for only a short time.

海岸上的危险区域被划分为若干区域,这些区域表明存在爆炸性气体-空气混合物的可能性,因此也表明有发生爆炸的可能性。

(1)区域0——该区域内的爆炸性气体-空气混合物是持续存在或长时间存在的。

(2)区域1——在正常运行中很可能产生爆炸性气体-空气混合物。

(3)区域2——在正常运行中不太可能产生爆炸性气体-空气混合物,即使产生,也只存在很短的一段时间。

An area which is not classified Zone 0, 1 or 2 is assumed to be a non-hazardous or safe area. Examples of this zoning applied to ships could be:

(1) Zone 0—Interior spaces of oil cargo tanks, pipes, pumps, etc.

(2) Zone 1—Enclosed or semi-enclosed spaces on the deck of a tanker, the boiler firing area on a gas carrier usingmethane boil-off as a fuel and battery rooms.

(3) Zone 2—Open spaces on the deck of a tanker.

未划分为区域0、区域1或区域2的区域被认为是无危险或安全的区域。适用于船舶的这种分区的例子有:

(1)区域0——油货舱、管道、泵等内部空间。

(2)区域1——油轮甲板上的封闭或半封闭空间、使用甲烷汽化作为燃料的气体运输船上的锅炉燃烧区和电池室。

(3)区域2——油轮上的甲板敞开空间。

The cargo pump rooms of tankers are, at present, considered as falling somewhere between Zone 0 and Zone 1.

目前,油轮的货油泵室被认为介于区域0和区域1之间。

7.3 Electrical Ignition of Gas 气体的电起火

In practice, three essential components must be present to start a fire or cause an explosion:

(1) A flammable gas or vapour (hazard);

(2) Air or oxygen to support combustion (oxidiser);

(3) Something to start the explosion (source of ignition).

实际上,要想引起火灾或爆炸,必须具备三个基本要素:

(1)可燃气体或蒸气(危险);

(2)支持燃烧的空气或氧气(氧化剂);

(3)引起爆炸的元素(火源)。

When all three of these components are brought together ignition can take place, often with devastating results.

当这三个要素结合在一起时,就会发生火灾,通常会带来毁灭性的后果。

The occurrence of a fire or ignition depends on the probability of the simultaneous occurrence of all three components shown in the fire triangle diagram shown in Fig. 7. 1.

火灾的发生取决于图 7. 1 所示的火灾三角图中的所有三种要素同时发生的概率。

Fig. 7. 1　Fire triangle

图 7. 1　燃烧三角形

Gases, when concentrated above the lower flammable limit (LFL), can be ignited by heat generated from various electrical sources e. g. :

(1) Arcing between switch contacts;

(2) Arcing between a live conductor and earth;

(3) An internal arcing fault within an electrical enclosure;

(4) Overheating causing hot spots;

(5) An electrostatic spark discharge between charged bodies or between a charged body and earth;

(6) Chemical action;

(7) Lightning strikes.

当气体浓度超过最低可燃限度(LFL)时,可由各种电源产生的热量点燃,例如:

(1)开关触点之间的电弧;

(2)带电导体与地面之间的电弧;

(3)电器外壳内部的电弧故障;

(4)过热导致热点;

(5)静电放电,带电物体之间或带电物体与接地之间的静电火花放电;

(6)化学作用;

(7)雷击。

As might be expected, the flammability of a gas-air mixture is dependent upon the ratio of gas to air. A ratio of 100% gas/air concentration will not burn and, as can be expected, 0% will also not burn. Furthermore, each gas is quite different and the flammability range depends on the gas type as shown in the Table 7. 1.

正如可以预料的那样,气体-空气混合物的可燃性取决于气体与空气的比例。100%的气体/空气浓度不会燃烧,正如预期的那样,0%的浓度也不会燃烧。此外,每种气体都有很大的不同,其可燃性范围取决于气体类型,如表 7.1 所示。

Table 7.1 Flammable range of several gases

表 7.1 几种气体的可燃范围

Gas 气体	Flammable limits 可燃范围	
	Lower 下限/%	Higher 上限/%
Acetylene 乙炔	1.5	100
Hydrogen 氢	4	75.6
Methane 甲烷	5	15
Butane 丁烷	1.5	8.5

The terms used to describe these limits are called: LFL-lower flammable limit, and UFL-upper flammable limit (previously called LEL and UEL-lower and upper explosive limits).

用来描述这些极限的术语称为爆炸下限(LFL)和爆炸上限(UFL)(以前称为 LEL 和 UEL)。

This is still not all that must taken into consideration, there is also the amount of minimum ignition energy required to ignite the gas, and the temperature at which the gas automatically ignites. Some examples are shown in the Table 7.2.

必须考虑的问题还有点燃气体所需的最小点燃能量,以及气体自动点燃时的温度。一些例子如表 7.2 所示。

Table 7.2 Minimum ignition energy of several gases

表 7.2 几种气体的最小点燃能量

Gas 气体	Auto ignition temperature 自燃温度/℃	Minimum ignition energy 最小点燃能量/mJ
Acetylene 乙炔	305	0.02
Butane 丁烷	365	0.25
Hydrogen 氢	560	0.02
Methane (firedamp) 甲烷(沼气)	595	0.29

The above table shows that hydrogen has a very low ignition energy, but a very high ignition temperature. Acetylene, however has a low ignition energy and low ignition temperature (beware, it is very easy to ignite). Methane with its very high ignition temperature and high ignition energy can prove quite difficult to ignite.

由表 7.2 可知,氢气的点燃能量很低,但点火温度很高,而乙炔的点燃能量和点火温度都很低(注意,它很容易着火)。甲烷具有很高的点火温度和较高的点燃能量,因此很难着火。

On the other hand, the amount of energy released (in MJ/m^3) by a given volume of gas does vary, methane containing three times as much energy as Hydrogen and Butane eleven times as much (Table 7.3). A medium size camping gas cylinder of butane can contain more than enough energy to destroy an average-sized household garage.

另一方面,给定体积的气体所释放的能量(单位 MJ/m^3)是不同的,甲烷的能量是氢的 3 倍,丁烷是氢的 11 倍(表 7.3)。一个中型的丁烷野营气瓶的能量足够摧毁一个普通大小的家庭车库。

Table 7.3 Net calorific value of several gases

表 7.3 几种气体的净热值

Gas 气体	Net calorific value 净热值/(MJ/m^3)
Acetylene 乙炔	51
Butane 丁烷	112.4
Hydrogen 氢	10.2
Methane 甲烷	34

7.4 Apparatus Gas Groups 仪器气体分组

The flammable gases in which explosion protected electrical equipment may have to operate are grouped according to the amount of electrical energy, in the form of an arc, which is needed to ignite the gas. Gases associated with the mining industry are fire-classed as GROUP I, all other industrial gases are classed as GROUP Ⅱ which are listed in three sub-groups according to their ease of ignition(Table 7.4).

可燃气体中的防爆电气设备操作需要分组,按点燃气体所需的电能(电弧形式)进行分组。与采矿工业有关的气体被列为防火等级第一类(Ⅰ),所有其他工业气体都被列为第二类(Ⅱ),根据其着火的容易程度,这些气体被列为三个子类(表 7.4)。

It should be noted that equipment certified for use in group ⅡC may also be used for ⅡA and ⅡB. Equipment certified for ⅡB may be used for ⅡA. Equipment certified for ⅡA may be used with no other group.

需要注意的是,经认证为ⅡC 组别的设备也可以用于ⅡA 和ⅡB 组别。经认证为ⅡB 的设备可用于ⅡA 组别。经认证为ⅡA 组别的设备不能使用于其他的组别。

Table 7.4 Gas classification

表 7.4 气体分类

Apparatus gas group 仪器气体分组	Gas or vapour 气体或气雾
I	Methane (firedamp) 甲烷(沼气)
ⅡA	Ammonia 氨 Industrial methane 工业甲烷 Blast furnace gas 高炉煤气 Carbon monoxide 一氧化碳 Propane 丙烷 Butane 丁烷 Pentane 戊烷 Hexane 己烷 Heptane 庚烷 iso Octane decane 辛烷癸烷 Benzene 苯 Xylene 二甲苯 Cyclohexane 环己烷 Acetone 丙酮 Ethyl methyl ketone 甲基乙基酮 Methyl acetate 乙酸甲酯 Ethyl acetate 乙酸乙酯 n-Propyl acetate 醋酸正丙酯 Butyl 丁基橡胶 Acetate 醋酸盐 Amyl acetate 乙酸戊酯 Chloroethylene 氯乙烯 Methanol 甲醇 Ethanol 乙醇 iso Butanol 丁醇 n-Butanol 正丁醇 Amyl alcohol 戊醇 Ethyl nitrite 亚硝酸乙酯
ⅡB	Buta-1, 3 diene 丁二烯 Ethylene 乙烯 Diethylether 乙醚 Ethylene oxide 环氧乙烷 Town gas 煤气
ⅡC	Hydrogen 氢

The gas grouping can affect the design and construction of some types of explosion protected equipment (Exd and Exi).

气体分组会影响某些类型的防爆设备(Exd 和 Exi)的设计和结构。

7.5 Temperature Class 温度等级

This defines the maximum surface temperature of the components in the electrical equipment under normal and fault conditions. This maximum surface temperature must not exceed the gas ignition temperature.

本节定义了电气设备中元件在正常和故障条件下的最高表面温度。此最高表面温度不得超过气体点火温度。

The temperature class is stated with reference to a maximum ambient temperature of 40 ℃, should any other reference temperature be adopted, regulations require that this temperature be shown on the equipment.

温度等级是参照最高 40 ℃的环境温度来划定的,如果采用任何其他参考温度,则要求在设备上标注该温度。

It is important to note that the apparatus gas grouping and temperature class are not related. For instance, hydrogen requires very little spark energy to ignite, but the surface temperature necessary for ignition is very high (560 ℃).

要注意,设备的气体分组和温度等级是不相关的。例如,氢的点火所需的点燃能量非常小,但点火所需的表面温度却非常高(560 ℃)。

The Table 7.5 relates the temperature class to the maximum surface temperature under fault conditions.

表 7.5 将温度等级与故障条件下的最高表面温度联系起来。

Table 7.5 Temperature class and maximum surface temperature

表 7.5 温度等级与最高表面温度

Temperature class 温度等级	Maximum surface temperature 最高表面温度/ ℃
T1	450
T2	300
T3	200
T4	135
T5	100
T6	85

For example, an electric motor may have a maximum surface temperature of 120 ℃ and would be classed as T4. Temperature classifications and apparatus groups for all group Ⅱ gases can be found in BS 5345 Part 1.

例如,电动机的表面温度最高可达 120 ℃,可归类为 T4。所有Ⅱ类气体的温度等级和设备可在 BS 5345 第 1 部分中找到。

7.6　Types of Explosion Protection 防爆类型

There are a number of different constructional techniques employed in preventing electrical equipment causing explosions in hazardous areas. Some techniques, such as flameproof enclosures, have long been established but others, such as intrinsic safety and increased safety are the result of developments in material and electrical/electronic circuit design. The Ex identification marks as shown in Fig. 7. 2.

为了防止危险区域电气设备引起爆炸,采用了许多不同的工艺结构。一些技术,如防爆外壳,早已创立,但其他技术,如本质安全型和增安型,是材料和电气/电子电路设计发展的结果。防爆标志如图 7. 2 所示。

Fig. 7. 2　Ex identification marks

图 7. 2　防爆标志

It has been internationally agreed that explosion protected equipment be identified by the symbol "Ex" followed by a letter Indicating the type of protection employed. The Table 7. 6 lists the types of protection.

国际上已公认,防爆设备由符号"Ex"后面加一个字母表示所采用的防护类型,如表 7. 6 所示。

Table 7. 6　Explosion proof symbols and protection types

表 7. 6　防爆符号与防护类型

Symbol 符号	Type of protection 防护类型
Exd 隔爆型	flameproof enclosure 防火外壳
Exi 本安型	intrinsic safety 本质安全
Exe 增安型	increased safety 增进安全
Exn 无火花型	non-sparking 无火花

Table 7.6(Continued)

表 7.6(续)

Symbol 符号	Type of protection 防护类型
Exq 充沙型	powder filled(not applicable to ships) 充沙(不适用于船舶)
Exo 充油型	oil immersed(not applicable to ships) 油浸(不适用于船舶)
Exp 正压型	pressurization 升压
Exs 特殊型	special protection 特殊防护

Some equipment may use more than one of these types of protection in its construction. In this case, the primary type of protection is quoted first. For example, an increased safety motor with a flameproof terminal box would be marked Exed. Equipment may also be marked with a prefix "E" which denotes compliance with European Standardse. g. EExed.

一些设备在其建造过程中可能会使用不止一种类型的防护措施。在这种情况下,首先引用的是主要类型的保护。例如,带有隔爆接线盒的增安型电动机将被标记为 Exed。设备也可以标记前缀"E",表示符合欧洲标准,如 EExed。

7.6.1 Exd Flameproof Enclosure 隔爆型防火外壳

Type "d" protection, code "EExd", uses a flameproof enclosure to contain the electrical apparatus. The internal apparatus may include parts which arc and surfaces which become hot. Gas may be inside the enclosure so it must fulfil three conditions:

(1) The enclosure must be strong enough to withstand an internal explosion without suffering damage.

(2) The enclosure must prevent the flame and hot gases from being transmitted to the external flammable atmosphere.

(3) The external surface temperature of the enclosure must remain below the ignition temperature of the surrounding gas under all operating conditions.

类型"d",代码"EExd",使用隔爆外壳来容纳电气设备。内部装置可包括起弧的部件和变热的表面。气体可能在外壳内,所以它必须满足三个条件:

(1)外壳必须足够坚固,以承受内部爆炸而不受损害。

(2)外壳必须防止火焰和热气体被传送到外部可燃环境中。

(3)在所有工作条件下,外壳的外表面温度必须保持在周围气体的点火温度以下。

The transmission of flame and hot gases from a flameproof enclosure is prevented because all joints, such as flanges, spigots, shafts and bearings are closely machined to achieve a small gap which is less than a defined maximum. The pressure of an internal explosion is then released through the small gap between machined faces which cools the gas sufficiently to prevent it from igniting any external flammable atmosphere.

火焰和热气体向防爆外壳外传播被阻止了,因为所有的接头,如法兰、插口、轴和轴承都经过紧密的加工,以实现一个小于规定最大值的小间隙。内部爆炸的压力通过加工表面之间的小间隙释放出来,从而充分冷却气体,防止它点燃任何外部可燃气体。

The maximum permitted gap depends upon three factors:

(1) The type of gas with which the apparatus is safe for use. This is indicated by Apparatus Group.

(2) The width of the joint (L).

(3) The volume of the enclosure (V).

允许的最大间隙取决于三个因素:

(1)该设备使用安全的气体类型。这是由设备组指出的。

(2)接头宽度(L)。

(3)防爆壳体积(V)。

These factors are illustrated in Fig. 7. 3 for a flanged enclosure.

对于法兰外壳,这些因素如图 7. 3 所示。

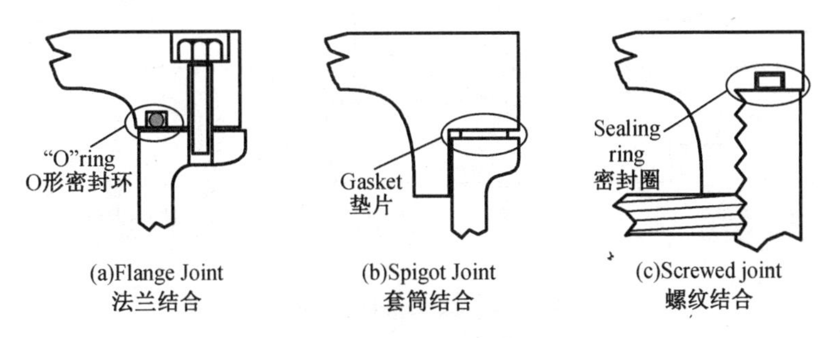

Fig. 7. 3 Exd flame paths

图 7. 3 隔爆型火焰路径

Question 思考题

A ship's battery room is fitted with a flameproof luminaire marked Exd ⅡC T4. Is this luminaire certified for use in the battery room?

一艘船的电瓶间装有标记为 Exd ⅡC T4 的隔爆灯具。这个灯具是否可以在电池室使用?

Answer 答案

Yes. The hazard is hydrogen gas from the batteries which requires apparatus designed for use in apparatus gas group ⅡC. The ignition temperature of hydrogen is 560 ℃ and the temperature classification of the luminaire is T4. This means that it's surface temperature will not exceed 135 ℃, so the temperature classificatio is satisfactory.

可以。危害是来自蓄电池产生的氢气,需要使用适用于ⅡC 类气体的设备。氢的点火温度为 560 ℃,灯具的温度等级为 T4。这意味着其表面温度不超过 135 ℃,因此该温度分类是令人满意的。

The cable entry into an Exd enclosure must also be maintained flameproof by using a certified Exd gland. This type of gland, shown in Fig. 7. 4, has a compound filling which forms a barrier between the individual conductors and prevents entry of explosive products from the enclosure entering the cable.

进入 Exd 外壳的电缆也必须使用经过认证的 Exd 密封盖来保持防火。这种类型的法兰如图 7. 4 所示,有一个复合填充,在单个导体之间形成一个屏障,防止爆炸性产物从外壳进入电缆。

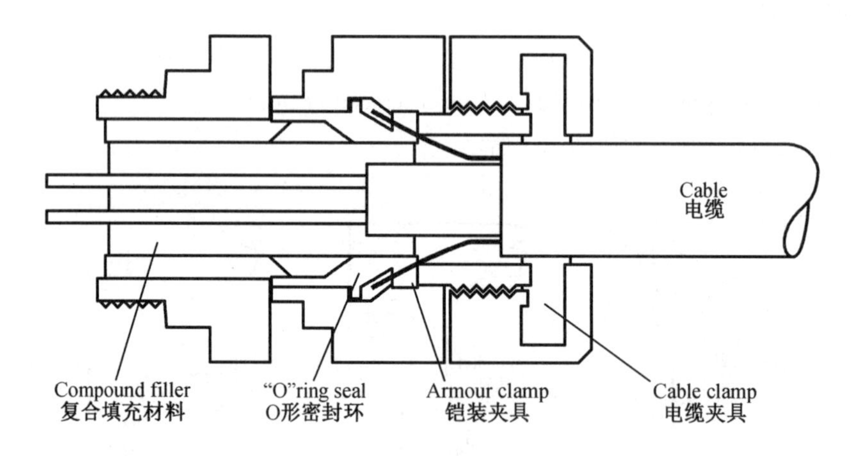

Fig. 7. 4 Exd cable gland

图 7. 4 隔爆型电缆固定头

7. 6. 2 Exi Intrinsic Safety 本安型

These are circuits in which no spark nor any thermal effect produced under prescribed test conditions (which include normal operation and specified fault conditions) is capable of causing ignition of a given explosive atmosphere. Generally, this means limiting the circuit conditions to less than 30 V and 50 mA. Naturally, this restricts the use of Exi protection to low power instrumentation, alarm and communication circuits.

在规定的试验条件下(包括正常运行和指定的故障条件),这些电路中没有火花或产生任何热效应,能够在给定的爆炸气体中引起点火。通常,这意味着将电路条件限制在 30 V 和 50 mA 以下。自然,这就限制了本安型防护措施在低功耗仪表、报警和通信电路中的使用。

The design of the circuit will depend on the type of gas present (gas grouping).

电路的设计将取决于存在的气体类型(气体分类)。

In the UK, two grades of intrinsic safety are recognised based on the safety factor of the equipment involved:

(1) Exia—The highest category based on a safety factor of 1.5 with two faults on the circuit.

(2) Exib—Based on a safety factor of 1.5 with one fault on the circuit.

在英国,根据有关设备的安全系数,认定两个本安等级:

(1) Exia——最高类别基于 1.5 的安全系数与两个故障的电路。

(2) Exib——基于 1.5 的安全系数和一个故障的电路。

In addition to apparatus in the hazardous area being rated as intrinsically safe, an electrical safety barrier may also be fitted to the circuit. The purpose of such a barrier is to limit voltages and currents in the hazardous area when faults occur on the circuit. A separate barrier is required for each Exi circuit and they must be fitted outside the hazardous area. See Fig. 7.5.

除了危险区域的设备被评为本安型外,还可以为电路安装一个电气安全屏障。这种屏障的目的是当电路发生故障时,限制危险区域的电压和电流。每个 Exi 电路都需要一个单独的屏障,并且必须安装在危险区域之外。如图 7.5 所示。

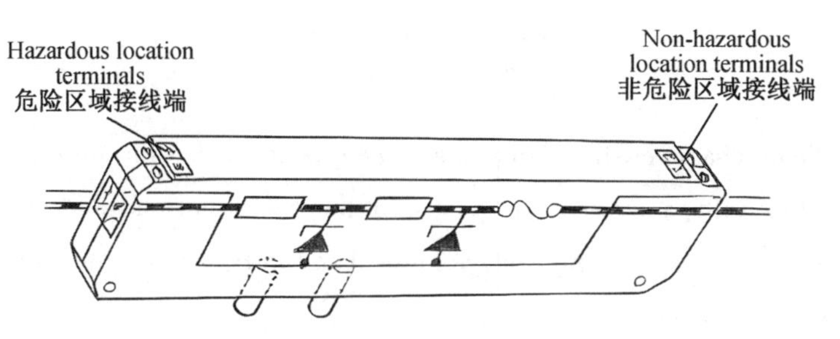

Fig. 7.5 Exi barrier contruction

图 7.5 本安型安全栅结构

A safety (or zener) barrier comprises:

(1) A fuse to limit the maximum current through the shunt (zener) diodes;

(2) A set of resistors to limit the maximumcurrent into the hazardous area;

(3) A set of shunt connected shunt (zener) diodes to limit the maximum voltage appearing on the circuit within the hazardous area.

安全(或齐纳)栅包括:

(1)限制通过分流(齐纳)二极管的最大电流的保险丝;

(2)一组电阻,以限制进入危险区域的最大电流;

(3)一组与分流器连接的分流(齐纳)二极管,用来限制在危险区域内电路上出现的最大电压。

All components are sealed into a compact package with clearly marked terminals at each end of the barrier.

所有组件都密封在一个紧凑的包装内,在隔栅的每一端都有明确标记的端子。

The circuit in Fig. 7. 6 shows a single channel zener barrier. It illustrates the preventive action in the event of a high voltage being accidentally applied to the non-hazardous terminals.

图 7.6 所示为单通道稳压隔板电路。它说明了在意外情况下将高压施加到非危险端子时的预防措施。

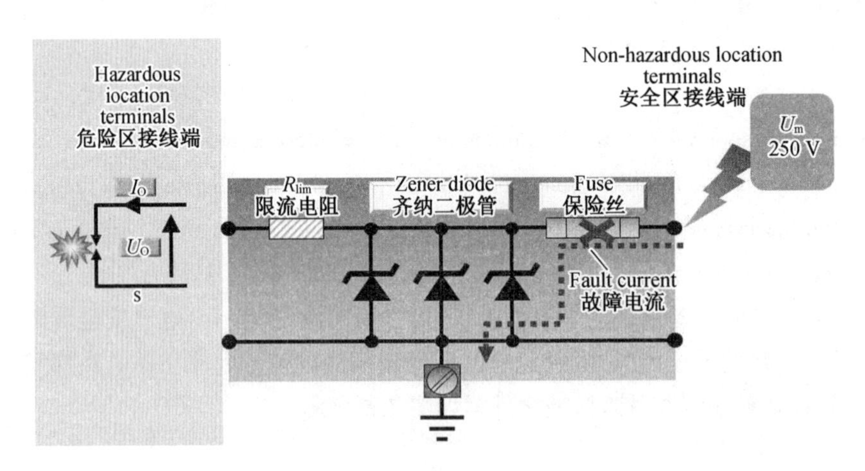

Fig. 7. 6　Zener barrier

图 7.6　齐纳栅

The zener diode characteristic shows that when connected with reverse bias it has an approximately constant voltage across it irrespective of the size of current flow. In normal operation the instrumentation circuit has a supply voltage lower than the U_z voltage rating of the zener diodes so no current flows through them.

齐纳二极管的特性表明,当与反向偏置电压连接时,它具有一个近似恒定的电压,与电流的大小无关。在正常工作时,仪表电路的供电电压低于齐纳二极管的额定电压 U_z,因此没有电流流过它们。

When an accidental high voltage appears at the input to the barrier, the diodes conduct to clamp their voltages to their U_z rating. This then limits the maximumvoltage appearing on the hazardous area wiring. While the zeners are conducting, the current level is designed to blow the fuse which now isolates the circuit to maintain safety in the hazardous area.

当在安全栅的输入端出现意外的高电压时,齐纳二极管将其电压钳位在 U_z。这就限制了危险区域线路上出现的最大电压。当齐纳二极管导通时,电流等级被设计成能熔掉保险丝,隔离电路以确保危险区域的安全。

In the event of a short-circuit on the hazardous area wiring or equipment, the in-line resistors within the barrier will limit the size of fault current while the fuse blows. Two or three zener-resistor combinations are used within a barrier to provide back-up voltage anchors while the fuse is blowing.

一旦危险区域的线路或设备发生短路,当保险丝熔断时,安全栅内的串联电阻将限制故障电流的大小。当保险丝熔断时,在一个安全栅内使用两个或三个齐纳电阻组合来提供备用电压锚定。

After clearing a fault, the complete zener barrier must be replaced with an identical unit. No alterations to the original is allowed — remember this is a certified Ex safety device.

清除故障后,需要更换整个齐纳栅。不允许对原始设备进行任何修改。记住,这是一个经过认证的 Ex 安全装置。

Cables for intrinsically safe circuits aboard ships should be separated from powercables and the crossing over of such cables should be at 90°. This is to minimise electromagnetic interference from the power cables affecting the intrinsically safe circuits.

船舶上本安型电路的电缆应与电力电缆分开,电缆交叉应在 90°。这是为了尽量减少电力电缆对本安型电路的电磁干扰。

The metallic cable screens of intrinsically safe circuits should be earthed at the power supply end only to prevent circulating currents within the sheath. See Fig. 7. 7.

本安型电路的电缆金属层应仅在电源端接地,以防止在护套内产生循环电流。如图 7. 7 所示。

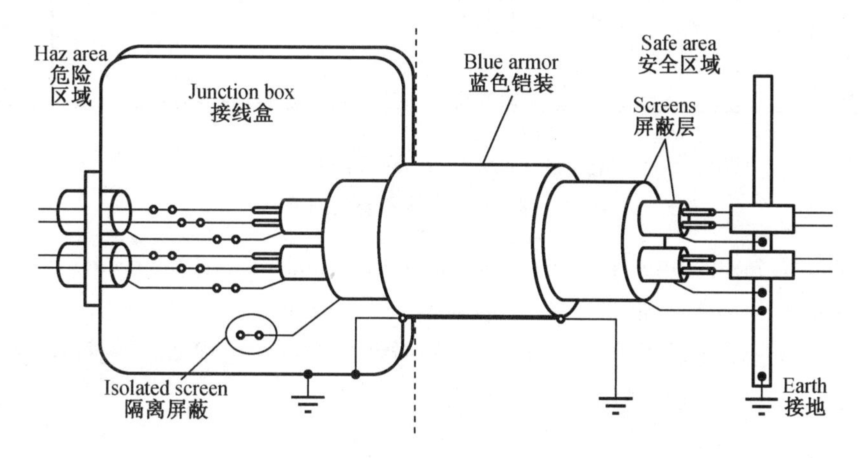

Fig. 7. 7　Exi cable terminations

图 7. 7　本安型电缆接线

Power and intrinsically safe cable runs should be separately identified. i. e. by labels or by using cables with a distinctive colour (typically blue for Exi).

电力电缆和本安型电缆应分开标识,即通过标签或使用特殊颜色的电缆(通常为用蓝色表示 Exi)。

7.6.3 Exe Increased Safety 增安型

Increased safety equipment is based primarily on the elimination of open sparking as at relay and switch contacts or on the commutators or slip-rings of motors and generators, and on the close control of surface temperatures.

增安型设备可以消除继电器和开关触点、换向器或电动机和发电机滑环上的开路火花,以及实现对表面温度的密切控制。

Also, the construction of the equipment is to a very high standard to prevent faults developing. Extra insulation is used, creepage distances between bare terminals are made longer and special enclosures to protect against damage due to entry of moisture and mechanical damage are also specified. See Fig. 7.8. The enclosure is made to withstand impact and to prevent ingress of solids and liquids.

此外,该类设备的结构标准非常高,以防止故障发生。使用了额外的绝缘材料,使裸露端子之间的爬电距离变长,还规定了使用特殊的外壳,以防止由于水分进入和机械损坏而造成的事故。如图 7.8 所示。外壳可以承受冲击,防止固体和液体的进入。

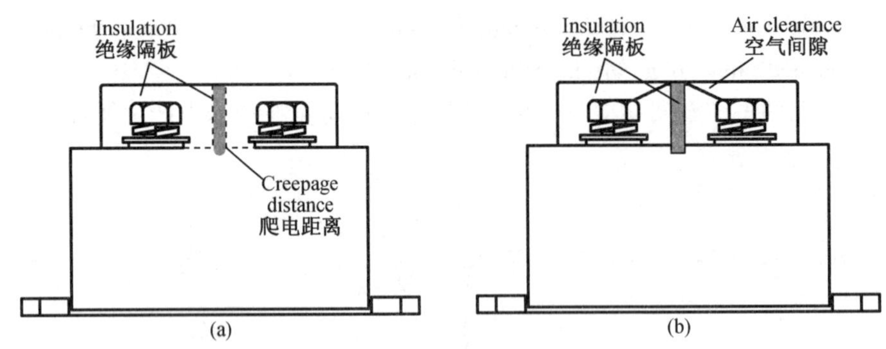

Fig. 7.8 Creepage and air clearecce

图 7.8 爬电距离和空气间隙

Applications include cage-rotor induction motors, luminaires and connection boxes. Special Exe cable glands, metal or plastic, are used with Exe apparatus.

应用范围包括笼型转子感应电动机、灯具和接线盒。专用的 Exe 电缆接头为金属或塑料制成,可与 Exe 设备配套使用。

7.6.4 Exn Non-Sparking 无火花型

Similar to Exe, the designation Exn applies to equipment which has no arcing contacts or hot surfaces which could cause ignition.

与 Exe 类似,Exn 这个名称适用于不会产生电弧的触头或不会引起点火的热表面的设备。

The Exn requirements are less stringent than for Exe, and designs are very close to that of normal electrical apparatus.

无火花型设备的要求没有增安型那么严格,而且设计非常接近于普通电气设备。

The main consideration is extra care to ensure locking of terminal connections to avoid any risk of electric sparking or flashover.

主要考虑的是确保锁紧终端连接,以避免存在任何电火花或闪燃的风险。

7.6.5 Exp Pressurised Enclosure 正压型

Clean, dry air or an inert gas is supplied to the equipment slightly above atmospheric pressure to prevent entry of the external flammable gas. This method is sometimes used for motors, instrumentation enclosures and lighting.

为防止外部可燃气体进入,向设备内提供略高于大气压力的干燥空气或惰性气体。这种方法有时用于电动机、仪表外壳和照明设备。

The diagrams in Fig. 7.9 show that the internal pressure may be maintained by leakage compensation or by continuous circulation. A pressurisation system requires a purge flow before the internal electrical equipment is permitted to operate. Also, the pressurised enclosure must be fitted with alarm and trip signal for a reduction of pressure which in turn will switch-off the enclosed electrical circuits.

图 7.9 显示,内部压力可以通过泄漏补偿或连续循环来维持。在内部电气设备允许工作之前,增压系统需要先换气。此外,增压外壳必须配备报警和跳闸信号,当压力降低时,能关闭整个电路。

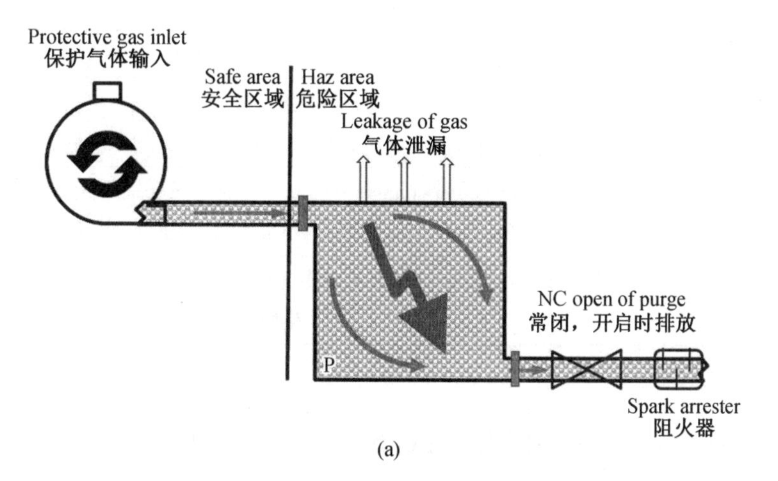

Fig. 7.9 Exp enclosure arrangement

图 7.9 正压型外壳布局

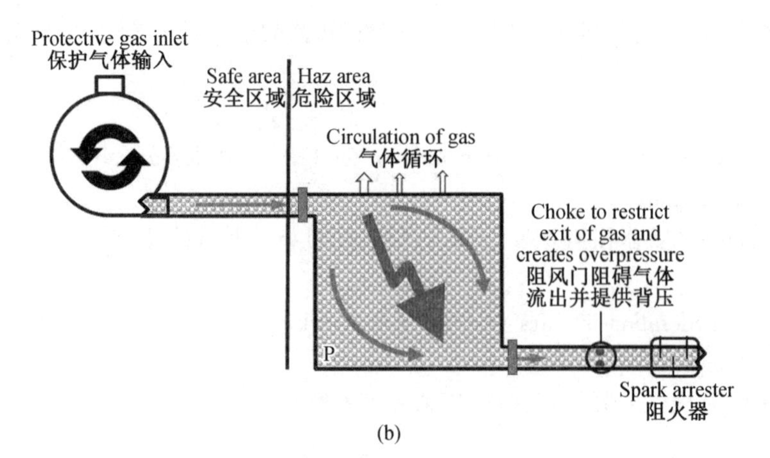

Fig. 7.9(Continued)

图 7.9(续)

7.6.6 Exs Special Protection 特殊防护型

This includes precautions taken to prevent explosions which are not specifically covered by the previous designations.

这包括为防止爆炸而采取的预防措施,而这些措施并没有列入前几次指定的具体范围。

The Table 7.7 below shows the type of protection which is allowed in the three hazardous zones.

表 7.7 显示了三个危险区域允许的防护类型。

Table 7.7 Protection types for different areas

表 7.7 不同区域对应的防护类型

Zone 区域	Type of protection 防护类型
0	Exia 本安型 a,特殊型 Exs(specially certified for use in zone 0,用于 0 区)
1	Any type of protection suitable for zone 0 and 1 设备适用于 0 区和 1 区: Exd,Exib,Exp,Exe,Exs 隔爆型,本安型 b,正压型,增安型,特殊型
2	Any type of protection suitable for zone 0 or 1 and 2 设备适用于 0 区或者 1 区和 2 区: Exn,Exo,Exq 无火花型,充油型,充沙型

7.6.7 Certification and Identification 认证和识别

When a manufacturer produces an item of explosion protected equipment, it must be tested and inspected to ensure that it complies with the required standards relating to that type of protection.

当制造商生产防爆设备时,必须对其进行测试和检查,以确保其符合与该类型防护相关的标准要求。

In the UK this work is carried out by BASEEFA (British Approvals Service for Electrical Equipment in Flammable Atmospheres) and SCS (SIRA Certification Service). BASEEFA/SCS issue a certificate for each explosion protected device they have tested. The BASEEFA certificate number is shown on the equipment name plate.

在英国,这项工作是由 BASEEFA(英国易燃环境下电气设备审批服务)和 SCS (SIRA 认证服务)进行的。BASEEFA/SCS 为他们测试的每一个防爆装置颁发证书。BASEEFA 证书编号显示在设备铭牌上。

Some other national certification authorities:

USA: There is no national certifying body in the USA. Two separate insurance basedorganisations carry out tests on equipment and issue approvals (listings) of apparatus and equipment acceptable to their published standards.

Canada:The Canadian Standards Association (CSA) is the national body responsible for certifying equipment forhazardous areas. CSA have an arrangement with BSI to allow UK equipment which has a BASEEFA approval to be certified to CSA Standards in the UK.

Australia: The Standards Association of Australia (SSA) is responsible for certification in Australia. SAA has an arrangement with BSI to help UK organisations to obtain SAA Approval.

South Africa:South African Bureau of Standards(SABS).

Germany: PTB are the testing and certification authority , certifying either to CENELEC Standards or to VDE Standards(VDE is the German equivalent of BSI).

Denmark:Danmarks Eleclriske Material-Kontrol(DEMKO). Denmark also recognises the CENELEC Standards.

Norway:Det Norske Veritas(DNV),an approvals body similar to Lloyds.

其他国家权威认证机构情况如下:

美国:美国没有国家认证机构。两个独立的保险机构负责对设备进行测试,并对符合其公布标准的仪器和设备下发批准(清单)。

加拿大:加拿大标准协会(CSA)是负责对危险区域设备进行认证的国家机构。CSA 与 BSI 达成协议,允许拥有 BASEEFA 证书编号的英国设备在英国获得 CSA 标准认证。

澳大利亚:澳大利亚标准协会(SSA)负责澳大利亚的认证工作。SAA 与 BSI 有协议,以帮助英国组织获得 SAA 批准。

南非:南非标准局(SABS)。

德国:PTB 是测试和认证机构,通过 CENELEC 标准或 VDE 标准进行认证(VDE 在德语中相当于 BSI)。

丹麦:丹麦电气材料控制(DEMKO)。丹麦也承认 CENELEC 标准。

挪威:挪威船级社(DNV),类似劳氏船级社的审批机构。

The Table 7.8 gives a reminder of the meaning of the Ex identification marks on a rating label for an item of explosion-protected apparatus.

表 7.8 中的例子提示我们防爆设备等级标签上 Ex 标识的含义。

Table 7.8 Meaning of the Ex mark on the explosion-proof equipment grade label

表 7.8 防爆设备等级标签上 Ex 标识的含义

Example: EExia ⅡC T4 No. BASEEFA 例如:EExia ⅡC T4 英国防爆电气设备审定局					
E	Ex	ia	ⅡC	T4	No.
European Standard EN50 020 欧洲标准	Explosion Protection 防爆	Type of Protection 防爆类型	Apparatus Group 设备类别	Temperature Class 温度组别	Certifying Authority and Certificate Number 认证机构和证书编号

Question 思考题

Explain the meaning of the Ex label listed in Table 7.8.

解释表 7.8 列出的 Ex 标签的含义。

Answer 答案

Intrinsically safe (Exi) to the highest safety factor (a) which is suitable for installation in Zone 0, apparatus group (ⅡC) is suitable for hydrogen, temperature class (T4) allows a maximum surface temperature of 135 ℃, the certifying authority is the UK test house BASEEFA.

本质安全型(Exi),安全系数最高(a),适用于安装在 0 区,仪器组别(ⅡC)适用于氢气,温度等级(T4)允许最高表面温度 135 ℃,认证机构是英国的 BASEEFA 测试机构。

7.7 Electrical Testing in Hazardous Areas 危险区域的电气测试

All electrical apparatus and associated circuits are required to be tested periodically in accordance with a definite testing routine with recorded test results.

所有电气设备和相关电路都需要按照规定的测试程序进行定期测试,并记录测试结果。

Insulation resistance, earth loop resistance and earth continuity resistance tests are required to be made, the last two in relation to the setting or rating of the protective devices associated with the apparatus and its circuitry.

要求进行绝缘电阻、接地回路电阻和对地电阻测试,最后两项测试与该设备及其电路有关的保护装置的整定或额定值有关。

It is important that insulation resistance tests are not made in such a way that the safety devices and insulation used inintrinsically safe apparatus and circuits are damaged by excess test voltages.

重要的是,绝缘电阻测试的方式不能因过高的测试电压而损坏本安型设备以及电路中使用的安全装置和绝缘。

No apparatus should be opened in a danger area until it has been made dead and effective measures (e. g. locking-off the isolating switch) have been taken to prevent its being made live again inadvertently.

在使设备不带电且没有采取有效措施(例如关闭隔离开关)以防止在无意中使其再次带电之前,不得在危险区域打开任何设备。

Where, for the purpose of electrical testing, it is necessary to restore thepower supply before the apparatus is reassembled, tests should be made using a suitable gas detector and continued during the operation to ensure that the combustible does not approach the explosive limit.

如果为了进行电气测试,需要在重新组装设备之前恢复供电,则应使用适当的气体探测器进行测试,并在操作期间进行持续的气体探测,以确保可燃物不会接近爆炸极限。

Unless the hazardous area can be made gas-free or otherwise safe, or the electrical equipment is removed from the area, then insulation resistance testing should be carried out using a 500 V DC tester of certified intrinsically safe (Exi) design.

除非危险区域可以做到无气体或其他安全方式,或电气设备被移出该区域,否则绝缘电阻测试应使用经本安认证(Exi)设计的 500 V 直流测试仪进行。

The testing and maintenance of flameproof or intrinsically safe equipment should be entrusted only to competent persons who have received instruction in the special techniques involved.

隔爆或本安型设备的测试和维护只能委托给受过有关特殊技术培训的人员进行。

The body material of instruments and tools required for maintenance purposes should be designed so that they will not make a hot spark when dropped.

维护所需的仪器和工具的主体材料应在跌落时不会产生热火花。

The energy output of all intrinsically safe instruments should be so small that they do not produce hot sparks. An insulation tester has a drooping characteristic to prevent high currents and may be intrinsically safe when applied to circuits of small inductance or capacitance but a risk may arise when such energy-storing properties of a circuit have an appreciable value.

所有本安型仪器的输出能量应该很小,以不至于产生热火花。绝缘测试仪具有降压的特性,可以防止大电流,当应用于小电感或小电容电路时,可能具有本安性能,但电路储存的能量达到一定值时,可能会产生风险。

Where such instruments are used the test leads should be firmly connected throughout and on completion of the test they should not be detached until the circuit has been discharged through the testing instrument (leave the tester for 1 min after test is finished).

在使用这类仪器时,测试引线应始终连接牢固,在测试完成时应在电路通过测试仪器放电后(测试仪测试结束 1 min 后)再将引线拆下。

7.8 Maintenance of Ex-protected Apparatus 防护装置的维护

The previous sections covering zoning, gas grouping, temperature classification and the various types of protection methods show that the design of electricalequipment for hazardous areas is very special. Maintenance of such apparatus must not, in any way, cause its operation to be less safe than in its original certified state.

前面几节涉及分区、气体分组、温度等级以及各种类型的防护方法,说明了危险区域电气设备的设计是非常特殊的。这种仪器的维护不得使其以比认证的状态更不安全的方式进行。

This most important point means that the maintenance must be carried out by a competent person. Temporary lash-ups, refitting with wrong sized components (e. g. lamps), failing to employ the correct number of cover bolts etc. , is absolutely forbidden.

最重要的一点是,维护必须由适任的人员进行。临时的应急措施,如用尺寸错误的部件再次紧固(如灯具)、没有使用正确数量的盖板螺栓等,此类措施是绝对禁止的。

The inspection and maintenance of Exd enclosures for luminaires, switches, junction boxes, push-buttons, etc. , requires meticulous care.

灯具、开关、接线盒、按钮等的隔爆外壳的检查和维护需要小心谨慎。

The following example gives a guide to the inspection and maintenance points as applied to a flameproof luminaire.

下面的例子给出了防爆灯具的检查和维护要点指南。

7.8.1 Corrosion 腐蚀

Corrosion will reduce the enclosure strength. To ascertain the extent of corrosion, remove dirt, loose paint and surface corrosion with a wire brush. If only the paintwork is deteriorating, the enclosure should be repainted to prevent further corrosion.

腐蚀会降低外壳强度。为了确定腐蚀程度,用钢丝刷清除污垢、松动的油漆和表面腐蚀。如果只是油漆恶化,应重新油漆外壳,以防止进一步腐蚀。

7.8.2 Bolts 螺栓

Make sure that there are no missing bolts. This is particularly important on flameproof luminaires because a missing bolt will invalidate the certification. Replacement bolts must be of equivalent strength as originals (usually high tensile steel).

确保没有缺失的螺栓。这对隔爆型灯具特别重要,因为缺少螺栓将使认证失效。替换螺栓的强度必须与原装螺栓(通常为高强度钢)一致。

7.8.3 Mountings 配件

Ensure all mountings are installed safely and reliably. Corrosion and vibration are severe on ships and can cause premature failure.

确保所有配件的安装都是安全可靠的。船舶上的腐蚀和振动非常严重,可能导致配件提前失效。

7.8.4 Flamepaths 火焰路径

Examine the flamepath for signs of corrosion or pitting. If the flamepath needs cleaning, this should be done with a non-metallic scraper and/or a suitable non-corrosive cleaning fluid.

检查火焰路径是否有腐蚀或点蚀的迹象。如果火焰路径需要清洁,应使用非金属刮刀和/或合适的非腐蚀性清洗液。

7.8.5 Cement 胶合剂

Examine the cement used around lampglass assemblies both inside and outside. If the cement is eroded, softened or damaged in any way, advice should be sought from the manufacturer regarding repair. If deterioration of the cement has occurred, a complete new lampglass assembly should be fitted.

灯罩内部和外部使用的胶合剂都要检查。如果胶合剂以任何方式被侵蚀、软化或损坏,应向制造商寻求修复建议。如果胶合剂发生了变质老化,应安装一个完整的新灯罩组件。

7.8.6 Lampglass 灯罩

Check lampglass, if cracked or broken a complete new lampglass assembly should be fitted.

Clean the lampglass.

检查灯罩,如果破裂或破碎,应安装一个完整的新灯罩组件。清洁灯罩。

When re-assembling an Exd enclosure you must ensure that the following points are covered:

(1) Lightly grease all flamepaths and threaded components with an approved form of non-setting silicone grease. Care must be taken to ensure that blind tapped holes are free from accumulated dirt or excessive greasewhich can prevent the correct closure of flamepaths, or cause damage to the tapped components. Fit new lamp of the correct rating.

(2) Ensure bolts are not over-tightened as this can distort flamepaths, cause excessive stress on lampglasses or distort weather proofing gaskets, if fitted, allowing the ingress of liquids and dusts.

(3) Check the luminaire is installed in accordance with the requirements of the installation, particularly the classification of the area if it is hazardous and that the correct rating of lamp is fitted.

(4) Remove any build-up of dust on the luminaire, this can cause overheating as well as acting as a corrosive agent.

当重新组装隔爆外壳时,必须确保以下几点:

(1)在所有火焰通路和螺纹组件上涂上经认可的非固结硅脂。必须小心确保非贯穿螺纹孔内没有堆积的污垢或过量的油脂,否则会妨碍火焰路径的正确关闭,或对螺纹部件造成损坏。安装正确等级的新灯泡。

(2)确保螺栓不要过紧,因为过紧会扭曲火焰路径,导致灯罩上的压力过大,或者扭曲防水垫圈(如果安装了的话),导致液体和灰尘进入。

(3)检查灯具的安装是否符合安装的要求,特别是检查灯具分类是否符合危险区域的使用要求以及是否安装了正确参数的灯泡。

(4)清除任何积聚在灯具上的灰尘,这些灰尘会导致灯具过热,并起到腐蚀的作用。

Before attempting any maintenance work on Exd equipment check for any particular inspection and overhaul instructions given by the manufacturer.

在尝试对隔爆型设备进行任何维护工作之前,请检查制造商给出的特定的检查和大修指南。

Chapter 8　Electrical Survey Requirements
第 8 章　电气检验要求

8.0　Introduction 介绍

The electrical equipment aboard ship is inspected and tested during the complete engine survey which occurs every four years. Such a survey is prescribed under the Rules and Regulations for the Classification of the Ship.

在每四年进行一次的发动机全面检查期间,船上的电气设备要进行检查和测试。这种检验是船级社的规则和规定要求的。

The electrical survey guidance given in this chapter is based on the periodical Survey regulations of Lloyds Register of Shipping, London. Other classification societies have their own rules which, although similar to Lloyds, should be consulted prior to an electrical survey.

本章的电气检验指南基于伦敦劳氏船级社的定期检验规则。其他船级社有其自己的规则,虽然类似于劳氏船级社,但也应该在电气检验之前咨询相关船级社。

8.1　SOLAS《国际海上人命安全公约》

The International Maritime Organization (IMO), which met for the first time in 1959, is a specialised agency of the United Nations devoted to maritime affairs. Its main interests can be summed up in the phrase "safer shipping and cleaner oceans".

国际海事组织于 1959 年成立,是联合国负责海事事务的专门机构。它的主要目标可以用"更安全的航运和更清洁的海洋"这句话来概括。

Of all the international conventions dealing with maritime safety, the most important is the *International Convention for the Safety of Life at Sea*, better known as SOLAS, which covers a wide range of measures designed to improve the safety of shipping.

在所有与海上安全有关的国际公约中,最重要的是《国际海上人命安全公约》(SOLAS),它涵盖了一系列旨在提高航运安全的措施。

SOLAS is also one of the oldest of its kind: The first version was adopted in 1914 following the sinking of the Titanic with the loss of more than 1,500 lives. Since then there have been four more versions of SOLAS. The present version was adopted in 1974 and entered into force in 1980.

SOLAS 也是同类公约中最古老的公约之一:第一个版本是在 1914 年"泰坦尼克号"沉

没,1 500 多人丧生之后通过的。之后又出现了四种版本的 SOLAS 修正案。目前的案文于 1974 年通过,并于 1980 年生效。

The Convention in its consolidated edition dated 1997 has eleven chapters. Electrical regulations are part of Chapter Ⅱ-1 which outlines the requirements for ship construction — sub-division and stability, machinery and electrical installations.

1997 年的 SOLAS 共有 11 章。电气规则是其中第 2 章的第 1 部分,概述了船舶建造的要求——分舱和稳定性,机械和电气装置。

This Chapter has five parts as follows:

Part A　General

Part B　Sub-division and stability

Part C　Machinery installations

Part D　Electrical installations

Part E　Additional requirements for periodically unattended machinery spaces

第 2 章分为以下 5 部分:

A 部分　通则

B 部分　分舱与稳性

C 部分　机器设备

D 部分　电气装置

E 部分　周期性无人值班机器处所的附加要求

The electrical installations (Part D) is sub-divided into regulations as:

Regulation 40　General

Regulation 41　Main source of electrical power and lighting systems

Regulation 42　Emergency source of electrical power in passenger ships

　Regulation 42-1　Supplementary emergency lighting for ro-to passenger ships

Regulation 43　Emergency source of electrical power in cargo ships

Regulation 44　Starting arrangements for emergency generator sets

Regulation 45　Precautions against shock, fire and other hazards of electrical origin

电气装置(D 部分)可细分为以下条例:

40 条　通则

41 条　主电源和照明系统

42 条　客船应急电源

　42-1 条　客滚船的附加应急照明

43 条　货船应急电源

44 条　应急发电机组的启动装置

45 条　触电、电气火灾及其他电气灾害的预防措施

8.2 Classification Societies 船级社

Some of the main Classification Societies for ships are: American Bureau of Shipping (ABS, New York); Bureau Veritas (Paris); Germanischer Lloyd (Hamburg); Nippon Kaiji Kyokai (ClassNK, Tokyo); Det Norske Veritas (Oslo); Registro Italiano Navale (Genoa).

国际上一些主要的船级社有:美国船级社(ABS,纽约);法国船级社(巴黎);德国劳氏船级社(汉堡);日本海事协会(东京);挪威船级社(奥斯陆);意大利船级社(热那亚)。

Electrical equipment and services aboard ship must also meet the minimum standards specified by various national and international organisations.

船上的电气设备和服务也必须满足各种国家和国际组织规定的最低标准。

For British registered ships in particular, it is necessary to comply with:

(1) *Regulations for the Electrical and Electronic Equipment of Ships* — Institution of Electrical Engineers. In conjunction with the British Standards Institute these Regulations are being combined with the Recommendations for the Electrical and Electronic Equipment of Offshore Installations.

(2) *The Merchant Shipping Rules*—Maritime and Coastguard Agency.

(3) SOLAS — IMO Convention.

(4) British Standards (BS).

(5) International Electrotechnical Commission.

特别是在英国注册的船舶,必须遵守以下规定:

(1)《船舶电气和电子设备规则》,由电气工程师学会颁布,与英国标准协会颁布的规则一起,正在与《海上装置电气和电子设备建议》合并。

(2)《商船规则》,由海事和海岸警备局颁布。

(3) SOLAS,由国际海事组织颁布。

(4)英国标准(BS)。

(5)国际电工委员会颁布的标准。

The standards specified by the above organisations are met when the ship is designed, built, approved and classified. It is for the shipowner and the operating staff to maintain the vessel and its electrical installation to the requirements of the Classification Society throughout the ship's lifetime. The periodical electrical survey is, therefore, to check that the installation is maintained to the Rules of the Classification Society.

船舶在设计、建造、批准和分类时,均符合上述机构的标准。船东和操作人员应在船舶的整个使用期内,按照船级社的要求,对船舶及其电气设备进行维护。因此,定期的电气检验是为了检查设备是否符合船级社的规则要求。

8.3 Main Electrical Survey Items 主要的电气检验项目

The inspection items listed in Fig. 8.1 are generally applicable to all ships.

图 8.1 所列检验项目普遍适用于所有船舶。

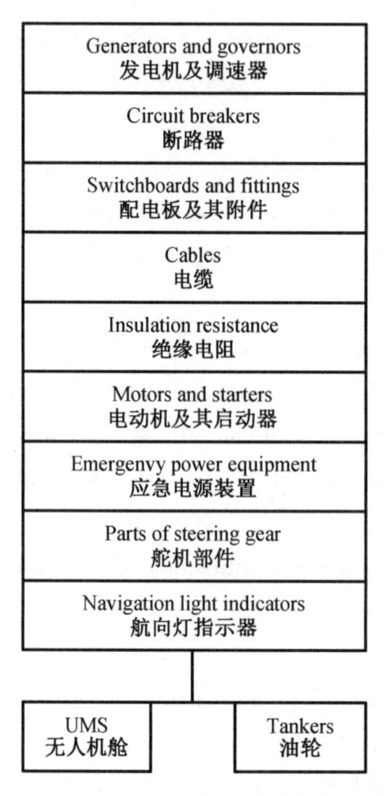

Fig. 8.1 Inspection items

图 8.1 检验项目

For UMS operation, a survey of the associated alarms, controls and fire detection is required.

对于无人机舱系统的运行,需要对相关的报警、控制和火灾探测进行检验。

For tankers/gas carriers and other ships transporting flammable cargo, an additional survey of all electrical equipment in hazardous areas is carried out during each docking survey and annual survey. This means that hazardous area electrical equipment is surveyed every year.

对于油轮/气体运输船和其他运输易燃货物的船舶,在每次停靠检验和年度检验期间,对危险区域的所有电气设备进行额外检验。这意味着每年都要对危险区域的电气设备进行检查。

8.4　Generators and Governors 发电机和调速器

The surveyor will require that main and emergency generators are clean, respond correctly to controls and load changes, and show stable operation when required to run in parallel with other generators.

主发电机和应急发电机应清洁干净,对控制和负载的变化能做出正确反应,并在需要与其他发电机并联运行时能稳定运行。

Generator windings on stator and rotor must be free of dust, oil and moisture. A visual check will be made for any obvious deterioration, abrasion or cracking of the insulation around the end winding coils on the stator.

发电机绕组上的定子和转子必须没有灰尘、油污和湿气。检查定子端部绕组线圈周围的绝缘是否有明显的劣化、磨损或开裂。

An insulation test to earth and between stator phase windings (if the neutral point can be disconnected at the terminal box) should be carried out while the machine is still hot after running on load.

对地和定子相绕组之间的绝缘试验(如果中性点可以在接线盒处断开)应在机器负载运行后仍发热时进行。

Question 思考题

Would an IR test result of 0.5 MΩ to earth be acceptable for a 440 V main generator?

对于 440 V 的主发电机,0.5 MΩ 对地的绝缘测试结果是否可以接受?

Answer 答案

Although a minimum of 1.5 MΩ is generally specified for new equipment, Lloyds rules suggest that 0.1 MΩ is acceptable in special cases. However, most surveyors would insist on at least 1 kΩ/V, i.e. 440 kΩ, or 0.5 MΩ as a reasonable minimum value for a 440 V generator. For HV equipment the usual recommended minimum IR level is (kV+1) MΩ. e.g. for a 6.6 kV motor, the acceptable minimum IR would be 7.6 MΩ.

尽管最低 1.5 MΩ 通常为新设备,劳氏船级社建议 0.1 MΩ 是可接受的特殊情况,然而大多数验船师会坚持至少 1 kΩ/V,即 440 kΩ,或者 0.5 MΩ 作为 440 V 特发电机合理的最小值。对于高压设备,通常推荐的最低绝缘等级为(电动机额定电压(kV)+1) MΩ。例如,对于 6.6 kV 的电动机,可接受的最小绝缘值为 7.6 MΩ。

Remember to disconnect all AVR equipment, instrument connections and generator heater supplies when testing for IR.

在进行绝缘测试时，请记住断开所有电压调节设备、仪表连接和发电机加热器电源。

The rotor circuits must also be tested for insulation value, taking care to short out the rotating shaft diodes of a brushless excitation system as the diodes usually have a low peak inverse voltage (PIV) rating.

必须测试转子电路绝缘值，注意短路无刷励磁系统的转轴二极管，因为二极管通常有一个低额定的峰值反向电压(PIV)。

Special attention to the contact surface of any commutator or slip-rings is required. The contact surfaces must be smooth and concentric without any signs of pitting or deep grooves. Carbon brushes must be of adequate length, maintained at the correct spring pressure and properly contoured onto its rotating commutator or slip-ring. Be sure to remove any excess carbon dust in the vicinity of the brush gear and around rotor coils.

需要特别注意任何换向器或滑环的接触面。接触表面必须光滑、同心，没有任何点蚀或深沟槽的迹象。碳刷必须有足够的长度，保持在正确的弹簧压力下，并在其旋转换向器或滑环上形成适当的轮廓。一定要清除电刷装置和转子线圈附近多余的碳灰尘。

Generator running tests, on load, should confirm the proper operation of governor and AVR controls with correct voltage, frequency and current values indicated on the generator control panel. Governor droop and its response to sudden load changes must be within the declared specification for the prime mover/generator combination. Stability of load sharing of kW and kVAr (or load current/power factor) between two or more generators running in parallel must be demonstrated.

发电机在带负载下运行试验时，应根据发电机控制面板上指示的电压、频率和电流值，确认调速器和电压调节控制器的正确运行。调速器下垂特性及其对突然变化的负载的响应必须在原动机/发电机组合的要求内。必须证明两台或多台发电机并联运行时有功功率和无功功率(或负载电流/功率因数)分配的稳定性。

8.5 Circuit-breakers 断路器

A visual examination of circuit-breakers in main, emergency and section boards will usually precede operational tests. The surveyor will particularly check the condition of main, arcing and auxiliary contacts for signs of wear, misalignment and overheating. A similar inspection of fixed and moving isolator contacts at the rear of a circuit-breaker will be made.

通常在运行试验之前，对主、应急和分配电板中的断路器进行目视检查。应特别检查主触点、电弧触点和辅助触点的状态，以确定是否存在磨损、错位和过热迹象。应对断路器后部的固定和移动隔离开关触点进行类似检查。

Arc chutes must be clean, free of arc debris and correctly aligned. All internal wiring should be in good condition and its end connections must be tight. All mechanical linkages will be checked for any signs of wear or stress.

弧槽必须清洁,无弧屑,并正确对齐。所有内部接线应完好,其端部连接必须牢固。所有的机械连接都要检查是否有磨损或应力的迹象。

Tests on a circuit-breaker will include close and trip operations while in its isolated position (i. e. not connected in circuit). The racking mechanism for moving the breaker from the service to the isolated position must be demonstrated to be free moving and the fixed main terminals must be seen to be shuttered off when the breaker is withdrawn. Emergency hand charging (if fitted) of the closing spring will be tested. Correct operation of the mechanical indicators to show whether the breaker is open, closed or isolated, is required.

断路器的测试将包括在隔离位置(即未连接到电路中)时的合闸和跳闸操作。必须证明用于将断路器从工作位置移动到隔离位置的机架机构能够自由移动,并且当断路器抽出时,必须看到固定主端子关断。合闸弹簧的紧急手动充能(如已安装)也要进行检验。机械指示器应正确动作,以显示断路器是否断开、闭合或隔离。

The undervoltage release mechanism and overcurrent trip settings for level and time delay may have to be demonstrated to the surveyor's satisfaction. An overcurrent trip for a generator breaker is typically set for 130% of FLC with a typical time delay of 3 s, but this has to suit the thermal capacity of the generator and be coordinated with the overall protection scheme for the power system.

欠压释放机构和过电流脱扣的等级及延迟时间的设置,必须向检查员演示并使其满意。发电机断路器的过电流脱扣通常设置为满载电流的130%,典型的时间延迟为3 s,但这必须与发电机的热容量相适应,并与电力系统的整体保护方案相协调。

Although the overcurrent and time delay settings on the breaker can be seen to be correctly adjusted to the desired values, only a proper current injection test will prove these settings against the manufacturer's I–t characteristics. In this test the circuit-breaker is isolated from the bus-bar and a set of calibrated currents from a current injection set are fed directly through the closed circuit-breaker (primary injection) or (more usually) through the overcurrent relay (secondary injection). This is generally a specialist task for an outside contractor.

尽管可以看出断路器上的过电流和延时设置已正确调整至所需值,但只有适当的电流注入试验才能证明这些设置符合制造商要求的I–t特性。在该试验中,断路器与母线隔离,电流注入装置中的一组校准电流直接通过闭合断路器(一次注入)或(通常)通过过电流继电器(二次注入)。这通常是外部承包商的专业任务。

Circuit-breaker time delay mechanisms with oil dash pots must have the pots filled to the correct level with clean oil of a type recommended by the manufacturer.

带有油缓冲罐的断路器延时机构必须使用制造商推荐类型的清洁油将缓冲罐加注至正确油位。

8.6 Switchboards and Fittings 配电板及其配件

An obvious survey requirement for any switchboard, section board or distribution board is that they are clean. This includes all internal surfaces as well as the external panel surfaces, instrument faces and control switches. A thorough cleaning job on the inside of the main switchboard can only be safely carried out when the board is completely dead (all generators stopped and prime movers locked-off).

对任何配电板、区域配电板或分配电板首先要检查清洁情况。这包括所有的内部表面以及外部面板表面、仪器和控制开关表面。对主配电板内部进行彻底的清洁工作前,配电板要完全失电(所有发电机停止工作,原动机停止)时才能安全进行。

All the main bus-bar and auxiliary connections throughout the boards should be checked for tightness during the dead period of a major internal clean up. Overheating signs at a connection junction are probably due to a loose joint. Direct heat testing on load with an infra-red thermal camera is now a very useful technique for locating hot-spots.

在主要内部清理的失电期内,应检查整个配电板的所有主母线和辅助连接的紧密性。连接处的过热迹象可能是由于接头松动造成的。使用红外热像仪对负载进行直接热量检测是目前定位热点的非常有用的技术。

Bus-bar supports will be examined for surface tracking and damage to the insulation material. All internal wiring within the switchboard panels must be securely fixed. Cable entries at the bottom of the switchboard should be sealed with a non-flammable material to exclude dirt and act as a fire stop.

检查母线支架的表面电弧径迹和绝缘材料的损坏。配电板内的所有内部布线必须牢固固定。配电板底部的电缆入口应用非易燃材料密封,以防止灰尘和作为防火屏障。

The main switchboard earth bar must be securely bonded to both the frame of the board and, of course, to the ship's hull. One secondary terminal of each CT and the metal cases of instruments and relays should be wired to the main earth bar. Hinged panel doors should be bonded with an earth strap to the main switchboard frame.

主配电板接地棒必须牢固地连接到配电板框架上,当然,还必须连接到船体上。每个电流互感器的一个二次绕组端子以及仪表和继电器的金属外壳应连接至主接地棒。铰链式面板门应通过接地条连接至主配电板框架。

Question 思考题

What is the reason for earthing one end of the secondary winding of a CT?
电流互感器二次绕组一端接地的原因是什么?

Answer 答案

Should the insulation between primary and secondary break down, the secondary circuit can be raised to full primary voltage, e. g. 440 V above earth which could damage the secondary insulation with a serious risk to personnel. By earthing one end of the CT, the circuit is anchored to zero volts. As a bonus, the earth connection will allow such a fault to be detected on the earth fault monitor.

如果一次和二次之间的绝缘发生故障,二次电路可以升高到一次电压,例如对地 440 V,可能损坏二次侧绝缘,对人员造成严重威胁。通过电流互感器的一端接地,二次电路固定在 0 V。另外,接地连接将使接地故障监视器能检测到此类接地故障。

Feeder isolator and fuse holder contacts must be checked for any mechanical wear or damage due to overheating or arcing at the contacts. A slight smear of a proprietary electrical contact lubricant on such moving contacts is usually recommended.

必须检查馈线的隔离器和保险丝座触点是否因触点过热或电弧而出现损坏或机械磨损。通常建议在此类动触点上涂抹少量专用触点润滑剂。

Operational tests on a main switchboard under this heading will focus on the synchronising controls and generator protection relays such as reverse power and preferential load shedding trips. Typical reverse power trip settings may range between 5% – 15% of the generator power rating, with a time delay of 0. 5–2. 5 s for a diesel drive. Equivalent settings for a turbo-generator may be 2%–5% and 5 s.

本节中主配电板的运行测试将重点关注同步控制和发电机保护继电器,如逆功率和优先脱扣跳闸。典型的逆功率跳闸可能设置在发电机额定功率 5% ~ 15% 之间,延时 0. 5~2. 5 s 给柴油机调整。涡轮发电机的同类设置可能为 2% ~5% 和 5 s。

Such time delay settings must allow for the operating practice on the ship. For example, cargo winches and cranes may, at times, feed power back into the supply network. Under light load conditions such regenerative feedback may cause a generator to trip on reverse power if its time delay was set too short.

这种时间延迟设置必须考虑到船上的实际运行情况。例如,起重绞车和起重机有时会将电力反馈回供电网络。在轻载条件下,如果它的时间延迟设置太短,则这种再生反馈可能导致发电机逆功率时跳闸。

8.7 Cables 电缆

Apart from an IR (megger) test on a main cable run (e. g. along the flying bridge of a tanker) the survey of cables and their installation is largely based on a close visual examination. Inspection would search for any external damage of a cable's outer sheath and wire or basket weave armouring (if fitted). The cable must, of course, be adequately supported along horizontal and vertical runs by suitable cable clips or ties.

除了对主电缆(例如沿着加油机的飞桥)进行绝缘测试外,电缆的测量和安装在很大程度上基于近距离的视觉检查。视觉检查将检查电缆的外护套和钢丝或篮织铠装(如果安装)的任何外部损伤。当然,电缆必须由合适的电缆夹或扎带在水平和垂直方向上充分支撑。

Where cable-runs along an open deck have expansion loops, these must be examined for abrasion and wear. Where cables pass though fire check bulkheads they must be correctly glanded or pass through stopper boxes which prevent the passage of fire between compartments.

如果沿露天甲板敷设的电缆具有膨胀伸缩弯头,则必须检查其磨损情况。当穿过防火检查舱壁时,电缆必须正确密封或穿过阻挡盒,以防止舱室之间形成火焰通路。

Probably the most common ship-board cable insulations used are ethylene propylene rubber (EPR) or butyl rubber which is sheathed with either polychloroprene(PCP) or chlorosulphonated polyethelene(CSP).

最常用的船用电缆绝缘材料可能是乙丙橡胶(EPR)或丁基橡胶,其护套为氯丁橡胶(PCP)或氯磺化聚乙烯(CSP)。

Question 思考题

What are the functions of EPR or butyl and PCP or CSP?

乙丙橡胶、丁基橡胶、氯丁橡胶、氯磺化聚乙烯的作用是什么?

Answer 答案

EPR or butyl rubber are good electrical insulators but are not mechanically strong or resistant to oil. This is why a sheath of PCP or CSP (which is stronger and has greater oil and fire resistance) is fitted around the inner insulation.

乙丙橡胶或丁基橡胶是良好的电气绝缘体,但机械强度或耐油性较差。这就是为什么在内部绝缘周围安装氯丁橡胶或氯磺化聚乙烯(强度更高,耐油性和耐火性更强)护套的原因。

Where EPR/butyl cable terminations may be subjected to oil vapour it is usual to tape or sleeve the cable ends to prevent deterioration of the insulation. Check that such taping is secure.

当乙丙橡胶/丁基橡胶电缆端子可能会受到油蒸气的影响时,通常用胶带或套管将电缆端子包裹,以防止绝缘恶化。应检查这种包裹是否可靠。

Flexible cables to light fittings, power tools, etc., should be inspected for mechanical damage. In normal operation a flexible cable may be repeatedly dragged and chafed so reducing its safety. If in doubt replace flexible cables.

灯具配件、电动工具等的软性电缆,应检查其是否有机械损坏。在正常运行中,软性电缆可能会被反复拖曳和摩擦,从而降低其安全性。如不确定是否损坏,请更换软性电缆。

A copper strap or flexible earthing braid/wire is used to bond the steel frame of all electrical motors and other equipment to the ship's hull.

一根铜带或柔性接地编织线/电线被用来将所有电动机和其他设备的钢制框架连接到船体上。

Question 思考题

Why is such an earth bonding required?

为什么需要这样的接地连接?

Answer 答案

Without an earth strap, a loose internal wire may touch the frame causing it to become live at mains voltage with obvious danger to operators. The earth strap electrically anchors the frame to the ship's hull (0 V) to eliminate the shock hazard to personnel.

如果没有接地母线,松动的内部导线可能会接触机架,导致机架在主电源电压下带电,这明显会对操作员造成危险。接地母线将框架以电气方式固定在船体上(0 V),以消除人员的触电风险。

8.8 Insulation Resistance 绝缘电阻

The surveyor will require a list which shows the results of recent insulation tests on all main 440 V and 220 V circuits.

船舶检验人员会要求提供一份清单,其中包含所有 440 V 和 220 V 主电路最近的绝缘测试结果。

Such a list should also indicate the test date's, weather conditions (hot, humid, etc.) together with any comments relevant to the test conditions (e.g. machine hot or cold).

该清单还应注明测试日期、天气条件(炎热、潮湿等)以及与测试条件相关的任何备注(如机器是热态或冷态)。

For essential items such as generators and main motors, the surveyor will be more interested in the IR trend, so a set of past results showing the insulation history of such machines may be requested.

对于发电机和主要电动机等重要设备,船检将对绝缘趋势图更感兴趣,因此可能需要一组显示此类设备绝缘的历史记录。

8.9 Motors and Starters 电动机和启动器

After checking through the IR test results list, a surveyor may ask to witness a repeat test on selected motors. A visual examination of a motor frame and terminal box will reveal any damaged or missing parts. General neglect will be suspected if the motor is covered with dirt, oil or rust.

在对绝缘测试结果清单进行检查后,船舶检验人员可要求见证对指定的电动机重复进行绝缘测试。对电动机机架和接线盒进行目视检查可发现任何损坏或缺失的零件。如果电动机上覆盖有污垢、油液或铁锈,则船舶检验人员会怀疑存在管理不善。

Totally enclosed fan ventilated (TEFV) induction motors require little attention as their windings are protected against the external atmosphere. The surveyor will be more likely to concentrate on motors with drip proof, weatherproof and deck-watertight enclosures. It may be necessary to open up such motors to check for ingress of oil and water which could damage insulation and cause internal corrosion.

全封闭风机(TEFV)的感应电动机不需要特别关注,因为它们的绕组受到保护,与外部大气隔绝。船舶检验人员可能更关注具有防滴漏、防风雨和甲板防水外壳的电动机。可能需要打开此类电动机,以检查是否有可能损坏绝缘并导致内部腐蚀的油和水进入。

Special machines such as d. c. commutator or a. c. slip-ring types used, for example, on an electric windlass, must have their rotary contacts and brush gear checked.

如电动起锚机上使用的直流换向器或交流滑环等特殊装置,必须检查其旋转触点和电刷装置。

Cargo cranes and winches are not strictly part of a survey as they are not considered essential to the safety of the ship.

货物克令吊和绞车严格来说不是检验的一部分,因为它们不是保障船舶安全必不可少的设备。

A running test on a motor will reveal any vibration problems, undue noise and worn out bearings. On-load, the motor running current (shown on the ammeter at the starter) should be checked against the value indicated on the motor rating plate.

对电动机进行运转测试将发现振动问题、过度噪声和轴承磨损。带负载时,应对照电动机铭牌上指示的额定值检查电动机运行电流(显示在启动机的电流表上)。

With starters and associated control gear such as remote stop/start buttons, regulating resistors etc., an inspection will check mainly for badly burned and misaligned contacts. The general condition of starter equipment will also be examined. This would include an inspection for loose connections, worn pigtails on moving contacts, badly carbonised arc-chutes and signs of overheating on coils, transformers and resistors. Dust and weather-proof sealing features on a starter must be in place and in a serviceable condition.

对于启动器和相关控制装置,如远程停止/启动按钮、调节电阻器等,将主要检查触点是否严重烧坏和错位,还将检查启动器设备的一般状况。这包括检查松动的连接、动触点上磨损的引线、严重碳化的灭弧罩以及线圈、变压器和电阻器上的过热迹象。启动器上的防尘和防风雨密封装置必须就位并处于可用状态。

Functional checks will test the normal operation of the starter from its local, remote and emergency control (if applicable) positions. Signal status lamps showing the motor/starter condition, e. g. running, off, tripped, etc., must be demonstrated as working correctly. Overcurrent trip settings should be compared with the motor FLC rating. Motor starter back-up fuse size and type may be checked against the ship's manufacturer's drawings and the motor rating.

功能检查将从本地、远程和紧急控制(如适用)位置测试启动器的正常运行。信号状态指示灯显示电动机/启动器的状态,如运行、关闭、跳闸等,必须演示其正常工作过程。过电流跳闸设置应与电动机满载电流额定值进行比较。可根据船舶制造商图纸和电动机额定值检查电动机启动器备用保险丝的尺寸和类型。

8.10 Emergency Power and Associated Equipment 应急电源及相关设备

This section surveys the operation of the emergency generator and/or battery power equipment (inspection of the emergency generator itself is covered under the heading of Generators and Governors).

本节检验应急发电机和/或蓄电池电源设备的运行情况(对应急发电机本身的检查在发电机和调速器章节)。

The emergency generator must be started, manually or automatically, while the initiation sequence and operation of starting equipment is observed.

应急发电机必须能手动或自动启动,同时观察启动设备的启动顺序和运行情况。

Electrical supplies taken from the emergency switchboard should be checked as receiving their rated voltage, current and frequency when powered from the emergency generator.

当从应急发电机供电时,应检查应急配电板是否接收了其额定电压、电流和频率的供电。

Emergency lighting, fire pump and other emergency electrical equipment must be functioning correctly. Electrical interlocking arrangements between main and emergency switchboard must be checked. Auto-start initiation relays, whether voltage or frequency operated, will be examined and tested.

应急照明、消防泵和其他应急电气设备必须正常工作。必须检查主配电板和应急配电板之间的电气联锁装置。检查和测试自动启动继电器,无论是电压控制的还是频率控制的。

The ship's emergency battery installation and its charging rectifier will be examined. In particular the battery environment must be dry and well ventilated. The battery tops must be clean with terminal posts and connections appearing free from corrosion.

对船舶应急蓄电池装置及其充电整流器进行检查。特别是电池环境必须干燥、通风良好。电池顶部应清洁,端子和连接处应无锈蚀。

Grease all connections with petroleum jelly. Battery electrolyte should be at its proper level and have the correct value of specific gravity (SG) as checked on a hydrometer. Safety notices and personnel safety clothes (gloves, apron and goggles) should be available adjacent to the batteries. The ventilation arrangements for the battery locker will be checked.

所有连接处涂上凡士林油。电池电解液应处于适当的液位,并用比重计检查其比重值,应正常。电池旁边应备有安全告示和人员安全服(手套、围裙和护目镜)。检查电池间的通风布置。

Battery charging equipment should be given the normal checks for dirt, overheating, loose connections and correct functioning of indicators, instruments and alarms.

应检查蓄电池充电设备是否有污垢、过热、连接松动以及指示灯、仪表和报警器是否能正常工作。

8.11 Parts of Steering Gear 舵机部件

An electrohydraulic steering gear system can be envisaged from the surveyor's viewpoint as being in three parts: Power unit, Steering control, Indications and alarms.

从船检的角度可将电液舵机系统分为三个部分:电源装置、转向控制和指示警报。

The power unit comprises duplicate electric motors and starters supplied from either side of the main switchboard.

电源装置包括从主配电板任一侧供电的双电动机和启动器。

On many ships one of the steering gear motors will be supplied via the emergency switchboard as recommended by the SOLAS requirements for certain vessel types, e. g. passenger ships and ferries.

在许多船舶上,根据 SOLAS 对某些船舶类型(如客船和渡轮)的要求,只是一台舵机电动机应由应急配电板供电。

The motors, starters and any changeover supply switch units will be inspected under the same criteria outlined earlier in the section on "Motors and Starters".

其电动机、启动器和任何电源转换开关装置将按照前面"电动机和启动器"一节中概述的相同标准进行检查。

Rudder control from the bridge position may be via an hydraulic telemotor or via an electric controller or both. Main and alternative electric supplies, including any changeover facilities for the electric control from the steering wheel and for the auto pilot, must be tested.

驾驶台位置的舵角控制可通过液压遥控马达或电子控制器或两者共同实现。必须对用于手动舵和自动舵的电气控制的任何转换设施的主电源和备用电源进行测试。

The steering gear and its control must be functionally tested for its response. This is generally specified to be that the rudder must be swung from 32° port to 32° starboard in 28 s. Note, a fully loaded response can only be obtained when the ship is loaded and under way at sea. Steering gear status indications must be operating correctly in the steering flat, main control room, on the bridge. The rudder position indicator on the bridge may be checked during the functional testing of the steering gear. The bridge indication should be compared with the direct mechanical indicator on the rudder stock in the steering flat.

必须对舵机及其控制装置的响应进行功能测试。这通常是指,舵必须在 28 s 内从 30°左舷转向 35°右舷。注意,满载响应只能在船舶装载并在海上航行时获得。舵机状态指示必须在舵机平台、主控制室、驾驶台上正确工作。在进行舵机功能试验时,可检查驾驶台上的舵角指示器。驾驶台指示应与转舵平台舵杆上的直接机械指示对比。

Motor overload alarms can be initiated by simulating the action of the overload relay. Remember that a steering gear motor does not have overload trip protection; the only main circuit protection being from the back-up fuses which are essential for short-circuit protection. Hydraulic fluid low level alarms, if fitted, must be checked for correct initiation by the oil level sensors.

可通过模拟过载继电器的动作来启动电动机的过载报警。记住,舵机电动机没有过载跳闸保护;唯一的主电路保护来自备用熔断器,这对于短路保护至关重要。液压油低液位警报(如已安装),必须通过油位传感器检查低液位报警是否正能确启动。

8.12 Navigation Light Indicators 航行灯指示器

Essentially, the surveyor will expect to prove that the navigation light indicator operates correctly and gives the appropriate alarms. A broken wire or lamp can be simulated by pulling the appropriate fuse.

基本上船舶检验人员都会希望验证航行灯指示器工作正常,并能发出适当的警报。通过拔出适当的熔断器,可以模拟电线或灯丝断路。

The power supply for the navigation lights must be duplicated (usually the alternative supply is obtained from the emergency switchboard) and the changeover facilities must be checked.

航行灯的电源必须有两路供电(通常备用电源从应急配电板获得),电源转换设施也必须检查。

Although the actual light fittings for navigation are part of the safety equipment survey, the electrical survey will include a check on the supply cables to the lights.

虽然实际的航行灯具是安全设备检验的一部分,但电气检验包括检查航行灯具的供电电缆。

8.13 UMS Operation 无人机舱操作

If your ship is classified for UMS operation, the electrical survey will be extended to include all the alarms, fire detection, controls and fail-safe features of such an installation.

如果你的船属于无人机舱船舶,电气检验内容将扩展到包括所有警报、火灾探测以及此类装置的控制和故障安全功能。

All alarms associated with the main engine, auxiliary machines, lubrication and cooling are to be tested for correct operation. Testing of the electrical circuits from the various sensors is relatively straightforward. This can be achieved by operating the sensor switch by hand or by simulating the switch action under the expected alarm condition. To prove that the overall sensor (pressurestat, flow switch, level switch, temperature switch, etc.) is functioning correctly is obviously more involved. Often, specialist contractors may be called upon to service and calibrate the sensors and alarm annunciators.

所有与主机、辅机、润滑和冷却有关的警报都要进行测试以确保能工作正常。对各种传感器的电路进行试验的方法相对简单。这可以通过手动操作传感器开关动作或模拟预设报警条件使开关动作来实现。证明所有传感器(压力开关、流量开关、液位开关、温度开关等)的正常工作状态显然更为重要。通常,可能会请专业承包商来维修和校准传感器和报警器。

Particular attention will be paid to the main engine and auxiliary generators in respect of their alarms for lubrication and cooling. Initiation and action of automatic shut-down features will be tested. Essential drives for lubrication, cooling and fuel supply are duplicated and arranged so that one pump can be selected on a duty/standby basis. Loss of pressure at the duty pump should automatically start up the standby unit.

会特别注意主机和辅机润滑及冷却的相关警报。会试验自动停机功能的启动和执行。润滑、冷却和燃料供应的基本驱动器是双套设备,这样就可以在运行/备用的基础上选择一个泵的工作状态。当运行泵失去压力时,备用泵应自动启动。

Automatic start-up of the emergency generator must be demonstrated. The emergency generator should run up to speed and supply voltage to the emergency switchboard. The initiation of the undervoltage or under-frequency relay can usually be accomplished by pulling the fuses in the detection unit.

应急发电机的自动启动必须演示。然后,应急发电机应达到额定转速并向应急配电板供电。欠压或欠频率继电器的动作通常可以通过拉动探测单元中的保险丝来实现。

UMS requirements demand that a standby main generator starts automatically on loss of the duty generator. The standby generator is to start and close onto the dead bus-bars within 45 s.

无人机舱的功能要求备用主发电机在运行主发电机失电时能自动启动。备用发电机将在45 s内启动并合闸向失电母线供电。

This is followed by automatic sequential re-starting of essential auxiliaries for lubrication, cooling, fuel and steering. The correct functioning of the system will be tested. The duplicate bilge level alarms together with automatic bilge pumping must be proven to the surveyor's satisfaction.

随后,润滑、冷却、燃油和舵机等重要辅助设备将自动顺序启动。系统的这个功能也会试验。必须向船舶检验人员证明双重的舱底液位警报以及自动舱底泵送符合要求。

The main and standby electric power supplies to the overall alarm monitoring system must be inspected and tested. The standby power arrangement usually includes battery back-up. It will be necessary to inspect the general condition of the battery and its trickle-charger.

必须检查和测试整个报警监控系统的主电源和备用电源。备用电源配置通常包括备用电池。有必要检查蓄电池及其涓流充电器的一般状况。

Tests are made on the UMS alarm system to verify:

(1)That alarms displayed on the main console in the engine control room are relayed to the smaller group alarm panel on the bridge.

(2)That the duty engineer call system is operating in the accommodation areas, i. e. in the cabin of the selected duty engineer and in the duty mess and lounges.

(3)That the selected duty engineer is allowed 2-3 min to respond to a machinery alarm. If the engineer has not reached the control room and acknowledged the alarm within this time, a engineer call alarm should be sounded generally in the alleyway adjacent to the engineers' accommodation.

对无人机舱报警系统进行试验以验证：

(1)在集控室的主控制台上显示的警报被传送到驾驶台上较小的组报警面板上。

(2)值班轮机员呼叫系统在生活区运行，即在选定值班轮机员的房间以及值班餐厅和休息室中运行。

(3)指定值班轮机员有 2~3 min 的时间对设备警报做出反应。如果值班轮机员未在这段时间内到达控制室并确认警报，通常应在轮机员住所附近的过道中发出失职警报。

A complete inspection and test of the fire detection apparatus must be performed. All smoke, heat and flame sensors must function correctly to initiate the appropriate audible and visual alarms on the bridge, in the main control room and in the accommodation. Hand operated fire-alarm switches of the break-glass type (Fig. 8. 2) must also be examined and tested to be in proper working order.

必须对火灾探测装置进行全面的检查和测试。所有感烟式、感温式火焰传感器必须正常工作，并在驾驶台、集控室和生活区启动适当的声光警报。必须检查和测试破碎玻璃型的手动火灾报警(图 8. 2)，以确定其处于正常工作状态。

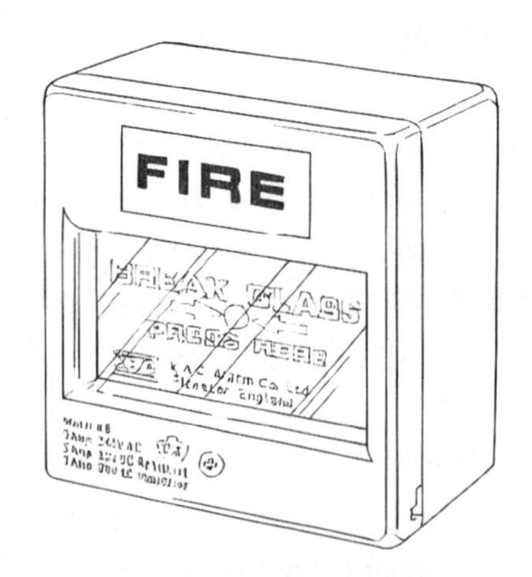

Fig. 8. 2 Break-glass switch

图 8. 2 玻璃开关

Main engine controls must function correctly and will be tested from the bridge position, engine control room and at the emergencycontrol alongside the engine. The operational features of the electrical equipment for main engine control and indication will be best demonstrated during a full engine test during an engine survey. Such electrical equipment and connections associated with engine control will be examined as usual for wear and tear, insulation level, cleanliness, loose connections and overheating.

主机的控制功能必须正常，并将在驾驶台控制位置、集控室控制位置和机旁紧急控制位置进行试验。主机控制和指示相关的电气设备运行功能将在主机全功能试验的检验期间得到良好的演示。要像往常一样检查与主机控制相关的电气设备和连接的磨损、绝缘等级、清洁度、连接松动和过热情况。

8.14　Tankers 油轮

Electrical equipment in the hazardous areas of oil/gas carriers and other ships carrying potentially dangerous cargo will be surveyed during the normal engine survey (every four years) and during docking and annual surveys. Consequently, the hazardous area electrical equipment is effectively surveyed every year.

石油/天然气运输船和其他运载有潜在危险货物的船舶的危险区域电气设备,将在正常的机舱检验(每四年一次)、船坞和年度检验期间进行检验。因此,每年要对危险区域的电气设备进行有效的检验。

The most common form of hazardous area electrical equipment is the flameproof enclosure type (marked Exd on the equipment certification label). This type of enclosure will be found on light fittings, motors, starters, push-buttons and alarm bells within the hazardous zones.

危险区域电气设备最常见的形式是具有隔爆型外壳(在设备认证标签上标注 Exd)。危险区域内的灯具配件、电动机、启动器、按钮和警铃上会采用这种类型的外壳。

The flameproof enclosure will be inspected for surface cleanliness (which affects the surface temperature), corrosion and secure mountings. On lighting fittings the support that bonds the lamp glass to its frame must be closely inspected for cracks. All bolts must be in place, evenly torqued-up and of the correct type.

应检查隔爆外壳的表面清洁度(影响表面温度)、腐蚀和安装是否牢固。在照明灯具上,必须仔细检查将灯罩固定在其框架上的支架是否有裂缝。所有螺栓必须安装到位,均匀拧紧,类型正确。

The edges of flame path flanged joints must not be painted over or impeded in any way. Exposed flameproof equipment on deck must be adjudged weatherproof with the correct (approved) gaskets or "O" rings in place.

火焰通路法兰接头的边缘不得以任何方式涂漆或受到阻碍。甲板上的外露隔爆设备必须采用正确的(经认证的)垫圈或 O 形圈进行防风雨处理。

An Exd fitting may be opened up to check the condition of its flamepath surfaces for corrosion, pitting or scratch marks.

可以打开隔爆型配件,检查其火焰通路表面是否有腐蚀、点蚀或划痕。

The Ex certification label and equipment rating label must not be painted over.

隔爆认证标签和设备等级标签不得涂刷。

Remember that no alterations to the Exd equipment are allowed without permission from the certification authority. This applies also to the lamp size and its rating for a particular light fitting — it must have the correct lamp fitted.

请记住,未经认证机构许可,不允许对隔爆设备进行任何改动。这一要求也适用于特定灯具的尺寸及其额定值——必须安装正确的灯泡。

Some pump rooms have pressurised light fittings (marked Exp on the certification label). Here it is necessary to confirm that the fittings are purged and pressurised before the light is allowed to be switched on. Similarly the lights should automatically be switched off if the air pressure drops below its set value.

一些泵房配有加压照明装置(认证标签上标有 Exp)。在允许开灯之前,有必要确认灯具已吹扫和加压。同样,如果空气压力降至设定值以下,灯应自动关闭。

Electrical instrumentation and communication equipment used in hazardous areas must be intrinsically safe (marked Exi on the certification label). In most cases, zener barriers, as shown in Fig. 8. 13, are connected in line with intrinsically safe circuits and are fitted in a safe area just outside the hazardous area.

用于危险区域的电气仪表和通信设备必须是本安型(在认证标签上标记 Exi)的。在大多数情况下,齐纳栅与本安型电路连接,并安装在危险区域外的安全区域内。

The surveyor cannot easily test zener barriers in situ as this would involve special equipment and it is generally accepted that such protection equipment will function correctly when circuit fault conditions arise. This is no different to accepting that a fuse will blow when a short-circuit occurs.

齐纳栅不易在现场进行测试,因为这将涉及特殊设备,并且一般认为,当出现电路故障时,此类保护设备应能正常工作。这与发生短路时保险丝会熔断没有不同。

However, the surveyor will visually inspect the zener barrier installation. The barriers must have secure connections and be properly bolted to an earth strap, which in turn, must be solidly bonded to the ship's hull.

然而,船检会通过视觉检查齐纳栅的安装情况。齐纳栅必须有可靠的连接,并用螺栓固定在接地编织带上,接地编织带必须牢固地连接到船体上。

Chapter 9 Electric Propulsion and High Voltage System
第9章 电力推进和高压电力系统

9.0 Introduction 介绍

The earliest electric propulsion for ships was demonstrated in Russia in 1832 with a DC. motor powered from a battery. In 1886 an electrically propelled vessel called the Volta crossed the English Channel. By 1888 the improvements to batteries and motors led to the first commercial applications in passenger launches on the River Thames in London. As with road transport, electric river boats were soon eclipsed by the arrival of the internal combustion engine.

1832年,俄罗斯展示了最早的船舶电力推进系统,其直流电动机由电池供电。1886年,一艘名为"沃尔特号"的电动船只横渡英吉利海峡。到1888年,电池和电动机的改进使得伦敦泰晤士河上的客轮首次将它们商业化应用。与公路运输一样,内燃发动机的到来很快使电动内河船黯然失色。

Electric propulsion for many new ships is now re-established as the popular choice where the motor thrust is governed by electronic switching under computer control.

现在许多新船舶又将电力推进作为一种流行的选择,其中电动机推力由计算机控制下的电子开关进行调节。

The high power required for electric propulsion usually demands a HV power plant with its associated safety and testing procedures.

电力推进所需的高功率通常需要高压电站及其相关的安全和测试程序。

9.1 Electric Propulsion Scheme 电力推进方案

Electric propulsion of ships has a long but somewhat chequered history. There have been periods when it has enjoyed popularity, with a significant number of installations being undertaken, whilst at other times it has been virtually ignored as a drive system.

船舶使用电力推进的历史很长,但有些曲折。有一段时间,它很受欢迎,并大量在船上安装,而在这段时间以外,对驱动系统的选择几乎都忽略了它。

Passenger ships have always been the largest commercial vessels with electric propulsion and, by their nature, the most glamorous. This should not, however, obscure the fact that a very wide variety of vessels have been, and are, built with electric propulsion. Early large passenger vessels employed the turboelectric system which involves the use of variable speed, and therefore variable frequency, turbo-generator sets for the supply of electric power to the propulsion motors directly coupled to the propeller shafts. Hence, the generator-motor system was acting as a speed reducing transmission system. Electric power for auxiliary ship services required the use of separate constant frequency generator sets.

客船一直以来都是最大的电力推进商业船舶,由于其特殊性才使用电力推进的。然而,这不应掩盖这样一个事实,即无论过去还是现在都有各种各样的船舶选择电力推进。早期的大型客船采用涡轮发电系统,该系统使用变速、变频涡轮发电机组为直接与螺旋桨轴连接的推进电动机供电。因此,发电机-电动机系统充当减速传动系统。船舶辅助设备的电力需要使用单独的恒频发电机组。

A system that has generating sets which can be used to provide power to both the propulsion system and ship services has obvious advantages, but this would have to be a fixed voltage and frequency system to satisfy the requirements of the ship service loads. The provision of high power variable speed drives from a fixed voltage and frequency supply has always presented problems. Also, when the required propulsion power was beyond the capacity of a single DC. motor there was the complication of multiple motors per shaft.

具有可用于向推进系统和船舶服务设施提供电力的发电机组系统具有明显的优势,但其必须是一个恒压和恒频系统,以满足船舶服务设施负荷的要求。通过恒压和恒频电源提供高功率变速驱动器一直存在问题。此外,当所需的推进功率超过单个直流电动机的容量时,每个轴上会出现需要多个直流电动机驱动的复杂情况。

Developments in high power static converter equipment have presented a very convenient means of providing variable speed AC and DC drives at the largest ratings likely to be required in a marine propulsion system.

大功率静态变频器设备的发展更便于船舶推进系统的交流和直流变速驱动器以最大额定值工作实现。

The electric propulsion of ships requires electric motors to drive the propellers and generator sets to supply the electric power. It may seem rather illogical to use electric generators, switchgear and motors between the prime-movers (e. g. diesel engines) and propeller when a gearbox or length of shaft could be all that is required.

船舶的电力推进系统需要电动机驱动螺旋桨,同时需要发电机组提供电力。在原动机(如柴油发动机)和螺旋桨之间增设发电机、开关设备和电动机似乎不合逻辑,因为需要考虑增设齿轮箱或轴的长度。

There are obviously sound reasons why, for some installations, it is possible to justify the complication of electric propulsion and some of the reasons advanced are:

(1) Flexibility of layout;

(2) Load diversity between ship service load and propulsion;

(3) Economical part-load;

(4) Ease of control;

(5) Low noise and vibration characteristics.

显然,对于某些装置而言,有充分的理由可以证明电力推进的复杂性是合理的,其中一些有优势的理由是:

(1)布局的灵活性;

(2)船舶服务负荷和推进负荷之间的分配性;

(3)部分负荷的经济性;

(4)控制的简易性;

(5)噪声低和振动小的特性。

The advantage of an electric transmission is that the prime-movers, and their generators, are not constrained to have any particular relationship with the load as a cable run is a very versatile transmission medium. In a ship propulsion system it is possible to mount the diesel engines, gas turbines etc., in locations best suited for them and their associated services, so they can be remote from the propeller shaft. Diesel generator sets in containers located on the vessel main deck have been used to provide propulsion power and some other vessels have had a 10 MW generator for ship propulsion duty mounted in a block at the stern of the vessel above the ro-ro deck. An example of an electric propulsion plant layout (for a large cruise ship) is shown in Fig. 9.1.

电力传输的优点是,由于电缆线路是一种非常通用的传输介质,因此原动机及其发电机与负载的位置关系不受限制。在船舶推进系统中,可以将柴油机、燃气轮机等安装在最适合它们及其相关服务装置的位置,以便它们可以远离传动轴。位于船舶主甲板上的集装箱中的柴油发电机组用于提供推进动力,其他一些船舶的滚装船甲板上方的船尾安装了一台 10 MW 的船舶推进系统发电机。图 9.1 所示为电力推进装置布局示例(适用于大型游轮)。

Another example of the flexibility provided by an electric propulsion system is in a semi-submersible, with the generators on the main deck and the propulsion motors in the pontoons at the bottom of the support legs.

电力推进系统灵活性的另一个例子是半潜式平台,在该平台中发电机位于主甲板上,推进电动机位于支撑腿底部的浮筒中。

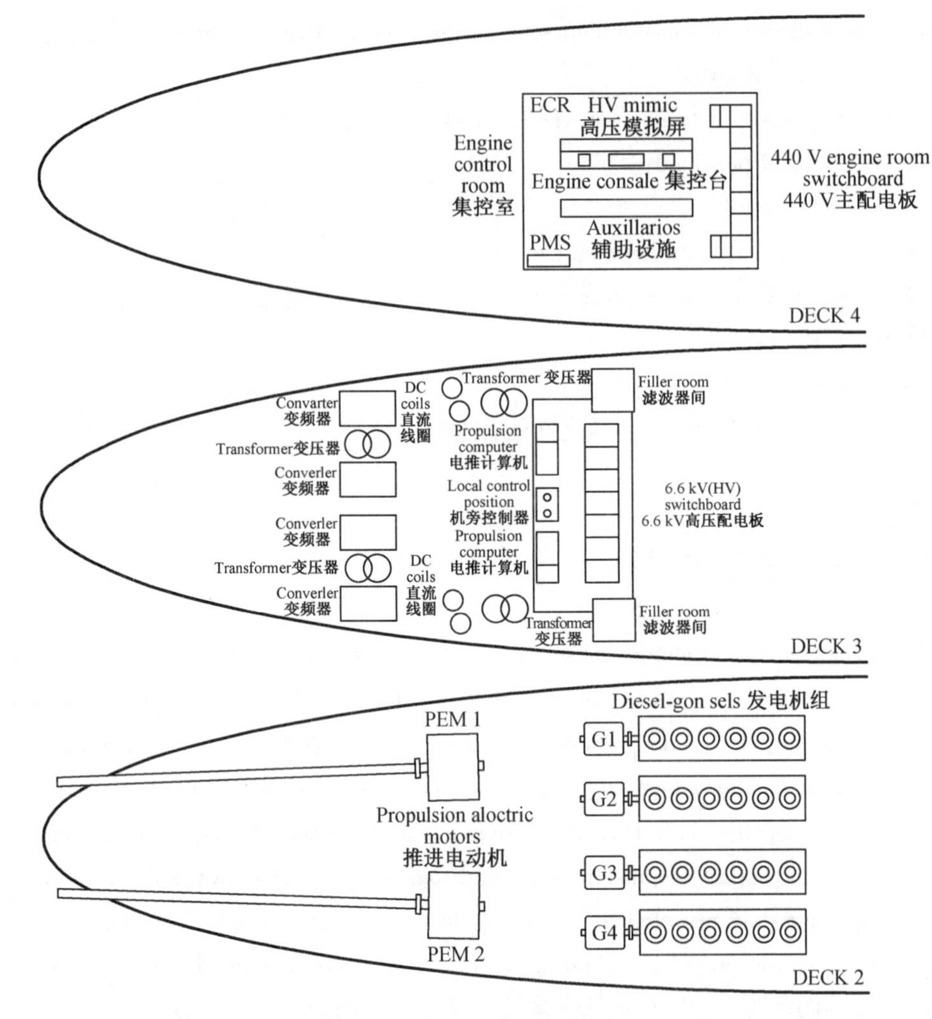

Fig. 9.1 Propulsion plant layout

图 9.1 推进装置布局

1. Load Diversity 负荷的分配性

Certain types of vessels have a requirement for substantial amounts of electric power for ship services when the demands of the propulsion system are low. Tankers are one instance of this situation and any vessel with a substantial cargo discharging load also qualifies. Passenger vessels have a substantial electrical load which, although relatively constant, does involve a significant size of generator plant. There are advantages in having a single central power generation facility which can service the propulsion and all other ship loads as required.

某些类型的船舶推进系统对功率需求较低,而需要大量的电力来供应船舶服务设施。油轮是这种情况,任何有大量货物要卸载的船只也符合这种情况。客船的电力负荷大,虽然负荷波动相对稳定,但需要容量大的发电站。有单独的中央发电设施是有优势的,它可以满足推进装置和所有其他船舶负载需要的负荷。

2. Economical Part-load Running 部分负荷运行的经济性

Again this is a concept that is best achieved when there is a central power generation system feeding propulsion and ship services, with passenger vessels being a good example.

同样,有一个为推进和船舶服务设施供电的中央发电系统,是实现以上要求的方式,客船就是一个很好的例子。

It is likely that a typical installation would have between 4-8 diesel generator sets and with parallel operation of all the sets it becomes very easy to match the available generating capacity to the load demand. In a 4 engine installation for example, increasing the number of sets in operation from 2 that are fully loaded to 3 partially loaded will result in the 3 sets operating at a 67% load factor which is not ideal but also not a serious operating condition, It is not necessary to operate generating sets at part-load to provide the spare capacity to be able to cater for the sudden loss of a set, because propulsion load reduction may be available instantaneously, and in most vessels a short time reduction in propulsion power does not constitute a hazard.

一种典型电力推进装置可能有 4~8 台柴油发电机组,所有机组并联运行后,很容易使可用发电容量满足负载需求。例如,在 4 台发动机的安装中,将运行中的机组数量从 2 台满载增加到 3 台部分负载将导致 3 台机组以 67%的负载系数运行,这不是理想的,但也不是严重的问题,无须在部分负荷下运行发电机组,以提供备用容量,以应对机组的突然损失,因为推进负荷的降低可能是瞬间发生的,并且在大多数船舶上,推进功率的短时降低并不带来风险。

The propulsion regulator will continuously monitor the present generator capability and any generator overload will immediately result in controlled power limitation to the propulsion motors. During manoeuvring, propulsion power requirements are below system capacity and failure of one generator is not likely to present a hazardous situation.

推进调节器将持续监测当前发电机的能力,任何发电机过载将立即导致推进电动机受到可控的功率限制。在机动航行过程中,推进功率要求低于系统容量,一台发电机的故障不太可能导致危险情况。

3. Ease of Control 控制的简易性

The widespread use of controllable pitch propellers(CPP) has meant that the control facilities that were so readily available with electric drives are no longer able to command the same premium. Electric drives are capable of the most exacting demands with regard to dynamic performance which, in general, exceed by a very wide margin anything that is required of a ship propulsion system.

可变螺距螺旋桨(CPP)的广泛使用意味着电力驱动的控制设施不再能够获得同样的优势。电力驱动装置能够满足动态性能方面最严格的控制要求,一般来说,其动态性能远远超过船舶推进系统所需的其他性能。

4. Low Noise 低噪声

An electric motor is able to provide a drive with very low vibration character-istics and this is of importance in warships, oceanographic survey vessels and cruise ships where, for different reasons, a low noise signature is required. With warships and survey vessels it is noise into the water which is the critical factor whilst with cruise ships it is structure borne noise and vibration to the passenger spaces that has to be minimized.

电动机能够提供具有极低振动特性的驱动器,这对军舰、海洋调查船和游轮非常重要,因为不同的原因,需要低噪声信号。对于军舰和勘测船,进入水中的噪声是重要因素,而对于游轮,必须将乘客空间的结构噪声和振动降至最低。

An overview of practical electric drive options is shown in Fig. 9. 2.

图 9. 2 所示为实际电力推进方案的概览。

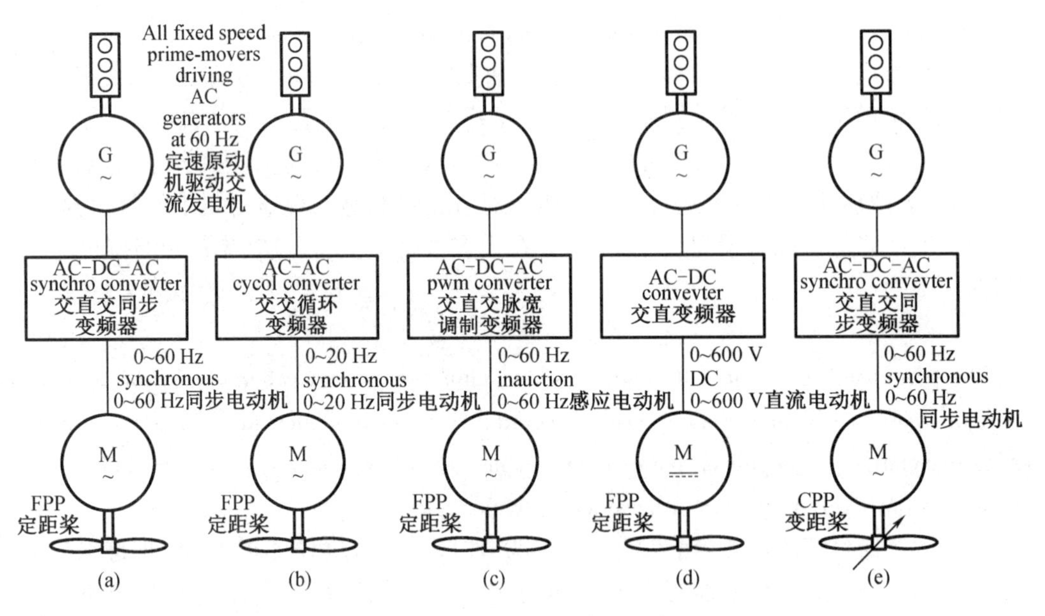

Fig. 9. 2　Electric propulsion options

图 9. 2　电力推进方案

For very high power, the most favoured option is to use a pair of high efficiency, high voltage AC synchronous motors with fixed pitch propellers (FPP) driven at variable speed by frequency control from electronic converters. A few installations have the combination of CPP and a variable speed motor. Low/medium power propulsion (1 - 5 MW) may be delivered by AC induction motors with variable frequency converters or by DC motors with variable voltage converters.

对于超高功率,最受欢迎的选择是使用一对高效、高压交流同步电机,带有固定螺距螺旋桨(FPP),通过电子变频器的频率控制实现变速驱动。一些装置结合了可变螺距螺旋桨和调速电动机。低/中功率推进装置(1~5 MW)可选择带变频器的交流感应电动机或带电压调节器的直流电动机。

The prime movers are conventionally constant speed diesel engines driving AC generators to give a fixed output frequency. Gas turbine driven prime movers for the generators are likely to challenge the diesel option in the future.

原动机通常为定速柴油发动机,用以驱动交流发电机,以提供固定的输出频率。用燃气轮机驱动原动机的发电机在未来可能会成为柴油发电机的竞争机型。

Conventionally, the propeller drive shaft is directly driven from the propulsion electric motor (PEM) from inside the ship. From experience obtained from smaller external drives, notably from ice-breakers, some very large propulsion motors are being fitted within rotating pods mounted outside of the ship's hull. These are generally referred to as azipods, as shown in Fig. 9.3, as the whole pod unit can be rotated through 360° to apply the thrust in any horizontal direction, i. e. in azimuth. This means that a conventional steering plate and stern side-thrusters are not required.

传统上,螺旋桨传动轴直接由船内的推进电动机(PEM)驱动。根据从小型外部驱动装置(尤其是破冰机)获得的经验,一些非常大的推进电动机安装在船体外部的旋转吊舱内。如图 9.3 所示,这些通常被称为 Azipod,因为整个吊舱单元可以旋转 360°以便在任何水平方向(即方位角)施加推力。这意味着不需要传统的转向盘和艉侧推。

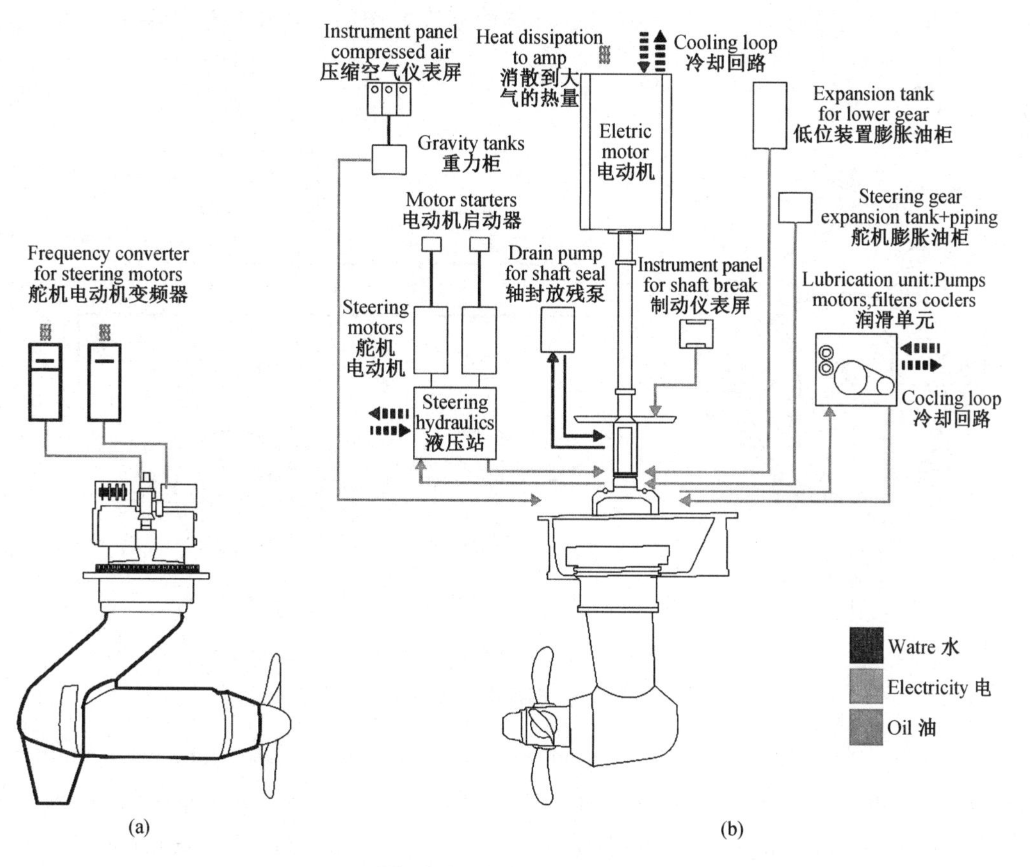

Fig. 9.3　Azipod drive unit

图 9.3　吊舱式驱动单元

Ship manoeuvrability is significantly enhanced by using azipods and the external propulsion unit releases some internal space for more cargo/passengers while further reducing hull vibration.

通过使用吊舱式驱动,船舶操纵性显著增强,船体外部推进装置为更多货物/乘客释放一些内部空间,同时还进一步降低了船体振动。

Gradual progress in the science and application of superconductivity suggests that future generators and motors could be super-cooled to extremely low temperatures to cause electrical resistance to become zero. In this condition, the electrical power losses (I^2R) are also zero so it is possible to drive extremely large currents (>100,000 A) through very thin wire coils to create an exceptionally large magnetic field. The combination of a large current and a large magnetic field will produce a very large electromagnetic force as $F \propto \Phi \cdot I$. One way of applying such a direct force into the water for ship propulsion (a long-term ongoing experiment in Japan) is outlined in Fig. 9. 4.

超导科学和应用的进展表明,未来的发电机和电动机可以被过冷到极低的温度,从而使其电阻变为零。在这种情况下,电功率损耗(I^2R)也为零,因此可以通过非常细的线圈驱动非常大的电流(>100 000 A),以产生非常大的磁场。由于 $F \propto \Phi \cdot I$,大电流在大磁场中将产生一个非常大的电磁力。图 9. 4 概述了将这种直接力作用于水中推进船舶的一种方法(日本正在进行长期试验)。

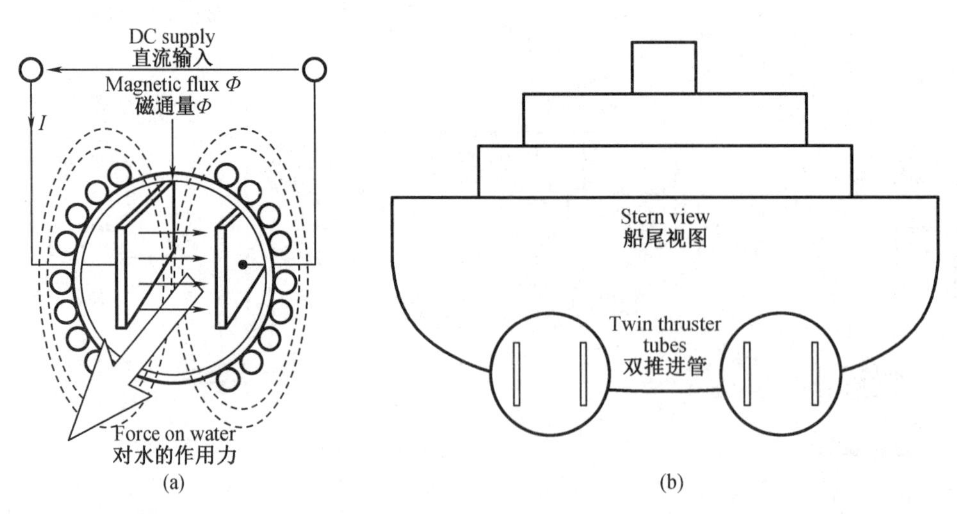

Fig. 9. 4 Linear electric propulsion

图 9. 4 线性电力推进

A large d. c. current is driven between metal plates mounted in a open tube below the hull. The conductor for this current is the sea water. Coils of wire at a superconducting temperature (e. g — 269 ℃ cooled by helium) are fitted around the propulsion tube to create a magnetic field 90° to the current flow. The combination of current and magnetic field produces a direct mechanical force on the conductor (water) to create a linear thrust without the need for a rotating propeller.

By dividing port and starboard thrust tubes into short sections along the hull, the size and location of thrust can be distributed so that conventional steering and side thrusters are not required. This is a very interesting experiment into the direct application of electromagnetic force for ship propulsion.

在安装在船体下方开口管中的金属板之间驱动较大的直流电流。这种电流的导体是海水。超导温度(例如,氦冷却至-269 ℃)下的线圈安装在推进管周围,以产生与电流成90°角的磁场。电流和磁场的结合在导体(水)上产生直接的机械力,从而产生线性推力,而无须旋转螺旋桨。通过沿船体将左舷和右舷推力管划分为短段,可以分配推力的大小和位置,从而不需要传统的转向和侧推。这是电磁力在船舶推进中直接应用的一个非常有趣的实验。

9.2 Marine High Voltage Power Supply Network 船舶高压供电网络

As the demand for electrical power increases on ships (particularly passenger ferries, cruise liners, and specialist offshore vessels and platforms) the supply current rating becomes too high at 440 V. To reduce the size of both steady state and fault current levels, it is necessary to increase the system voltage at high power ratings.

随着船舶(尤其是客运渡轮、邮轮和专业海上船舶及平台)对电力需求的增加,440 V 额定电压供电时电流变得过高。为了减小稳态和故障电流等级,有必要在高额定功率下增加系统电压。

Note: In marine practice, voltages below 1,000 V are considered LV. HV is any voltage above LV. Typical marine HV system voltages are 3.3 kV or 6.6 kV but 11 kV is used on some offshore platforms and specialist oil/gas production ships e.g. on some floating production, storage and offloading(FPSO) vessels.

注:在海上实践中,低于 1 000 V 的电压被视为低压。高压是高于低压(1 000 V)的任何电压。典型的海上高压系统电压为 3.3 kV 或 6.6 kV,但在一些海上平台和专业油气生产船上使用 11 kV,例如浮式生产储卸装置(FPSO)。

By generating electrical power at 6.6 kV instead of 440 V the distribution and switching of power above about 6 MW becomes more manageable.

通过用 6.6 kV 代替 440 V 的电压发电,使超过约 6 MW 的功率分配和切换变得更易于管理。

e.g. A three-phase 6 MW ships load on a 440 V system supplied by 3×2 MW, 0.8 power factor diesel-generator units requires the switchboard fault level to be about 90 kA and each generator circuit breaker and system cabling has to handle a FLC of:

$$I=2,000,000/\sqrt{3}\cdot 440\cdot\ 0.8=3,300\ \text{A}$$

例如：由 3 台 2 MW、功率因数为 0. 8 的柴油发电机组提供的 440 V 系统上的三相 6 MW 船舶负载要求配电板故障等级约为 90 kA，每个发电机断路器和系统电缆必须承受以下满负载电流：

$$I=2\ 000\ 000/\sqrt{3}\cdot 440\cdot\ 0.8=3\ 300\ \text{A}$$

The same system at 6. 6 kV requires the HV switchboard and cables to be rated for a fault level of about 9 kA with generator circuit breakers rated only for an FLC of 220 A.

6. 6 kV 的同一系统要求高压配电板和电缆的额定故障等级约为 9 kA，发电机断路器的额定故障水平仅为 220 A。

The component parts of an HV supply system are now standard equipment with HV diesel generator sets feeding an HV main switchboard. Large power consumers such as thrusters, propulsion motors, air-conditioning compressors (A/C) and HV transformers are fed directly from the HV switchboard.

高压供电系统的组成部分现在是标准设备，高压柴油发电机组向高压主配电板供电。大型用电设备，如推进器、推进电动机、空调压缩机(A/C)和高压变压器，直接由高压配电板供电。

An economical HV system must be simple to operate, reasonably priced and require a minimum of maintenance over the life of the ship. Experience shows that a 9 MW system at 6. 6 kV would be about 20% more expensive for installation costs. The principal parts of a ship's electrical system operated at HV would be the main generators, HV switchboard, HV cables, HV transformers and HV motors. An example of a high voltage power system is shown in Fig. 9. 5.

具有高性价比的高压电系统必须操作简单，价格合理，并且在船舶的整个寿命期内需要最少的维护。经验表明，6. 6 kV 的 9 MW 系统的安装成本将增加约 20%。在高压电下运行的船舶电气系统，其主要组成是主发电机、高压配电板、高压电缆、高压变压器和高压电动机。高压电力系统的示例如图 9. 5 所示。

In the example shown the HV generators form a central power station for all of the ship's electrical services, On a large passenger ship with electric propulsion, each generator may be rated at about 10 MW or more and producing 6. 6 kV, 60 Hz three-phase AC voltages.

在示例中，高压发电机构成船舶所有电气服务的中央电站，在配备电力推进装置的大型客船上，每台发电机的额定功率约为 10 MW 或以上，并发出 6. 6 kV、60 Hz 三相交流电压。

The principal consumers are the two synchronous AC propulsion electric motors (PEMs) which may each demand 12 MW or more in the full away condition. Each PEM has two stator windings supplied separately from the main HV switchboard via transformers and frequency converters. In an emergency a PEM may therefore be operated as a half-motor with a reduced power output.

主要用电设备为两台同步交流推进电动机(PEM),在全速下,每台电动机可能需要12 MW或更高的功率。每台电动机有两个定子绕组,分别通过变压器和变频器从主高压配电板供电,因此在紧急情况下,同步交流推进电动机可用一个绕组运行,功率输出降低。

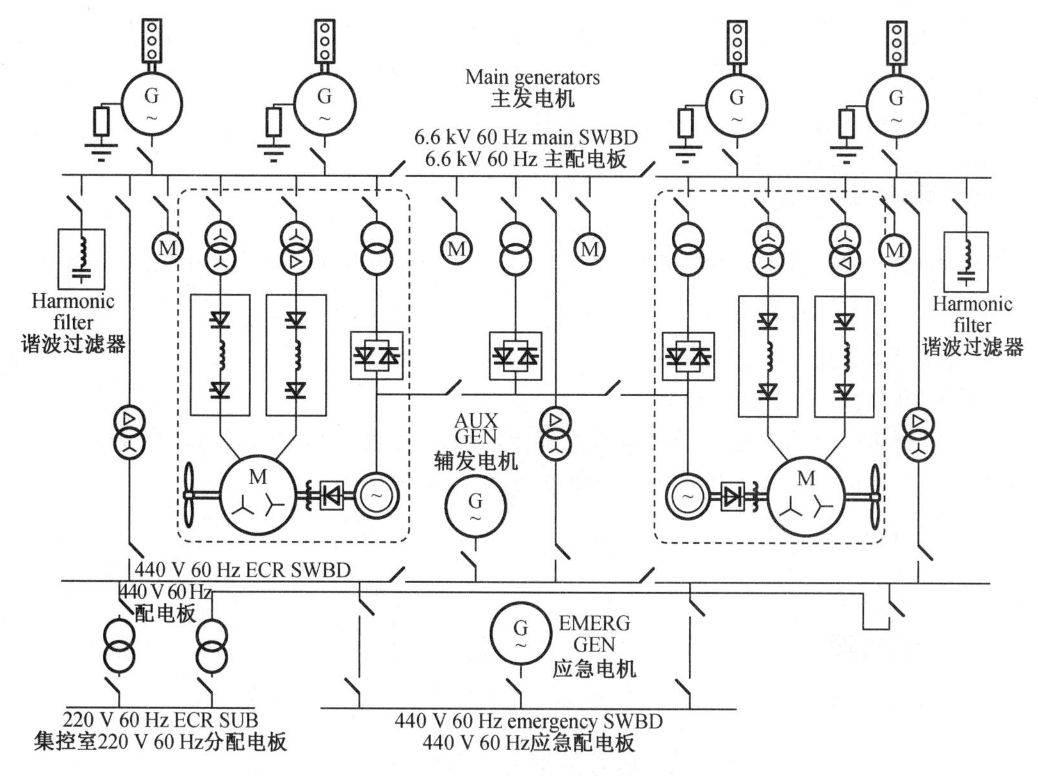

Fig. 9. 5 HV power system

图 9. 5 高压电力系统

A few large induction motors are supplied at 6. 6 kV from the mainswitch board with the circuit breaker acting as a direct-on-line (DOL) starting switch. These motors are: Two forward thrusters and one aft thruster, and three air conditioning compressors.

一些大型交流异步电动机从 6. 6 kV 主配电板直接供电,断路器作为直接启动方式的(DOL)启动开关。这些电动机是两台艏侧推器和一台艉侧推器,以及三台空调压缩机。

Other main feeders supply the 440 V engine room sub-station (ER sub) switchboard via step-down transformers. An interconnector cable links the ER sub to the emergency switchboard. Other 440 V substations (accommodation, galley etc.) around the ship are supplied from the ER sub. Some installations may feed the ships sub stations directly with HV and step-down to 440 V locally.

其他主馈线通过降压变压器向 440 V 机舱分站(ER sub)配电板供电。母联电缆将机舱分站连接至应急配电板。船舶的其他 440 V 分站(生活区、厨房等)由机舱分站供电。还有一些装置可由船舶高压电站直接供电,再就地降压至 440 V。

The PEM drives in this example are synchronous motors which require a controlled low voltage excitation supply current to magnetise the rotor poles. This supply is obtained from the HV switchboard via a step-down transformer but an alternative arrangement would be to obtain the excitation supply from the 440 V ER sub switchboard.

本例中的同步交流推进电动机驱动器为同步电动机,需要可控低压励磁电源提供电流来磁化转子磁极。高压配电板通过降压变压器向此电源供电,但另一种方式是从 440 V 机舱分站获得励磁电源。

Question 思考题

Assuming 100% efficiency, calculate the FLC then estimate the DOL starting current for a three-phase, 100 kW,0.9 power factor induction motor supplied at:

(a)440 V;

(b)6.6 kV.

假设电动机效率为 100%,计算满载电流,然后估算三相 100 kW、功率因数为 0.9 的交流异步电动机在以下条件下供电的直接启动电流,供电电压为:

(a)440 V;

(b)6.6 kV。

Answer 答案

(a)145.8 A,729 A;

(b)9.7 A,49 A [assuming $I_{DOL}=5I_{FLC}$(取 $I_{DOL}=5I_{FLC}$)]。

9.3 Review of Motor Operation 回顾电动机的运行特性

Electric motors for ship propulsion duty may be of the DC or AC type. The AC versions may be the induction or synchronous models. The following is a brief review of the basic action and control possibilities for the various types.

船舶推进电动机可为直流或交流型。交流型可以是异步式或同步式。以下是对不同类型电动机基本运行和控制状态的简要回顾。

9.3.1 DC Motors 直流电动机

The DC motor drive is still used where very high torque and/or precise speed control is acquired. Traction drives such as electric trains, submarines and offshore drilling rigs use DC motors. The torque is governed by: $T \propto \Phi \cdot I_A$ and the speed is due to: $n \propto V/\Phi$ where Φ is the magnetic field flux and I_A is the armature current. See Fig. 9. 6.

在需要进行大扭矩和/或精确调速时,仍采用直流电动机驱动。电力列车、潜艇和海上钻机等牵引驱动装置使用的就是直流电动机。转矩调节:$T \propto \Phi \cdot I_A$ 和转速调节 $n \propto V/\Phi$,其中 Φ 是磁通量,I_A 是电枢电流。如图 9. 6 所示。

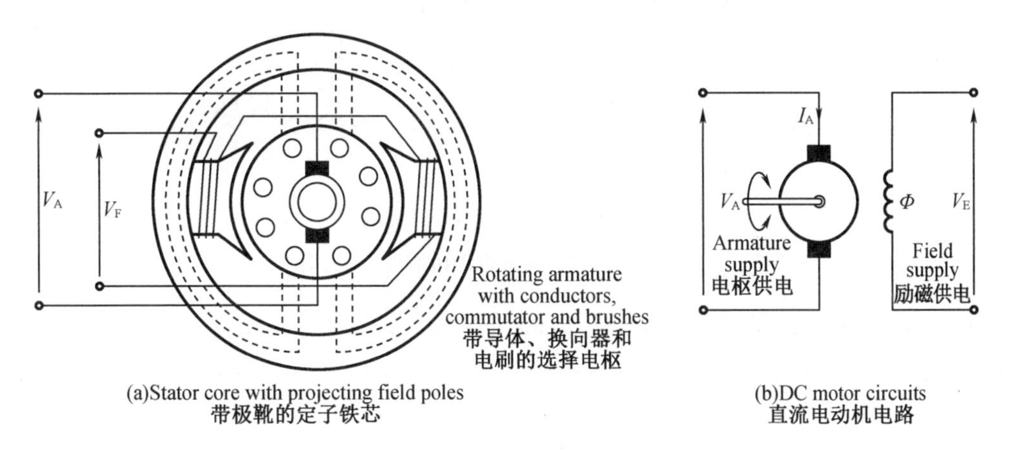

Fig. 9. 6 DC motor circuit

图 9. 6 直流电动机电路

As the armature current and field flux can be independently controlled, the DC motor is able to provide very useful torque/speed characteristics for power drives.

由于电枢电流和磁通量可以单独控制,因此直流电动机能够为电力传动提供非常有效的转矩/调速特性。

The major drawback of a DC motor is that the necessary switching of the armature current is achieved by a mechanical "commutator" on the rotating shaft. Apart from the maintenance required for the commutator and its carbon brushes, the applied voltage for the armature is limited to about 750 V DC. Many regional "Metro" train systems run at 1,500 V DC where two DC motors are connected in series across the supply voltage.

直流电动机的主要缺点是,电枢电流的必要切换是通过转轴的机械"换向器"实现的。除换向器及其碳刷所需的维护外,电枢的外加电压被限制在直流 750 V 左右。许多地区"地铁"列车系统在直流 1 500 V 电压下运行,其中需要两个直流电动机串联后接入供电电压。

9. 3. 2 a. c. Motors 交流电动机

1. Induction Type 异步型

The most common motor drive is a three-phase AC, induction motor with a cage-rotor because it is extremely robust as there are no electrical connections to the rotor. See Fig. 9. 7.

三相交流异步电动机是最常见的电动机驱动装置,它带有笼型转子,非常强劲,且转子没有电气连接。如图 9.7 所示。

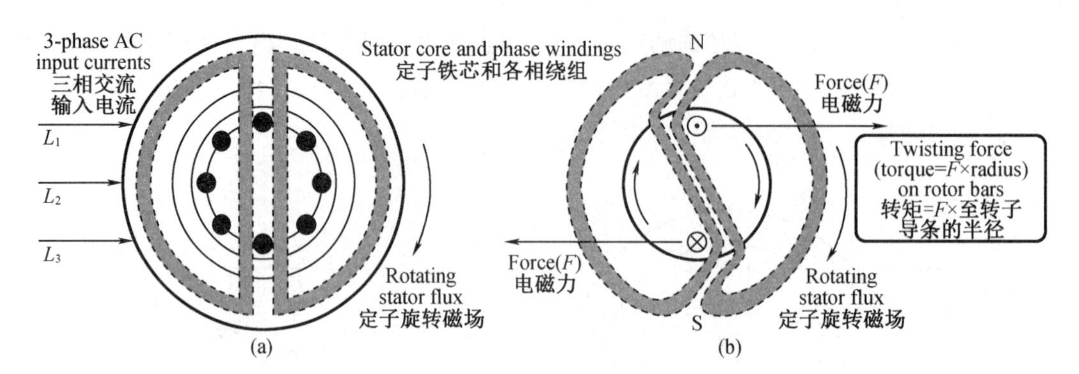

Fig. 9.7　Induction motor action

图 9.7　感应电动机原理

Three time-displaced supply currents to the three stator windings produce a rotating magnetic field which induces currents into the cage winding on the rotor. The interaction of stator flux Φ and rotor current I_R produces a torque on the shaft from $T \propto \Phi \cdot I_R \cdot \cos\varphi$, where φ is the phase angle between Φ and I_R. To be able to induce currents into the rotor, its running speed must be slightly lower than that of the stator rotating field. This difference is called the slip speed and ranges between 1%–5% over the load range for a standard induction motor.

三相定子绕组的三个有相位差的电流产生旋转磁场,从而使转子上的笼型绕组产生电流。定子磁通量 Φ 和转子电流 I_R 的相互作用在轴上产生扭矩 $T \propto \Phi \cdot I_R \cdot \cos\varphi$,其中 φ 是 Φ 和 I_R 之间的相位角。为了能够在转子中产生电流,转子的转速必须略低于定子旋转磁场的转速。这种差异称为转差率,在标准异步电动机额定负载范围内,其大小为 1%~5%。

The speed n_s(synchronous speed) of the rotating flux produced by the stator is fixed by the number of winding pole-pairs "p" and the supply frequency "f" as: $n_s = f/p$(r/s).

定子产生的旋转磁场的转速 n_s(同步速度)由绕组磁极对数 p 和电源频率 f 决定:$n_s = f/p$(r/s)。

An example: for a motor designed for 4-poles ($p=2$) to run on a 50 Hz supply with a full-load slip of 4%, the speed of the rotating flux is $n_s = 50/2 = 25$ r/s (1,500 r/min) but the actual rotor speed will be $n_R = 96\%$ of $25 = 24$ r/s or 1,440 r/min.

例如:对于设计成 4 极($p=2$)的电动机,在 50 Hz 电源上运行,满载时转差率为 4%,旋转磁场的转速为 $n_s = 50/2 = 25$ r/s(1 500 r/min),但实际转子速度为 $n_R = 96\% \times 25 = 24$ r/s 或 1 440 r/min。

While the cage-type induction motor is simple and low-cost it has some practical disadvantages. When supplied with a fixed voltage and frequency the motor runs at an almost constant speed and has a high starting current of typically 5–7 times its full load value.

笼型异步电动机结构简单、成本低，但在实际应用中存在一些缺点。当电压和频率恒定时，电动机以几乎恒定的转速运行，并且启动电流通常为其满载电流的 5~7 倍。

If the motor in the above example is designed for 440 V with a full load rated output of 100 kW with an efficiency of 90% and a power factor of 0.8 lagging, its full load supply current will be found from the three phase power formula:

$$P=\sqrt{3}\cdot V_L\cdot I_L\cdot\cos\varphi$$

so, the electric power input is 100/90% = 111.1 kW and

$$I_L=(111.1\times10^3)/\sqrt{3}\times440\times0.8=182.2\ \text{A}$$

then the initial starting current surge is about 911 A(5 times).

如果上述示例中的电动机设计为 440 V，满载额定输出功率为 100 kW，效率为 90%，功率因数为 0.8 滞后，则其满载电流可由三相功率公式得出：

$$P=\sqrt{3}\cdot V_L\cdot I_L\cdot\cos\varphi$$

所以，输入电动机的功率为 100/90% = 111.1 kW，则

$$I_L=(111.1\times10^3)/\sqrt{3}\times440\times0.8=182.2\ \text{A}$$

则初始启动电流为 911 A(取 5 倍)。

2. Synchronous Type 同步型

This is a three-phase synchronous motor that produces a magnetic field rotating at a speed of $n_s=f/p$ (r/s) just like the induction motor type. The rotor has a set of magnetic poles with DC excitation which locks in synchronism with the stator rotating flux. This means that the shaft is always running at the synchronous speed set by the supply frequency, See Fig. 9.8.

这是一台三相同步电动机，产生的磁场以 $n_s=f/p$(r/s) 的速度旋转，与异步电动机类似。转子有一组直流励磁磁极，与定子旋转磁场同步旋转。这表示转轴始终以和供电频率相同的同步转速转动，如图 9.8 所示。

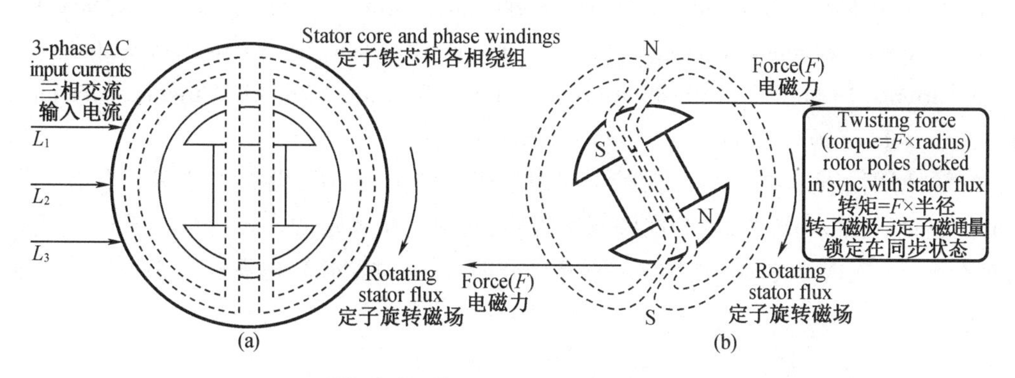

Fig. 9.8　Synchronous motor action

图 9.8　同步电动机原理

To start the motor from standstill can be a problem — it is either:

(1) Pulsed forward at a very low frequency with the rotor poles excited;

(2) Dragged up to slip speed as an induction motor with an embedded cage rotor then locked into synchronism by energising the d. c. rotor field.

从静止状态启动同步电动机有一定难度。启动方式有:

(1)转子磁极有励磁时,以低频脉冲启动;

(2)嵌入笼型转子,通电后使同步电动机像异步电动机一样产生转速差而启动,然后转子再接通直流电以同步转速转动。

For normal running, the operating power factor of a synchronous motor can be lagging or leading as this is determined by the size of the DC excitation field current.

正常运行时,同步电动机的功率因数可能是滞后的或超前的,这取决于直流励磁磁场电流的大小。

(1) Basic Speed Control of Motors 电动机的基本转速控制

Many industrial installations can benefit from direct and smooth speed control of a drive which is moving the process material (water, compressed air, oil, conveyor belts, lifts etc.). Smooth, controlled acceleration and deceleration also reduces shock loading in the system. For a DC motor on a fixed voltage supply, this is easily achieved by using resistance in the armature or field circuits to control the armature current or field flux (or both). The disadvantage is the overall loss of efficiency due to the power losses in the external control resistance(s).

许多工业装置的直接平稳的转速控制得益于中间介质(水、压缩空气、油、传送带、升降机等)的移动。平稳、受控的加速和减速也降低了系统内的冲击负荷。对恒压电源的直流电动机,通过控制电枢或磁场电路中的电阻来控制电枢电流或磁场磁通量(或两者)很容易实现。缺点是由于外部控制电阻带来的功率损耗而导致整体效率下降。

For an AC induction motor or synchronous motor on a fixed voltage and frequency supply, resistance control would only affect the size of operating current but the speed is constant due to the fixed supply frequency. This can only be overcome by changing the frequency of the stator supply currents. To prevent overheating (by over-fluxing) of the motor while frequency changing, the supply voltage must be changed in direct proportion.

对于使用恒压、恒频电源的交流异步电动机或同步电动机,控制电阻只会影响工作电流的大小而不会影响转速,因为电源频率恒定,转速也是恒定的。转速只能通过改变定子电源的频率来实现。为防止电动机在频率变化时过热(过励磁),电源电压必须保持与频率成正比。

(2) Advanced Speed Control 先进的转速控制

Computer controlled variable speed drives (VSDs) are now applied to DC and AC motor types of all sizes. The most popular application is for induction motors for the main industrial power range but synchronous motors are used in large installations e. g. marine electric propulsion.

计算机控制的变速驱动器(VSD)现在应用于各种尺寸的直流和交流电动机中。最常见的是应用于主要工业负载范围的异步电动机中,而同步电动机用于大型装置,如船舶电力推进装置。

The AC motor drives produce a variable frequency output by fast voltage switching from a transistor or thyristor converter which may be AC-DC-AC(PWM and synchroconverter) or AC-AC(cycloconverter). These drives use a mathematical model of the motor and the computer controls the converter output to precisely match the set inputs for speed, torque, acceleration, deceleration, power limits etc.

该交流电动机驱动器通过晶体管或晶闸管变频器对电压的快速转换产生变频输出,该变频器可以是交-直-交(脉冲宽度调制器和同步变频器)或交-交(循环变频器)形式的。这些驱动器使用电动机的数学模型和计算机来控制变频器的输出,以精确匹配转速、扭矩、加速、减速、功率限制等输入设定值。

Such drives may even be tuned to create optimum conditions for run-up/down, braking and energy savings against the connected shaft load.

此类驱动器甚至可以针对轴带负荷的加/减速、制动和节能条件实现最佳的运行状态。

(3)Problems Arising 存在的问题

The fast switching (or chopping) of the voltages to VSDs will produce a distorted waveform which includes high frequency harmonic components whose frequencies are exact multiples of the fundamental (base frequency) value.

变速驱动器的电压快速转换(或斩波),将使电压波形产生畸变,其中包括高频谐波分量,其频率为基频值的整数倍。

For example a 7th harmonic of a 60 Hz fundamental will be at 420 Hz. Such harmonics create additional heating in equipment and possible interference (often called radio frequency interference or RFI).

例如,60 Hz 基波的 7 次谐波为 420 Hz。此类谐波会使设备产生额外的发热和可能的干扰(通常称为射频干扰,RFI)。

Practical solutions to a harmonic problem include good initial system design, filtering and suppression.

谐波问题的实际解决方案包括良好的初始系统设计、滤波和抑制。

9.4 Controlled Rectification and Inversion 可控整流与逆变

The generated three-phase AC, electrical power supply on a ship has a fixed voltage and frequency. This is generally at 440 V and 60 Hz but for high power demands it is likely to be 6.6 kV and 60 Hz.

船舶上产生的三相交流电是恒压和恒频的，通常为 440 V 和 60 Hz，但对于高功率需求，可能需要 6.6 kV 和 60 Hz。

Speed control for a propulsion motor requires variable voltage for a DC drive and variable frequency+voltage for an AC drive. The set bus-bar AC voltage must be converted by controlled rectification (AC→DC) and/or controlled inversion (DC→AC) to match the propulsion motor type.

推进电动机的转速控制要求直流驱动采用可变电压，交流驱动采用变频+变压。根据推进电动机类型来设置的母线交流电压，其必须通过可控整流（交流变直流）和/或受控逆变（直流变交流）进行转换。

A basic rectifier uses semiconductor diodes which can only conduct current in the direction of anode (A) to cathode (K) and this is automatic when A is more positive than K. The diode turns-off automatically when its current falls to zero. Hence, in a single-phase AC circuit a single diode will conduct only on every other half-cycle and this is called half-wave rectification. Other single-centre-tapped transformer with two diodes will create full-wave rectification. Similarly, four diodes in a bridge formation will also produce a full-wave DC voltage output. An equivalent three phase bridge requires six diodes for full-wave operation. A diode, having only two terminals, cannot control the size of the DC output from the rectifier.

基本整流器使用半导体二极管，二极管只能沿阳极（A）到阴极（K）的方向传导电流，当阳极电位比阴极电位高时，二极管自动导通。当反向时其电流降到零，二极管自动截止。因此，在单相交流电路中，一个二极管每隔半个周期导通一次，称为半波整流。其他单中心抽头变压器和两个二极管组成全波整流。类似地，四个二极管组成的桥式结构也将产生全波整流的直流输出电压。三相电桥式整流需要六个二极管才能进行全波整流。二极管只有两个端子，无法对其进行控制从而无法控制整流器的直流输出大小。

9.4.1 Controlled Rectification Process 可控整流过程

For controlled rectification it is necessary to use a set of three-terminal devices such as thyristors (for high currents) or transistors (for low/medium currents).

对于可控整流，有必要使用一组三端装置，如晶闸管（用于大电流）或晶体管（用于中/低电流）。

A basic AC→DC control circuit using a thyristor switch is shown in Fig. 9. 9. Compared with a diode, a thyristor has an extra (control) terminal called the gate (G). The thyristor will only conduct when the anode is positive with respect to the cathode and a brief trigger voltage pulse is applied between gate and cathode (gate must be more positive than cathode). Gate voltage pulses are provided by a separate electronic circuit and the pulse timing decides the switch-on point for the main (load) current. The load current is therefore rectified to DC (by diode action) and controlled by delayed switching. In this circuit an inductor coil (choke) smoothes the DC load current even though the DC voltage is severely chopped by the thyristor switching action. An alternative to the choke coil is to use a capacitor across the rectifier output which smoothes the DC voltage.

基本的交流变直流控制电路使用晶闸管开关控制,如图 9.9 所示。与二极管相比,晶闸管有一个称为栅极(G)的额外(控制)端子。晶闸管仅在阳极电位高于于阴极电位,并且在栅极和阴极之间施加短暂的触发电压脉冲(栅极与阴极对比必须为正)时导通。栅极电压脉冲由单独的电子电路产生,脉冲定时决定主(负载)电流的接通时间点。因此,负载电流被整流为直流(通过二极管通断)电,并由延时开关控制。在该电路中,即使直流电压由于晶闸管开关动作产生严重波动,电感线圈(扼流线圈)也能使直流负载电流波形变得平滑。扼流线圈的替代方案是在整流器输出端并联电容器,以使直流电压输出波形变得平滑。

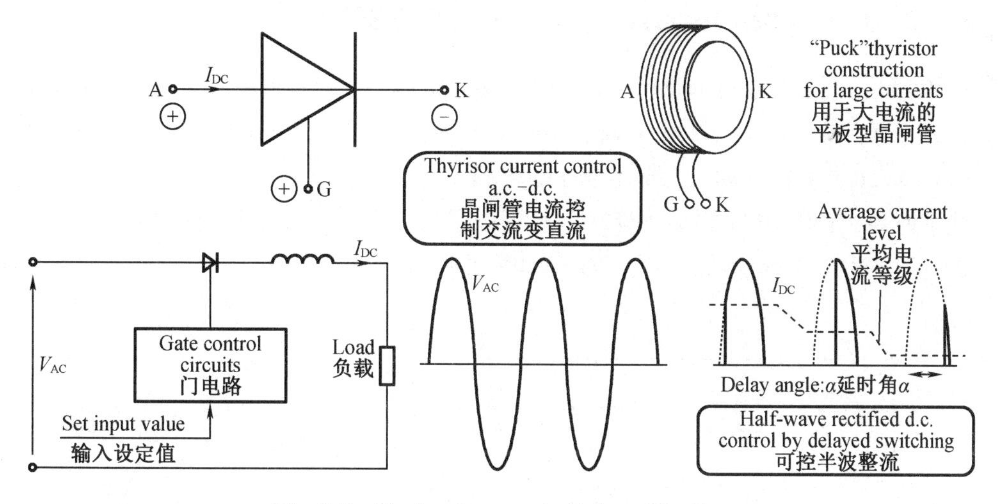

Fig. 9. 9　Single-phase controlled rectification

图 9.9　单相可控整流

Full wave controlled rectification from a three-phase AC supply is achieved in a bridge circuit with six thyristors a shown in Fig. 9. 10.

三相交流电源的全波整流在带有六个晶闸管的桥式整流电路中实现,如图 9.10 所示。

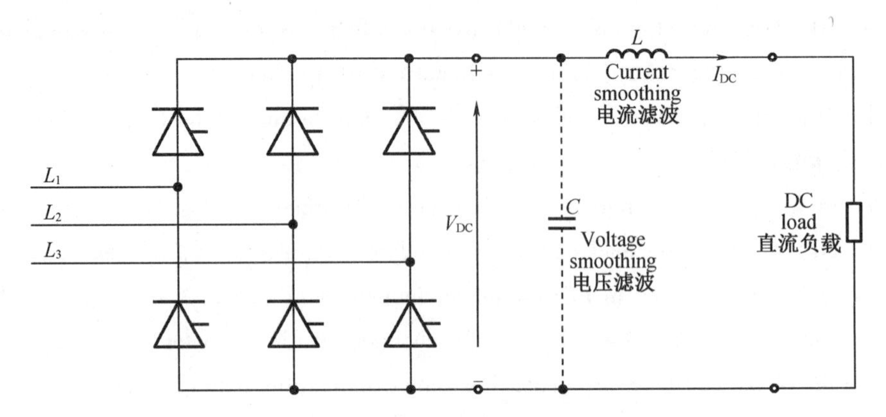

Fig. 9. 10　Three-phase controlled rectifier bridge circuit

图 9. 10　三相可控桥式整流

For a 440 V (r. m. s.) AC line voltage the peak voltage is $440\times\sqrt{2}=622$ V. The equivalent maximum DC average voltage output is taken to be about 600 V as it has a six-pulse ripple effect due to the three-phase input waveform.

对于 440 V(均方根)交流线电压,峰值电压为 $440\times\sqrt{2}=622$ V。等效最大直流平均输出电压约为 600 V,因为三相输入波形产生六脉冲纹波干扰。

9. 4. 2　Controlled Inversion Process 可控逆变过程

A DC voltage can be inverted (switched) repeatedly from positive to negative to form an alternating (AC) voltage by using a set of thyristor (or transistor) switches. A controlled three-phase thyristor bridge inverter is shown in Fig. 9. 11.

通过使用一组晶闸管(或晶体管)开关,可以将直流电压的正负反复反转(切换),以形成交流电压。受控三相晶闸管桥式逆变器如图 9. 11 所示。

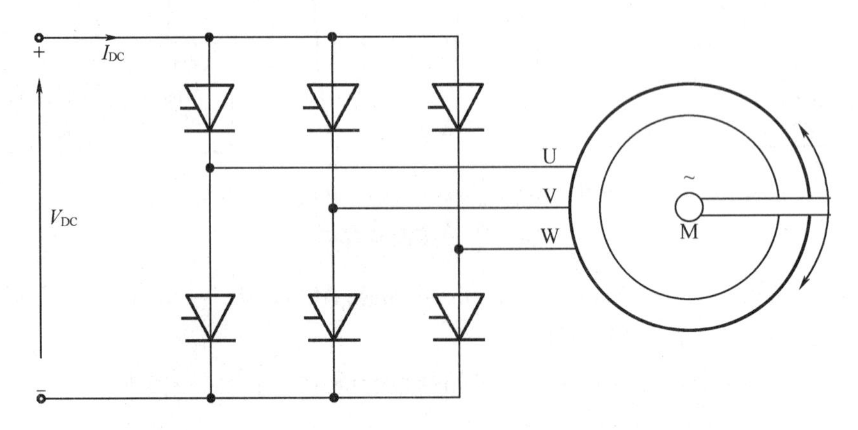

Fig. 9. 11　Three-phase inverter circuit and induction motor

图 9. 11　三相电动机逆变电路

The inverter bridge circuit arrangement is exactly the same as that for the rectifier. Here, the DC voltage is sequentially switched onto the three output lines. The rate of switching determines the output frequency. For AC motor control, the line currents are directed into (and out of) the windings to produce a rotating stator flux wave which interacts with the rotor to produce torque.

桥式逆变电路的布置与桥式整流电路完全相同。此电路中,直流电压依次切换到三条输出线上。开关速率决定输出频率。对交流电动机的控制,线电流被导入(或流出)绕组,以使定子产生旋转磁场,该磁场的磁通量与转子相互作用而产生转矩。

9.5 Converter Types 变频器类型

The processes of controlled rectification and inversion are used in converters that are designed to match the drive motor. The principal types of motor control converters are:

(1) AC-DC (controlled rectifier for DC motors);

(2) AC-DC-AC (PWM for induction motors);

(3) AC-DC-AC (synchro converter for synchronous motors);

(4) AC-AC (cycloconverter for synchronous motors).

变频器的可控整流和逆变过程与驱动电动机相匹配。电动机控制变频器的主要类型有:

(1)交-直(用于直流电动机的可控整流器);

(2)交-直-交(用于交流异步电动机的脉冲宽度调制器);

(3)交-直-交(用于同步电动机的同步变频器);

(4)交-交(用于同步电动机的循环变频器)。

9.5.1 AC-DC Converter 交-直变频器

This is a three-phase AC controlled rectification circuit for a DC motor drive. Two converters of different power ratings are generally used for the separate control of the armature current (I_A) and the field current which produces the magnetic flux. Some systems may have a fixed field current which means that the field supply only requires an uncontrolled diode bridge as shown in Fig. 9.12.

这是一个驱动直流电动机的三相交流可控整流电路。通常使用两个不同额定功率的变频器分别控制电枢电流(I_A)和产生磁通量的励磁电流。一些系统可能有一个固定的励磁电流,这意味着励磁电源只需要一个不可控的二极管整流桥,如图 9.12 所示。

Motor torque is determined from $T \propto \Phi \cdot I_A$ and the speed is controlled from $n \propto V_A / \Phi$. Shaft rotation can be achieved by reversing either the field current or the armature current direction. Ship applications for such a drive would include cable-laying, offshore drilling, diving and supply, ocean survey and submarines.

电动机转矩由 $T \propto \Phi \cdot I_A$ 确定,转速基于 $n \propto V_A/\Phi$ 控制。轴的转向可以通过改变励磁电流或电枢电流方向来实现。应用这种驱动的船舶包括电缆敷设、近海钻探、潜水和补给、海洋调查和潜艇。

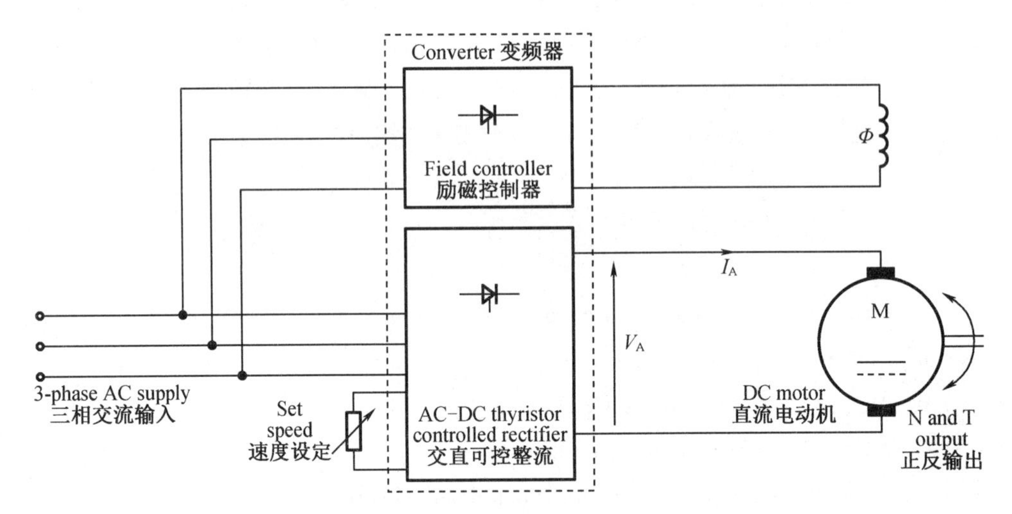

Fig. 9.12 controlled rectification converter

图 9.12 可控整流变频器

9.5.2 AC-DC-AC PWM Converter 交-直-交脉冲宽度变频器

This type of converter is used for induction motor drives and uses transis tors as the switching devices. Unlike thyristors, a transistor can be turned on and off by a control signal and at a high switching rate (e.g. at 20 kHz in a PWM converter). See Fig. 9.13.

这种类型的变频器用于驱动感应电动机,并使用晶体管作为开关设备。与晶闸管不同,可以通过控制信号控制晶体管以高开关速率(例如,在脉冲宽度变频器中为 20 kHz)通断。如图 9.13 所示。

The input rectifier stage is not controlled so is simpler and cheaper but the converter will not be able to allow power from the motor load to be regenerated back into the mains supply during a braking operation. From a 440 V AC supply, the rectified DC voltage will be smoothed by the capacitor to approximately 600 V.

输入整流级不受控制,因此它更加简单和便宜,但在制动过程中,来自电动机负载的电能无法通过变频器重新回馈到主电源。通过输入 440 V 交流电源,电容器将整流后的直流电压稳压至约 600 V。

The DC voltage is chopped into variable-width, but constant level voltage pulses in the computer controlled inverter section using insulated gate devices(IGBTs, e.g. programmable logic bipolar transistors). This process is called pulse width modulation or PWM. By varying the pulse widths and polarity of the DC voltage it is possible to generate an averaged sinusoidal AC output over a wide range of frequencies typically 0.5-120 Hz. Due to the smoothing effect of the motor inductance, the motor currents appear to be nearly sinusoidal in shape. By sequentially directing the currents into the three stator windings, a reversible rotating magnetic field is produced with its speed set by the output frequency of the PWM converter.

在计算机控制的逆变器部分,使用绝缘栅器件(IGBT,如可编程逻辑双极晶体管)将直流电压斩波为脉冲宽度可变但恒定电平的电压脉冲。这个过程称为脉冲宽度调制(PWM)。通过改变直流电压的脉冲宽度和极性,可以在宽频率范围内(通常为0.5~120 Hz)产生平均正弦交流输出。由于电动机绕组的电感滤波效应,电动机电流的波形近似正弦。通过将电流依次导入三个定子绕组,产生可逆的旋转磁场,其转速由脉冲宽度变频器的输出频率设定。

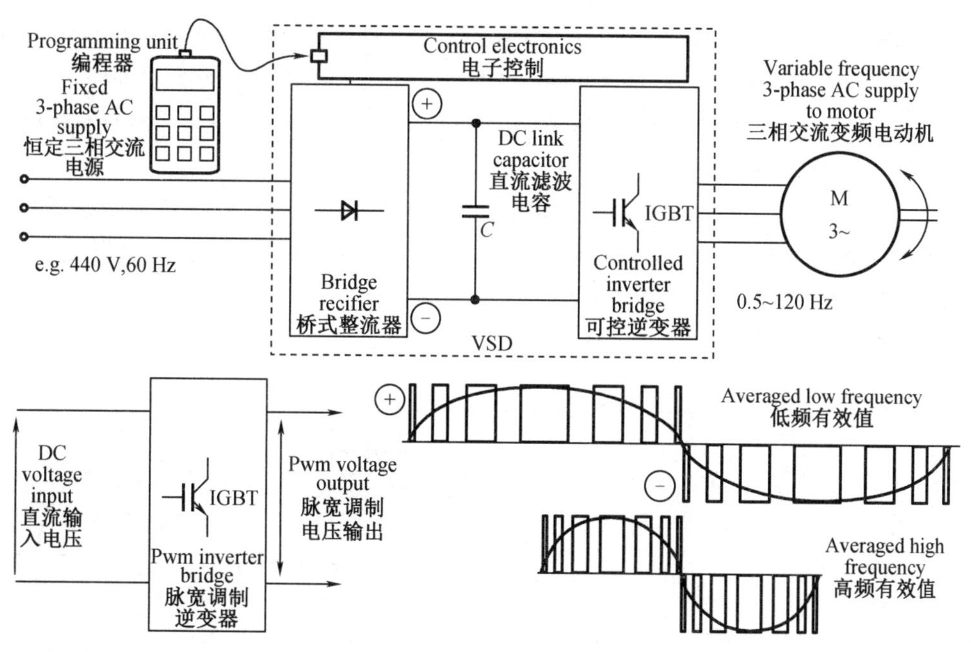

Fig. 9.13 PWM converter

图 9.13 脉冲宽度调制变频器

Accurate control of shaft torque, acceleration time and resistive braking are a few of the many operational parameters that can be programmed into the VSD, usually via a hand-held unit. The VSD can be closely tuned to the connected motor drive to achieve optimum control and protection limits for the overall drive. Speed regulation against load changes is very good and can be made very precise by the addition of feedback from a shaft speed encoder.

对转轴的转矩、加速时间和制动电阻的精确控制是可以编程到变速驱动器中的多种运行参数中的一部分,通常通过手持式装置编程。变速驱动器可与连接的电动机驱动器保持高度同步,以实现对整个驱动器的最佳控制和极限保护。针对负载变化的转速调节效果非常好,通过增加编码器反馈轴的转速信号,可以实现非常精确的转速调节。

VSDs, being digitally controlled, can be easily networked to other computer controllers (PLCs) for overall control of a complex process.

变速驱动器采用数字控制,可以轻松地与其他计算机控制器(PLC)联网,以便对复杂过程进行全面控制。

9.5.3 AC-DC-AC Synchroconverter 交-直-交同步变频器

This type of converter is used for large AC synchronous motor drives (called a synchrodrive) and is applied very successfully to marine electric propulsion.

这种变频器用于大型交流同步电动机驱动上(称为同步驱动),并成功地应用于船舶电力推进。

A synchroconverter, as shown in Fig. 9. 14, has controlled rectifier and inverter stages which both rely on natural turn-off (line commutation) for the thyristors by the three phase AC voltages at either end of the converter. Between the rectification and inversion stages is a current-smoothing reactor coil forming the DC link.

如图 9. 14 所示,同步变频器的整流和逆变阶段都依赖于三相交流电压下变频器两端晶闸管的自然关断(线路换相)。在整流级和逆变级之间是一个电流滤波的电抗器线圈,形成直流链路(隔交通直)。

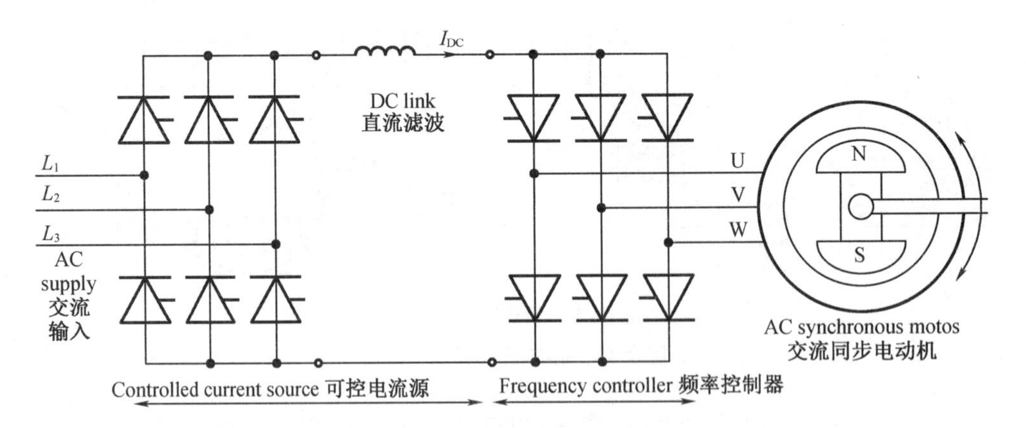

Fig. 9. 14 Synchroconverter circuit

图 9. 14 同步变频器电路

An operational similarity exists between a synchrodrive and a DC motor drive. This view considers the rectifier stage as a controlled DC supply and the inverter/synchronous motor combination as a DC motor. The switching inverter acts as a static commutator.

同步驱动器和直流电动机驱动器的运行特性相似。此观点是将整流级作为一个可控直流电源,逆变器/同步电动机组合作为直流电动机。开关逆变器作为静态换向器。

The combination of controlled rectifier and d. c. link is considered to be a current source for the inverter whose task is then to sequentially direct blocks of the current into the motor windings as shown in Fig. 9. 15.

可控整流器和直流链路的组合被认为是逆变器的电流源,逆变器的任务是依次将电流组引导到电动机绕组中,如图 9. 15 所示。

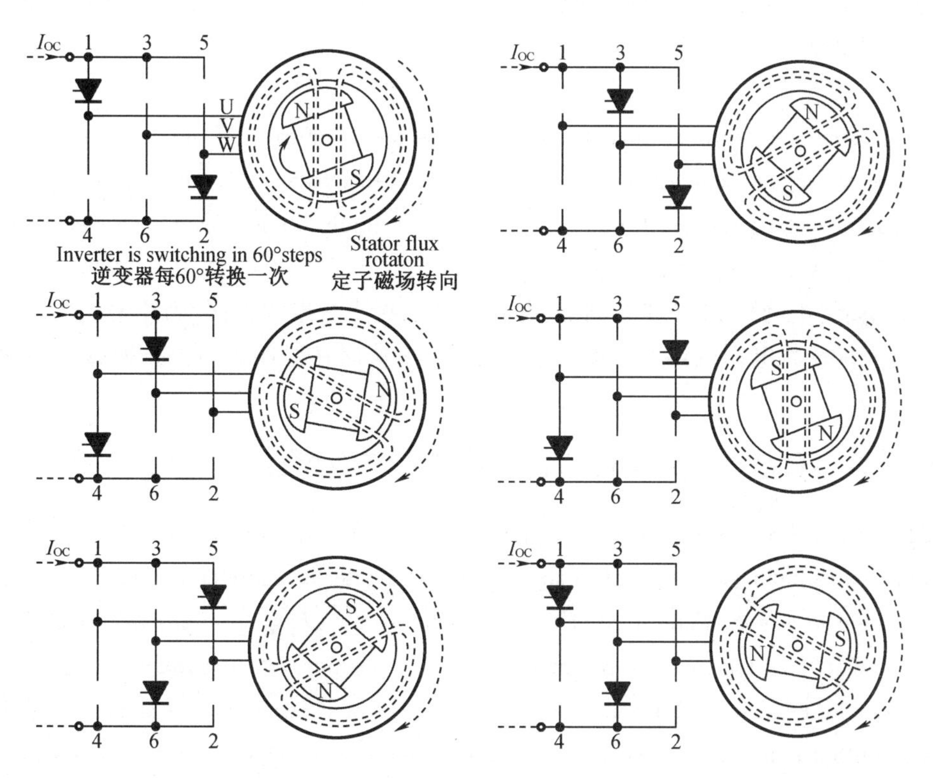

Fig. 9. 15 Inverter current switching sequence

图 9. 15 逆变器通断顺序

The size of the DC current is set by the controlled switching of the rectifier thyristors. Motor supply frequency (and hence its speed) is set by the rate of inverter switching. The six inverter thyristors provide six current pulses per cycle (known as a six-pulse converter).

直流电流的大小是由整流晶闸管的通断控制决定的。电动机的供电频率(和它的转速)是由逆变器的开关速率决定的。六个逆变晶闸管每周期提供六个电流脉冲(称为六脉冲变频器)。

A simplified understanding of synchroconverter control is that the current source (controlled rectification stage) provides the required motor torque and the inverter stage controls the required speed. To provide the motor e. m. f. which is necessary for natural commutation of the inverter thyristors, the synchronous motor must have rotation and magnetic flux in its rotor poles. During normal running, the synchronous motor is operated with a power factor of about 0. 9 leading (by field excitation control) to assist the line commutation of the inverter thyristors. The DC rotor field excitation is obtained from a separate controlled thyristor rectification circuit.

对同步变频器控制的简单理解是,电流源(受控整流级)提供所需的电动机转矩,而逆变器级按需求控制转速。使电动机产生电动势需要逆变器晶闸管的自然换向,同步电动机在其转子磁极中必须具有转速和磁通量。在正常运行时,同步电动机以约0.9超前的功率因数(通过励磁控制)运行,以辅助逆变器晶闸管的线路换相。直流转子磁场励磁通过单独控制的晶闸管整流电路获得。

As the supply (network) and machine bridges are identical and are both connected to a three-phase AC voltage source, their roles can be switched into reverse. This is useful to allow the regeneration of motor power back into the mains power supply which provides an electric braking torque during a crash stop of the ship.

由于电源(电网)和电桥是相同的,并且都与三相交流电源连接,因此它们的作用可以互换。这有助于将电动机再生电能反馈回主电源,从而在船舶紧急停止时提供电磁制动转矩。

9.5.4 AC-AC Cycloconverter 交-交循环变频器

While a synchroconverter is able to provide an output frequency range typically up to twice that of the mains input (e. g. up to 120 Hz), a cycloconverter is restricted to a much lower range. This is limited to less than one third of the supply frequency (e. g. up to 20 Hz) which is due to the way in which this type of converter produces the a. c. output voltage waveform. Ship propulsion shaft speeds are typically in the range of 0-145 r/min which can easily be achieved by the low frequency output range of a cycloconverter to a multi-pole synchronous motor. Power regeneration from the motor back into the main power supply is available.

同步变频器的输出频率范围通常可达电源输入频率的两倍(例如,可达120 Hz),而循环变频器的输出频率范围则要低得多。它被限制在电源频率的三分之一以下(例如,可达20 Hz),这是由此类变频器产生交流输出电压波形的方式造成的。船舶推进轴转速通常在0~145 r/min的范围内,可通过循环变频器的低频输出至多极同步电动机实现这个调速范围。电动机的再生电能可回馈至主电源。

A conventional three phase converter from AC to DC can be controlled so that the average output voltage can be increased and decreased from zero to maximum within a half-cycle period of the sinusoidal AC input. By connecting two similar converters back-to-back in each line an AC output frequency is obtained. The switching pattern for the thyristors varies over the frequency range which requires a complex computer program for converter control.

通过控制从交流变直流的传统三相变频器,在正弦交流输入的半个周期内可以使平均输出电压由零升高或降低至最大幅值。通过将两个相似的变频器背靠背地连接在每条线路中,就可以输出交流频率信号。需要一个复杂的计算机程序对变频器进行控制,使晶闸管的开关模式根据频率变化。

The diagram in Fig. 9. 16 gives a basic circuit arrangement for a cycloconverter together with an approximate voltage waveform for the low frequency output. The corresponding current waveform shape (not shown) will be more sinusoidal due to the smoothing effect of motor and line inductance.

图 9. 16 中的图表给出了循环变频器的基本电路布置以及低频输出的近似电压波形。由于电动机和线路电感的滤波效应,相应的电流波形(未显示)将更接近正弦波。

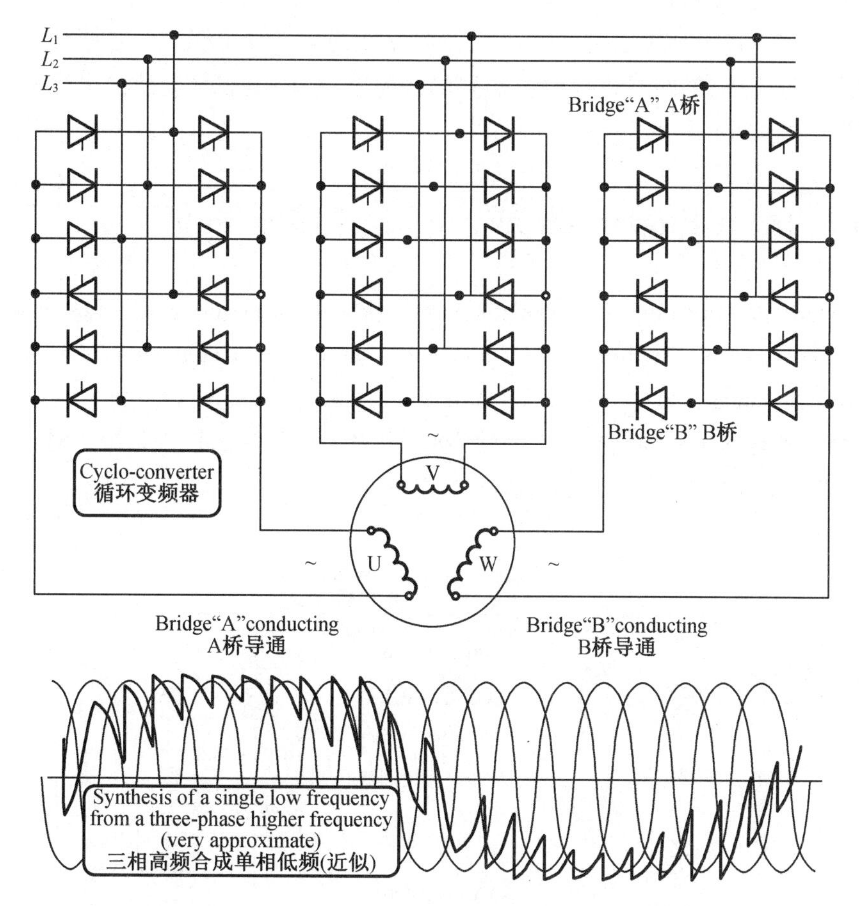

Fig. 9. 16　Cycloconverter circuit and output waveform

图 9. 16　循环变频器电路及输出波形

The output voltage has a significant ripple content which gets larger (worse) as the output frequency is raised and it is this feature that limits the maximum useful frequency.

输出电压含有显著的纹波,纹波随着输出频率的升高而增大(更糟),正是这个特性限制了可用频率上限。

There is no connection between the three motor windings because the line converters have to be isolated from each other to operate correctly to obtain line commutation (natural) switching of the thyristors.

三个电动机绕组之间没有连接,因为线路变换器必须相互隔离才能正确地动作,以获得线路换相(自然)对应的晶闸管开关状态。

The converters may be directly supplied from the HV line but it is more usual to interpose step-down transformers. This reduces the motor voltage and its required insulation level while also providing additional line impedance to limit the size of prospective fault current and harmonic voltage distortion at the main supply bus-bar.

变频器可以直接由高压线路供电,但却通常采用降压变压器供电。这降低了电动机电压及其要求的绝缘等级,同时也提供了额外的线路阻抗,以限制预期故障电流和主汇流排谐波电压畸变的大小。

9.6 Electrical Propulsion System 电力推进系统

This section describes the overall operation of a propulsion system and is based on a diesel-electric arrangement with synchroconverter frequency control. For a large ship, the power system will employ high voltage (HV) generation as in the diagram in Fig. 9. 17.

本节介绍具有同步变频器频率控制的柴油-电力传动装置的推进系统。对于一艘大型船舶来说,电力系统将采用高压发电,如图 9. 17 所示。

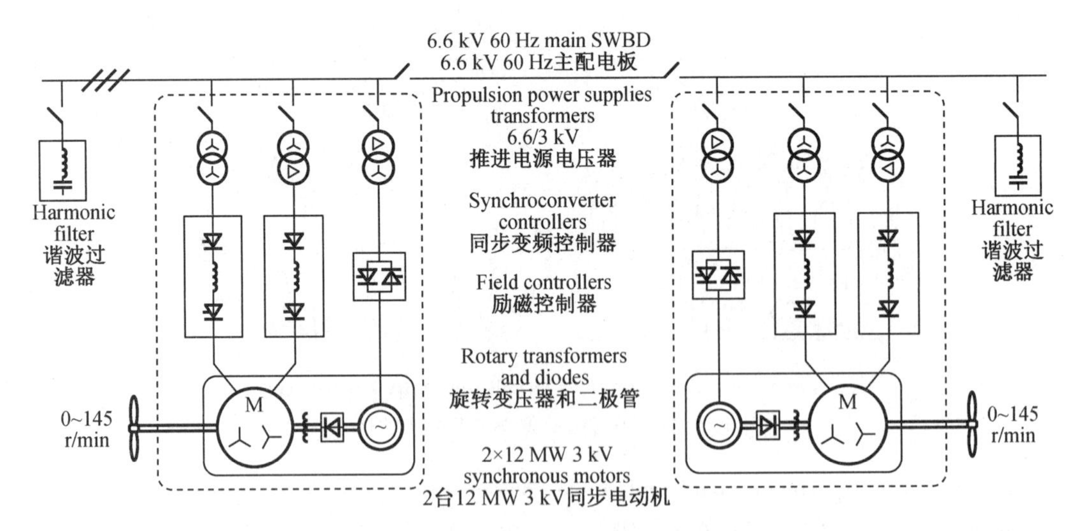

Fig. 9. 17 HV propulsion power system

图 9. 17 高压电力推进系统

In this example each 12 MW, 3 kV propulsion motor has two separate 6 MW stator windings and each half winding is supplied from a 6. 6/3. 0 kV propulsion transformer and a static six-pulse synchroconverter. The 24 pole motors have a shaft speed range of 0–145 r/min controlled from the converter output frequency range of 0–29 Hz.

在本例中,每个 12 MV, 3 kV 推进电动机有两个独立的 6 MW 定子绕组,每个独立绕组由 6.6/3.0 kV 推进变压器和静态六脉冲同步变频器供电。24 极电动机转轴转速范围为 0~145 r/min,由输出频率为 0~29 Hz 的变频器控制。

By using two converters feeding two separate stator windings fitted 30° apart, a 12-pulse shaft torque is achieved to minimize shaft vibration. A more complicated arrangement of supply transformers and converters can produce a 24-pulse shaft torque.

通过两个变频器分别为两个相差 30°的定子绕组供电,就可获得 12 脉冲转轴转矩,以最大限度地减少轴振动。电源变压器和变频器通过更复杂的布局可产生 24 脉冲的转轴转矩。

Motor brushless excitation is also obtained from the HV bus-bars via a 6.6/0.44 kV static transformer, a thyristor controller, an AC to AC rotary transformer (inside the motor) and a set of shaft mounted diodes for the final conversion to DC.

高压母线的高压交流电通过 6.6/0.44 kV 静态变压器、晶闸管控制器、交流变交流旋转变压器(电动机内部)和一组轴装二极管整流装置变成直流电向无刷电动机提供励磁。

The related physical arrangement of the main components in the propulsion system is shown in Fig. 9.18.

推进系统中主要部件的相关硬件布局如图 9.18 所示。

Control throttle stations for both shafts are installed on the bridge (in wheelhouse and on the wings), engine control room and local (in HV switchboard room) positions. At sea the shaft speed commands are set from the bridge and repeated in the ECR. In port the control position is transferred to the ECR. The local control position is mainly used for testing and maintenance duties but also acts as an emergency control station. Selection of the command position is determined by a switch on the propulsion console in the ECR.

两个推进轴的转速控制站安装在驾驶台(驾驶室内和两翼上)、集控室和机旁(高压配电间)位置。在海上,转速指令从驾驶台设定,并在 ECR 中复示。在港时控制位置被转换到 ECR。机旁控制位置主要用于测试和维护,但也作为一个紧急控制站使用。控制位置的选择由 ECR 推进控制台上的一个选择开关确定。

An emergency push-button telegraph giving set speed commands (dead-slow, half-ahead etc.) is available at each control station. The ship propulsion regulator and side-thruster regulators can be combined into a master joy-stick controller to give overall directional control for accurate manoeuvring in port.

每个控制站都有一个带紧急按钮的车钟,可发出速度指令(慢速、半速等)。船舶推进调节器和侧推调节器可以组合成一个主操纵杆控制器,提供全方向控制,以便在港进行精确船舶操纵。

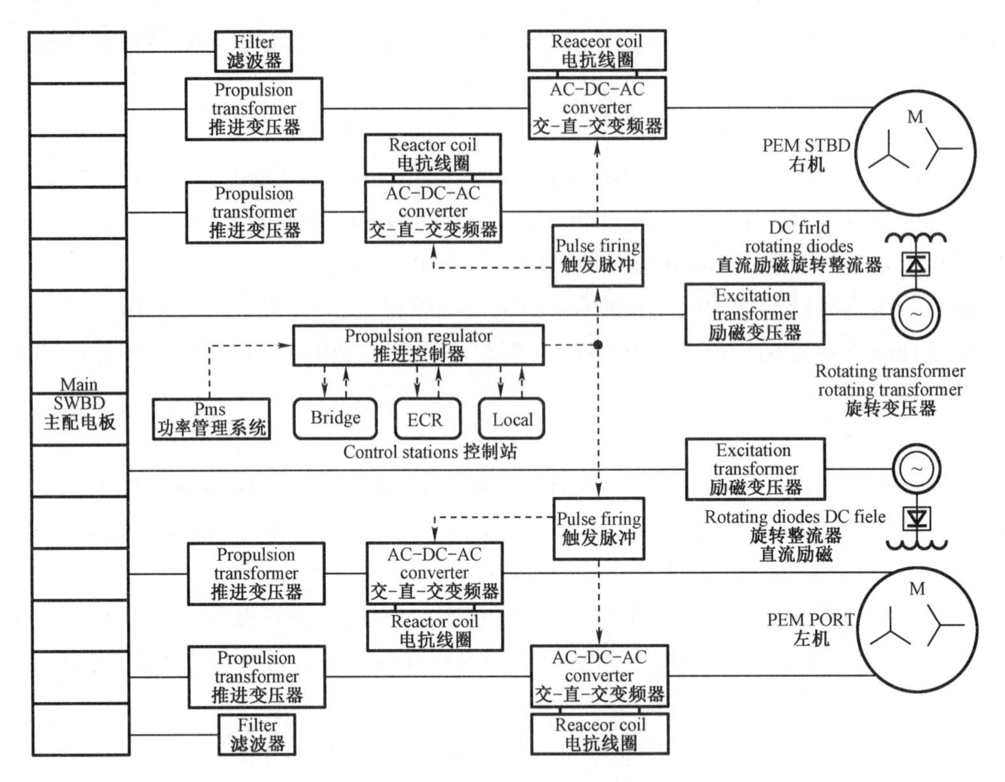

Fig. 9. 18　Interconnection of main propulsion components

图 9. 18　主要推进部件的互联

In a synchrodrive system as shown in Fig. 9. 19, the computer receives a command (set speed) input and many feedback signals (voltage, current, power, frequency etc.), but the obvious regulating item is the actual shaft speed feedback forming a closed control loop. The principal parameters to be controlled are the size of motor stator current (to set motor torque) and the motor frequency (to set the shaft speed). In addition, the DC motor field current has to be continually controlled from the propulsion regulator via the excitation converter.

在如图 9. 19 所示的同步驱动系统中,计算机接收一个指令(设定的转速)输入和许多反馈信号(电压、电流、功率、频率等),但最显著的调节项目是形成闭合控制回路的实际轴转速反馈。需要控制的主要参数是电动机定子电流的大小(用来设定电动机转矩)和电动机频率(用来设定转轴转速)。此外,直流电动机励磁电流必须由推进调节器通过励磁变换器持续控制。

In normal running and full-away with both propulsion motor speeds within 5% of each other, the bridge can select a shaft synchro-phasing mode which applies momentary acceleration/deceleration to bring the propeller blades into an alignment which minimizes shaft vibration into the hull. Speed and position are derived from detectors on the non-drive end of the motor shaft.

在正常运行和全速时,两台推进电动机的转速相差在 5%以内,驾驶台可以选择转轴同步相位模式,即瞬时加速/减速,使螺旋桨叶片排成一条直线,从而最大限度地减少轴向船体的振动。转速和位置信号来自电动机转轴非驱动端的传感器。

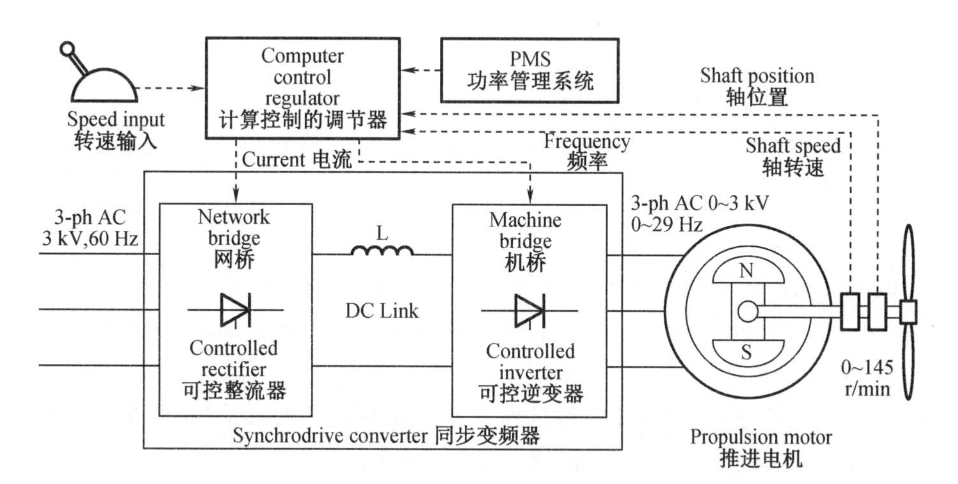

Fig. 9. 19 Synchrodrive system

图 9. 19 同步驱动系统

At speeds of less than 10%, the motor does not generate sufficient back e. m. f. to cause automatic thyristor switch-off (line commutation). Remember that a thyristor can only switch off when its current becomes zero. This problem is overcome by pulse-mode operation where the current is momentarily forced to zero by the thyristors in the controlled rectifier stage. This allows the inverter thyristors to turn-off so that the controller can regain control. The decision is now which thyristor and which sequence of switching is required to maintain the required shaft direction of rotation. It is necessary to know exactly the position of the rotor poles and this is provided by the shaft position encoder for low-speed, pulse-mode operation. When kicked above 10% speed, the motor e. m. f. will be large enough to allow the converter to revert to its normal line-commutation mode for synchronous operation.

当转速小于10%时,电动机不会产生足够的反向电动势,从而导致晶闸管自动关断(线路换相)。请记住,晶闸管只能在其电流为零时关闭。该问题可通过运行脉模式解决,在脉冲模式下,受控整流器级的晶闸管将电流瞬间强制归零。这样逆变器晶闸管就能关断,以便控制器能够重新获得控制。现在决定需要哪个晶闸管导通和通过什么顺序来导通以保持所需的旋转方向。必须准确地知道转子磁极的位置,这由低速脉冲模式运行时,转轴末端的编码器提供。当踢机转速超过10%时,电动机电动势将大到足以允许变频器恢复到其正常线路换相模式,以进行同步运行。

Question 思考题

If the individual inverter thyristors are not switched off (commutated) at the necessary instant a serious problem arises. Explain the likely consequences.

如果个别的逆变器的晶闸管没有在必要的时刻关断(交换)会出现一个严重的问题。

解释说明可能的后果。

Answer 答案

If two or more inverter thyristors are unable to be switched-off naturally they will apply a full short-circuit fault path across the DC link.

如果两个或两个以上的逆变器晶闸管不能自然关断,它们将在直流链路上形成一个完全短路故障的路径。

For normal running, above about 10% speed, the operation is switched to synchronous mode where the thyristors in both bridges are switched off naturally (line commutated) by their live AC voltages from supply and motor.

约10%以上的转速正常运行时,运行模式就切换到同步模式,其中两个电桥中的晶闸管通过电源和电动机的交流电压自然关断(线路换向)。

To reverse the shaft rotation the forward/ahead phase sequence of motor supply currents is reversed by the inverter thyristors. This reverses the direction of stator flux rotation and hence shaft direction to astern. The rate of deceleration to zero speed must be carefully controlled before a shaft reversal to avoid large power surges in the system.

为使转轴反向旋转,逆变器晶闸管使电动机电源电流向前/正车的相序反向。这将使定子磁通量的转向反向,从而使转轴向倒车方向转动。在轴反转之前,必须小心控制减速至零的速率,以避免系统中出现大功率浪涌。

For a motor braking operation, the inverter bridge can be considered as a rectifier bridge when viewed from the live AC supply produced by the motor e. m. f. If the network (rectifier) bridge thyristors are switched with a delay angle greater than 90° the DC link voltage reverses causing power flow from the motor back to the supply (motor braking). In this mode the roles of the network and machine bridges are swapped over.

电动机制动运行时,将电动机感应电动势视作带电交流电源,逆变器电桥视为整流电桥,如果网络(整流器)电桥晶闸管以大于90°的延迟角导通,则直流链路电压反向,导致电能从电动机回流至电源(电动机制动)。在此模式下,网络和设备电桥的角色互换了。

Overall system power control is provided by a computer controlled power management system (PMS) which effectively coordinates power demand with its supply.

整个系统的功率控制由计算机控制的功率管理系统(PMS)实现,该系统有效地协调了功率需求和电力供应。

Broadly, the PMS functions are:

(1) Control

①Automatic power limitation for propulsion motors;

②Auto-start, synchronising and load sharing of standby generators;

③ Control of re-generation from the propulsion motors during braking and reversing manoeuvres;

④Power limitation for main generators;

⑤Load shedding by preferential tripping;

⑥Dynamic limitation of propulsion motor acceleration.

(2) Monitoring

①Load sharing;

②Diesel performance;

③Proposal to start/stop a generator;

④Running time for generators and propulsion motors;

⑤Status arid data display.

总的来说,PMS 的功能包括:

(1)控制

①推进电动机的自动功率限制;

②自动启动,同步和备用发电机的负荷转移;

③控制推进电动机在制动和换向操纵时产生的再生电能;

④主发电机功率限制;

⑤优先脱扣卸载;

⑥推进电动机加速过程的动态限制。

(2)监测

①负荷分配;

②柴油机性能;

③启动/停止发电机的条件;

④发电机和推进电动机的运行时间;

⑤状态和数据显示。

9.7 Harmonics 谐波

The input current to a static power converter has in general, a high harmonic content due to the way the current is switched (chopped) from phase to phase. Harmonic currents are important because they cause distortion of the supply voltage waveform which may result in the malfunction and additional heating of other equipment connected to the supply system.

一般来说,静态电源变频器的输入电流通常含有高次谐波,这是由电流在相间切换(斩波)的方式造成的。谐波电流很重要,因为它会引起供电电压波形的畸变,从而导致连接到供电系统的其他设备故障和额外发热。

The size and frequencies of the harmonic currents and voltages depend on the converter type, the pulse number and method of control (e. g. synchroconverter, cycloconverter or PWM).

电压、谐波电流及频率的大小取决于变频器的类型、脉冲数和控制方式(例如同步转换器、循环转换器或脉冲宽度变频器)。

Typical waveforms for a six-pulse synchroconverter are shown in Fig. 9. 20.

6 脉冲同步变频器的典型波形如图 9. 20 所示。

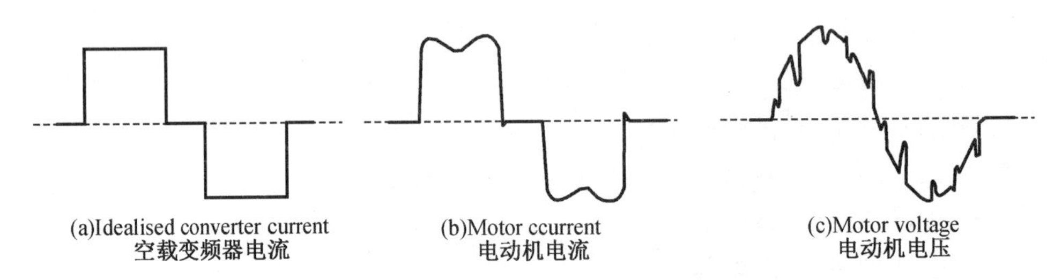

Fig. 9. 20　Typical synchroconverter waveforms

图 9. 20　同步变频器典型波形

In general, harmonic frequencies are integer multiples (e. g. 3, 5, 7, 11, 13, etc.) of the fundamental (supply) frequency. Hence, a 7th harmonic in a 60 Hz AC voltage has a frequency of 420 Hz and an 11th has a frequency of 660 Hz. Harmonic amplitudes are roughly the reciprocal of the harmonic number, i. e. 20% (1/5) for the fifth, 14. 3% for the seventh, 9. 1% for the eleventh, etc. The particular shape of the resulting supply voltage will depend on harmonic currents causing additional harmonic voltages in the supply reactance (inductive and/or capacitive). See example in Fig. 9. 21.

通常,谐波频率是基频(电源)的整数倍(例如 3 倍、5 倍、7 倍、11 倍、13 倍等)。因此,60 Hz 交流电压中的第 7 次谐波的频率为 420 Hz,第 11 次谐波的频率为 660 Hz。谐波幅值大致是谐波次数的倒数,即 5 次谐波为 20% (1/5),7 次谐波为 14. 3%,11 次谐波为 9. 1%,等等。电源电压的特征波形将取决于谐波电流在电源电抗(感性和/或容性)中引起的谐波电压。如图 9. 21 所示。

Some harmonics are eliminated by careful system design e. g. by adding more circuit inductance, using phaseshifting transformers (star-star and star-delta) and increasing the converter pulse number. The 30° phase-shifted transformers effectively double the current pulses drawn by the motor so a 6-pulses converter system appears to be 12-pulses as viewed from the supply point.

通过细致的系统设计,例如通过增加电路电感,使用移相变压器(星形-星形和星形-三角形)和增加变频器脉冲数,可以消除一些谐波。整流级增加 30° 移相变压器能有效地使电动机汲取的电流脉冲数加倍,因此从电源输出来看,三相变频器系统的 6 脉冲变为 12 脉冲。

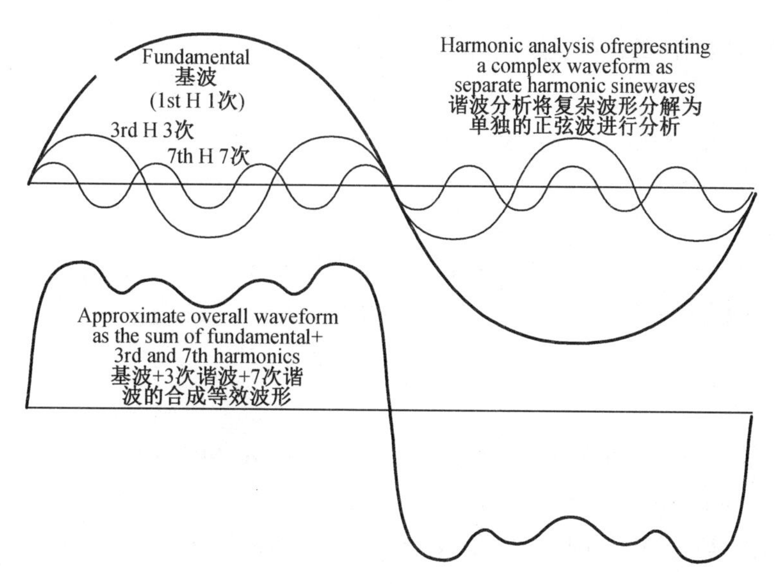

Fig. 9. 21　Harmonic analysis of waveforms

图 9. 21　波形的谐波分析

For a generator sinusoidal AC voltage waveform with identical positive and negative shapes, all even numbered harmonics are cancelled out. In a three-phase a. c. system, all harmonics that are a multiple of three are also automatically cancelled. That leaves harmonic numbers of 5th, 7th, 11th, 13th, 17th, etc. as potential problems. For a pair of six-pulses synchroconverters supplied by a pair of phase-shifted transformers the significant harmonic problem is reduced to the 5th, 11th and 17th.

对于具有相同正负波形的发电机正弦交流电压波形来说,所有偶次谐波都被抵消。在三相交流电系统中,所有 3 次谐波也会自动消除。这样还剩 5 次、7 次、11 次、13 次、17 次谐波等的潜在问题。对于由一对移相变压器供电的一对 6 脉冲同步转换器,严重的谐波问题减少到 5 次、11 次和 17 次。

The actual voltage waveshape can be examined with an oscilloscope or calculated into its harmonic content with a harmonic/spectrum analyzer. To accurately measure the useful level of voltage or current in a non-sinusoidal AC supply it is necessary to use true rms (root-mean-square) indicating instruments.

实际电压波形可以用示波器检查,也可以用谐波/频谱分析仪计算出谐波数量。为了准确地测量非正弦交流电源中电压或电流的有效值,必须使用真有效值(均方根)指示仪表。

The harmonic content of the AC input to a synchroconverter also has components that are related to the motor operating frequency. The DC link reactor coil reduces the ripple in the link current so that the effect on the AC supply side is reduced.

同步变频器的交流输入谐波也包含与电动机工作频率相关的分量。直流链路电抗器线圈可降低链路中电流的纹波,从而降低对交流电源侧的影响。

The total heating effect of distorted (non-sinusoidal) current waveform is calculated from the rms sum of all harmonics including the fundamental (or 1st harmonic). e. g. for a waveform with three significant harmonics, total rms value is:

畸变(非正弦)电流波形的总热效应以包括基频(或第 1 次谐波)在内的所有谐波电流的平方和的均方根来计算。例如,三个主要谐波的总均方根电流为:

$$I=\sqrt{I_1^2+I_5^2+I_{11}^2+I_{17}^2}$$

The % total harmonic distortion (THD) is found from the ratio of the sum of rms harmonics to the rms value of the fundamental:

总谐波的失真百分比(THD)是由谐波平方和的均方根与基波的均方根之比得出的:

$$\text{THD}=\sqrt{I_5^2+I_{11}^2+I_{17}^2}/I_1$$

Question 思考题

A distorted 440 V, 60 Hz voltage waveform is found to include harmonics of: 20%,5th ; 9%,11th ; and 6%,17th. Determine the rms size of each harmonic voltage and the overall THD.

发现失真的 440 V,60 Hz 电压波形包括:20%的 5 次谐波;9%的 11 次谐波; 6%的 17 次谐波。求每个谐波电压的有效值大小和总谐波的失真百分比。

Answer 答案

The 1st harmonic voltage rms level is 440 V. The 5th harmonic voltage is 20% of 440=88 V. Similarly the 11th harmonic voltage is 40 V and the 17th harmonic voltage is 26 V. The overall rms value of the three harmonics is

$$V_H=\sqrt{88^2+40^2+26^2}=100\text{ V}$$

so the THD=100/440=0. 227 or 22. 7%.

1 次谐波电压有效值 V_1 为 440 V。5 次谐波电压为 440 V 的 20%等于 88 V。同理,11 次谐波电压为 40 V,17 次谐波电压为 26 V。三个谐波的总均方根值为:

$$V_H=\sqrt{88^2+40^2+26^2}=100\text{ V}$$

所以总谐波的 THD=V_H/V_1=100/440=0. 227 或 22. 7%。

Most ship classification societies demand that the THD of the mains voltage is less than 10% but in practice this is usually less than 5%.

大多数船级社要求电源电压的失真百分比小于 10%,但实际上它通常小于 5%。

To minimize the size of voltage distortion it is necessary to connect filters which are tuned to the troublesome harmonics. The filters are the combination sets of inductance (L) and capacitance

(C) each resonantly tuned to a particular frequency in a series/parallel circuit. Additionally, some resistance (R) is included to act as a harmonic current limiting (damping) effect.

为了使电压失真最小化,需要连接滤波器来调整有害谐波。滤波器由电感(L)和电容(C)组合而成,电感和电容将串联/并联电路调整到特定频率。此外,还可增加一些电阻(R)以限制谐波电流(阻尼)。

The simplest way to view the overall system is to consider that the converter injects harmonics while the filter absorbs them. Filtering is not perfect over the variable frequency range so the harmonic problem is not completely solved but is minimized.

概括整个系统最简单的方法是认为变频器发出谐波的同时滤波器吸收谐波。滤波在可变频率范围内不能完全吸收谐波,因此谐波问题没有被完全解决而是被最小化了。

Practical harmonic filtering installations in power systems are physically large and will create power losses and heat in the components.

电力系统中实际谐波过滤装置的体积较大,会在部件中产生功率损耗和热量。

A cycloconverter drive employs complex thyristor switching to create a variable low frequency output. The associated harmonics range is wide, variable and difficult to predict so static filtering is difficult. With large cycloconverter drives (e. g. on a cruise ship) it is usual to employ a pair of motor-generator sets (instead of transformers) between the 6.6 kV and 440 V switchboards. This arrangement provides a clean (harmonic free) supply which does not transmit HV voltage variations to the LV side due to the rotational mechanical inertia of the M-G sets.

循环变流驱动器采用复杂的晶闸管开关电路来产生可变的低频输出。相关的谐波范围很宽、多变且难以预测,因此很难实现静态滤波。对于大型循环变流驱动器(例如在游轮上),通常在6.6 kV和440 V配电板之间使用一对电动机-发电机组(而不是变压器)。该装置提供纯净的(无谐波)电源,不会因电动机-发电机机组的旋转机械惯性而将高压侧电压变化传输至低压侧。

e. g. 230 V, 50 Hz and 110 V, 60 Hz for instrument power on ocean survey ships with DC converters where clean LV supplies are essential, it is usual to provide separate diesel-generator sets for that purpose. In this case, the main power system would probably not employ harmonic filters but is likely to use capacitive voltage surge suppression to minimize over-voltage spikes on the main bus-bar supply.

例如,配备直流转换器的海洋勘测船上的230 V,50 Hz和110 V,60 Hz仪表电源,就需要纯净的低压电源,为此通常需要单独的柴油发电机组。在这种情况下,主电网系统可能不会使用谐波滤波器,而使用容性浪涌电压抑制,将主母线电源上的过电压尖峰最小化。

The general problem of interference (noise) in electrical systems is how to minimize it at source and/or limit its transmission into adjacent susceptible equipment to prevent circuit malfunction. Consider the interference to TV reception caused by the nearby operation of an electric power tool or unsuppressed motor bike ignition. The coupling between source and reception devices can be inductive (magnetic), electric (capacitive) or conductive (directly through the conductors). All of this is the subject of electromagnetic compatibility or EMC which is a complicated analysis due to the wide range of possibilities for interference coupling. Manufacturers of electrical/communication equipment have to test their designs to prove and declare acceptable levels of compatibility.

电气系统干扰(噪声)的共性问题是如何从源头上将干扰最小化,以及/或限制其传输到邻近易受影响设备,以防止电路产生故障。想一想电视附近电动工具的运转或摩托车的点火未被抑制时对电视接收信号造成的干扰。电源和接收器件之间的耦合可以是感应的(磁性的)、电的(电容的)或导体的(直接通过导体)。这些都是电磁兼容性或 EMC 的对象,这是一个复杂的分析,因为可能产生耦合干扰的范围很广。电气/通信设备的制造商必须测试他们生产的设备,以证明和说明可接受的兼容性级别。

Harmonic filtering and circuit screening are two methods of limiting interference effects but no single method can be perfect.

谐波的滤波和电路的屏蔽是限制干扰效应的两种方法,但没有一种单一方法是完美的。

The most important factor that compromises a screen performance is its coverage of the circuit. Think of radiated noise as visible light. A light bulb that is enclosed in a full metal box with no holes or gaps in any of the seams ensures that no light escapes from the box (in electrical terms this is a faraday cage or fully screened room). If any holes exist in the box for cable entry/exit or the box seams are not perfect then light energy will escape. The amount of energy which can escape is dependent on the maximum linear dimension (L) of any aperture and the wavelength (X) of the radiation, which is the principle used in microwave oven doors where visible light which has a short wavelength can pass through the door but microwaves with a longer wavelength cannot.

影响屏蔽性能的最重要因素是它对电路的覆盖程度。把辐射噪声想象成可见光。一个灯泡被放在一个全封闭的金属盒子里,在任何接缝处都没有孔或缝隙,确保没有光从盒子里逃逸出去(在电气术语中,这是一个法拉第笼或完全屏蔽室)。如果在电缆出/入口存在任何孔洞,或者盒子接缝不完美,那么光就会逃逸出去。逃逸所需的能量取决于孔径的最大线性尺寸(L)和辐射的波长(X),这是微波炉门中使用的原理,在微波炉门中,波长较短的可见光可以通过门,但波长较长的微波无法通过。

Apertures can occur in door fittings, gaskets, ventilation holes, spaces for instruments, seams on boxes, cable entry and exit points etc.

门配件、垫圈、通风孔、仪表空间、接线盒上的接缝、电缆出入口等处都可能出现孔洞。

An important issue for interference is the coverage of screened and armored cables, which is often far from ideal and allows leakage of radiation from the effective apertures caused by the braid knitting, and by the connection at either end of the screen/armor. The more expensive screened/armored cables do have a better coverage and are to be preferred, but the effect can be negated by poor screen/armor termination.

干扰的一个重要问题是屏蔽和铠装电缆的覆盖效果,这通常很不理想,会造成辐射干扰从编织层和屏蔽/铠装末端的连接处的有效孔径泄漏。较昂贵的屏蔽/铠装电缆确实具有较好的覆盖效果,应优先考虑,但屏蔽/铠装末端连接不良会降低这种效果。

9.8 Propulsion Auxiliaries and Protection 推进装置辅助设备及其保护

The electric propulsion motors and its shaft bearings, converters, control regulators, transformers reactor coils and harmonic filters all generate heat which must be continually removed by auxiliary cooling services. An over-temperature condition must be managed by load limitation or disconnection.

电力推进电动机及其轴承、变频器、控制调节器、变压器、电抗器线圈和谐波过滤器都会产生热量,必须通过辅助冷却服务持续排出热量。温度超限必须通过限制或断开负荷来管理。

High current electrical components are generally cooled by forced air or by forced air/water circulation. In a large propulsion motor (Fig. 9.22), an internal shaft mounted fan circulates air through the rotor and stator spaces. This air is forced by electric fans to flow through a fresh water cooler, usually mounted on top of the machine, which removes the heat into the main cooling system.

大电流电气部件通常通过强制通风或强制空气/水内循环进行冷却。在大型推进电动机中(图9.22),安装在轴上的内部风扇使空气在转子和定子之间循环。风机迫使空气流过淡水冷却器,淡水冷却器通常安装在推进设备顶部,它能将空气热量转移到主冷却水系统中。

The motor enclosure will be typically rated as IP56 up to the shaft line and IP44 above the shaft line.

推进电动机外壳至轴线处的额定防护等级通常为IP56,轴线以上的防护等级为IP44。

Insulation plays a great role in high voltage installations. It can determine the capacity of the machine by temperature and temperature raise; it also affects the life span of electrical installations. Low insulation can lead to fire and personal injury during daily operation.

绝缘在高压电设备中扮演着重要角色。它决定了设备的温度和温升容量;它也影响电气设备的寿命。在日常运行中绝缘低会导致失火和人身伤害。

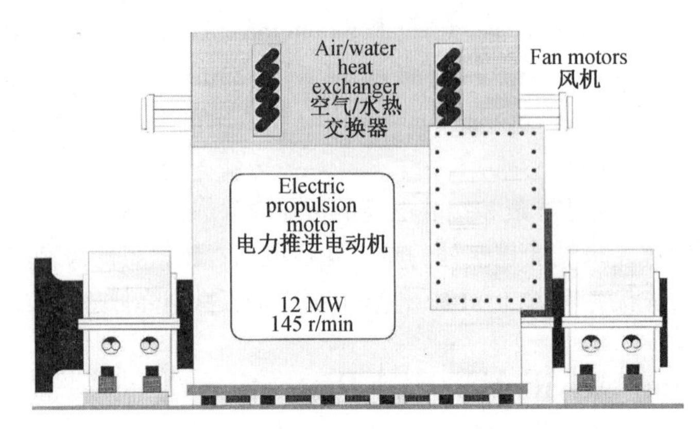

Fig. 9. 22　Propulsion motor construction

图 9. 22　推进电动机的结构

General purpose insulating materials for supporting conductors shall withstand the temperatures to which they are likely to be exposed. This is normally ambient temperature plus the heat from the conductor itself during full load, see Fig. 9. 23.

支撑导体的通用绝缘材料应当能耐受其处所的温度,即满负荷状态下的空气温度加上导体的发热温度,如图 9. 23 所示。

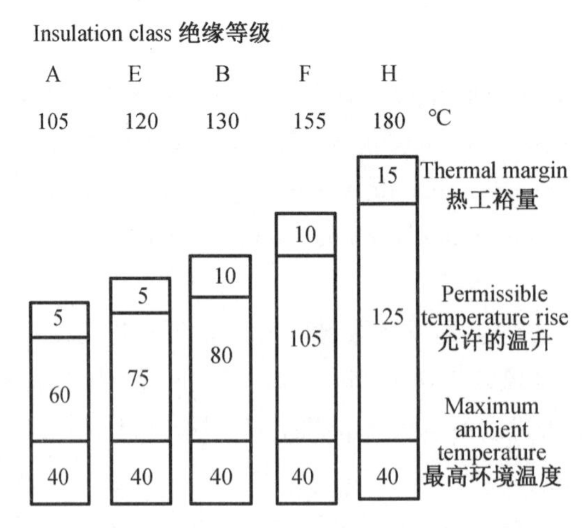

Fig. 9. 23　Insulation class table

图 9. 23　绝缘等级表

In order to prevent insulation break down, proper cooling of the electrical machine is important for preventing insulation break down. Stator winding, cooling air and water temperatures are monitored for display in the ECR. It is essential that general and hot-spot temperature limits are not exceeded.

为了防止绝缘失效，采取适当的冷却很重要。定子绕组、冷却空气和水的温度被监测，并在集控室显示。它们的普通温度和热点温度都不能超限。

Question 思考题

Which major feature of an electrical machine is principally degraded by over-temperature?
电气设备的哪个主要特征主要是由于温度过高而退化的？

Answer 答案

The winding insulation around the stator and rotor. Large HV machines are generally insulated with class F materials which have a maximum permitted temperature of 155 ℃ but will be normally operated well below this limit.

定子和转子绕组的绝缘。大型高压电设备通常用 F 级材料绝缘，这种材料的最大允许温度为 155 ℃，但在正常情况下，其运行时的温度远低于这个限值。

Large motors and generators have internal electric heaters (space heater) that are activated when the machine is disconnected. The requirement is to raise the internal temperature to about 3 ℃ above ambient which will prevent condensation settling on the motor insulation. Typically, an anti-condensation heater rated at about 4 kW at 220 V would be fitted in a large HV machine.

大型电动机和发电机内部有电加热器（空间加热器），当它们停止运行时，加热器就会启动。加热器的作用是将设备内部温度提升到高于环境温度约 3 ℃以上，以防止冷凝水沉积在电动机绝缘上。通常，在大型高压电设备中安装 220 V 额定电压，约 4 kW 额定功率的防冷凝加热器。

Semiconductor components are particularly sensitive to temperature. In particular, the temperature of large-current switching thyristors in the converters must be carefully managed. A perfect closed switch has no voltage drop across it so its power loss is zero when conducting. A thyristor, however, develops a small voltage drop (typically up to 2 V) when conducting its current. For a thyristor carrying an average current of, say, 2,000 A its power loss could be up to 4,000 W which would rapidly destroy the device unless the internal heat is efficiently removed.

半导体元件对温度特别敏感。必须小心管理变频器中大电流开关晶闸管的温度。一个完全闭合的开关在其两端没有电压降，因此在导电时其功率损耗为零。然而，晶闸管在传导电流时会产生很小的电压降（通常达 2 V）。对于平均电流为 2 000 A 的晶闸管而言，其功率损失可能高达 4 000 W，除非有效地去除内部热量，否则晶闸管将迅速发热损坏。

Fig. 9. 24 shows how large power thyristors are clamped between large area metal heat sinks which conduct the internal heat away from the device. The heat sink is itself cooled by clean and dry forced air which is circulated through the converter cubicle, air filters and an air-water heat exchanger. A more effective method is to pump de-mineralised fresh water directly through the thyristor heat sinks and then circulate it through an external water-water heat exchanger.

图 9.24 显示了大功率晶闸管是如何夹持在大面积金属散热器之间的,金属散热器将内部热量传导到远离该装置的地方。散热器本身由清洁干燥的空气冷却,空气通过变频器柜、空气过滤器和空气-水热交换器循环。一种更有效的方法是通过晶闸管散热器直接泵送脱矿淡水,然后通过外部水-水热交换器循环。

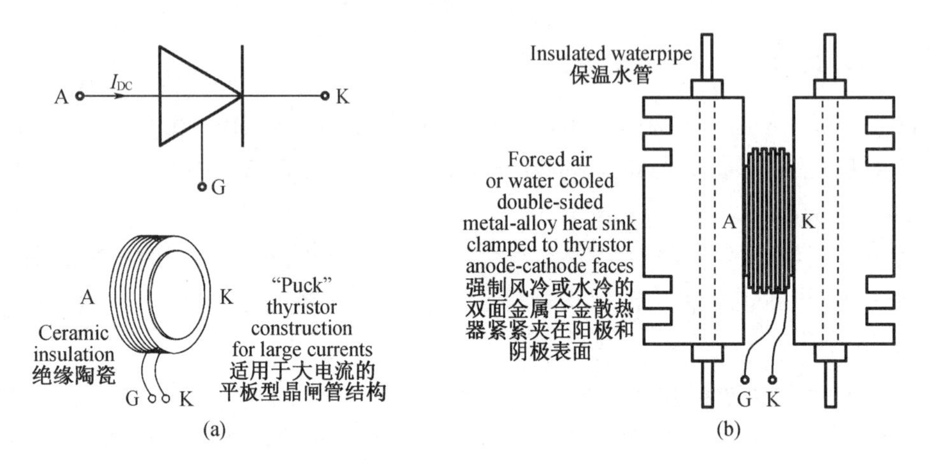

Fig. 9.24 Thyristor cooling arrangements

图 9.24 晶闸管的冷却布局

Question 思考题

The water used for heat sink cooling must be of exceptionally high purity. Why?

用于散热片冷却的水必须具有极高的纯度,为什么?

Answer 答案

The metal alloy heat sinks form the electrical connections to anode and cathode so are live at a high voltage level. Insulated, plastic, piping is used and the electrical resistance of the water must be extremely high to avoid accidental connection between adjacent thyristors via the cooling medium.

合金散热器与阳极和阴极形成电气连接,因此在高电压下带电。使用绝缘的塑料管,其中水的电阻必须非常高,以避免相邻晶闸管之间通过冷却介质意外导通。

The instrument used to measure the conductivity is similar to that used in a salinometer. Conductivity is measured in the units of micro-Siemens (μS) with acceptable values of less than 5 μS for thyristor cooling duty. If the set conductivity limit is exceeded the test instrument will signal alarm and trip conditions depending on the severity of the fault.

用来测量电导率的仪器与盐度计类似。电导率测量单位为微西门子(μS),晶闸管冷却负荷的可接受值小于 5 μS。如果超过设定的电导率极限,测试仪器将根据故障的严重程度发出警报和跳闸信号。

Protection of electrical power components requires that they be operated within their normal current, voltage and temperature ratings. A special case arises for the protection of large semiconductors, e. g. thyristors, which can additionally be destroyed by a fast rate-of-change of voltage and current caused by rapid switching. Fig. 9. 25 shows thyristor protection.

为了保护电力元件,要求它们在额定电流、电压和温度范围内工作。对大型半导体的保护有一种特殊情况,例如晶闸管,它还可能被快速通断时引起的电压和电流的高频变化损坏。图 9. 25 所示为晶闸管的保护。

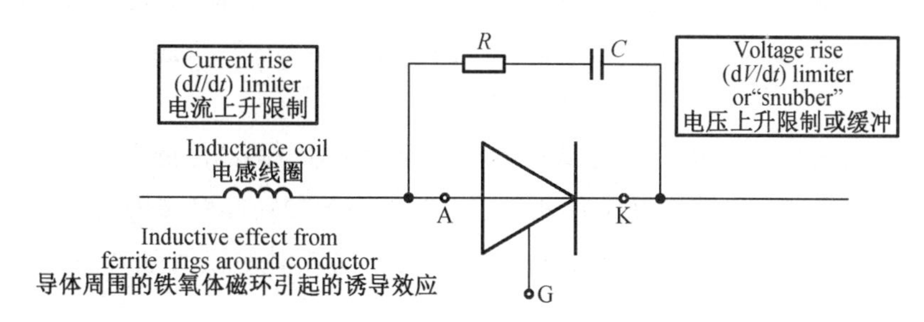

Fig. 9. 25　Thyristor protection

图 9. 25　晶闸管的保护

To suppress a rapid overvoltage rise (dV/dt) across a thyristor an R-C snubber circuit is used. Its action is based on the fact that voltage cannot change instantaneously across a capacitor. The series resistor limits the corresponding current surge through the capacitor while it is limiting the voltage across the thyristor. Significant heat will be produced by the resistor which, in some applications, is directly cooled by a water jacket.

为了抑制晶闸管过快的过电压变化率(dV/dt),使用了 R-C 缓冲电路。它的作用是基于这样一个事实:电压不能在与之并联的电容器上突变。串联电阻器限制通过电容器的电流浪涌,同时限制与之串联的晶闸管的电压。电阻器会产生大量的热量,在某些应用中,电阻器可以通过水冷套筒直接冷却。

An in-line inductive effect will limit the rate-of-change of current (dI/dt) through the thyristor, Its action is based on the fact that current cannot change instantaneously through a inductor. Special fast-acting line fuses may be used as back-up overcurrent protection for the thyristors.

串联电感效应将限制通过晶闸管的电流变化率(dI/dt)。它的作用是基于这样一个事实:电流不能在与之串联的电感器上突变。特殊的快速熔断器可用作晶闸管线路的备用过电流保护。

Circuit protection for the electric propulsion units (including excitation and harmonic filters) principally employs coordinated protective relays which monitor current, voltage, earth leakage and temperature.

电力推进装置的电路保护(包括励磁和谐波滤波装置)主要采用保护继电器,它可监测电流、电压、对地漏电流和温度。

The settings of protection relay parameter level (overcurrent, undervoltage etc.) and their tripping times are critical to the circuit protection under fault conditions. Such settings have been very carefully matched to the circuit and its components. Confirmation testing of protective relays requires calibrated current and voltage injection which is generally regarded as a specialist task for an outside contractor. Such testing is normally performed during a major survey during a drydocking period.

保护继电器参数(过流、欠压等)的设置及其跳闸时间对电路的故障保护至关重要。这类设置已经非常谨慎地与电路及其组件匹配。保护继电器的功能测试需要注入校准电流和电压,这由第三方服务商执行。这种测试通常是在坞修时的重大船级社检验期间进行的。

9.9 High Voltage on Ships 船舶高压电力系统

For ships with a large electrical power demand it is necessary to utilise the benefits of a HV installation. For marine practice, HV means >a. c 1,000 V. The design benefits relate to the simple ohms law relationship that current size (for a given power) is reduced as the voltage is increased. Working at high voltage significantly reduces the relative overall size and weight of electrical power equipment. HV levels of 3.3 kV, 6.6 kV and 11 kV are employed onboard for power distribution and HV motor drives.

对于电力需求大的船舶,就需要利用高压电装置的优势。在海上实践中,船舶高压电是指大于 1 000 V 的交流电压。高压电设计的优势与简单的欧姆定律有关,即电流随着电压的增加而减小(功率一定)。设备在高电压下工作显著地降低了电力设备的整体尺寸和质量。船舶上使用 3.3 kV、6.6 kV 和 11 kV 等级的高压电进行配电和高压电动机驱动。

The main disadvantage perceived by the user/maintainer, when working on an HV installation, is the very necessary adherence to stringent safety procedures.

当进行高压电设备工作时,用户和维护人员必须严格遵守安全工作程序。

Most electrical accidents occur because people are working on or near the equipment that is:

(1) Thought to be dead but which is live;

(2) Know to be live but those involved do not have adequate training or appropriate equipment to prevent injury, or they have not taken adequate precautions.

大多数电气事故的发生是由于人们在电气设备或其附近作业时:

(1)认为带电设备没电;

(2)知道设备带电但是没有经过适当的培训,或没有合适的防护装备,或没有采取适当的预防措施。

The Maritime and Coastguard Agency(MCA) published the code as best practice guidance for improving health and safety on board ship. It is intended primarily for merchant seafarers on UK-registered ships. Chapter 20 includes work on high voltage system. For example:

20.14.3 Work on high-voltage equipment/installations

No work shall be carried out on high-voltage equipment/installations unless an agreed switching plan has been developed and implemented so that the equipment/installations are:

a) Dead;

b) Isolated and all practicable steps have been taken to lock off live conductors, voltage transformers (except where the connections are bolted) and dead conductors that may become live;

c) Earthed at all points of disconnection of high-voltage supply and caution notices attached in English and any other working language of the vessel;

d) Released for work by the issue of a permit to work or a sanction for test.

Also, the competent person designated to carry out the work should fully understand the nature and scope of the work to be carried out and have witnessed a demonstration that the equipment/installation is dead at the point of work.

A limitation of access instruction should be used to give written instructions defining the limits of work to be carried out in the vicinity ofbut not on high-voltage equipment/installations.

英国海事和海岸警卫署(MCA)出版了 MCA 商船海员安全工作守则,作为改善船上健康和安全的最佳实践指南。它主要是为在英国注册船舶的商船海员设计的。第 20 章包括高压系统的工作。例如:

20.14.3 对高压电设备/装置施工

除非已制定并实施协定的转换计划,使设备/装置具备以下情况,否则不得对高压电设备/装置施工:

a)不带电;

b)已截断,并已采取一切可行步骤分隔带电导体、变压器(接线已截断者除外)及可能带电的不带电导体;

c)高压供电的所有断电点均已接地,并以英文和船上任何其他工作语言附上警告告示;

d)通过发出工作许可或测试许可批准工作。

此外,被指派工作的合格人员应充分了解作业性质及范围,并目测确认该设备/装置在工作点不带电。

应使用限制进入指引,对于高压电设备/装置附近（但非在其上)作业的工作限制做出书面指示。

In the ships power network shown in Fig. 9. 26, all of the equipment indicated above the dotted line is considered as HV. For the purposes of safety, this includes the LV field system for a propulsion motor as it is an integrated part of the overall HV equipment, From the HV generators, the network supplies HV motors (for propulsion, side thrusters and main L. O pump motor etc.) and the main transformer feeders to the 440 V switchboard. Further distribution links are made to interconnect with the emergency switchboard.

在如图 9.26 所示的船舶电网中,虚线上方的所有设备均视为高压电设备。出于安全目的,推进电动机的低压磁场系统也视为高压电,因为它是整个高压设备的一个组成部分,由高压发电机、高压电网向高压电动机(用于推进器、侧推器和主滑油泵等)和向 440 V 配电板供电的主变压器供电。还有配电线路与应急配电板互连。

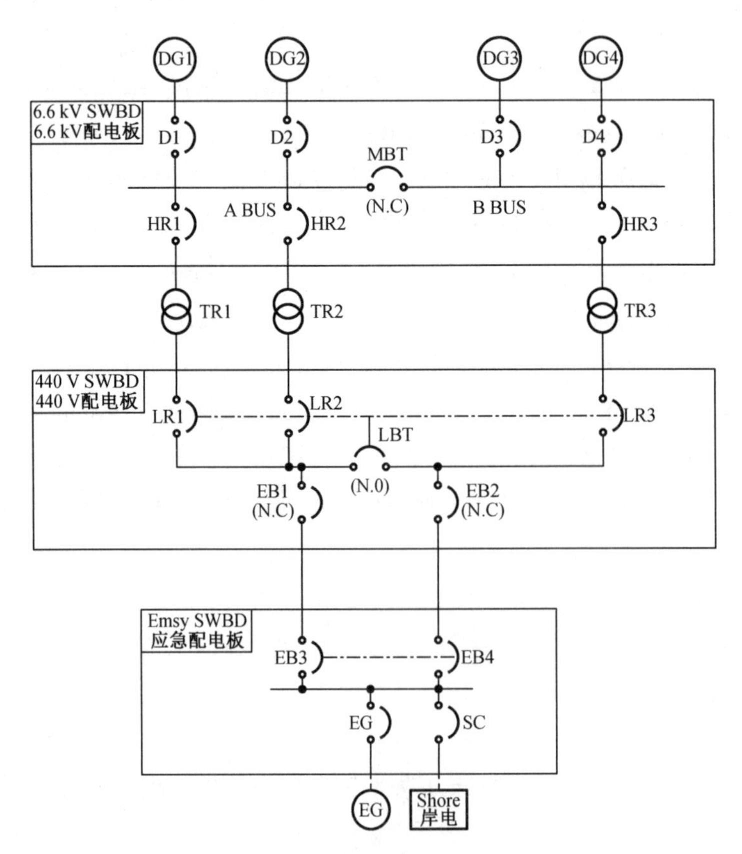

Fig. 9. 26 HV/LV power supply system

图 9. 26 高压/低压电力系统

9.9.1 HV Circuit Breakers and Contactors 高压断路器和接触器

Probably the main difference between a HV and an LV system occurs at the HV main switchboard. For HV, the circuit breaker types may be air-break, oil-break, gas-break using SF_6 (sulphur hexafluoride) or vacuum-break. Of these types, the most popular and reliable are the vacuum interrupters, which may also be used as contactors in HV motor starters, See Fig. 9. 27.

高压和低压系统之间的主要区别可能体现在高压主配电板上。对于高压电,断路器类型可以是空气断路器、油断路器、使用 SF_6(六氟化硫)气体的断路器或真空断路器。在这些类型中,最受欢迎和最可靠的是真空灭弧断路器,它也可用作高压电动机启动器的接触器,如图 9. 27 所示。

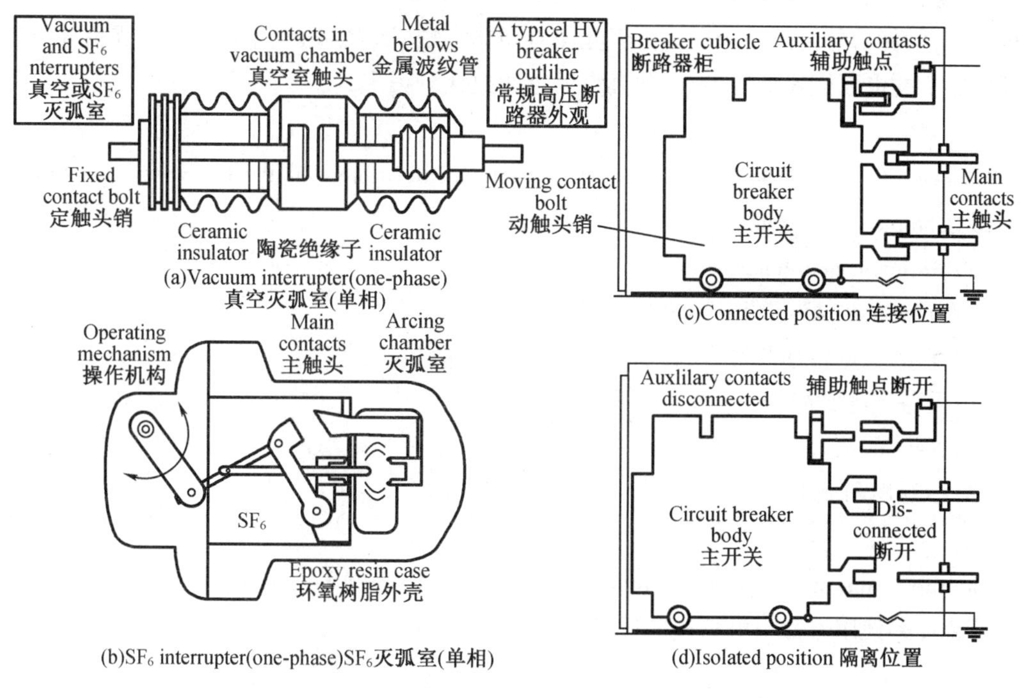

Fig. 9. 27 Vacuum and SF_6 interrupter/circuit breaker position

图 9. 27 真空和 SF_6 灭弧器/断路器位置

Each phase of a vacuum circuit breaker or contactor consists of a fixed and moving contact within a sealed, evacuated envelope of borosilicate glass. The moving contact is operated via flexible metal bellows by a charging motor/spring or solenoid operating mechanism. The high electric strength of a vacuum allows a very short contact separation, and a rapid restrike-free interruption of the arc is achieved.

真空断路器或接触器的每相由硼硅酸盐玻璃密封真空外壳内的定触头和动触头组成。动触头由储能电动机/弹簧或电磁阀操作机构通过弹性金属波纹管进行操作。真空的高耐电强度允许动静触头间非常短暂地分离、接触,并实现电弧的快速无重燃中断。

When an alternating current is interrupted by the separating contacts, an arc is formed by a metal vapour from the material on the contact surfaces and this continues to flow until a current zero is approached in the a. c. wave form. At this instant the arc is replaced by a region of high dielectric strength which is capable of withstanding a high recovery voltage. Most of the metal vapour condenses back on to the contacts and is available for subsequent arcing. A small amount is deposited on the shield placed around the contacts which protects the insulation of the enclosure. As the arcing period is very short (typically about 15 ms), the arc energy is very much lower than that in air-break circuit-breakers so vacuum contacts suffer considerably less wear.

当交流电被分断触点中断时,触头表面间形成电弧,触头材料产生的金属蒸气维持电弧电流,直到交流波形中接近电流零点。此时,电弧熄灭形成一个能够承受高恢复电压的高介电强度区域。大部分金属蒸气凝结于触点,可用于后续电弧;少量沉积在触点周围的保护层上,以保护外壳的绝缘层。由于起弧时间非常短(通常约 15 ms),真空电弧能量比空气断路器中的电弧能量低得多,因此真空触点的损耗少得多。

Because of its very short contact travel, a vacuum interrupter has the following advantages:

(1) Compact quiet unit;

(2) Minimum maintenance;

(3) Non-flammable and non-toxic.

由于它的触点行程非常短,真空断路器有以下优点:

(1)设备紧凑安静;

(2)维护量小;

(3)不易燃和无毒。

The life of the unit is governed by contact erosion but could be up to 20 years.

该装置的使用寿命由触点侵蚀程度决定,可长达 20 年。

In the gas-type circuit breaker, the contacts are separated in an SF_6 gas which is typically at a sealed pressure chamber at 500 kPa or 5 bar (when tested at 20 ℃).

在气体式断路器中,触点在 SF_6 气体中分离,这种气体通常处于 500 kPa 或 5 bar(在 20 ℃下测试压力)的密封压力室中。

9.9.2 System Earthing 系统接地

There are two kinds of systems: insulated system and earthed neutral system. 98% of fault is line-to-ground fault. System earthing can create a controlled path for earth currents, limit the size of earth fault currents, and detect Earth fault.

有两种接地系统:中性点不接地系统和中性点接地系统。98%的故障是单相对地故障。系统接地可以为接地电流创造回路,限制接地故障电流的大小,并且使故障电流可检测。

Question 思考题

Some HV systems have the neutral point of a generator earthed to the ships via a neutral earthing resistor (NER). What is this connection for?

一些高压电系统的发电机中性点通过中性点接地电阻(NER)与船体连接。这样连接有什么作用?

Answer 答案

To minimize the size of earth fault current. A hard (zero resistance) earth fault causes a short circuit across a generator phase winding, so the fault current is V_{PH}/R_{NER}. e. g. in a 6. 6 kV system with a 200 Ω NER, the $V_{PH}=6,600/\sqrt{3}=3,810$ V and the maximum earth fault current is 3,810/200 = 19 A.

使接地故障电流最小化。硬(接地电阻为零)接地故障会导致发电机相间绕组短路,因此一相故障电流为 V_{PH}/R_{NER}。例如,在具有 200 Ω 接地电阻的 6. 6 kV 系统中,相电压 $V_{PH}=6\,600/\sqrt{3}=3\,810$ V,最大接地故障电流为 3 810/200 = 19 A。

9.9.3　HV Insulation Requirements 高压绝缘要求

The HV winding arrangements for generators, transformers and motors are similar to those at LV except for the need for better insulating materials such as micalastic or similar.

高压发电机、变压器和电动机的高压绕组布置与低压绕组相似,但需要更好的绝缘材料,如云母或类似材料。

The HV windings for transformers are generally insulated with an epoxy resin/powdered quartz compound. This is a non-hazardous material which is maintenance free, humidity resistant and tropicalised.

变压器的高压绕组通常用环氧树脂/粉末石英化合物绝缘。这是一种无害材料,免维护、耐潮湿、耐热。

Conductor insulation for an HV cable requires a more complicated design than is necessary for an LV type. However, less copper area is required for HV conductors which allow a significant saving in space and weight for an easier cable installation. Where the insulation is air (e. g. between bare-metal live parts and earth within switchboards and in terminal boxes) greater clearance and creepage distances are necessary in HV equipment.

高压电缆的导体绝缘设计要求比低压电缆更复杂。然而,高压导线所需的铜面积较小,从而大大节省了体积和质量,便于高压电缆安装。如果绝缘介质为空气(例如配电板和接线盒内的裸露金属带电部件和接地之间),则高压电设备需要更大的间隙和更长的爬电距离。

Question 思考题

Would a 500 V megger test be suitable to determine the insulation integrity of a 6. 6 kV motor?

500 V 兆欧表是否适合用来确定 6. 6 kV 电动机的绝缘完整性?

Answer 答案

No. It would give a rough guide to the IR value but at 500 V, the tester is not properly stressing the insulation. For 6. 6 kV equipment, a 5,000 V IR tester is required.

不适合。它会给出粗略绝缘值,但在 500 V 时,兆欧表没有正确地对绝缘施加电压应力。对于 6. 6 kV 设备,需要 5 000 V 绝缘测试仪。

9. 10 High Voltage Safety 高压用电安全

Making personal contact with any electric voltage is potentially dangerous. At high voltage (>1,000 V) levels the electric shock potential is lethal. Body resistance decreases with increased voltage level which enhances the current flow, see Fig. 9. 28. Remember that an electric shock current as low as 30 mA can be fatal.

人体接触任何电压都有潜在风险。在高电压(>1 000 V)下,触电电压是致命的。人体电阻随着电压等级的增加而减小,从而增强了电流,如图 9. 28 所示。牢记,低至 30 mA 的触电电流是可致命的。

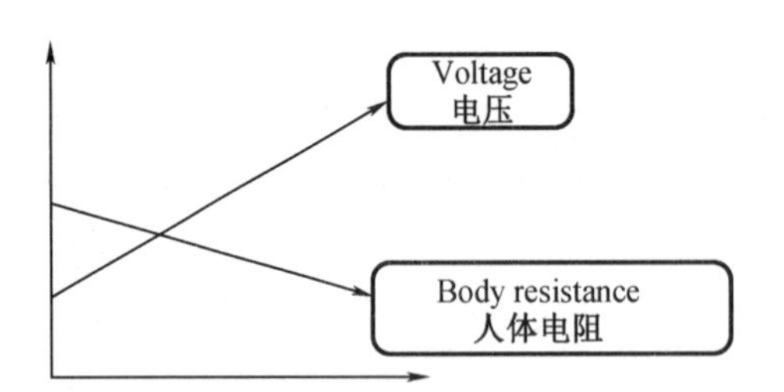

Fig. 9. 28 Voltage vs body resistance

图 9. 28 电压与人体电阻

The risk to people working in HV areas is greatly minimized by the diligent application of sensible general procedures and company safety regulations and procedures. Personnel who are required to routinely test and maintain HV equipment should be trained in the necessary practical safety procedures and certified as qualified for this duty. Approved safety clothing, footwear, eye protection and hard hat ,gloves,ear muff should be used where danger may arise from arcs, hot surfaces and high voltage etc.

通过认真合理地应用一般程序和公司的安全规程,在高压电区域工作的人员的风险会大大降低。需要对高压设备进行常规测试和维护的人员应接受必要的安全程序实操培训,并通过资格认证。在存在电弧、高温表面和高电压等可能发生危险的地方,应使用经认证的安全服、鞋、护目镜和安全帽、手套、耳罩。

The access to HV switchboard and equipment must be strictly controlled by using a permit-to-work scheme and isolation procedures together with live-line tests and earthing-down before any work is started.

必须严格管控进入高压配电板和设备,在开始任何工作之前,要使用工作许可证制度和隔离程序以及验电和接地。

The HV warning notice is shown in Fig. 9. 29.

高压警示标志如图 9. 29 所示。

Fig. 9. 29　HV warning notice

图 9. 29　高压警示标志

All work to be carried out on HV equipment is subject to an Electrical Permit to Work (EPTW).

在高压设备上进行的所有工作前均需获得电气工作许可证(EPTW)。

9. 10. 1　EPTW 电气工作许可证

The format of a permit will vary for different companies and organizations. The broad guidelines for the necessary declarations and procedures are outlined below.

许可证的格式因公司和机构而异。关于必要的公告和程序的通用准则概述如下。

Before work is commenced on HV equipment an EPTW must be issued. This permit is usually the last stage of a planned maintenance task which has been discussed, prepared and approved by the authorising person to be carried out by the responsible person. The copied permit, signed by the responsible person, usually has at least five sections with the first stating the work to be carried out. The next section is a risk assessment declaring where electrical isolation and earthing has been applied and where danger/caution notices have been displayed then the permit is signed as authorised by the Chief Electrotechnical Officer (CETO) or Chief Engineer. In the third section, the person responsible for the work signs to declare that he/she is satisfied with the safety precautions and that the HV circuit has been isolated and earthed. Section four relates to the suspension or completion of the designated work. Finally, the fifth section cancels the permit with a signature from the authorising person. A Permit-to-Work is usually valid only for 24 h.

开始在高压电设备上工作之前,必须签发电气工作许可证。该许可证通常是计划维护任务的最后阶段,该任务已与授权人员讨论、准备并获得授权人员批准,由负责人员执行。由负责人签署的许可证复印件通常至少有五个部分,第一部分说明要进行的工作内容。第二部分是风险评估,说明在何处进行了电气隔离和接地,以及在何处展示了危险/警告通知,然后由首席电子电气员(CETO)或轮机长授权签署许可证。在第三部分,负责工作的人员签字声明,他/她对安全预防措施感到满意,并且高压电路已被隔离和接地。第四部分涉及暂停或完成指定工作。最后,第五部分取消许可证,并由授权人员签字。工作证的有效期通常只有 24 h。

Some marine and offshore companies will also require an associated Electrical Isolation Certificate to declare and record exactly where the circuit isolation and earthing has been applied before the EPTW can be authorised. A Sanction to-Test safety certificate may also be required when an electrical test (e. g. an electrical insulation test) is to be applied. This is necessary as the circuit earth generally has to be removed during such testing.

一些海运和海洋公司还需要相关的电气隔离证书,以准确声明和记录在电气工作许可证授权之前,已应用电路隔离和接地的位置。在进行电气试验(如电气绝缘试验)时,可能还需要获得测试安全许可证书的批准。这是必要的,因为在此类测试期间,通常必须移除电路的接地。

Before earthing-down the particular circuit or equipment declared in the EPTW it must be tested and proved dead after disconnection and isolation. This can only be carried out by using an approved HV tester as shown in Fig. 9. 30. The tester itself must be proven before and after such a test. This is checked by connecting the tester to a known HV source (supplied either as a separate battery operated unit or included as an internal self-test facility).

在将电气工作许可证中的特定电路或设备接地之前,必须对其进行验电,并在断开和隔离后证明其不带电。这只能通过使用认可的高压验电器进行,如图 9. 30 所示。必须在测试前后对高压验电器本身进行验证。通过高压验电器接触到已知的高压电源(由单独的电池装置提供,或内部自检设施提供)进行检查。

At least two people should always be together when working on HV equipment.

在高压电设备上工作时,应始终保持至少两人。

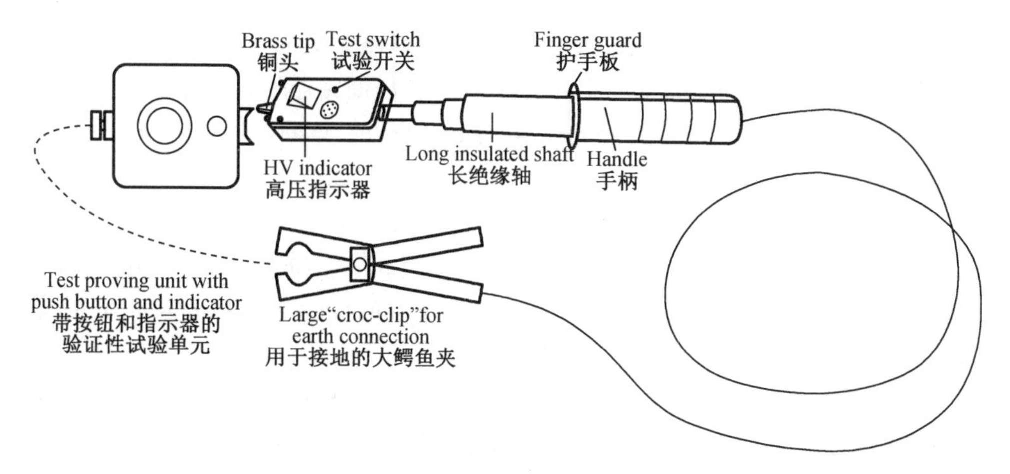

Fig. 9. 30 HV tester

图 9. 30 高压验电器

9. 10. 2 Earthing-down 接地

Before work can be allowed to commence on HV equipment it must be earthed to the hull for operator safety.

在许可高压设备工作之前,必须将其接地至船体,以确保工作人员的安全。

As an example, consider the earthing arrangements at an HV switchboard. Here, the earthing-down method is of two types:

(1) Circuit Earthing: After disconnection from the live supply, an incoming or outgoing feeder cable is connected by a manually operated switch to connect all three conductors to earth. This action then releases a permissive-key to allow the circuit breaker to be withdrawn to the TEST position. The circuit breaker cannot be re-inserted until the earth has been removed and the key restored to its normal position.

(2) Bus-bar Earthing: When it is necessary to work on a section of the HV switchboard bus-bars, they must be isolated from all possible electrical sources. This will include generator incomers, section or bus-tie breakers and transformers (which could back-feed) on that bus-bar section. Earthing down is carried out at a bus-section breaker compartment after satisfying the permissive key exchanges. In some installations the application of a bus-bar earth is by a special earthing circuit breaker which is temporarily inserted into the switchboard solely for the bus-bar earthing duty.

例如,考虑高压配电板的接地布置。这里,接地方式有两种类型:

(1)电路的接地:断开电源后,通过手动接地开关连接进/出馈线电缆,将所有三相导线连接到地。这个动作会解锁一把许可钥匙,以允许抽出断路器至测试位置。只有断开接地开关,许可钥匙恢复到正常位置后,才能重新插入断路器。

(2)汇流排的接地:当需要在高压配电板母线的某一段上工作时,必须将其与所有可能的电源隔离。隔离对象包括发电机进线、分段或母线联络开关以及该母线段上的变压器(可反向馈电)。在满足许可钥匙交换条件后,在母线分段断路器隔间进行接地。在某些装置中,母线接地的应用是通过一个特殊的接地断路器进行的,该断路器临时插入配电板,仅用于母线接地。

For extra confidence and operator safety, additional earthing can be connected local to the work task with approved portable earthing straps and an insulated extension tool, e. g. at the terminals of an HV motor as shown in Fig. 9. 31.

为了接地更加可靠和确保操作人员安全,可使用经批准的便携式接地线和绝缘延伸工具将附加接地线连接到工作任务的本地,例如连在高压电动机的端子处,如图 9. 31 所示。

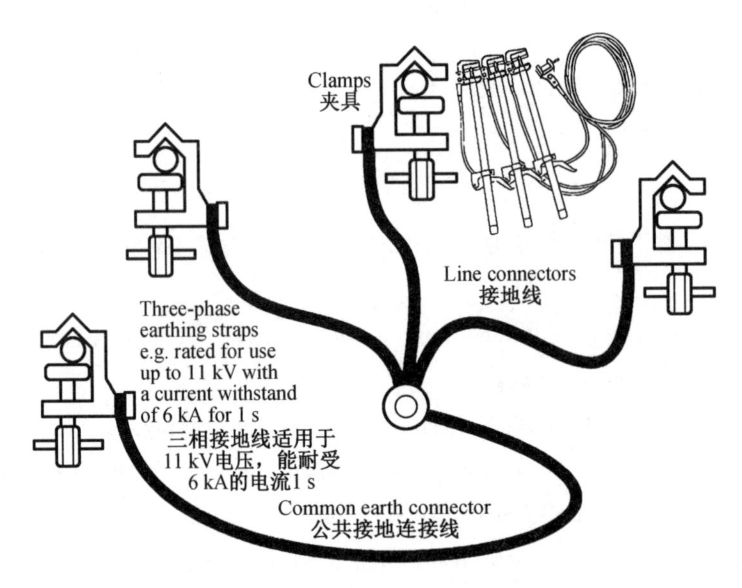

Fig. 9. 31　Portable earthing straps

图 9. 31　便携式接地线

Remember to always connect the common wire to earth first before connecting the other wires to the three phase connections. When removing the earthing straps, always remove the earth connection last.

记住,在将便携式接地线与三相连接之前,始终先将公共接地端连接地。拆除接地线时,务必最后拆除接地连接。

Question 思考题

Why is earthing down considered essential during HV maintenance?

为什么在高压电维护期间接地是必要的?

Answer 答案

So that the worker can be assured that the equipment (and himself) cannot experience any accidentally applied voltage because the earth connection bonds the circuit to earth (zero volts).

这样，工作人员可以确信设备（和他自己）不会经历任何意外电压，因为接地连接已将电路接地（0 V）。

9.11 High Voltage Equipment Testing 高压电设备的测试

The high voltage (e. g. 6.6 kV) installation covers the generators, main supply cables, switchgear, transformers, electric propulsion (if fitted) and a few large motors e. g. for side-thrusters and air conditioning compressors. For all electrical equipment the key indicator to its safety and general condition is its IR and this is particularly so for HV apparatus. The IR must be tested periodically between phases and between phases and earth. HV equipment that is well designed and maintained operated within its power and temperature ratings should have a useful insulation life of 20 years.

高压（如 6.6 kV）安装包括发电机、主电源电缆、开关设备、变压器、电力推进装置（如安装）和一些大型电动机，如侧推器和空调压缩机。对于所有电气设备，衡量其安全性和一般状况的关键指标是绝缘电阻，对于高压电设备尤其如此。必须定期测试相间以及相与地之间的绝缘电阻。设计和维护良好的高压设备，在额定功率和温度范围内运行的有效绝缘寿命应为 20 年。

An IR test is applied with a high DC voltage which applies a reasonable stress to the dielectric material (insulation). For 6.6 kV rated equipment, a periodical 5,000 V DC insulation resistance (megger) test is recommended. The IR test should be applied for 1 min and temperature corrected to a standard of 40 ℃. The minimum IR value is usually recommended as (kV+1) MΩ where kV is the equipment voltage rating. e. g. 7.6 MΩ would be an acceptable IR value for a 6.6 kV machine. For machines with healthy insulation, an IR test result may indicate a value up to 100 times greater than the recommended minimum.

在直流高压电下进行绝缘测试，该电压对电介质材料（绝缘层）施加合理的应力。对于额定 6.6 kV 的设备，建议定期用直流 5 000 V 进行绝缘电阻（兆欧表）测试。应在温度校正至标准的 40 ℃时，持续试验 1 min。通常建议最小绝缘电阻值为[设备额定电压（kV）+1] MΩ。例如，对于 6.6 kV 的机器，7.6 MΩ 是可接受的绝缘电阻值。对于具有良好绝缘的机器，绝缘电阻测试的结果可比建议的最小值高出 100 倍。

A more involved IR test (the polarization index or PI) is used when the insulation value may be suspect or recorded during an annual survey. The PI value is the ratio of the IR result after 10 min of testing to the value recorded after 1 min. For class F insulation materials the recommended

PI value is 2. 0. To apply a PI test over a ten minute period requires a special IR tester that has a motor-driven generator or an electronic converter powered from a local 220 V AC supply.

一种更复杂的绝缘测试(极化指数,PI),在年度检验时可能会要求测试或记录。极化指数是测试 10 min 后的绝缘电阻结果与 1 min 后的绝缘电阻结果的比值。对于 F 级绝缘材料,建议的极化指数值为 2. 0。要进行 10 min 以上的极化指数测试,需要一个特殊的绝缘测试仪,该测试仪具有一个电动机驱动的发电机或一个由本地 220 V 交流电源供电的电子变频器。

The condition of HV insulation is governed by many factors such as temperature, humidity, surface condition and operating voltage level. Be guided by the manufacturers recommendations when testing and maintaining HV insulation.

高压绝缘材料的状况受温度、湿度、表面条件和工作电压等级等多种因素的影响。对高压绝缘材料进行测试和维护时,应遵循制造商的建议。

Before applying an IR test to HV equipment its power supply must be switched off, isolated, confirmed dead by an approved live-line tester and then earthed for complete safety in accordance with the current EPTW regulations.

在对高压电设备进行绝缘测试之前,根据现行电气工作许可证法规,其电源必须关断、隔离,并通过经认可的带电线路测试仪确认其无电,然后进行接地以保证绝对安全。

The correct procedure is to connect the IR tester to the circuit under test with the safety earth connection ON. The safety earth may be applied through a switch connection at the supply circuit breaker or by a temporary earth connection local to the test point. This is to ensure that the operator never touches a unearthed conductor. With the IR tester now connected, the safety earth is disconnected (using an insulated extension tool for the temporary earth). Now the IR test is applied and recorded, the IR tester switched off. The safety earth is now reconnected before the IR tester is disconnected. This safety routine must be applied for each separate IR test.

正确的步骤是在安全接地已连接的情况下,将绝缘测试仪连接到被测电路。安全接地可通过电源断路器处的开关连接或测试点本地的临时接地线连接。这是为了确保工作人员不会接触未接地导体。现在绝缘测试仪已连接,就可断开安全接地(使用绝缘延长工具断开临时接地线)。绝缘测试完成并记录后,关闭测试仪。在绝缘测试仪断开之前,先重新连接安全接地。每次单独的绝缘测试都必须执行该安全程序。

Large currents flowing through machine windings, cables, bus-bars and main circuit breaker contacts will cause a temperature rise due to resistive heating (I^2R). Where overheating is suspected, e. g. at a bolted bus-bar joint in the main switchboard, the local continuity resistance may be measured and checked against the manufacturers recommendations or compared with similar equipment that is known to be satisfactory. A normal ohmmeter is not suitable as it will only drive a few mA through the test circuit. A special low resistance tester or micro-ohmmeter (traditionally called a ducter) must be used which drives a calibrated current (usually $I=10$ A) through the circuit while measuring the voltage-drop (V) across the circuit. The meter calculates R from V/I and displays the test result. For a healthy bus-bar joint a continuity of a few mΩ would be expected.

当大电流流过机器绕组、电缆、母线和主断路器触点时,它们会由于电阻发热(I^2R)引起温升。在可能过热的地方,如在主配电板的母线螺栓连接处,可以根据制造商的建议测量和检查局部连接电阻,或与已知连接良好的类似设备进行比较。普通欧姆表不适合这样的测量,因为它只能驱动几毫安的电流通过测试电路。必须使用特殊的低电阻测试仪或微欧姆计(传统上称为导管),在测量电路的电压降(V)时,驱动经过校准的电流(通常为 $I=10$ A)通过电路。该仪表根据 V/I 计算 R,并显示测试结果。对于一个健康的母线接头来说,应该有几毫欧的电阻。

Normally the safe testing of HV equipment requires that it is disconnected from its power supply. Unfortunately, it is very difficult and unsafe to closely observe the on-load operation of internal components within HV enclosures. This is partly resolved by temperature measurement with an recording infra-red camera from a safe distance. The camera is used to scan an area and the recorded infra-red image is then processed by a computer program to display hot-spots and a thermal profile across the equipment. To examine internal components, e. g. busbar joints, a camera recording can be made immediately after the equipment has been switched off and isolated in accordance with an EPTW safety procedure. Alternatively, some essential equipment, e. g. a main switchboard, can be monitored on-line using specially fitted and approved enclosure windows suitable for infra-red testing. These windows are small apertures with a permanently fixed steel mesh through which the camera can view the internal temperature from a safe position. An outer steel plate fixed over the window mesh maintains the overall enclosure performance during normal operation.

通常情况下,高压电设备的安全测试要求其与电源断开。遗憾的是,近距离观察高压设备外壳内部部件的有载运行是非常困难和不安全的。通过在安全距离内使用红外热像仪进行温度测量在一定程度上可以克服这个困难。热像仪用于扫描一个区域,然后由计算机程序处理记录的红外图像,以显示设备上的热点和热轮廓。为了检查内部部件,例如母线接头,可按照电气工作许可证安全程序在高压电设备关闭和隔离后立即使用红外热像仪进行记录。或者,一些必要设备,例如主配电板,可以通过专门安装且认可的适用于红外测试的外壳窗口进行在线监控。这些窗户带有永久固定钢网的小孔,通过它热像仪可以从安全位置查看内部温度。固定在窗户网格上的外部钢板在正常运行期间能保持外壳的整体防护性能。

A conventional photograph of the equipment is taken simultaneously to match the infra-red image and both are used as part of a test report. Such testing is usually performed by a specialist contractor who will prepare the test report and propose recommendation/repair advice to the ship operator. Fig. 9. 32 gives typical results from an infra-red camera test on a bus-bar connection.

测温的同时拍摄设备的常规照片以匹配红外图像,并将两者作为测试报告的一部分。此类测试通常由专业服务商进行,该服务商将编制测试报告并向船舶运营商提出意见/维修建议。图 9. 32 给出了一个典型的红外图像结果,来自红外热像仪测试对母线连接处的测试。

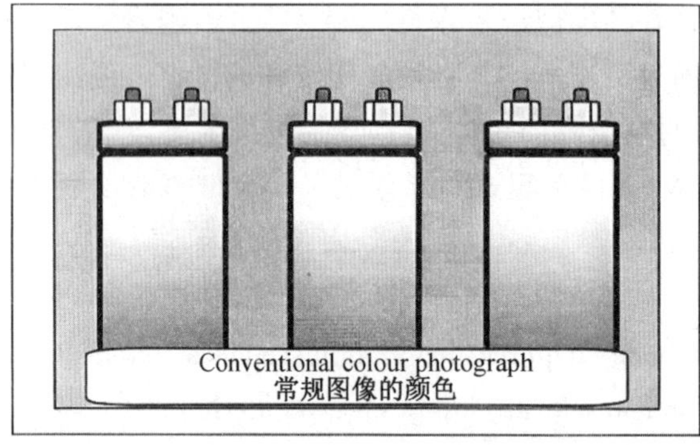

Location/identification 位置/名称	
area:	6.6 kV main board
equipment:	Gen 2 breaker
component:	copper bus-bars
date/time:	22/03/99/15:45

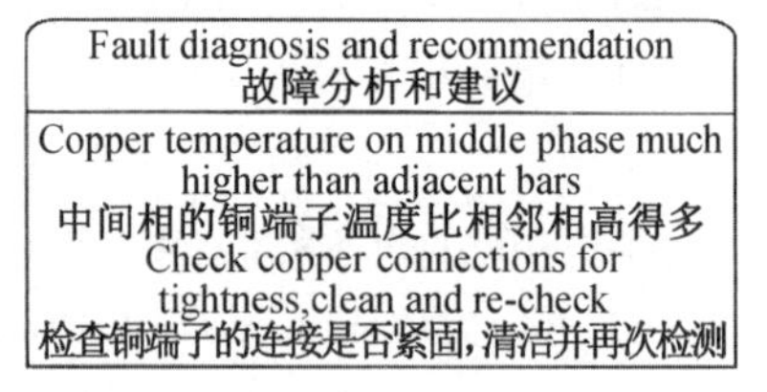

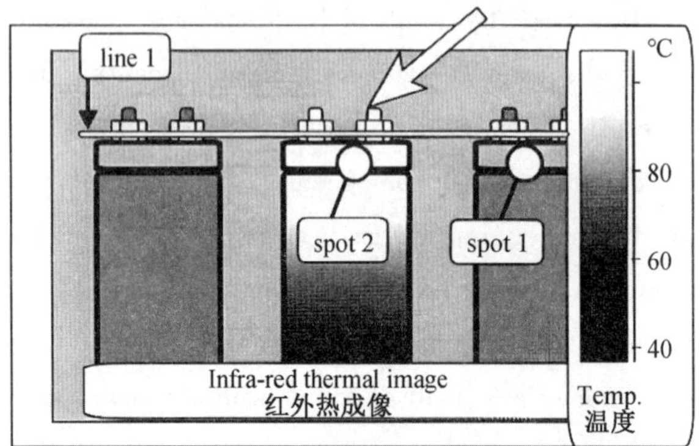

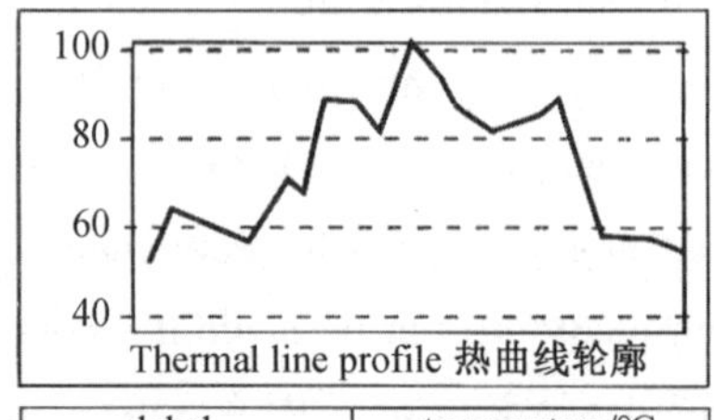

label	temperature/°C
spot 1	55.2
spot 2	100.3
line 1:max	99.0
line 1:min	50.6

Fig. 9. 32 Infra-red thermal image

图 9. 32 红外热成像

In this on-line test, the camera recorded hot-spot temperatures up to 100 ℃ and the report recommended that this copper connection is checked for tightness as it is running very hot compared to that on the neighboring copper-work.

在该在线测试中,热像仪记录了高达 100 ℃的热点温度,报告建议检查该铜线连接的紧密性,因为与相邻铜线上的连接相比,该铜线连接处过热。

To test the insulating integrity of an HV vacuum-type circuit breaker requires a special high voltage impulse test. The tester produces a short duration voltage pulse, of typically 10 kV for a 6. 6 kV circuit, which is connected across the open breaker contacts. Any weakness in the insulating strength of the vacuum in the interrupter chamber will be detected as a current flow and the tester will display the condition as a pass or fail.

为了测试高压真空断路器的真空度,需要进行特殊的高压冲击试验。该测试仪产生一个持续时间较短的电压脉冲,6.6 kV 电路的电压脉冲通常为 10 kV,分别与分断的断路器的一对触点连接。真空灭弧室中真空度的任何减弱将产生电流流动并被测试仪检测到,测试仪将显示真空度为正常还是失效状态。

Gas (SF_6) HV circuit breakers rely on the quality and pressure of the gas acting as the insulation between the contacts. A falling gas pressure can be arranged to initiate an alarm from pressure switches fitted to each switching chamber. Normal gas pressures are typically 500 kPa or 5 bar.

气体(SF_6)高压断路器触点之间的绝缘取决于气体的质量和压力,可以设置气体压力下降时的下限压力,可通过安装在每个开关室的压力开关启动警报。正常的气体压力通常为 500 kPa 或 5 bar。

Overall circuit protection of HV equipment is supervised by coordinated protective relays. These must be periodically tested to confirm their level settings (for current, voltage, frequency etc.) and their tripping times. This requires the injection of calibrated values of current and voltage into the protective relays which is usually performed by a specialist contractor during a main ship survey while in dry-dock.

高压电设备的综合电路保护由保护继电器监控。必须定期对其进行测试,以确认其保护设定值(电流、电压、频率等)及其跳闸时间。这需要将经过校准的电流和电压信号发送至保护继电器,通常在干坞中进行船舶检验时由专业服务商进行该项测试。